Rehabilitation Consultant's Handbook

Roger O. Weed, PhD
Timothy F. Field, PhD

Elliott & Fitzpatrick, Inc.

Rehabilitation Consultant's Handbook
Fourth Revised Edition, 2012

Roger O. Weed, PhD
Timothy F. Field, PhD

ISBN 978-0-9855538-07

Elliott & Fitzpatrick, Inc.
1135 Cedar Shoals Drive
Athens, GA 30605
Phone: (706) 548-8161 (GA); (800) 843-4977
Fax: (706) 227-2204

website: www.elliottfitzpatrick.com

Table of Contents

Preface

The *Rehabilitation Consultant's Handbook – Fourth Edition* represents an evolution of several books, chapters and articles in which the authors have participated. The primary goal is to provide a *practical* foundation for the practice of rehabilitation consulting. The intended audience includes a wide spectrum of rehabilitation professionals, such as rehabilitation counselors, rehabilitation masters students, rehabilitation nurses, and rehabilitation psychologists who are practicing in public sector rehabilitation, workers' compensation, long-term disability, social security, and personal injury litigation.

The origin of this edition can be traced to 1981, when Field and Sink published a pamphlet titled *The Vocational Expert* in which the authors addressed many of the issues relevant to the work of the vocational expert in judicial hearings. In 1986, Field, Weed, and Grimes published the *Vocational Expert Handbook*, which represented a vastly expanded version of that early work and includes several new sections not earlier addressed in the 1981 publication. In 1988 Field and Weed published *Transferable Work Skills*, which enhanced book texts in an area (transferable skills) that has been written into many workers' compensation laws. This edition expands on the previous editions of the *Rehabilitation Consultant's Handbook* (1990, 1994, and 2001) with updates reflecting contemporary rehabilitation practice. This fourth edition embraces the most important concepts and processes of the above mentioned publications and identifies major changes in thinking and procedures. Additionally, every attempt has been made to identify and discuss the emerging issues in the field of private sector rehabilitation, especially as it relates to the work of the rehabilitation consultant.

Chapter 1 provides an introduction and overview of the general field of rehabilitation. Reference is made to public sector rehabilitation with a brief overview of important legislation that funds and maintains these rehabilitation programs. The listing and brief overview of important legislation has been extensively revised and updated. An introductory general discussion of the Social Security, workers' compensation, state-federal system, and personal injury approaches to disability determination is offered along with related issues of transferability of skills, labor market access, cultural considerations, and future lost earnings. Dr. Ann Landes has a special interest in multiculturalism and contributed a section to the foundations chapter to reflect contemporary thought on this topic.

Chapter 2 provides a more specific overview of the work of the rehabilitation expert across all types of settings. Issues such as credentials, areas of expertise, varieties of work performed, and guidelines for performance is presented and discussed. Suggestions are made with respect to what the expert should or should not do in various work settings, along with some further suggestions for effective presentation of vocational expert testimony.

Chapter 3 is a discussion on the role of the rehabilitation consultant in workers' compensation cases and is co-authored by an experienced worker's compensation professional, Dr. Berens. Although workers' compensation segment of the industry has experienced trying times since the last edition, it continues to be a viable profession, especially for "good" consultants. This chapter includes concepts specific to this specialized profession with an attempt to include information that is relevant throughout the United States. However, since each state has significant differences, the rehabilitation consultant is strongly urged to obtain the laws or undertake specialized training in the state in which they intend to practice.

Chapter 4 is a discussion on the preparation of a case for a hearing involving the one who has been designated a "vocational expert." Particular attention is given to the definitions provided by the Social Security Administration and how the Vocational Expert (VE) must attend to these issues in the preparation of testimony. The Social Security regulations for vocational expert testimony always serve as a useful guideline for similar testimony prepared for presentation in either workers' compensation hearings or in civil court. Included is a step-by-step approach to evaluating and preparing a case. This section is intended to interface with *Transferable Work Skills* and the new O*Net. Discussion is also presented on the workers' compensation hearing as well as the deposition and issues related to trial by jury.

Chapter 5 is a discussion of approaches to vocational assessment and evaluation. This area of information is absolutely essential in the development of vocational expert testimony. Included in this chapter are the important areas of information that must be attended to and addressed in nearly all cases being prepared for presentation. The discussion includes such topics as vocational history, psychological and educational testing, the vocational interview, and work sample assessment. Various approaches to job analyses are also included.

Chapter 6 encompasses the "meat" of the transferable work skills including references to the O*Net. Because of the aging DOT and the lack of an alternative for assessing pre- vs. post-injury work capabilities, suggestions for addressing these challenges are offered. The DOT arrangement and forms are provided with examples and a step-by-step guided tour is included.

Chapter 7 provides an overview of the necessary elements included in the labor market survey. This chapter, based on a peer-reviewed article by Roger Weed and Celeste Taylor, offers suggestions, format, and a checklist. Celeste Taylor is a vocational evaluator and licensed professional counselor in private practice in Athens, Georgia. The purpose of this information gathering is to identify the vocational outlook of a particular occupational choice. This is an alternative to the reliance on published statistics, which often are outdated. The labor market survey provides the foundation for the feasibility of pursuing a vocational plan before spending time and money on a plan potentially leading to failure.

Chapter 8 is the logical next step from the labor market survey. Once a potential vocational outcome is identified, it may be that close scrutiny would reveal that the occupation is beyond the client's capabilities. The job analysis is a detailed analysis of the job requirements and functional capabilities required to perform the essential and other functions of the job. It is the second step in the foundation for the feasibility of pursuing a vocational plan before spending time and money on a plan potentially leading to failure. This article includes the contribution of Celeste Taylor and Dr. Terry Blackwell. Dr. Blackwell is professor in the Rehabilitation and Mental Health Counseling Program at Montana State University-Billings.

Chapter 9 incorporates job placement basics based on "in the trenches" experience by one of the authors. Included topics are client preparation, resumes, job search, and employer issues. It also offers references, resources, Internet addresses, and practical information for the beginning rehabilitation professional.

Chapter 10 offers a comprehensive overview of the tenets, process, and methodology for the life care planner. This chapter has been extensively revised to include the information from the booklet by one of the authors, *Life Care Planning: A Step-by-Step Guide*, also published by E&F, Inc. Several checklists are offered as well as an example plan. The various issues to be addressed in the Life Care Plan are extensively reviewed.

Chapter 11, Forensic Rehabilitation, has been updated to reflect certain court rulings that have had an effect on professional practice (e.g., *Daubert and Kumho Tire* rulings). This chapter also addresses labor market access and earnings capacity analysis. Increasingly, the vocational expert is retained to provide expert opinions with respect to the loss of employment opportunity and the impact on future lost earnings of the injured child or adult with and without a work history. This chapter discusses the general issue of labor market analysis as it relates to the vocational assessment of the injured worker and discusses how such an assessment relates to labor market information. Additional discussion centers around wage loss analysis, including factors that are important in determining future wage loss. The various approaches to wage loss analysis are also discussed and are compared to each other through the analysis and comparison of a case presentation. A suggested approach with example and a checklist outline are included. This chapter is another important source for the professional who expects to testify. Explanations of the deposition, testifying at trial, and subpoenas are incorporated.

Chapter 12, Admissible Testimony and Clinical Judgment, has been added as an adjunct to Chapter 11. The authors have presented at various conferences on the topic of actual litigation cases which involve rehabilitation experts. Audience reactions have been very enthusiastic about the value of the information (which is not an academic exercise). Litigation cases (court appeals and such) relating to both the vocational expert and the life care planner are presented with commentary and suggestions. The contribution of Tony Choppa, an experienced rehabilitation litigation consultant, is gratefully acknowledged.

Chapter 13 provides ADA and reasonable accommodation information with updates from the 2008 ADA Amendments Act. As predicted in the first and second editions, the rehabilitation consultant will be involved in job accommodation, which often utilizes technology. Many Centers for Rehabilitation Technology have evolved over the past few years and an association (RESNA) for professionals interested in technology for persons with a disability has flourished. This chapter includes an overview and resources for high and low technology as well as pertinent ADA definitions and law content. Numerous reasonable accommodation examples for various disabilities are offered. Photographs are offered as examples of actual workstations used by clients.

The appendices include several areas of information that will prove helpful to the rehabilitation consultant. One of the important inclusions is an extensive review on how to give a deposition. A comprehensive glossary of terms will assist the professional in rounding out his or her vocabulary as it applies to this legal arena. A bibliography identifies many essential and excellent resources available to the rehabilitation consultant. Other items included are a code of ethics as developed by the Commission on Rehabilitation Counselor Certification (CRCC), an Interview Worksheet, the Labor Market Survey Worksheet, a Functional Capacities Consideration worksheet, the Transferable Skills Worksheet, a Job Analysis Worksheet, definitions of the DOT Worker Traits, a Deposition Checklist, and important new sections of the Federal Rules of Evidence.

Acknowledgments

Several people deserve special recognition for their assistance. The editing by Tessa Johnson (who devoted most of her vacation and discretionary time to the project) was invaluable. Contributions by the co-authors mentioned above have significantly broadened the base of information. The editing and production assistance by Janet Field brought this text to completion. Editorial help, contributions, suggestions, comments and general research support by Dr. Debbie Berens, Dr. Ann Landes, Susan Sherman, MS, CRC, past Program Director for Georgia vocational rehabilitation and past president of the National Rehabilitation Association (and current doctoral student), and state agency Program Manager, Mary Abercrombie, MS, CRC, were extremely helpful. To all of them we add our heartfelt thanks for a job well done!

In addition to the persons cited above, the authors wish to thank their many friends and colleagues in the business rehabilitation consulting. These many associations and shared experiences have contributed greatly to the formulation and ultimate development of this publication. In a very real sense, the contents reflect the work that is already in practice by many professionals in the field of rehabilitation.

ROW & TFF

Chapter 1
Rehabilitation Foundations

Introduction

Although this text is intended to be a practical guide to help rehabilitation professionals accomplish high-level and complex tasks, it is beneficial to know something about the historical foundations of the profession. Additional workers' compensation history is located in the appropriate chapter. Readers who are interested in more detailed information about the foundations of public sector rehabilitation are referred to Obermann's extensive review in *A History of Vocational Rehabilitation in America* (1967), a summary of history in Wright's Total Rehabilitation (1980), and the chapter Historical Roots of Modern Rehabilitation Practices from the text *Foundations Vocational Rehabilitation Process* by Rubin & Roessler (2008) and Maki & Tarvydas (2012) (see also McGowan & Porter, 1967).

Public Related Vocational Rehabilitation Programs

Public sector vocational rehabilitation, as we know it, is a fairly recent phenomenon. The beginnings are well entrenched in the past but enjoyed little financial support from governments until mid 1900s. During ancient times, treatment of people with disabilities was said to have ranged from neglect to abuse (Rubin & Roessler, 2008). Children born as Spartans who were considered less than adequate were left exposed to die (Rubin & Roessler, 2008). However, after the turn of the 20th century, a number of changes rapidly occurred. This was termed the "age of interdependence" (Allen, 1965, p. 21) and indicated the changes brought on by industrialization and the prevailing philosophy of rugged individualism (Rubin & Roessler, 1978). After the advent of the taxation system in 1913 (providing the foundation for the income tax of 1 to 6%), ground was laid for various laws that would allow the government to provide social welfare and vocational rehabilitation services and would allow wealthy persons to make contributions claimed as deductions, which would help people with disabilities (Rubin & Roessler, 2008).

One of the first efforts for extending rehabilitation and vocational training was the result of the **War Risk Insurance Act** of 1914, which provided rehabilitation and vocational training to veterans injured in military service (Bitner, 1979). Later, the **Smith-Hughes Act** of 1917 signaled the beginning of the vocational rehabilitation movement by providing funds for vocational education to dislocated industrial workers and unskilled youth migrating to cities. The idea of vocational rehabilitation of people with disabilities gained acceptance, and the term "residual capacities" was coined (Rubin & Roessler, 2008, p. 25).

The **Soldiers Rehabilitation Act** of 1918 was designed to help veterans who were disabled regardless of which war. People who experienced the injury as far back as the Revolutionary War were provided medical and vocational services. The Federal Board for Vocational Education was responsible for vocational education or retraining for all veterans, provided that

(1) the injury was received while serving in the military,

(2) the injury was a handicap to employment, and

(3) the education provided a feasible plan to employment (Obermann, 1965). The criteria are similar for public sector federally funded vocational rehabilitation services provided currently.

The civilian version was initially proffered in 1918 but by 1920 had survived substantial attack and was passed as the **Smith-Fess Act**. The Act was a temporary measure until extended in 1924 (Rubin & Roessler, 2008). The incentive for states to support this endeavor came from the plan that for every dollar the state contributed, the federal government would match it (50/50 matching funds). However, smaller states received a minimum of $5,000. As with the military act, the Federal Board for Vocational Education was the designated agency for providing the services, and the minimum age was set at 16.

In 1935 with the passage of the **Social Security Act**, vocational rehabilitation programs became a permanent part of federal services, which could be deleted only if by action of Congress. To enhance the employment of persons who were blind or visually impaired, the **Randolph-Sheppard Act** in 1936 passed with a provision that people with blindness could operate vending stands on federal property. To enhance the lives of people with blindness further, the **Wagner-O'Day Act** of 1938 required federal purchase of specified products from workshops for the blind (Rubin & Roessler, 2008).

In 1943 the **Borden-LaFollette Act** broadened the definition of eligibility to include the mentally ill and "retarded," and expanded services for physical restoration, living expenses, and people who were blind. In 1944 the **Servicemens' Readjustment Act** provided a variety of services, including training, tuition, subsistence, direct loans, unemployment allowances, readjustment benefits, preferential employment, and referral services. This program is administered by the Veterans' Administration (Obermann, 1967).

In 1954 the **Vocational Rehabilitation Act** authorized services for people with more severe disabilities, provided funds for graduate training and research and improving facilities at workshops and other rehabilitation settings (Obermann, 1967). In 1965 the **Vocational Rehabilitation Act amendments** authorized construction of rehabilitation facilities, established extended evaluation, and included persons with socially handicapping conditions. Also, economic need was eliminated as a requisite for rehabilitation services. The act was again **amended in 1967** to separately provide rehabilitation services for migratory workers, the elimination of state residency requirements for serving people with disabilities in need of rehabilitation services, and the construction and operation of a national center for deaf-blind youth and adults (Bitner, 1979; Sink & Field, 1981).

Amendments to the Vocational Rehabilitation Act of 1968 included approval to expend funds for new construction of rehabilitation facilities and an authorization to provide vocational evaluation work-adjustment services to disadvantaged persons by reason of age, education, ethnic, or other factors (Sink & Field, 1981).

An important act in rehabilitation legislation history, the **Rehabilitation Act of 1973**, emphasized services to people with more severe disabilities and involvement in the consumers' rehabilitation process, which included an individual written rehabilitation plan (see Table 1.1 for relevant sections). It also provided for annual evaluations of eligibility and programs of affirmative action (Sink & Field, 1981). This act continues to be relevant (especially for educational institutions).

Another important piece of legislation, the **Education for All Handicapped Children Act** (EAHCA and sometimes shortened to Education for Handicapped Act, EHA), PL94-142, was passed in 1975 and was directed toward children with disabilities. Services initially began at age three and, if the disability was severe enough to meet certain requirements with regard to public education, continued through the age of 21. In 1986, the law was revised to include an infant and toddler component. In 1990 the law changed names to become the **Individuals with Disabilities Education Act** (PL101-476) but was update to EHA to specifically include brain injury, autism, and transition services. Another revision in 2004, titled **Individuals with Disabilities Education Improvement Act** (PL108-446), cleared the way to help some students who, prior to this change, had to fall behind in school before interventions could be initiated (IDEA notebook, 2005). The regulations released in September 2011 included rules (known as Part B for ages 3 through 21 and Part C for birth through age 2) and provided the criteria for an Individualized Family Service Plan (IFSP). A model form is available at http://idea.ed.gov/ part-c/search/new. For an overview of the revised Part B and Part C, visit http://idea.ed.gov/.

In 1978 Public Law 95-602 established the **Rehabilitation, Comprehensive Services, and Developmental Disabilities Act**, which created a national council for people with disabilities, the National Institute of Handicapped Research, independent living services, and continued emphasis on vocational services to the severely handicapped. However, vocational rehabilitation was provided separately to representatives of veterans' groups by the Veterans' Administration.

The **Assistive Technology Act**, often called the Tech Act for short, was first passed in1988. Reauthorized in 1994, 1998, and 2004, it provides federal funding support to states. In Georgia, for instance, Tools for Life is affiliated. The Tech Act is intended to:

> . . . *promote people's awareness of, and access to, assistive technology (AT) devices and services. The Act seeks to provide AT to persons with disabilities, so they can more fully participate in education, employment, and daily activities on a level playing field with other members of their communities. The Act covers people with disabilities of all ages, all disabilities, in all environments (early intervention, K-12, post-secondary, vocational rehabilitation, community living, aging services, etc.)* (National Dissemination Center for Children with Disabilities [NICHCY], 2009, p. 1). (Editors note: NICHCY was origi-

nally the National Information Center for Handicapped Children and Youth, but the terms have changed for appropriateness. Because NICHCY was so well known, the initials are still used even though the initials do not match the official name.)

The **Americans with Disabilities Act** (ADA) of 1990 was a landmark accomplishment that prohibits discrimination against people with disabilities in regard to several factors, including employment (Title I), transportation (Title II), and public accommodations and activities by public, state, and local government such as buses and trains (Title III). The ADA also provides for requiring communications accommodations such as relay services (Title IV). Title V, a miscellaneous category, provides insurance-related rules and amendments to the rehabilitation Act of 1973. Many advocates believed that the ADA would have a pervasive impact on the rights and privileges extended to people with disabilities. Indeed the first award from litigation produced a verdict of $572,000, which was subsequently reduced to $222,000 by United States Magistrate Judge Ronald Guzman (Southeast Disability and Business Technical Assistance Center, 1993). As observed in the third edition of this text, it was thought that the law would make good employers better and bad employers more clever. Although the ADA has dramatically affected the lives of many, a study of the first decade post-ADA revealed no significant change in the employment of people with disabilities (Lee, 2003). Not surprisingly the intent of the original ADA law was circumvented which resulted in a substantive revision referred to as the ADA Amendments Act (ADAAA) in 2008 (P.L. 110-325), which became effective on January 1, 2009 (ADA, 2011). The aim of the amendments is to reduce the emphasis on "disability" and reinvigorate efforts to reduce discrimination. As Lee writes (2003) "The threshold issue—whether or not the employee meets the ADA definition of 'disabled'—has been extremely difficult for plaintiffs to establish" (p. 16). With the reinvigoration, advocates are hopeful that true change will occur. Chapter 13 offers more detailed and practical information concerning the importance of this law for practicing professionals.

In 1996 the **Health Insurance Portability and Accountability Act** (HIPAA), became Public Law 104-191 on August 21, 1996. This law affects nearly everyone who visits a health care professional, and probably every reader of this chapter has been required to fill out privacy forms. For the rehabilitation professional, there are at least two practical consequences. First, many rehabilitation professionals must comply with HIPAA requirements as part of their practice, particularly in the private sector. Disclosures as part of the automatic signatures attached to emails are commonplace. Secondly, many private practitioners are engaged in consulting or expert-witness activities with attorneys and insurance companies and are required to abide by business associate rules (see below). The U.S. Department of Health and Human Services has published a Guide that is useful, and pertinent selections are reprinted below (Department of Health and Human Services, 2003).

The U.S. Department of Health and Human Services ("HHS") issued the Privacy Rule to implement the requirement of the **Health Insurance Portability and Accountability Act** of 1996 ("HIPAA"). The Privacy Rule standards address the use and disclosure of individuals' health information—called "protected health information" by organizations subject to the Privacy Rule — called "covered entities," as well as standards for individuals' privacy rights to understand and control how their health information is used. Within HHS, the Office for Civil Rights ("OCR") has responsibility for implementing and enforcing the Privacy Rule with respect to voluntary compliance activities and civil money penalties.

The Privacy Rule, as well as all the Administrative Simplification rules, applies to health plans, health care clearinghouses, and to any health care provider who transmits health information in electronic form. *Health plans* include health, dental, vision, and prescription drug insurers, health maintenance organizations ("HMOs"), Medicare, Medicaid, Medicare+Choice and Medicare supplement insurers, and long-term care insurers (excluding nursing home fixed-indemnity policies). Health plans also include employer-sponsored group health plans, government and church-sponsored health plans, and multi-employer health plans.

Every *health care provider*, regardless of size, who electronically transmits health information in connection with certain transactions, is a covered entity. These transactions include claims, benefit eligibility inquiries, referral authorization requests, or other transactions for which HHS has established standards under the HIPAA Transactions Rule. Using electronic technology, such as email, does not mean a health care provider is a covered entity; the transmission must be in connection with a standard transaction. The Privacy Rule covers a health care provider whether it electronically transmits these transactions directly or uses a billing service or other third party to do so on its behalf. Health care providers include all "providers of services" (e.g., institutional providers such as hospitals) and "providers of medical or health services" (e.g., non-institutional providers such as physicians, dentists, and other practitioners) as defined by Medicare, and any other person or organization that furnishes, bills, or is paid for health care.

In general, a business associate is a person or organization, other than a member of a covered entity's workforce, that performs certain functions or activities on behalf of, or provides certain services to, a covered entity that involves the use or disclosure of individually identifiable health information. Business associate functions or activities on behalf of a covered entity include claims processing, data analysis, utilization review, and billing. Business associate services to a covered entity are limited to legal, actuarial, accounting, consulting, data aggregation, management, administrative, accreditation, or financial services.

When a covered entity uses a contractor or other nonworkforce member to perform *"business associate"* services or activities, the Rule requires that the covered entity include certain protections for the information in a business associate agreement (in certain circumstances governmental entities may use alternative means to achieve the same protections).

The Privacy Rule protects all *"individually identifiable health information"* held or transmitted by a covered entity or its business associate, in any form or media, whether electronic, paper, or oral. The Privacy Rule calls this information *"protected health information (PHI)."*

"Individually identifiable health information" is information, including demographic data, that relates to the individual's past, present, or future physical or mental health or condition, the provision of health care to the individual, or the past, present, or future payment for the provision of health care to the individual that identifies the individual or for which there is a reasonable basis to believe that it can be used to identify the individual. Individually identifiable health information includes many common identifiers (e.g., name, address, birth date, Social Security Number).

All covered entities, except "small health plans," must be compliant with the Privacy Rule by April 14, 2003. Small health plans, however, have until April 14, 2004 to comply (pp. 1-4).

In 1998, the **Workforce Investment Act** (WIA) (P.L. 105-220) and the Technical Amendments to the Workforce Investment Act (Public Law 105-277) were added to provide assistance to states interested in establishing a statewide and local workforce investment system (Department of Labor, Employment and Training Administration [DOLETA], 2004). It is also the foundation for "one-stop" delivery systems where clients seeking or receiving services from multiple agencies can reduce the time and conflict experienced when those agencies are scattered in various locations. According to the law, the purpose of the WIA:

> . . . is to provide workforce investment activities, through statewide and local workforce investment systems, that increase the employment, retention, and earnings of participants, and increase occupational skill attainment by participants, and, as a result, improve the quality of the workforce, reduce welfare dependency, and enhance the productivity and competitiveness of the Nation (DOLETA, 1998, p. 11).

From a practical perspective, the WIA authorizes the use of federal job training funds for adults, dislocated workers, and youth, including people with disabilities. Services can include vocational assessment, vocational and employment information, unemployment insurance assistance, and job counseling and placement assistance. Part of the relevant content in this Act is the requirement for personnel to be qualified as a rehabilitation counselor, which essentially means graduating with a master's degree from an accredited rehabilitation counseling program and obtaining certification such as the Certified Rehabilitation Counselor (CRC) (Rubin & Roessler, 2008).

The long awaited **Ticket to Work and Work Incentives Act** (TWWIA) of 1999 (P.L. 106-170) was signed into law on December 17, 1999. One of the critical issues for people with disabilities who are receiving public assistance is health insurance. This act, which is administered by the Social Security Administration, improves social security disability insurance (SSDI) and supplemental security income (SSI) benefits by giving states the option to allow recipients to purchase Medicaid (usually if they were receiving SSI) or continuing Medicare coverage (if they were or are receiving SSDI). This change is an attempt to reduce the significant disincentives for people with disabilities to remain on benefits rather than seek employment. From the Social Security Administration's (SSA) website:

> Social Security's Ticket to Work Program is free, voluntary, and available to most people who receive Social Security Disability Insurance (SSDI) or Supplemental Security Income (SSI) benefits because they are disabled or blind. Eligible beneficiaries may choose to assign their Ticket to an Employment Network (EN) of their choice or to a State Vocational Rehabilitation (SVR) agency to obtain employment services and supports necessary to achieve a work goal. The EN/SVR, if they accept the Ticket, will coordinate and provide appropriate services to help the beneficiary find and maintain employment (SSA, 2011a, p. 1).

There are two sections and four purposes. The sections are as follows:

- Improved access to employment training and placement services for people with disabilities.
- Provides provision for work without fear of losing Medicare and Medicaid coverage. Government can charge for premiums part or fully depending on income.

The purposes [Section 2(b) of the Act] are as follows:

- To provide health care and employment preparation and placement services to individuals with disabilities that will enable those individuals to reduce their dependency on cash benefit programs.
- To encourage states to adopt the option of allowing individuals with disabilities to purchase Medicaid coverage that is necessary to enable such individuals to maintain employment.
- To provide individuals with disabilities the option of maintaining Medicare coverage while working.
- To establish a return to work ticket program that will allow individuals with disabilities to seek the services necessary to obtain and retain employment and reduce their dependency on cash benefit programs.

Although the "tickets" are typically used in public rehabilitation agencies, there are opportunities for private sector rehabilitation counselors to enter into an agreement with the Social Security Administration and accept clients (Enrique Vega, personal communication, December 15, 2011).

The above listed laws and countless sets of regulations have firmly established the intent of the government to provide necessary assistance to people with disabilities or other disadvantages in order that they, as much as possible, may enjoy the benefits of the American way of life. Also, the well noted militancy of many persons with disabilities in the early 70s resulted in much more public awareness as well as additional funding (Weed & Field, 1989).

As a result of the legislation accompanied by research that consistently shows favorable cost-benefit ratios of providing services to people with disabilities, vocational rehabilitation has enjoyed a steady growth from its inception. However, government spending has become enough of a burden to the taxpayer that funding has been reduced and demands have been placed on rehabilitation counselors to do more with less (Rubin & Roessler, 2008). The past few years of the "Great Recession" have taken their toll on the U.S. economy and have hit hard human services organizations (Khimm, 2011).

Workers Compensation

Another specialized group requiring rehabilitation are people injured while on the job (see also chapter on this subject). The concepts that underlie workers' compensation were imported primarily from Germany. As early as 1884, Germany had legislated plans for injured workers, followed by Austria in 1887. In 1902 Maryland enacted a cooperative insurance law of benefits to be awarded an injured worker without suing his employer or proving negligence. One of the first on-the-job injury law efforts in the United States was related to workers' compensation, with the Civil Employees Act in 1908. The 1909 Montana law, which provided for injured employees of the coal mining industry, and the 1910 compulsory New York state law quickly followed. In 1911 ten states enacted compulsory workers' compensation laws. In 1920 the Smith-Fess Act provided counseling, training, prosthetic appliance, and job placement to persons with physical disabilities from industrial injuries. The Smith-Fess Act was a major impetus for laws for the injured worker, and by 1921, forty-five of the states and territories had laws on the books, although they were not uniform (Obermann, 1967). It was not until 1948, when Mississippi passed a workers' compensation law, that all states (at the time) had such legislation (Safilios-Rothschild, 1970, as cited in Rubin & Roessler, 2008).

The initial workers' compensation laws did not specifically provide for vocational rehabilitation, and the people who supported vocational rehabilitation generally stopped at insisting on medical and wage compensation to injured employees. In 1916, New York State provided for vocational rehabilitation of the injured worker who needed the service. This is the first notion of the "second injury fund" (Obermann, 1967). Although workers' compensation acts preceded the vocational rehabilitation acts, thereby apparently recognizing an interest in assisting injured workers, the vocational rehabilitation aspects have been slow to catch on for this group. Laws collected from all fifty states and the U.S. Chamber of Commerce's evaluation of various workers' compensation laws note that many states still do not provide vocational rehabilitation to injured workers. Several states, which had mandatory rehabilitation evaluations for injured workers, have repealed the laws, and others have provisions for vocational rehabilitation, although not mandatory (U.S. Chamber of Commerce, 2000). Georgia, Florida, Washington, Alaska, and Colorado are examples of states where mandatory rehabilitation laws have been repealed, reportedly to attempt to reduce costs.

The rehabilitation of injured workers takes several forms. The basic premise is that employers employing persons (usually one, two, or three full-time employees depending on the state) are required to have workers' compensation insurance. Many others are insured through their own special law. For example, railroad workers are covered by the **Federal Employers Liability Act**. Federal workers (Office of Workers Compensation Programs) have their own insurance program as do harbor workers, longshoremen, and persons who work at sea (Weed & Field, 2001).

Essentially, workers' compensation laws were designed to provide employers immunity from litigation for damages (Sink & Field, 1981; White, 1983). Prior to the passage of such laws, workers injured on the job were forced to sue the employer, which was expensive and time consuming, leading to financial ruin for numerous people. Moreover, it was presumed that a worker would enter into the employment arrangement knowing that it was dangerous and therefore accepting the risk (Obermann, 1967). Furthermore, if the person who was injured could be shown to have been negligent in any way, they would not receive compensation (Obermann, 1967). The theory proposed was to remove the "at fault" issue. If employer and employees accepted the premise that after an injury occurred, the worker was, regardless of the reason for the injury, to receive reasonable medical care and be otherwise compensated if they could not return to work, then costs and conflict should be reduced. In fact, as a result of these laws, employees were, and are, not permitted to sue the employer covered by state workers' compensation laws. There are other workers' compensation related laws where that is not true (e.g., Federal Employees Liability Act - FELA).

Unfortunately, the goals have not always been accomplished (Washburn, 1992; White, 1983). Since the form of workers' compensation rules varies depending on the industry and state, counselors must be thoroughly educated in the industry in which they choose to work. For example, as noted above, the railroad industry is covered by a law (FELA), which is based upon comparative negligence, whereas federal employees, longshore harbor workers, and people who work at sea each have a separate act (Jones Act) (U.S. Chamber of Commerce, 2005; Deneen, 1981; Huneke, 1982; Lynch, 1979; Matkin, 1985; Mason, 1982; Shrey, 1979). It is clear, through various studies, that injured workers often are perceived to be more difficult clients, and many state rehabilitation counselors avoid working with this population (Deutsch & Sawyer, 2000; Rasch, 1985; Shrey, 1979). In fact, this is a significant enough issue that a national task force has been in existence for years to discuss problems of vocational rehabilitation of the industrially injured, and the U.S. Chamber of Commerce has undertaken the study of the various workers' compensation laws in all fifty states (International Association of Industrial Accident Boards and Commissions [IAIABC], 2011; U.S. Chamber of Commerce, 2011).

With regard to an incentive for controlling costs, in 2011, The Occupational Safety and Health Administration (OSHA) estimated that employers pay almost $1 *billion* per week for direct workers' compensation costs alone (OSHA). The total economic costs in 2004 were estimated at $142.2 billion with another effect of 120 million lost workdays (American Society of Safety Engineers, 2011). With rising costs of medical expenses and payment of lost wages for the industrially injured, a number of companies began to look at possible ways to contain costs as well as to have more control over rehabilitation of injured workers. Many insurance companies found that state rehabilitation counselors were placing injured workers into two or more years of training, thereby obligating insurance carriers to continue compensation payments until clients had completed training programs. As early as 1970, INA Insurance Company primarily employed rehabilitation nurses to oversee medical management, review case records for over-payments to hospitals and doctors, and return injured workers to employment. In the last 30 years, a dramatic increase in professionals representing nurses, rehabilitation counseors, and others is clearly noted (Field, 1981; Matkin, 1982; Matkin & Rigger, 1985; Shrey, 1979; Weed & Field, 2001). It appears that these efforts have been successful both in reducing costs to insurance companies and in placing people in employment (Weed & Lewis, 1994). However, a review of some of the larger national companies, like Crawford & Company, has revealed a significant reduction in the offering of vocational rehabilitation services with a shift to interest in "risk management."

It is apparent that the rise of the private rehabilitation sector is associated with the changing workers' compensation laws, the reduction of public funding, a greater public awareness of the cost of injured employees, and the general social attitude toward assisting persons with disabilities (NIHR, 1985). In addition, with the training programs available to rehabilitation professionals, certification of rehabilitation professionals has been implemented. Since 1974 professionals have been certified as rehabilitation counselors (CRC) if they

Table 1.1
Summary of Rehabilitation Laws Relevant to the Rehabilitation Counselor

Law	Emphasis	Year
Federal Employees Workers' Comp Act	Alternative to suing an employer for on-the-job injuries.	1908
War Risk Act (PL 65-90)	Provided rehabilitation and vocational training. Gave the U.S. Government the authority to insure ships at sea.	1914
Smith-Hughes Act (PL 64-347)	Promoted vocational education to dislocated industrial workers and unskilled youth migrating to cities.	1917
Smith-Sears Act or Soldiers Rehabilitation Act (PL 65-178)	Helped veterans who were disabled and were provided medical and vocational services through the Federal Board for Vocational Education.	1918
Smith-Fess Act (PL 66-236)	Counseling, training, prosthetic appliances, and job placement to people with physical disabilities from work injuries.	1920
Social Security Act (PL 74-271)	Vocational rehabilitation programs became a permanent part of federal services.	1935
Randolph-Sheppard Act	People who were blind could operate vending stands on federal property.	1936
Wagner-O'Day Act	Required federal purchase of specified products from workshops for the blind.	1938
Borden-LaFollette Act	Broadened the definition of eligibility to include the mentally ill and "retarded," expanded services for physical restoration, living expenses, and people who were blind.	1943
Vocational Rehabilitation Act (PL 83-565) aka Hill-Burton Act	Authorized services for more severely disabled, provided funds for graduate training and research and improving facilities at workshops and other rehabilitation settings.	1954
Vocational Rehabilitation Act amendments (PL 89-333)	Authorized construction of rehabilitation facilities, established extended evaluation, and included persons with socially handicapping conditions.	1965
Amendments to the Vocational Rehabilitation Act (PL 90-391)	Included approval to expend funds for new construction of rehabilitation facilities and an authorization to provide vocational evaluation work-adjustment services to disadvantaged persons by reason of age, education, ethnic or other factors.	1968
Rehabilitation Act (PL 92-112)	A *significant* revision of the serves provided to persons with disabilities that affects rehabilitation services to this day. Emphasized services to people who were more severely disabled and involvement in the consumers' rehabilitation process, which included an individual written rehabilitation plan (IWRP) now known as "Individual Plan for Employment" (IPE)	1973
	Section 501: Affirmative Action in Federal Hiring. Mandates nondiscrimination by the Federal government in it own hiring practices	
	Section 502: Architectural and Transportation barriers Compliance. Insure compliance on accessibility of buildings constructed with federal funds.	
	Section 503: Affirmative Action by Federal Contract Recipients. Requires affirmative action on the part of businesses that receive contracts from the federal government that exceeds $2,500.	
	Section 504: Equal Opportunities. Prohibits the exclusion based on disability of otherwise qualified persons with disabilities from participating in any program or activity that receives federal financial assistance.	

Table 1.1 (Continued)
Summary of Rehabilitation Laws Relevant to the Rehabilitation Counselor

Education for All Handicapped Children Act (EAHCA) aka Education for Handicapped Act (EHA) (PL 94-142)	Although educational laws are not typically relevant to rehabilitation counselors, the EACHA-IDEA relates to children with disabilities who transition to work (approximately 16 years of age potentially through the age of 22). Services initially began at age three and if the disability was severe enough to meet certain requirements with regard to public education, continued through the age of 21. The mission was to provide free appropriate, public education for all children with disabilities in the "least restrictive alternative."	1975 with revisions
	Revised to include infant and toddlers (birth through age 2).	1986
Re-titled to the Individuals with Disabilities Education Act (IDEA) (PL 101-476)	When re-titled to IDEA, it was updated to specifically include brain injury, autism and transition services.	1990
	Amended to broaden "access" which included access to schools as well as curriculum. Be educated along side students without disabilities.	1997
	Another revision, titled Individuals with Disabilities Education Improvement Act (PL108-446), cleared the way for finding ways to help some students who, prior to this change, had to fall behind in school before interventions could be implemented.	2004 with Rules change in 2011
	The regulations released in September, 2011 included rules (known as Part B for ages 3 through 21 and Part C for birth through age 2) and provides the criteria for an Individualized Family Service Plan (IFSP).	
	Note: For rehabilitation counselors who author pediatric life care plans, IDEA will be a consideration since education includes occupational, speech/language, and physical therapies which assists the child in their education (they may need additional services for medical rehabilitation/habilitation therapies). Public agency rehabilitation counselors are involved in transition from school to work.	
Rehabilitation, Comprehensive Services, and Developmental Disabilities Act (PL 95-602)	Created the National Institute of Handicapped Research, a national council for people with disabilities, independent living services, and continued emphasis on vocational services to the severely handicapped.	1978
Rehabilitation Act Amendments (PL 99-506)	Added rehabilitation engineering and supported employment programs.	1986
Assistive Technology Act aka Tech Act (PL 105-394)	Federal funding support for assistive technology in 3 ways.	1988 and reauthorized in 1994, 1998, and 2004
	1. The establishment of assistive technology (AT) demonstration centers, information centers, equipment loan facilities, referral services, and other consumer-oriented programs;	
	2. Protection and advocacy services to help people with disabilities and their families, as they attempt to access the services for which they are eligible;	
	3. Federal/state programs to provide low interest loans and other alternative financing options to help people with disabilities purchase needed assistive technology.	
Americans with Disabilities Act (ADA) (PL 101-336)	Prohibits discrimination on the basis of disability in employment, State and local government, public accommodations, commercial facilities, transportation, and telecommunications. Applies to the United States Congress also.	1990
	An individual with a disability is defined by the ADA as a person who has a physical or mental impairment that substantially limits one or more major life activities, a person who has a history or record of such an impairment, or a person who is perceived by others as having such an impairment.	

Table 1.1 (Continued)
Summary of Rehabilitation Laws Relevant to the Rehabilitation Counselor

Americans with Disabilities Act (ADA) (PL 101-336) [Continued]	Title I: Employment. Requires employers with 15 or more employees to provide qualified individuals with disabilities an equal opportunity to benefit from the full range of employment-related opportunities available to others. Examples include discrimination in recruitment, hiring, promotions, training, pay, social activities, and other privileges of employment. Key terms: qualified person with a disability, essential functions of the job, reasonable accommodation, undue hardship.	1990
	Title II: State and local government activities and public transportation. Covers all activities of State and local governments regardless of the government entity's size or receipt of federal funding. Requires that state and local governments give people with disabilities an equal opportunity to benefit from all of their programs, services, and activities (to include public education, employment, transportation, recreation, health care, social services, courts, voting, and town meetings). Covers public transportation services, such as city buses and public rail transit. All newly purchased transportation must be accessible and trains manufactured before the ADA law must have at least one accesible car.	
	Title III: Public Accommodations. Covers businesses and nonprofit service providers that are public accommodations, privately operated entities offering certain types of courses and examinations, privately operated transportation, and commercial facilities. Public accommodations are private entities who own, lease, lease to, or operate facilities such as restaurants, retail stores, hotels, movie theaters, private schools, convention centers, doctors' offices, homeless shelters, transportation depots, zoos, funeral homes, day care centers, and recreation facilities including sports stadiums and fitness clubs. Transportation services provided by private entities are also covered.	
	Title IV: Telecommunications Relay Services. Requires common carriers (telephone companies) to establish interstate and intrastate telecommunications relay services (TRS) 24 hours a day, 7 days a week. Also requires closed captioning of Federally funded public service announcements.	
	Title V: Miscellaneous. Includes insurance issues, amendment to the rehabilitation act, development of technical assistance materials, coverage of congressional agencies and prohibits state immunity from remedies. This title specifies certain mental disorders which are not covered by the ADA, including transvestism or other sexual behavior disorders, compulsive gambling, kleptomania or pyromania, or substance use disorders resulting from current illegal use of drugs. Source: http://www.ada.gov/cguide.htm	
ADA Amendments Act (ADAAA) (P.L. 110-325)	The effect of the amendments are to reduce the emphasis on "disability" and reinvigorate efforts to reduce discrimination. This change is expected to have substantial effects on the rights of persons with disabilities in relation to work.	2008
Health Insurance Portability and Accountability Act (HIPAA), (PL 104-191)	HIPAA standards address the use and disclosure of individuals' health information—called "protected health information" by organizations subject to the Privacy Rule — called "covered entities," Key issue is related to technology transmission of health information. This includes email.	1996
Workforce Investment Act (WIA) (PL 105-220) and (PL 105-277)	Authorizes the use of federal job training funds for adults, dislocated workers and youth which includes people with disabilities. Services can include vocational assessment, vocational and employment information, unemployment insurance assistance, and job counseling and placement assistance. Foundation for "one-stop" shop for clients.	1998
Ticket to Work and Work Incentives Act (TWWIA) (P.L. 106-170)	Authorizes clients who receive Social Security Disability Insurance (SSDI) or Supplemental Security Income (SSI) benefits because they are disabled or blind, to choose to assign their Ticket to an Employment Network (EN) of their choice or to a State Vocational Rehabilitation (SVR) agency to obtain employment services and supports necessary to achieve a work goal.	1999

meet certain minimum standards and pass a written examination. Since 1984 professionals can be certified as disability management specialists (CDMS) and, beginning in 1993, as a Certified Case Manager (CCM) when they meet certain minimum standards and pass a written examination. In 1966 the Certified Life Care Planner (CLCP) was added. Another certification, Certified Vocational Evaluator (CVE), is available for work evaluators as well. Through the Council on Rehabilitation Education (CORE), university programs have recognized the clear trend for more private rehabilitation counseling and placed greater emphasis on such topics as private rehabilitation and job placement (CORE, 2011; Cottone, 1985; Matkin, 1981). In addition, historically there appears to be role strain and frustration associated with rehabilitation counseling in the public sector, and many persons in the profession appear to be interested in practicing in their own business (Chase, 1983; Rubin & Emener, 1979; Smits & Ledbetter, 1979). There may also be some evidence that there are certain personality characteristics that rehabilitation professionals have which are different between private and public sectors (Bernhard, 1984; Matkin, 1986, 1993).

In any case, based on the dramatic rise in membership for various organizations representing private sector rehabilitation and the decline of similar membership in the National Rehabilitation Counselors Association, it seems clear that private rehabilitation is here to stay (Field, 1981; Field, 1994; Weed & Field, 1989). The term "managed care" has appeared in many publications, and "case managers" are uniting to form organizations with common interests and purposes. Several journal articles and books, already cited elsewhere in this chapter, are predicting that private rehabilitation will continue to grow while public funding for rehabilitation will increase at a much slower pace (Brodwin, 2008).

It is also notable that many corporations and entities include in-house or contract with rehabilitation professionals to work with their injured employees (Huneke, 1982; Mason, 1982; Shrey, 1979; Taylor, Golter, Golter & Backer, 1985). It appears that some of these corporations believe that rehabilitation professionals working in a particular field must be intimately familiar with the laws that apply to the industry as well as the idiosyncrasies of the particular business. There also appears to be evidence that professionals need to be familiar with pain syndromes, substance abuse, secondary gain issues, disability insurance provisions, and their impact on vocational rehabilitation. For example, most agree that persons who are receiving compensation take substantially longer to return to work or heal from their injuries than other groups (Berkowitz, 1980; Deutsch & Sawyer, 1999; Lamb & Rogawski, 1978; Matkin, 1985; Rasch, 1985; Rubin & Roessler, 1978; Walls, 1982; Walls, Masson, & Werner, 1977), and those who have attorneys tend to take longer to return to work and cost more to rehabilitate (Jones, 1985). Private rehabilitation appears to be able to maintain much smaller case loads with intense rehabilitation efforts than their public counterparts (Lynch, 1979; Shrey, 1979; Weed & Field, 2001). In addition, at one point the various graduate training programs in rehabilitation encouraged their students to consider private rehabilitation due to the lack of jobs available in the public sector. This is apparently having an impact on students' attitudes and goals (Crawford, 1982). However, one study (Crisler, 1992) reveals that many public sector professionals are planning to retire within the next few years, and rehabilitation counselor training programs are graduating only about one-half of the counselors needed to fill expected slots. As of 2011, there continues to be a shortage of rehabilitation counselors particularly in state/public rehabilitation agencies (University of Iowa, 2010).

It should be noted that some private sector counselors also work with Social Security cases, personal injury lawsuits, private corporations, divorce actions, and employment agencies, although this represents relatively few job opportunities (Brodwin, 2008, Havranek, 1993; Goodwin, 1982; Matkin, 1982; May, 1983; Weed, 1990; Weed & Field, 2001). Most counselors in private practice work in concert with insurance companies, and it may be that insurance companies feel that rehabilitation counselors who receive direct payment are more responsive to their needs. This may present professional and ethical challenges not evident in the past (Banja, 1995; Cottone, 1985; Matkin, 1985; Matkin & May, 1981). Even more complicating for the professional is the insurance company that directly employs them (Taylor, Golter, Golter & Backer, 1985). In any case, consultants working in the private sector face influences from which the public sector counselors are usually shielded (Cross, 1979; Treon, 1979; Trimble, 1977). Table 1.2 identifies some of the differences between private and public sector rehabilitationists.

The Contemporary Rehabilitation Counselor

Given the rather significant differences between the private and public sector rehabilitation professionals, i.e., the populations served and work performed, the definition of vocational rehabilitation may not be the same for the private sector counselor as it is for the public sector counselor. For example, Townsend (1966) defined vocational rehabilitation as the restoration of persons with handicaps to the fullest physical, mental, social, vocational, and economic usefulness of which they are capable. For professionals working in the pri-

Table 1.2
Similarities and Differences Between Vocational Rehabilitation
in the Public and Private Sectors

Differences (Partial Listing)

Public	Private
Funded primarily by public money. Usually Fed/State matching.	Funded primarily through fee for services with occasional govt. contracts.
Usual staff are vocational counselors.	Usually very diverse backgrounds including nurses, job development specialists etc.
Wide variety of caseloads, e.g. developmental disabilities, learning disabled, congenital and medical disorders, emotionally disturbed	Primary caseload is with work injured.
Work setting is almost always a part of a large bureaucracy.	Most are associated with small companies (comparatively).
Vocational rehabilitation usually to the maximum potential.	Vocational rehabilitation to preinjury wage level.
Clients must meet eligibility requirements.	No eligibility requirements and occasionally assist people with no disability.
Usually do not actively engage in medical management.	Frequently monitor medical progress.
Arrange for basic medical and other diagnostic exams.	Usually do not require basic medical and often do not arrange diagnostic exams.
Cases records must meet fed/state requirements.	Case recording generally reflect style of the individual company with occasional reporting similarities based on individual state requirements, or federal contract requirements.
Do not review medical bills for accuracy and correctness.	Some companies specialize in reviewing medical bills for accuracy.
Less actively involved in job placement, labor market survey, and related work.	Usually active in job placement, labor market surveys and related activity.
Usually avoid expert testimony.	Often utilized as expert witness.
Caseloads often 100 or more.	Caseloads usually 20-30.
Less active in professional associations.	Usually very active in professional associations.
Salary not based on production.	Salary often partially based on commissions or production.
Promotions and wage increases usually weighted in favor of length of service.	Promotions heavily influenced by professional success.
Usually not actively involved with business practices such as time sheets or marketing.	Frequently involved with business practices such as time sheets and marketing.

Similarities

Overall there are probably more similarities than differences. Both are interested in the employment of persons with disabilities, represent similar attitudes and goals, practice counseling, evaluate, develop and write vocational plans, etc. Much of the research tends to indicate similar activities with differing emphasis. For example, one study lists 298 competencies for the rehabilitation counseling with a large number of similarities between the rehabilitation counselor and the vocational evaluator. To reproduce them here would be beyond the scope of the table. (Chase, 1983; Field, 1981; Matkin, 1980; Matkin, 1983; Rubin, Matkin, Ashley, Beardsley, May, Onstott, and Puckett, 1983; Sink, Porter, Rubin, Painter, 1979; Weed, 1981).

vate sector, much of the focus is on returning persons to work for compensation similar to what they were earning at the time of injury, whereas the public sector counterpart may be assisting the client to achieve his highest potential (Brodwin, 2008; Rasch, 1985). In some cases, the person receiving services may not even have his job interests considered as a condition for returning to work (Deutsch & Sawyer, 1999; U.S. Department of Health and Human Services, 1981). A more accepted definition of rehabilitation counseling for present times may be:

> "A process in which a counselor and a client are involved which will help the client understand his or her problems and potential and to help the client make effective utilization of personal and environmental resources for the best possible vocational, personal and social adjustment." (Jacques, 1970)

This definition allows the client and counselor to consider the effects of the disability insurance requirements and boundaries.

Knowledge Domains

With regard to contemporary rehabilitation counseling scope of practice, the Commission on Rehabilitation Counselor Certification (CRCC) has undertaken role-and-function studies to generally provide an empirically derived description of the functions associated with the practitioner's role (CRCC, 2011). Research published in 1993 with updates provided empirical support that the following 12 knowledge domains (with subtopics) represented a valid "core" of the types of knowledge and skills needed for rehabilitation counseling practice as of 2011 (*Source: http://www.crccertification.com/pages/crc_ exam_overview/120.php*):

1. Career Counseling and Assessment

    - Theories of career development and work adjustment
    - Tests and evaluation techniques for assessing clients
    - Psychometric concepts related to measurement
    - Interpretation of assessment results for rehabilitation planning purposes
    - Computer and Internet-based career resources
    - Transferable skills analysis
    - Assistive technology

2. Job Development and Placement Services

    - Vocational implications of functional limitations
    - Job readiness including seeking and retention skills
    - Techniques used to conduct labor market surveys
    - Occupational and labor market information
    - Job-matching strategies
    - Employer development for job placement
    - Employment support services
    - Employment settings

3. Vocational Consultation and Services for Employers

    - Employer practices that affect the employment or return to work of individuals with disabilities
    - Marketing rehabilitation services and benefits for employers
    - Educating employers on disability-related issues
    - Disability prevention and management strategies
    - Job analysis and/or job description development
    - Job modification, accommodation, and restructuring including ergonomic assessment
    - Work conditioning or work hardening resources and strategies

4. Case and Caseload Management

- Case management process including time management and prioritization, rehabilitation planning, service coordination, and referral to and collaboration with other disciplines
- Principles of caseload management including case recording and documentation
- Professional roles, responsibilities, functions, and relationships with clients and other human service providers
- Negotiation, mediation, and conflict resolutions strategies
- Techniques for working effectively in teams across disciplines

5. Individual Counseling

- Individual counseling theories
- Individual counseling practices and interventions
- Behavior and personality theory
- Human growth and development
- Multicultural counseling theories and practices related to individual counseling

6. Group and Family Counseling

- Family counseling theories
- Family counseling practices and interventions
- Group counseling theories
- Group counseling practices and interventions
- Multicultural counseling theories and practices related to family and group counseling

7. Mental Health Counseling

- Diagnostic and Statistical Manual
- Rehabilitation techniques for individuals with psychiatric disabilities
- Multicultural counseling theories and practices related to mental health counseling
- Medications as they apply to individuals with psychiatric disabilities
- Dual diagnosis
- Substance abuse
- Treatment planning
- Wellness and illness prevention concepts and strategies

8. Psychosocial and Cultural Issues in Counseling

- Individual and family adjustment to disability
- Psychosocial and cultural impact of disability on the individual
- Psychosocial and cultural impact of disability on the family
- Attitudinal barriers for individuals with disabilities
- Societal issues, trends, developments as they relate to rehabilitation
- Working with individuals from various socioeconomic backgrounds
- Working with individuals with English as a second language
- Gender issues
- Human sexuality and disability issues

9. Medical, Functional, and Environmental Aspects of Disabilities

- Medical aspects and implications of various disabilities
- Medical terminology
- Medications as they relate to vocational goals and outcomes
- Functional capabilities of individuals with physical, psychiatric, and/or cognitive disabilities

- Environmental barriers for individuals with disabilities
- Rehabilitation terminology and concepts

10. Foundations, Ethics, and Professional Issues

- Philosophical foundations of rehabilitation
- Legislation or laws affecting individuals with disabilities
- Ethical decision-making models and processes
- Ethical standards for rehabilitation counselors
- Advocacy for individuals with disabilities
- Theories and techniques for providing clinical supervision
- Interpretation and application of research findings
- Evaluation procedures for assessing the effectiveness of rehabilitation services, programs, and outcomes

11. Rehabilitation Services and Resources

- Financial support/funding resources for rehabilitation services and programs
- Organizations/programs providing rehabilitation services
- Community referral resources and services for rehabilitation planning
- Services available from one-stop career centers
- Services available relating to ergonomics, assistive technology, kinesiology, and rehabilitation engineering
- Services available through client advocacy programs
- Programs for specialty populations
- Forensic rehabilitation services

12. Health Care and Disability Systems

- Managed care concepts
- Insurance programs
- Health care benefits
- Workers' compensation laws and practices
- Social Security programs, benefits, work incentives, and disincentives

Scope of Practice

In addition, the CRCC has published the scope of rehabilitation counseling as a systematic process which assists persons with physical, mental, developmental, cognitive, and emotional disabilities to achieve their personal, career, and independent living goals in the most integrated setting possible through the application of the counseling process. The counseling process involves communication, goal setting, and beneficial growth or change through self-advocacy, psychological, vocational, social, and behavioral interventions. The specific techniques and modalities utilized within this rehabilitation counseling process may include, but are not limited to:

- assessment and appraisal
- diagnosis and treatment planning
- career (vocational) counseling
- individual and group counseling treatment interventions focused on facilitating adjustments to the medical and psychosocial impact of disability
- case management, referral, and service coordination
- program evaluation and research

- interventions to remove environmental, employment, and attitudinal barriers

- consultation services among multiple parties and regulatory systems

- job analysis, job development, and placement services, including assistance with employment and job accommodations

- the provision of consultation about and access to rehabilitation technology

Source: http://www.crccertification.com/pages/crc_ccrc_scope_of_practice/43.php

Definitions (CRCC)

The following definitions are related to the Scope of Practice Statement for Rehabilitation Counseling as of 2011 (*Source: http://www.crccertification.com/pages/crc_ccrc_scope_of_practice/43.php*):

Appraisal: Selecting, administering, scoring, and interpreting instruments designed to assess an individual's aptitudes, abilities, achievements, interests, personal characteristics, disabilities, and mental, emotional, or behavioral disorders as well as the use of methods and techniques for understanding human behavior in relation to coping with, adapting to, or changing life situations.

Diagnosis and Treatment Planning: Assessing, analyzing, and providing diagnostic descriptions of mental, emotional, or behavioral conditions or disabilities; exploring possible solutions; and developing and implementing a treatment plan for mental, emotional, and psychosocial adjustment or development. Diagnosis and treatment planning shall not be construed to permit the performance of any act which rehabilitation counselors are not educated and trained to perform.

Counseling Treatment Intervention: The application of cognitive, affective, behavioral, and systemic counseling strategies which include developmental, wellness, pathologic, and multicultural principles of human behavior. Such interventions are specifically implemented in the context of a professional counseling relationship and may include, but are not limited to: appraisal; individual, group, marriage, and family counseling and psychotherapy; the diagnostic description and treatment of persons with mental, emotional, and behavioral disorders or disabilities; guidance and consulting to facilitate normal growth and development, including educational and career development; the utilization of functional assessments and career counseling for persons requesting assistance in adjusting to a disability or handicapping condition; referrals; consulting; and research.

Referral: Evaluating and identifying the needs of a client to determine the advisability of referrals to other specialists, advising the client of such judgments, and communicating as requested or deemed appropriate to such referral sources.

Case Management: A systematic process merging counseling and managerial concepts and skills through the application of techniques derived from intuitive and researched methods, thereby advancing efficient and effective decision-making for functional control of self, client, setting, and other relevant factors for anchoring a proactive practice. In case management, the counselor's role is focused on interviewing, counseling, planning rehabilitation programs, coordinating services, interacting with significant others, placing clients and following up with them, monitoring progress, and solving problems.

Program Evaluation: The effort to determine what changes occur as a result of a planned program by comparing actual changes (results) with desired changes (stated goals), and by identifying the degree to which the activity (planned program) is responsible for those changes.

Research: A systematic effort to collect, analyze, and interpret quantitative or qualitative data that describe how social characteristics, behavior, emotions, cognition, disabilities, mental disorders, and interpersonal transactions among individuals and organizations interact.

Consultation: The application of scientific principles and procedures in counseling and human development to provide assistance in understanding and solving current or potential problems that the consultee may have in relation to a third party, be it an individual, group, or organization.

Determining Disability: State-Federal

For persons to receive services from either the private or public sector, they must have a disability. The definition of what constitutes a disability varies depending on source of funding, location in which the client resides, prevailing jurisdiction (i.e., personal injury vs. state court vs. federal court vs. workers compensation vs. Jones Act), and other factors. In order to determine whether an individual is eligible for vocational rehabilitation services from the state agency, the individual will apply. According to Mary Wareham (personal communication December 22, 2011), all applicants have a right to assessment and evaluative services. However, in order to qualify for services leading to employment, certain requirements must be met (Susan Sherman, personal communication, December 21, 2011).

Eligibility requirements:

- A determination by qualified personnel that the applicant has a physical or mental impairment
- A determination by qualified personnel that the applicant's physical or mental impairment constitutes or results in substantial impediment to employment for the applicant
- A determine by a qualified rehabilitation counselor employed by the public VR agency (Designated State Agency or DSU) that the applicant requires VR services to prepare for, secure, retain, or regain employment consistent with the applicant's unique strengths, resources, priorities, concerns, abilities, capabilities, interests, and informed choice

The public vocational rehabilitation program must presume that an applicant who meets the eligibility requirements can benefit in terms of an employment outcome unless there is clear and convincing evidence that the applicant is incapable of benefitting as such due to the severity of the applicant's disability. (Code of Federal Regulations [CFR], Parts 300-399, revised as of July 1, 2008)

The order of selection criteria differs from State VR Agency to State VR Agency (Susan Sherman, personal communication, December 21, 2011). There is no consistent criterion except as defined in 361.36 of the Federal Register (CFR, revised as of July 1, 2008). In establishing an Order of Selection, a state agency is saying that it is unable to serve everyone and that it is first serving individuals who are most significantly disabled. Individuals who do not meet the Order of Selection must have access to services provided through the public agency's information and referral system.

Once an individual has submitted an application for services, an eligibility determination must be made within 60 days unless (1) there are exceptional and unforeseen circumstances beyond the control of the public state agency (DSU) and (2) both the public state agency and the individual agree to a specific extension (Susan Sherman, personal communication, December 21, 2011).

Historically, Bitner (1979) notes the counselor must make at least two professional judgments: that the handicap is related to the disability and the services provided are likely to help the client become employed. In this case, the counselor relies on the physician to determine the disability through medical diagnosis. By 1994, a new definition and criteria for services was implemented nationwide. Although similar to what is referenced above, in the case of funding shortages there are subtle differences with an accent on serving the "most significantly disabled," then "significantly disabled" and then "disabled" in that order (Mary Wareham, personal communication, December 22, 2011). Refer to Table 1.3 for the expected eligibility criteria. In order close a case as successfully rehabilitated, the person must remain employment for at least 90 days. Additionally, the case file is kept for three years. During that time, a client may qualify for post-employment services if those services will ensure continuing employment (Mary Wareham, personal communication, December 21, 2011).

In order to manage the flow of work, the State-Federal system developed a series of codes to represent stages or client status; however, the use of status codes is not mandated, and not all state agencies use status codes today (Susan Sherman, personal communication, December 22, 2011). The primary goal is to prepare a client (or "customer") for work with an individual plan for employment (IPE). The client must participate in and approve the plan, which is documented in the file. Because of numerous complaints of delays, the law requires that clients be moved from applicant status (02) to plan development (10) within 60 days unless an extension or an extended evaluation (06) can be specifically justified. In the event an extended evaluation is necessary, the file must document the reason and be re-evaluated every 90 days. Any evaluation lasting more than 180 days must be justified in the file. In order to close a file as rehabilitated status (26), the client must maintain employment for at least 60 days. Even if a file is closed, under some circumstances additional funds can be expended if the action will help the client stay employed. See Public Sector Status Codes in Figure 1.1.

Table 1.3
Eligibility for State-Federal Rehabilitation Services

1. The applicant with a disability must have a physical or mental impairment which:

   a) must be stable or slowly progressive.

   b) cannot be acute or of an emergency nature.

   c) must be documented in the file.

2. The impairment must constitute or result in a substantial impediment to employment.

3. The applicant must benefit from rehabilitation services with respect to employment.

Source: PL 102-569

Determining Disability: Social Security

The Social Security Administration relies on an elaborate determination process that takes into account such factors as age, education, and work experience, and confirms a person possesses either a physical or mental disabling condition that will preclude him/her from the national labor market for a period of at least one year (Social Security, 1981; Blackwell, Field, & Field, 1993). In 1978 the Social Security Administration introduced the concept of the medical-vocational grid to assist the administrative law judge in making disability determinations without the benefit of a vocational expert. Based on the medical evidence, age of the claimant, education, and medical factors, certain rulings regarding disability could be found (*Heckler v. Campbell*, 1983). According to the above referenced case, the guidelines were established to improve the uniformity and efficiency of disability determinations since, "... vocational experts were frequently criticized for their inconsistent treatment in similarly situated claimants" (p. 1954). These guidelines relieved the secretary of the need to rely on vocational experts by establishing through rule-making the types and numbers of jobs that exist in the national economy. In addition, the client's interests, personality traits, and the specific location of residence are not considered. As Rasch (1985) notes, vocational opinions relative to Social Security are far more structured than for workers' compensation and personal injury cases, "and vocational experts must follow set guidelines in developing opinions" (p. 158).

Determining Disability: Workers' Compensation

State workers' compensation programs attempt to identify the degree of disability of the injured worker by classifying the person as having a disability that is (a) temporary total; (b) temporary partial; or (c) permanent (American Academy of Orthopaedic Surgeons, undated; U.S Chamber of Commerce, 2000). Furthermore, as part of the state law, most states have published schedules of injuries that identify an actual percentage loss of total functioning of the person taking into account the area of injury with their body. This approach has been well founded in the precedent of the *American Medical Association's Guides to the Evaluation of Permanent Impairment*, 6th edition (AMA, 2007) and the *Manual for Orthopaedic Surgeons* (undated), which establish an actual percentage of loss of bodily functioning due to loss of a body part or a reduced level of bodily function. The Guides present information detailing the percentages of loss that should be assigned to each of the areas given the precise definition of the body part or function involved. The procedure for determining the percentage rating is currently the sole responsibility of the physician. Most physicians are careful to note the assessment as an "impairment" estimate and not a "disability" rating since disability ratings are intended to consider the loss of employment opportunities and/or functioning in the worker's future (American Academy of Orthopaedic Surgeons, undated). Of interest, determining the amount of disability for the work injured and personal injury cases falls into the sphere of the vocational counselor, but little discussion is available in the literature to address this significant issue. It appears the vocational expert is called upon to offer an opinion without benefit of training on effective ways to accomplish this task. For example, a person who is employed as a dancer, whose job requires a great deal of balance and agility, might purport that there is a direct relationship between the loss of functioning in the amputation of the big toe and potential loss of functioning on the job. This determination is a significant factor in the personal injury case and for those states that provide for lost wage earning capacity in workers' compensation (e.g., Florida) (Rasch, 1985; *Walker v. New Fern Restorium*, 1982). Only a few sources provide a modicum

Figure 1.1.
Public Sector Status Codes

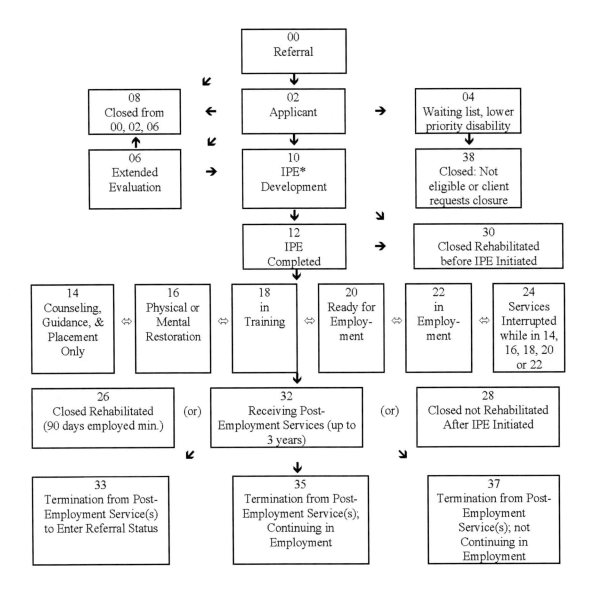

Note. IPE = Individual Plan for Employment; Also see explanations at http://dese.mo.gov/vr/CSG/100.pdf (effective 4/21/09); Not all state agencies use codes.

of information regarding this subject to the rehabilitation counselor (Deutsch & Sawyer, 1999; Dillman, 1993; Field, 1993; Field & Weed, 1986; Weed, 1990; Weed, 1993; Weed & Field, 1994; Wolf, 1985).

Determining Disability: Personal Injury

Personal injury cases result when a person suffers an injury and another party has some liability for the injury that may entitle the person to compensation for damages (Field, 1993; Rasch, 1985; Weed & Field, 2001). Examples are vehicle or aircraft accidents (*Malczewski v. McReynolds*, 1981; *Marks v. Mobile Oil*, 1983). Factors to be litigated may include pain and suffering, medical costs, loss of wages, loss of earning capacity, punitive, and other damages (Brookshire & Smith, 1990; Dillman, 1988; Deutsch & Sawyer, 1999;

Rasch, 1985; *Kemp v. Miami Quality Concrete*, 1982). For purposes of this book, only earnings capacity and future care costs will be considered in detail. The process is discussed in a later chapter under the headings of forensics, earnings capacity and life care plans. Generally speaking, the process for determining disability is similar to the workers' compensation system described above. However, the financial consequences can be significantly greater (Deutsch & Sawyer, 1999).

Benefits of Rehabilitation

Since its inception, private sector vocational and medical case management rehabilitation services have faced close examination concerning the cost-effectiveness of services. Indeed workers' compensation benefits vary from state to state and are based, at least in part, on perceived benefit (Lewin et al., 1979, Knoblach & McNabb, 1993; U.S. Chamber of Commerce, 1999; Weed & Field, 2001). Throughout the United States, benefits vary from required rehabilitation to no rehabilitation. Many states such as Alaska, California, Georgia, Florida, Hawaii, and Washington that at one time provided for rehabilitation services for persons who are injured have either terminated or limited these services (Mulholland, Sniderman, & Yankowski, 1994; Sharf, Donham, Williams, & Ryan, 1987; Thompson, 1992; U.S. Chamber of Commerce, 1994; Weed & Field, 1994).

One argument in support of limiting services seems to be doubt regarding the cost-effectiveness of rehabilitation services. Many states promote that the cost of rehabilitation does not justify the provision of the services to an injured person, as demonstrated by these states' legislative moves to reduce access to vocational and other rehabilitation for injured workers (CARP, 1992). In order to objectively survey this topic, an analysis of available literature with regard to cost-to-benefit was undertaken (Weed & Lewis, 1994).

Cost Benefit Analysis

Thornton (1985) defines cost-benefit analysis (CBA) as ". . . . whether the various outcomes justify their costs in terms of economic efficiency" (pg. 226). Dymond (1969) notes that in its purest sense, CBA takes into account only economic measures. Rehabilitation, however, is not a field that has only economic goals. Indeed, some goals may be impossible to measure in economic terms (Weed & Field, 1990). Regarding costs, Rehabilitation International (1981) lists the following: "special services and case expenditures; administrative salaries and overhead; social costs; specialized health services; counseling; technical aids; training centers" (pp. 5-6). These authors also observe that the following benefits may be derived: "reduced costs for future care; production benefits; and reduced administrative costs for transfer payments" (pp. 104-105). Of the above, social costs (money spent on rehabilitation that may be spent elsewhere) is the most difficult to quantify (Rehabilitation International, 1981).

Hardin (1969) and Hardin and Borus (1971) point out that the end product of money spent on rehabilitation is increased disposable income that is earned by people with disabilities. This income is recycled back into the economy giving more money for the population at large. Several authors state that it is impossible to precisely quantify this recycling because accurate CBA is confounded by various uncontrollable factors (Dymond, 1969; Hardin, 1969; Hardin & Borus, 1971; Thornton, 1985). Included are such intangibles as increased self-esteem, increased well-being, and reduced pain, anxiety, and discomfort, all of which are difficult to measure monetarily (Rehabilitation International, 1981). Conley (1965) notes that the greatest difficulty is placing value on a human life, a task that most people cannot accomplish. Therefore, CBA for rehabilitation may be greatly underestimated.

Rehabilitation services have been provided to assist injured veterans with working in American society as far back as World War I, and workers' compensation benefits, primarily for medical services, have been offered in the United States since the early 1900's (Weed & Field, 1990). Conley (1965) noted that between its inception in 1920 and 1963, the number of persons enjoying public vocational rehabilitation services multiplied over 10 times. Of persons receiving vocational rehabilitation services in 1963, almost all were placed in either gainful employment or in homemaker duties. Without taking into account the estimated wages for homemakers and other non-paid positions, the average salary for rehabilitates doubled. However, Conley asserts that if estimations for non paid-services were included, the wage increase would have been much larger.

Another study done by Conley (1969) demonstrated the cost-effectiveness of rehabilitation services. In surveying differences between subclasses of claimants, he found a 5 to 1 benefit and cost ratio for the year 1967.

He did not find differences between subgroups and found that all persons use equal amounts of rehabilitation monies.

Bellante (1972) noted that Conley did not find differences among subgroups in CBA because he did not control for various subcategories, also known as cross-classification. Bellante conducted a partial replication of Conley's study using methodology to control for cross-referencing across different groups. He concurred in an overall observation that the CBA for rehabilitation justifies the provision for services; however, breaking the study participants down into different factors (such as sex, age, education, and type of disability) changed the view of the benefits. Using 1969 closed cases in Florida, Bellante concluded that not all groups advanced equally from rehabilitation services, and that those who are younger and whose earnings are higher benefit the most. Bellante surmised that despite the variations amongst subgroups, it is desirable to use rehabilitation monies to help persons from all groups, even if that means shifting the relative shares of funds to different groups.

In another study, Worrall (1978) studied the amount of wages earned by rehabilitates. He found two important results: (1) similar to Conley, a benefit and cost ratio of 5 to 1 for the rehabilitates was evident, and, (2) successful rehabilitates are young, married, and nonwhite, a finding similar to Bellante.

To determine CBA, Walls, Dowler, and Misra (1985) reviewed the relationship between vocational rehabilitation expenditures and client earnings. They found that about half of the participants were earning above the minimum wage. In comparing vocational rehabilitation cost with earnings, the authors found that vocational rehabilitation's outlay would be recovered within 20 weeks (for clients earning at the minimum wage). Walls et al. (1985) did note that disability type must be taken into account when determining overall CBA. For example, the authors assert that clients with a mental disability are more likely to have funds spent on services other than training and restoration. However, several authors (Cho et al., 1980; Hill & Wehman, 1981; Noble & Conley, 1987) have found that this money is well spent in terms of the CBA. Including, for example, for the period of 1976-1978 where the Job Corps realized a 1.05 to 1.69 CBA (Cho & Schuermann, 1980).

Another issue affecting CBA is the proximity between time of injury and time of referral. Gardener (1991), based on a Florida study, found that early referral (defined as 6 months post injury or less) greatly increased rehabilitation success. Boschen (1989), CARP (1993), and Olsheski and Growick (1987) found similar results. One article specifically studying private sector rehabilitation in California found that in cases of total temporary disability, referral 180 or more days post injury cost on the average of $7,321.72 as compared to $1,918.43 in cases referred earlier (Lewis & Matkin, 1990). The study concluded that outcome and cost-effectiveness were greatly enhanced by early referral. Additionally, Yankowski and Sniderman (1991) note that the time between initial referral and initiation of the rehabilitation process extends the amount of time that clients are within the system. The Yankowski and Sniderman study also found that post-injury wages are higher when the rehabilitation process is accomplished in a timely fashion.

Workers' Compensation Research Institute (WCRI) (1988) compared the cost of rehabilitating a claimant when referral is at three months rather than at six months. The authors found that time to referral significantly affected cost of services. In comparing intervention times, they found great increases in cost as time between injury and referral increased. Gardener (1988) found that not only do overall costs decrease with early referral, but also factors such as weekly earnings and program completion increase.

Farrell, Knowlton, and Taylor (1989), in a Northwestern Life Insurance study, found a saving of $30 for every $1 spent on rehabilitation. Along with the 30 to 1 ratio, the authors also found that less money is being spent on rehabilitation than was previously spent, and, similarly to Bellante, persons with higher pre-injury incomes are more likely to be employed than are those with lower incomes.

Hester & Decelles (1991) have summarized several positive findings in their National Institute on Disability and Rehabilitation Research (NIDRR) funded study of International Association of Rehabilitation Professionals (IARP) member specialists, a group of primarily for-profit practitioners. They studied 1,013 cases nationwide and found that not only is rehabilitation cost effective (they hypothesized a 5 to 1 ratio and called for further study) but also that 59% of men studied returned to work with rehabilitation services as compared to 47% without those services. Related to this topic, a study in California reports that 84% of injured workers who completed a vocational rehabilitation program went back to work (CARP, 1993).

The literature search results surveying thirty years of data overwhelmingly support rehabilitation for people with disabilities regardless of referral or payment source. In fact, all research articles reviewed support the provision of rehabilitation services (see Table 1.4) as a cost-effective approach to assisting people with disabilities to work and suggest that earlier referral reduces the cost of rehabilitation and increases the likelihood of employment.

Evaluating Vocational Potential

Tests

As noted above, the private sector rehabilitation professional is more likely than the public sector counselor to testify in court. In either case, in order to estimate the work potential or earnings capacity of the person with an injury, a variety of approaches may be used. To assess work potential, information relating to medical, psychological, social, educational, and vocational aspects should be considered (Rubin & Roessler, 2008; Havranek, Grimes, Field, & Sink, 1994; McGowan & Porter, 1967; Sink, 1977). To assess these skills and traits, counselors often use various tests to perform a vocational evaluation (Anastasi, 1982; Weed & Field, 2001). A vocational evaluation may be defined as a process that attempts to predict work behaviors and vocational potential through the application of a variety of techniques and procedures (Nadolsky, 1971). The use of these tests by themselves has several problems. For example, the tests may require highly skilled and trained technicians to give and interpret them, and the tests may not adequately measure traits (Anastasi, 1982). Persons responsible for interpreting the tests may provide an incomplete or inadequate assessment of the client's potential, actual vocational skills, and other factors (Rubin & Roessler, 2008). It is also possible the professional may be biased and select information that supports his/her view (*Ryals v. Home Insurance*, 1982). (Also see Chapter 5).

Transferability of Skills

This section assumes that the client has a work history and sustains an injury. In the case of a 40 year-old plumber who suffers a high-level spinal cord injury leaving him a tetraplegic, the loss of employability and resultant loss of income seems clear. In this case the person with a long work history may be 100 percent disabled and have lost all ability to be competitively employed. On the other hand, a carpenter with a back injury may have the residual capacity to work at a lighter job. The challenge to the counselor is to find the setting that provides suitable employment. This has been termed the identification of transferable skills. (Also see Chapter 6 for much more information relating to the transferable skills process).

Some might wonder what suitable employment means. A brief review reveals the following. In Florida:

> *Employment or self-employment which is reasonably attainable in light of the individual's age, education, previous occupation, and injury and which offers an opportunity to restore the individual as soon as practical and nearly as possible to [his] average weekly earnings at the time of injury (Source: http://www.flsenate. gov/Laws/Statutes/2011/440.49).*

Maryland similarly defines suitable, gainful employment as:

> *. . . employment, excluding self-employment, that restores the disabled covered employee, to the extent possible, to the level of support at the time that the disability occurred" (Workers Comp Law, LE, 9-670, p 212). The law further states that in determining whether employment is suitable, gainful employment, the following shall be considered: (1) the qualifications, interests, incentives, pre-disability earnings, and future earnings capacity of the covered employee; (2) the nature and extent of the disability of the covered employee; and (3) the current and future condition of the labor market.*

Georgia, in the workers compensation law, states:

> *All job search plans (written for no more than one year) should be accompanied by documentation of labor market surveys or other information which documents a reasonable possibility of suitable employment in the job objectives listed on the plan. The plan must be submitted along with a current release to return to work from the authorized treating physician(s). Employment goals should be reasonably consistent with the employee's prior vocational status, including average weekly wage, as well as within the employee's current physical abilities. All treating physicians must concur that the employee is released to return to work (p. 7).*

> *Rehabilitation suppliers shall provide appropriate services as needed to return the injured worker to suitable employment consistent with prior occupational levels or to restore the injured worker to optimal physical functioning (p. 17).*

Table 1.4
Summary of Rehabilitation Cost Benefit Research

Author	Year	Rehab Useful?	Cost Benefit	# subjects (If identified)	Notes
Conley	1965	yes	–	clients served between 1921 and 1963	Reporting of cases taken by VR between 1921 and 1963
Conley	1969	yes	5 to 1	clients served between 1958 and 1967	Did not control for cross classification.
Bellante	1972	yes	–	13,888	Replication of Conley.
Worrall	1978	yes	5 to 1	10,000	Found similar results to Bellante.
Cho & Schuermann	1980	yes	1.05 to 1.69	34	Measured both sheltered workshops and regular employment (Job Corps).
Hill & Wehman	1981	yes	–	33	Study with moderately and severely mentally retarded clients.
Walls, Dowler, & Misra	1985	yes	–	157,785	Compared expenditures to wages.
Olsheski & Growick	1987	yes	–	85	Ohio Industrial Commission for injured workers found early referral superior.
Noble & Conley	1987	yes	–	Subjects taken from 6 programs	Study of mentally retarded subjects in supportive employment.
Gardener	1988	yes	–	1,173	Overall costs decrease and weekly earnings increase.
WCRI	1988	yes	–		Early referral more effective.
Boschen	1989	yes	–		Early referral means less rehab cost.
Farrell, Knowlton & Taylor	1989	yes	30 to 1	2,212	Northwestern Mutual Life Insurance study of clients with back injuries.
Lewis & Matkin	1990	yes	early referral costs: $1,918 vs. $7,321	332	California workers' compensation cases.
Hester & Decelles	1991	yes	5 to 1	1,013	NIDRR funded national study of IARP member cases.
Yankowski & Sniderman	1991	yes	–	343	Early initiation of services significantly improves post-injury salary.
Gardener (also see 1988)	1991	–	–	1,173	Found that early referral (6 months or less) is the most beneficial to rehab

Source: State Board of Workers' Compensation, 2011

The concept of transferable skills within the context of Social Security is defined to be the assessment of work functions acquired from performance of skilled/semi-skilled jobs which can be applied to meet other skilled/semi-skilled jobs (Field & Weed, 1988; U.S. Department of Health and Human Services, 1981). In rehabilitation literature, this concept is primarily related to Social Security and the private sector. In one book this is termed a new concept (Taylor, Golter, Golter, & Backer, 1985). Generally, the public sector counselor has been trained to believe that "... education is a feasible and common means to an end, employment" (p. 238). In workers' compensation, however: "Using acquired skills has proven to be the most cost-effective means of returning the injured worker to gainful employment" (p. 238). Further, transferable skills can be used in all aspects of vocational rehabilitation and can make the difference in a person working or not working (Sink & Field, 1981). Deutsch and Sawyer (1999) list source books for use in identifying transferable skills and offer an example case to show how they arrive at decisions. Rasch (1985) notes similar resources, but endorses the VDARE (Vocational Diagnosis and Assessment of Residual Employability) process as an organized way to assess transferable work skills (Field, 1993). (Note: Although many experienced rehabilitation counselors still use the term VDARE, the process has been revised and renamed to transferable work skills to more accurately reflect the concept.) Rasch points out the possible problems associated with relying on global data utilizing average worker traits. Rasch offers the suggestion to closely review a detailed work history for job skills, leadership qualities, machine skills and other work relevant attributes. Deutsch and Sawyer (1999) also urge the counselor to consider leisure time, hobbies, and other non-work activities.

Transferability Process

The process uses the client's work history as the basis to build the assessment of client vocational functioning capacities. The following is intended to be a general overview of the procedure. For a detailed description see Transferable Work Skills (Chapter 6) in this text. An important note is that the *Dictionary of Occupational Titles* (DOT) (DOL, 1991) was last updated in 1991 and therefore is an aging resource. For career planning the government supported O*Net has replaced the DOT as the resource of choice. However, the O*Net is not designed to determine pre- vs. post-injury comparisons which are needed for social security, personal injury litigation, and some workers' compensation claims. Therefore, the practicing rehabilitation counselor particularly in the private sector will need to know and understand the process. This is an important issue that resulted in the establishment of Occupational Information Development Advisory Panel (OIDAP) to resolve this increasingly challenging conundrum (Social Security Administration [SSA], 2011b)

The jobs are translated into trait profiles by looking up the job title in the *Dictionary of Occupational Titles* (DOT) (DOL, 1991) to verify the definition, then looking up the DOT number in the *Transitional Classification of Jobs* (Field & Field, 2004) and recording the worker trait information on the form specifically designed for this purpose. In the most recent edition of the *Dictionary of Occupational Titles* (1991), there are 72 factors which are listed under the headings of physical demands, working conditions, general educational development, specific vocational preparation, aptitudes, work activities, and work situations (see the transferable work skills chapter for more detail). The client may have worked at several jobs, and the highest demonstrated level of capability is recorded. Each factor is studied to determine if a trait should be adjusted up or down depending on any testing or medical information. For example, in the case of a back injury there may be lifting or other limitations. After the worker trait profile is established and all adjustments have been considered, the residual functional capacity (RFC) can be entered into a computer program (such as the on-line SkillTRAN, see Truthan, 2010), and jobs that match the remaining capability can be identified. It is also possible to use a manual process of cross-referencing various jobs through Industry, Work Field, Census, etc., codes (Field & Field, 1992; Weed & Field, 2001) to identify job titles that may be within the worker's profile. (Also see Chapter 6).

Labor Market Access and Lost Earnings or Earnings Capacity

Once the transferability of skills process is used to identify potential vocational options, the counselor has gathered any other appropriate data, wages associated with probable employment are revealed, and the evidence of likelihood of placement through labor market research, the vocational expert may be called upon to testify about the financial impact of an accident and the personal loss of access to the labor market. Very little has been published in this area. Rasch (1985) notes the expert in personal injury litigation may be asked to opine about placeability, employability, and wage loss, but does not specifically offer a method. Deutsch and Sawyer (1999) offer a general method of identifying jobs an injured person can do and the resulting wages. This is used as a foundation for an economist to project lost earnings. They note the process of calculating the diminished earning capacity " . . . is not as easy as some counselors and attorneys make it out to be" (p. 8.01). Deutsch and Sawyer focus on the lost earning capacity rather than the loss of access to the labor market. Also considered is an emphasis on work history with earning capacity (rather than actual earned dollars) and the impact of the accident on the individual's capacity to earn. Rules of thumb are offered for various considerations such as age, work identity, years of experience, and other factors when trying to estimate the post-injury earnings potential. Since, in this method, professional judgment is pivotal, a major contribution is the listing of 23 sources for obtaining statistical data on employment.

The most elaborate method apparently available was first promoted in 1981 under the title "Labor Market Access" (LMA) (Vander Vegt, Summit, & Field, 1981), revised in 1984 (Field, Choppa, & Shafer); in 1992 (Field & Field) and 2000 (Field & Field). The value of the procedure was based on the assumption that the legal community was increasingly asking the vocational expert to testify about employability and earning capacity, and the "LMA as a method of adding objectivity to the work of the vocational expert" (introduction). The Labor Market Access was based on the completed pre-injury and post-injury worker trait profiles using the VDARE (a transferability) process. An enhancement of this approach, designed to help the vocational consultant with the rationale, was later completed (Field & Weed, 1987; Weed & Field, 1994; Field & Field, 1992).

The authors found the most complete and consistent available nationwide datato be the *Dictionary of Occupational Titles* for job titles, *Classification of Jobs* for worker traits, Census for the number of jobs associated with various job titles, and Bureau of Labor Statistics for median weekly wage.

In order to complete the Labor Market Access, the rehabilitation professional utilized a transferability process to determine the Residual Functional Capacity. This was accomplished by identifying all prior jobs and the significant characteristics and levels of functioning for the pre-injury profile. Next, the nature and extent of the disabling conditions were listed. Third, the transferability process was used to adjust the pre-injury level of functioning to a post-injury level of functioning on all relevant factors. This adjusted level of functioning was the Residual Functional Capacity.

After the Residual Functional Capacity was established, the rehabilitation professional identified the percentage of jobs, not job titles, which were available to the worker before the injury and the number of jobs available after the injury. Census surveys with annual updates to adjust for labor market fluctuations were used as the basis of data (available for national and regional/local areas). The census arrangement was then assigned 1988 wage data (with annual updates) derived from the Bureau of Labor Statistics.

A disability rating was calculated by subtracting the number of jobs (civilian labor force) available to the worker after the injury from the number of jobs available prior to the injury and dividing the result by the number of jobs available to the person prior to injury. For example, if the number of jobs available before the injury were 2,000,000 and the number of jobs available after the injury are 1,500,000, then 1,500,000 from 2,000,000 is 500,000. 500,000 divided by 2,000,000 equals 25 percent which represents the *personal* loss of access to the employment market.

The next step was to take the Census arrangement and assign wage data derived from the Bureau of Labor Statistics. Finally, the rehabilitationist reviewed the average weekly wage data and number of jobs associated with the Census codes from the Labor Market Surveys (Field, J., 1993). By subtracting the pre-injury expected average weekly wage from the post-injury expected average weekly wage, lost earnings were estimated. After hand calculating percentages and wages, a process taking up to several hours, the consultant could offer an opinion regarding the impact of the disability on employability and/or placeability and earnings. Computer technology, on the other hand, searches through 72 worker traits on 12,741 DOT titles and cross-references across all Census codes, including wage data, in less than one hour.

No studies researching the accuracy of any LMA method were located. The efficacy of the Labor Market Access rationale has been scrutinized through the litigation process and apparently has worked well enough to be singled out for trial news reporting ("$110,000 for fractured wrist", 1983; "$190,000 to truck driver", 1984; "$800,000 settlement", 1984; "Botched diagnosis", 1984). Specific wage loss analysis procedures are described in a later chapter under the title of earnings capacity analysis.

Work Alternatives

Thirty years ago, there were no real alternatives for rehabilitation counselors to be employed outside of a State agency. All textbooks reflected federal rules and regulations for employment in offices of vocational rehabilitation. Indeed, many basic text books still place a heavy emphasis on public sector practice, yet many graduates from the Georgia State University's accredited rehabilitation counselor training program have found employment outside of the public agency. It is likely that many other universities have had similar experiences. (See Marketing Checklist for initiating a private practice located at end of chapter).

Nurses in private practice also had limited choices. It was not until 1969 that a large insurance company formed International Rehabilitation Associates to more effectively manage workers' compensation cases. Since then, with accelerating changes over the past twenty years, a large number of choices exist for both professions:

State Rehabilitation. As noted earlier in this chapter, historically rehabilitation counselors have found positions working for the State agency. Articles have been written suggesting that many of these people are retiring, and a new spurt of hiring has materialized. Other related occupations include rehabilitation counselor for the Veterans Administration, state and federal probation/parole offices, Indian Affairs, and other government-based rehabilitation counseling jobs. It is of interest to note that in the late 1990's Federal Law was changed to require qualified rehabilitation counselors for public sector rehabilitation offices. This places a renewed emphasis on the CRC credential.

Workers' Compensation. One of the most widespread professions for rehabilitation counselors and rehabilitation nurses has been specializing in on-the-job injuries. This alternative varies widely from state to state and is subject to state workers' compensation law changes. Related to this are specialty areas of federal employee workers' compensation (Office of Workers' Compensation Programs), longshore and harbor workers, and people who work on the sea (Jones Act).

In-House Rehabilitation. Many larger manufacturing companies employ nurses to handle minor wounds and to facilitate treatment for serious injuries. Others, such as railroads, rely upon in-house trained rehabilitation counselors as a cost effective way to manage placement of injured workers. They also have been trained in the highly specialized requirements of the disability insurance "policy." Some businesses are large enough to justify the cost of hiring their own vocational rehabilitation consultants to provide prompt services.

Rehabilitation Technology Consulting. The Center for Environmental Access and Assistive Technology at Georgia Institute of Technology has rehabilitation counselors advising clients, employers, families, and others about options for job accommodation. Some rehabilitation training programs are also offering a rehabilitation technology subspecialty.

Job Accommodation. Many nurses and rehabilitation counselors are assisting employers by consulting on ADA and Section 504 requirements.

Job Coaching. Several students have historically earned a part-time living through school by providing job coaching services to persons with acquired brain injuries or emotional disabilities. One graduate directed a job coach program that involved hiring, training and administering a grant.

Case Management. This option continues to expand. In general, the case manager is responsible for effectively coordinating services for a person with a disability. Sometimes this involves catastrophic impairments, requiring a high level of knowledge and experience. Many of these professionals have nursing backgrounds, and emerging specialty areas include pediatric services and working with the elderly. For certification in this area, visit http://www.ccmcertification.org/.

Program Managers. Many rehabilitation consultants have moved into program direction and management. Settings include traumatic brain injury rehabilitation, counseling for victims of spouse and child abuse, drug and alcohol addictions counseling, rehabilitation for persons with eating disorders, treatment for persons with mental disabilities or psychiatric needs, sheltered workshops, and many others.

Career Guidance. This option extends beyond guidance for people with disabilities. One rehabilitation counselor reported that career counseling with a person without a disability was a "breeze" and has attempted to develop a business catering to displaced workers.

"Out Placement" Programs. Related to the above is the expanding practice of many large businesses that provide career counseling for people who are laid off or displaced due to a variety of factors. Considering the economic environment at the time of this edition, displaced workers are a major topic.

Testing. The most obvious testing is associated with vocational evaluations of people with disabilities. However, some have found employment opportunities by testing for career guidance as well as promotions or placement firms looking for specific qualities.

Development of New Tests. Although a niche opportunity vocational, psychological, functional capacity, and other tests are often developed by rehabilitation professionals.

Executive Director/Owner. A large number of private rehabilitation companies are owned by practicing rehabilitation counselors and registered nurses. Others work for large companies and have achieved executive level status where they are involved in high-level decision and policy making. Settings extend far beyond workers compensation related businesses.

Development of New Products. Several companies that develop rehabilitation products utilize rehabilitation consultants to brainchild the items. Historically, some of the better known include Valpar, Jist, and Elliott & Fitzpatrick.

Publishing. Books, articles, journals, and newsletters bring us the discoveries and shape the future of rehabilitation. All rehabilitation professionals are urged to contribute to this segment of the profession in order to advance the knowledge and sophistication of our services.

Training. Training includes university-level education toward degrees in our area of specialization and continuing education courses to enhance the practice of those who have already entered the field. Some have developed "home study" courses based on audio, video, or written media. Since in rehabilitation counseling the master's degree is considered the terminal degree, doctoral level rehabilitationists are in demand.

Divorce Evaluations. A small number of counselors have been retained to provide professional opinions about outlook of soon-to-be ex-spouse work or to develop a program to assist with resolving divorce disputes. One rehabilitation counselor is working as a divorce mediator.

Aging/Geriatric. Another emerging area of concern is the well being of senior citizens. Many retired individuals need productive outlets or assistance with overcoming barriers associated with limitations from the aging process and medical case management. Professionals with a rehabilitation background are uniquely suited for this alternative.

Psychotherapy. Certainly many people with disabilities need to seek treatment for adjusting to their situation. Many counselors do not have the education in the medical and psychological aspects of disability and may be less well equipped to perform this service than someone with rehabilitation training and experience. Many professional counselors have experience in disability programs. Another segment is helping people adjust by specifying aids for independence.

Hospital/Rehabilitation Treatment Centers. All hospitals employ nurses. This probably represents the main opportunity for nurses. Many hospitals and rehabilitation centers employ job placement specialists, vocational counselors, and vocational evaluators. A few utilize rehabilitation professionals to conduct research.

In-Home Health Care. This alternative applies primarily to nurses. This represents a fairly rapidly growing profession, which is expected to accelerate in light of the move toward national managed health care and an aging population.

Prevention. Some companies have developed programs to advise employers about worker qualifications to avoid on the job injuries or to set pre-employment physical standards which meet federal ADA guidelines.

Employee Assistance Programs. Many larger businesses have developed procedures that facilitate treatment for employees with personal, family, drug, and alcohol problems. Others encourage "well behavior" in an attempt to avoid business-debilitating problems.

Marketing Health Care Programs/Products. Professionals who have attended conferences certainly are aware that many booths are available to educate the attendee about services and products that are available to other rehabilitation professionals. Obviously many of the marketers have worked, or been educated, in rehabilitation.

Sales of Health Care Related Products. A closely related option is associated with selling of products. This can range from books to durable medical equipment. One could make direct contact with customers or provide services by phone.

University Students with Disabilities Coordinator. Many universities employ rehabilitation counselors to eliminate or reduce barriers to education for people with disabilities. This may include accommodation issues as well as sensitizing, or desensitizing, others to the plights of students with disabilities.

Personal Injury Litigation. Both nurses and rehabilitation counselors have developed thriving businesses by cultivating work related to litigation. Most professionals who choose this area have extensive experience and must be able to tolerate a highly stressful atmosphere. Nurses (primarily) have developed "behind the scenes" options associated with medically related cases. Many attorneys hire nurses full-time for reviewing and summarizing depositions, developing deposition questions, finding experts, summarizing and explaining medical records, and conducting research. Some have become paralegals, which broadens their participation.

Life Care Planner. Many rehabilitation consultants, after gaining considerable experience, work with complex medical cases to determine future care costs. Life care planners may work independently or with an insurance company. Duties may include estimating life-time costs for health care, auto, or workers' compensation insurance companies, damages in personal injury claims, life-time costs for estate planning, and divorce cases.

Disability Management. In the mid to late 1990s many organizations and government entities began taking a more active role in working with their injured employees. The foundation is based on early intervention, outcomes research, psychosocial issues and proven strategies (Shrey & Lacerte, 1995, p. 3). The process encourages labor and management to work together to solve problems, offer disability prevention programs, and design safe return-to-work programs. These individuals may be an employee of a company or run programs through a contract. For certification in this specialty visit http://www.cdms.org/.

Centers for Independent Living. Commonly people who work at independent living centers are peer counselors and/or masters' degree professionals with a disability. As the name implies, the goals are to help people with disabilities to live as independently as possible, exercise as much control over life as possible, minimize reliance on others, and minimize dependence on agencies and institutions. Topics include transportation and mobility, communications, self-care and appearance, socialization, functional reading and computation, and domestic capabilities.

Ethics

Years ago, many of us practiced rehabilitation counseling before there was certification and ethics. Over the years, it became evident that counseling abuse was adversely affecting our profession, and in the early 1970s, the Certified Rehabilitation Counselor (CRC) was launched. An instrumental part of the credential was associated with developing ethics that were agreed upon by professionals. Over the years the ethics statements were re-evaluated and modifications were made to reflect changes in the industry. For example the CRC was updated in 2010 and is now 34 pages long (excluding the glossary and reference). Most professional associations also have their own ethics statements, which theoretically reflect the particular rehabilitation consulting profession. The associations also recognized that certification was not commonly a requirement in order to be a member. In spite of the safeguards, there are still many who choose to "bend the rules" to accomplish personal, NOT professional, goals. Sex with clients, failure to advocate for a person with a disability, fraudulent credentials, breach of duty, and financial deceit are a few examples (Weed & Golem, 1996; Weed, 2000). The client-counselor relationship is also an issue for rehabilitation counselors. For example, in a 1999 published article of a survey of private practice professionals in Virginia, 64.5% of the practitioners reported the "client" to be the injured worker whereas 58.3% of the managers disagreed (Sinsabaugh & Martin, 1999). This means that some believed the company paying the bills was the "client." First, the general problem with this concept is that many choose to modify good, solid rehabilitation principles and comply with what the bill payer (i.e., client) wants. Second, this study demonstrates differences between management and counselors with regard to priorities. For purposes of this text, the client refers to the person with a disability, with one caveat. For professionals practicing in the litigation specialty (forensics), there is no client-counselor relationship, and most organizations, including the certification commission for rehabilitation counseling, have adopted the position that the person with the disability is not the client in that instance [see Barros-Bailey, Carlisle, Graham, Neulicht, & Taylor, 2008 as reprinted in the *Journal of Life Care Planning, 7*(3), 125–132; See also Appendix I]

The reader is invited to review the various ethical statements included at the end of this book. Professionals who provide quality, ethical service will be rewarded personally, professionally, and financially.

Diversity Issues

In America alone, it is estimated that approximately 54 million people, or one-fifth of the population, have a disability (Bryan, 1999). Furthermore, surveys on the percentages of disabilities in America indicate that among racial minorities and females, there is a higher rate of disabilities as compared to Caucasian males. Additional information relates that 68% of working age, adult Hispanic/Latino Americans and 72% of African Americans with disabilities have severe disabilities, as compared to 52% of Euro-Americans. As a group, Native Americans have a disproportionately higher rate of disabilities, about 1.5 times that of the general population (Marshall, 2001). In fact, Bryan relates that when categorizing minority groups according to prevalence of disabilities, Native Americans are the highest ranked group, followed by African Americans, Caucasians, persons of Hispanic/Latino origin, and finally, Asian/Pacific Islanders. When women are considered as an aggregate, without regard to racial background, data indicates that females have a higher rate of disability than males.

Studies published by the Census Bureau (1990) prognosticate that during the twenty-first century, America will experience a demographic shift. Essentially, it is predicted that an aggregate group consisting of Hispanics/Latinos, African Americans, Asians, and Native Americans will outnumber Euro-Americans, historically the numerical majority. This shift will also result in a change in the labor force make-up. Specifically, minorities, females, and immigrants will embody 85% of the workforce. Asian/Pacific Americans and Native Americans, African Americans, and Hispanics/Latinos, will compose 4%, 12%, and 10% of the work force, respectively. Sixty-one percent of all American women will be employed, equivalent to 47% of the women comprising the total labor force. Finally, individuals thirty-five to fifty-four years in age will comprise 51% of the workforce, while persons between ages sixteen to twenty-four will decline to approximately 8%.

The number of persons with disabilities is expected to increase and generally come from minority populations (Bryan, 1999). Hence, it is predicted that most of America's needs and future work will not only be met by racially diverse populations, but also by those persons within these populations who have disabilities. Because of predicted demographic shifts, many helping professionals have focused on issues of multiculturalism. Rubin and Roessler (1995) communicate that multiculturalism has become particularly evident in the helping philosophy of professionals who work with persons with disabilities.

The helping profession's focus on multiculturalism increased as a result of several developments (Rubin & Roessler, 2008). A primary development was the realization that minorities were either being underserved or excluded from counseling-related services. Review of rehabilitation counseling literature confirms that, compared to Euro-Americans with disabilities, ethnic and racial minorities with disabilities are rejected at a disproportionately higher frequency for rehabilitation services. When minority clients are accepted as clients, one study asserts they are rendered less effective services resulting in unsatisfactory rehabilitation outcomes. Therefore, it is not surprising to learn that the earnings of minorities with disabilities are even lower than Caucasians with disabilities (Sue & Sue, 1999). In order to improve the treatment of persons with disabilities from minority populations, it is imperative that helping professionals be trained in and proficient at multicultural counseling. A meta analysis of four studies of African-Americans compared to Caucasians who were either deaf/hard-of-hearing or were diagnosed as "mentally retarded" confirmed the findings of Sue & Sue (Moore et al., 2009).

Helping professionals must understand that minorities with disabilities are to be perceived from two perspectives – a person with a disability and a minority of a minority population (Giles, 1992). This identity with two groups that have historically been marginalized by society can often lead to a type of double discrimination. According to Bryan (1999), the 1992 report by the National Council on Disability revealed that persons who engender this description encounter a disproportionate amount of biased treatment as compared to their Caucasian or European counterparts. For helping professionals, the added complexity associated with needing to consider both identities in the evaluation of a minority client with a disability can be quite daunting. However, to truly bring about successful rehabilitation outcomes, helping professionals must be knowledgeable and sensitive to the cultural and disability-related needs of each client.

Furthermore, people with disabilities have been portrayed as objects to be pitied, sick, burdens to society, ugly and sexless, incompetent, menaces or threats to society, cursed by God, gifts or tests from God, freaks, and perpetual children (Mackleprang & Salsgiver, 2009; Wright, 1980). In some cultures, for an example, the loss of an arm may mean that the person was caught stealing. These stereotypes add additional barriers to achieving parity in most societies.

The following is a general outline/checklist of areas for consideration when working with minority clients with disabilities.

1. Self-Assessment

This is a significant first step for any counselor, but especially for professionals working with minorities with disabilities.

- Be knowledgeable about your heritage and how it affects your thoughts, ideas, beliefs, and actions toward others. In addition, be cognizant of how your cultural background impacts others' perception of and interactions with you; this is particularly important if you are of the dominant culture.

- Gain awareness of how you see the dominant culture. What attitudes (positive and negative) have you adopted from the dominant culture, specifically those areas concerned with disabilities and minorities? How vested are you in these beliefs?

- Acknowledge and address issues that might hinder you from working effectively with minority clients with disabilities, such as biases, fears, superstitions, prejudices, expectations, stereotypes, etc.

- Educate yourself concerning society's discreet and not-so-subtle attitudes toward minority persons with disabilities.

- Determine your current level of expertise relating to different cultures and various disabilities, specifically those on your caseload. Do you have resources (persons experienced in this area, books, etc.) for learning more about different cultures and disabilities? Devote some effort into learning about other cultures and their history.

- Be comfortable with asking clients for help in learning more about their culture. Bryan (1999) asserts that through this request rapport is often increased, for many clients perceive this as a demonstration of the professional's commitment to helping.

- Learn about legislation that might affect minorities with disabilities, as well as their rights in employment and educational settings.

2. Client Assessment

A. Determine the Client's Current Support Systems

- Family Involvement: Due to the fact that family is a paramount influence in most persons' lives, the assessment of family structure is of utmost importance (Bryan, 1999). When considering persons with disabilities, family system is of particular interest, for the presence or absence of such a structure affects the unit's ability to manage life stressors, such as disability.

- Determine the family structure: Is it nuclear (i.e., parents or parents and unmarried children at home) or extended (i.e., parents, children, grandparents, uncles, aunts)?

- Identify the authority figures of the family, roles of family members, how decisions are made, and child-rearing practices.

- Evaluate the historical stability of the family unit: Have there been other stressful situations in the family's past? If so, how well did the unit manage?

- Assess the family's current ability to handle the situation.

- Determine the family's current resources for managing the issues at hand.

- Obtain information regarding the strengths and weaknesses of the family structure: This is particularly important for judging the family's problem-solving ability.

- Be knowledgeable of each client's environment (e.g., local surroundings, neighborhood, city) and its associated beliefs toward disabilities.

- Community Involvement: Typically, many minorities do not participate in formal types of activities (e.g., social and civic organizations), but find a sense of belonging through informal activities, such as places of worship. Hence, helping professionals need to be aware of both formal and informal sources of support.

- If the client and/or family is in need of additional resources outside of the family unit, it is imperative that the helping professional locate community connections for these individuals. During this process of making connections, one must be conscious of the comfort level of the client and/or family regarding outside services. In other words, while some individuals openly accept outside aid, others may indicate resistance, due to cultural issues.

Possible areas for additional support: affordable respite services, advocacy training, psychological services, legal advice, financial counseling and assistance, emotional support/support groups, education on issues concerning the specific disability, employment training, rehabilitative technology, etc.

B. Evaluate the Client's Acculturation Level

Though assimilation and acculturation are often used interchangeably, their meanings are different (Bryan, 1999). Acculturation is the acquisition of cultural patterns of the dominant society. Assimilation, on the other hand, involves a contribution to the dominant culture that is revered as equally important and respected as practices of the dominant culture. Stated in other terms, assimilation indicates equal inclusion in the dominant society, whereas acculturation denotes little contribution and/or relinquishment of some of one's culture in the process of joining the dominant society.

When assessing level of acculturation of minority individuals with disabilities, helping professionals must first determine client's and/or family's levels of acculturation with respect to the following factors: attitudinal, marital, behavioral, structural, civic, and identification. Assessments of clients and/or families will mainly pertain to attitudes, due to the fact that attitudinal barriers are the major hindrances to persons with disabilities. The assessment is aimed at gaining information regarding how much the client and/or family has "bought into" the dominant culture's negative doctrines toward disabilities.

C. Gain Insight into Client's Worldview

Tied into people's uniqueness is their own worldview. Worldview has been generally defined as the manner in which a person understands his or her position in the world and how that world operates. Through interactions with others, a person's perceptions are formed. It is these perceptions, or interpretations, of life occurrences that constitute one's worldview. When working with minority individuals, helping professionals must have a clear delineation of their own worldview and the client's, in order to reduce the possibility of unsatisfactory rehabilitation outcomes.

Points to remember when assessing worldviews of minorities with disabilities:

- Remember that persons in this group may have a worldview from a minority and disability standpoint. Try to evaluate how each aspect affects the attitudes, beliefs, etc. of the client and/or the family.

- Examine the client's locus of control and locus of responsibility (Sue & Sue, 1999). Locus of control can be either internal (the individual believes s/he has the power to enact change) or external (the individual attributes outside forces as the controlling factor of life). Locus of responsibility deals with the degree of responsibility or blame a person places on the himself/herself or the system for one's situation in life.

- The way people relate to others may be quite different from one culture to the next. For instance, Asians traditionally adhere to lineal, or hierarchical, relationships, while some adopt individualism (U.S.). Still other groups maintain egalitarian, or collateral alliances.

- Different cultures vary in the way they perceive time (Sue & Sue, 1999). Some groups may focus on the here and now, whereas others may see only the distant future or tradition and the past.

- Differences can also occur in the way people approach activity. For example, one culture may value a being orientation, while another may adhere to a doing attitude.

- Distinctions can occur between the way cultures view people. Sue and Sue (1999) state that culture and societies may socialize individuals to being trusting or suspicious. By way of illustration, some groups, due to their minority status, may acquire suspiciousness toward institutions and people.

- The manner in which people interact with nature is another point of contrast. For instance, while Caucasians tend to place importance upon overpowering nature, American Indians strive for peace with the earth.

- Gain an understanding of the client's beliefs and attitudes toward himself/herself and his/her disability.

- Ascertain opinions of the family's worldview with respect to both disabilities and the client's life situation.

Although this is not meant to be an exhaustive list, an understanding and application of these concepts will allow the professional to gain insight into the client's needs and ability of coping with life's difficulties. This insight will in turn provide direction for counseling interventions that will be more appropriate and effective for minorities with disabilities.

(Appreciation is extended to Dr. Ann Landes, for the above contribution. She is a graduate of the Georgia State University doctoral program and has personal experiences relating to this topic.)

Summary

This chapter has reviewed the literature relating to the foundations of rehabilitation in the private and public sectors, elements of disability determination, and the concepts of the transferability of skills. We have seen support mounting for objective and comprehensive rehabilitation procedures that minimize inadvertent or purposeful tampering of data by the professional. Most professionals will agree that demand for accountability is increasing. Support also exists for a procedure that reduces error from a lack of training. Ethical issues must be balanced with the offering of credible professional opinions and more of an effort to standardize the profession seems in the offing. Issues on diversity are gaining in significance to the principal that all people in our society should be considered for human and rehabilitation services when appropriate.

Figure 1.2
Marketing of Private Sector Rehabilitation Services

☑ **Credentials** as the number one priority. Develop a resume that reflects as much talent and experience as possible. This seems to be more important for those likely to end in court such as personal injury cases.
  ➤ Be credentialed/certified (CRC, CRRN, CCM, CVE, LPC, QRP, etc.)
  ➤ The more education and experience (degrees and CEUs) the better

☑ Give superior **Professional** service. Word of mouth marketing of services is the best. When you are in the business and giving good service, very few of the tips on this page are needed.

☑ **Dress and appearance**. Be reasonable and moderate in all areas.
  ➤ Weight
  ➤ Clothing
  ➤ Hair style
  ➤ Etc.

☑ **Professional involvement**. Be an active member of your association.
  ➤ Shows commitment
  ➤ Creates network
  ➤ Gives image of being the expert

☑ RN (and possible CRC) do no charge **file reviews** for insurance companies.

☑ CRC (possibly RN) do no charge **consulting** with attorneys.

☑ Offer insurance companies **in-service training** on various topics and/or "brown bag seminars." Brown bag seminars are open to a variety of people and usually involve a series of topics with physicians as guest speakers. A *Certificate of Participation* is often popular.

☑ **Teach** or guest speak at the local University. This helps with "expert" image. Also creates network.

☑ Help put on **conferences**; be a speaker.

☑ Volunteer to **speak** at public events or conferences outside of your profession. Or if you are helping with certain events, allow yourself to make television appearances to advertise employing the handicapped to make public appearance on telethons, etc.

☑ Provide **rapid response** to the client and the people who retain you. Or, do what you say you will do when you say you will do it!

☑ Consider **reduced fee**s at the start. Or, provide some services at no charge and send a bill showing the services provided at no expense; i.e., bring it to their attention.

☑ **Take** attorneys, insurance **representatives to lunch or dinner**. Or, put on open houses or buy people drinks at the end of the day. Be personable.

☑ Go to **adjuster luncheons** (e.g., monthly assoc. meetings), attend annual Christmas parties, and attend conferences that attract insurance and attorney representatives.

☑ **Publish** articles, books, etc., or consider writing and distributing newsletters for loss control and related information. Make people **aware** of you and your services.

Chapter 2
The Vocational Rehabilitation Expert

Introduction

Many rehabilitation professionals have served as a vocational expert (VE) in a variety of settings. Probably the most structured setting is the federal Social Security system. The text below is specifically related to this system. However, many terms and concepts are used across other areas as well, and guidelines are provided that relate to all professionals serving as a vocational expert in a variety of venues. Later in the chapter are guidelines for rehabilitation counselors and rehabilitation nurses for all settings.

The VE Defined

Within the field of guidance and counseling there are individuals who specialize in the area of vocational counseling and vocational rehabilitation counseling. Vocational counselors specialize in assisting individuals in the choosing of a career and will typically work with clients who span an age range from late adolescence to advanced age. Vocational counselors will sometimes work primarily with individuals who are psychologically or physically impaired. When they assume this role, they are referred to as vocational rehabilitation counselors.

Over the past thirty years, vocational specialists have been increasingly called upon to provide assistance to courts and attorneys in identifying the effect of injury on an individual's capacity to perform work and earn money. The admissibility of expert testimony has become a major concern in cases that become litigated in federal courts. While the Social Security Administration maintains specific criteria for vocational experts with the Bureau of Hearings and Appeals, federal and state courts are being influenced significantly by the U.S. Supreme Court rulings of Daubert and Kumho. At a minimum, a vocational expert (specialist) must possess "specialized knowledge and technical skills" that are clearly germane to the profession of vocational rehabilitation. The Social Security Administration does set forth specific criteria for those desiring to be eligible for VE work with the administration, but other programs (types of hearings) may be open to rigorous cross-examination. It is generally conceded that the following list of credentials will serve the VE in good stead.

Education:

• Baccalaureate degree in behavioral sciences

• Master's degree in specific vocational field

• Master's degree from CORE (Council on Rehabilitation Education)-accredited university programs (preferred)

• Doctorate degree in counseling, psychology, and/or rehabilitation (not essential)

• Related technical courses, seminars, or training sessions that would increase skills

Experience:

• Worked as a rehabilitation specialist

• Worked with "similar" clients

• Worked in vocational assessment

• Worked in job analysis and placement

- Worked on resolving forensic issues such as transferable skills analysis (TSA), estimating lost employment and earnings, estimating future earnings and worklife, and life care plans

Professionalism:

- Belong to one or more relevant professional associations
- Be familiar with current professional literature
- Become certified by the most relevant association (to one's work - list not exclusive):
  - CRC (Certified Rehabilitation Counselor) certification and licensure (if provided by state)
  - NBCC (National Board of Certified Counselors) certification and licensure (if provided by state)
  - CDMS (Certified Disability Management Specialist) certification
  - CCM (Certified Case Manager) certification
  - CLCP (Certified Life Care Planner) certification

One qualification that generally supersedes other qualifications for expert status is the attainment of a terminal degree or doctorate in a vocationally related area such as guidance and counseling, vocational counseling, and/or vocational rehabilitation counseling. Publication in professional journals will typically enhance the recognition of the vocational specialist as an expert, as will a vocationally related professorial appointment at a college or university (i.e., adjunct status). Some of the more relevant journals to the profession of forensic rehabilitation consulting are

- *The Rehabilitation Professional* (International Association of Rehabilitation Professionals)
- *Journal of Life Care Planning* (International Academy of Life Care Planners)
- *Journal of Forensic Rehabilitation Research* (Academy of Forensic Rehabilitation Research)
- *Forensic Rehabilitation and Economics: A Journal of Debate and Discussion* (E & F, Inc.)
- *Journal of Vocational Forensic Analysis* (American Board of Vocational Experts)

Preparing the Vocational Expert

Assuming the vocational expert (VE) is a well-qualified individual who possesses adequate or more than adequate credentials for the task, the preparation of the VE's testimony should be a relatively simple process. VEs who are experienced understand their particular role in the litigation process. They have a good grasp of their area of expertise and should have no difficulty assisting the attorney in preparing for the hearing presentation. It may be useful to review the critical areas of the work of the VE in order to understand the type of presentation that the VE can deliver. The areas of VE involvement include areas of expertise, varieties of work performed, and presentation of results.

Areas of Expertise

The vocational expert is a professional who should possess the following specific areas of expertise related to assessment, rehabilitation planning, and employment/wage analysis of vocational issues of the injured worker.

1. Be familiar with the general field of vocational rehabilitation, including federal and state laws and regulations of pertinent programs, e.g., Workers' Compensation, Jones Act.

2. Be knowledgeable of vocational, educational, and psychological assessment procedures, including tests, work samples, and measures often used in the assessment of vocational potential.

3. Be familiar with and able to utilize standard references covering issues of occupations, employment, labor market, and wage resources, e.g., *Dictionary of Occupational Titles* (1991), the *Transitional Classification of Jobs* (6th ed., 2004), the *O*NET* database, and related documents (see references).

4. Be familiar with the concept of "transferability of skills" and able to utilize this analysis process in determining loss of vocational functioning due to injury.

5. Be knowledgeable of competencies involved in "job analysis" of the worker's previous jobs, as well as jobs in general as they exist in a local economy.

6. Be able to determine the potential for future employment of the injured worker based upon the worker's transferable skills and capacity for work, especially as the worker's potential relates to the worker's own labor market. The VE should also be able to estimate a loss of access to particular jobs that exist in the economy as a result of the injury to the worker.

7. Be knowledgeable of wage and earnings data for jobs that exist in the economy and be able to offer an opinion regarding a wage loss based upon the worker's loss of access to employment to the economy. The VE should be able to assist the attorney in estimating the loss of power to earn money as a result of the injury and be able to provide sufficient employment and job data to an economist for the purposes of calculating the loss of future earnings.

8. Be familiar with procedures, processes, and resources for rehabilitation planning and/or training relative to the physical and/or psychological needs of the injured worker. This area of work would include utilizing client interviewing skills; referring clients to appropriate consultants for functional assessment (e.g., physicians, psychologists, physical therapists, etc.); planning for services such as medical treatment, education, etc.; coordinating services during the rehabilitation process; providing necessary job analyses, training and orientation, and job placement; and most importantly, writing comprehensive and relevant reports and summaries on all aspects of the worker's situation. This may include skills related to the development of a life care plan.

9. Be able to serve as a consultant to a variety of other professionals involved in the total rehabilitation/litigation process of the injured worker by offering clear, concise, and pertinent information to the relevant issues involved.

10. Be skilled in the area of vocational presentation in depositions and judicial hearings relative to all areas of the vocational rehabilitation process of the injured worker.

11. Under the rules of the Daubert and Kumho rulings, the VE (or any expert) is required to offer testimony that can meet the test(s) of relevant and reliable information as the basis for testimony. While it appears that the Kumho ruling is more relevant to the work of the vocational consultant, the specific criteria for testimony under Daubert cannot be ignored (see Field, 2006, 2010).

12. Consistent with the point above, the VE must be cognizant of the requirements for being clear and consistent about methodologies used in the preparation of expert testimony. Reliable and relevant sources of data and information must be utilized in the formulation of opinion.

Varieties of Work Performed

There are two major divisions within the work performed. The first is that one may be appointed as a VE by the Social Security Administration (SSA) to appear at an appeals hearing for an applicant for SSDI. The professional is compensated directly by the SSA and may have many cases to review in one day. The VE will not have prior access to the SSDI applicant (sometime called a "client", but there is no counselor-client relationship), so no interview will occur. The VE is expected to review available records and listen to testimony, and the VE may be allowed to ask clarifying questions during the hearing. The administrative law judge (ALJ) will ask hypothetical questions that resemble the characteristics of the applicant. The VE will be asked to render an opinion about the employability of the person seeking SSDI. The ALJ will then render a judgment and order based on all of the information presented.

The second division is that the VE is retained by an attorney or representative to appear at the hearing (SSA and others). The VE will be compensated by the attorney or representative. The VE will have the benefit of interviewing the evaluee, obtaining records, initiating testing, conducting a labor market survey, etc. (See below for additional details.)

The work of the VE is basically described above. However, the following are examples of specific types of work performed by the VE:

1. Conduct an initial interview with the worker for the purpose of gathering pertinent personal, family, and social information.

2. Complete a thorough vocational history from the worker.

3. Solicit varieties of consultants' reports and incorporate these data in an analysis of vocational function of the worker.

4. Complete a transferable skills process based upon job history, functional limitations, and consultants' reports.

5. Administer selected vocational and educational tests and measures in determining levels of vocational functioning.

6. Refer clients to appropriate and selected consultants and/or rehabilitation personnel to provide a general coordination of services on behalf of the worker.

7. Analyze, synthesize, and integrate all relevant information into a reasonable and coherent report of the worker's background and current functional level, including appropriate rehabilitation and/or vocational recommendations.

8. Perform job analyses and labor market surveys, including relevant wage and earnings data.

9. Conduct, when appropriate, analyses related to the loss of earnings capacity or worklife expectancy, and/or compile a life care plan.

10. Present written and/or oral reports containing relevant information on the worker in a variety of settings, e.g., individual consultations, depositions, hearings, and/or trials.

Guidelines for Performance

While performing the duties of the VE, the professional should be guided by prescribed ethical and professional standards of practice, ethics statements, and a document sometimes referred to as a scope of practice. Standards, such as those developed by professional organizations, are set forth as guidelines for the work of the vocational professional. The following list of associations that have published standards relevant to the professional's work is as follows:

*   International Association of Rehabilitation Professionals
*   National Rehabilitation Association
*   National Rehabilitation Counseling Association
*   Rehabilitation Counselors and Educators Association
*   Vocational Evaluation & Work Adjustment Association
*   American Rehabilitation Counseling Association
*   National Council on Rehabilitation Education
*   Council on Rehabilitation Counselor Certification
*   National Board of Counselor Certification
*   American Board of Vocational Experts
*   American Nurses Association
*   International Academy of Life Care Planning
*   Academy of Forensic Rehabilitation Research

In addition, several states have passed laws pertaining to the licensing of counselors and related professionals. In some instances, licensure is required in order to perform work as a professional in the counseling area. Nearly all states require that a rehabilitation professional be "qualified" to perform work in cases dealing with workers' compensation (for an application process to each state's Workers' Compensation Board, see Chapter 3). In addition, some states license rehabilitation counselors as "professional counselors" (e.g., Georgia), some states have a specific license for rehabilitation counselors (e.g., Louisiana), and some states do not require rehabilitation counselors to be licensed (e.g., South Dakota).

Questions for the VE

The VE can expect to address a series of questions from attorneys in either depositions or court presentations. The following list of questions is typical of items that will be asked of the VE:

1. Do you have knowledge of physical and mental disabilities and their relationship to employment potential?

2. How did you obtain this information?

3. Do you have knowledge of jobs and their requirements common to the labor market?

    a. How did you obtain this knowledge?

    b. Have you had experience in job analysis?

    c. Can you give me examples of local industries in which you have observed and analyzed jobs?

4. Will you describe for the court the parameters of previous employment, including

    a. Work performed

    b. Occupationally significant characteristics of the jobs

    c. Tools used

    d. Supervision given and received

    e. Communication skills required

    f. Temperaments needed for jobs

    g. Interest needed for jobs

    h. Typical salaries for such jobs

    i. Physical demands

    j. Use of arms, hands, fingers, legs, back, etc.

    k. General intelligence requirements

5. Define for the court or to the administrative law judge (ALJ) the occupational significance of the physical (or mental) conditions as defined by the physician.

6. Define for the court how the physical (or mental) conditions relate to previous jobs.

7. Define for the court the occupational significance of the client's daily (social, avocational, recreational) activities.

8. Are there jobs in the labor market (in this city) that may be done by the client without additional training? If so, what are they, and where are they located (by industry)?

9. Have you talked with these employers?

10. Would they hire the client?

11. What would be the salary level?

12. What would be the anticipated income in one year and in five years?

13. How does that income compare with previous income? How much can the client expect to gain or lose as a result of changing jobs?

14. Are there jobs in the labor market in which the client could be employed with additional training or education? If so, what are they?

15. What kind of training would it require?

16. What would be the cost of such training?

17. Is the client qualified for acceptance into the training program?

18. What are those qualifications?

19. How long is the training program?

20. If the client has had a vocational evaluation, the following additional questions will be asked:

    a. Would you define for the court the types of psychological tests administered during the evaluation process?

    b. What are those tests supposed to evaluate?

    c. Could you tell the court what the validity of those tests is?

    d. Describe in layman's terms what a work sample is.

    e. Describe for the court each of the work samples that were administered.

    f. What are their purposes?

    g. What are they supposed to measure?

    h. What is the validity of each?

    i. To what types of skills or jobs do the work samples relate?

    j. Are they related to industrial requirements?

21. Describe the method you used for such activities as TSAs and estimation of earnings and employment loss.

22. Have the methods used been peer reviewed and generally accepted by the rehabilitation community?

These questions should not be considered inclusive of all the questions asked of a vocational specialist while testifying in court. They do, however, help define the parameters of topics that may be covered. An examination of the questions with an interpretation that is applicable to the vocational specialist will be useful. When appropriate, the vocational specialist should answer the questions in terms of magnitude, frequency, and duration. For example, if lifting is incumbent to a job, the vocational specialist should be able to state how much weight must be lifted (magnitude), how often the weight must be lifted (frequency), and how long the weight must be held (duration). If a particular job requirement does not occur often enough to prevent the client from entering that vocation due to his disabling condition, then it may be possible to restructure or modify the job requirement(s) to fit the client's residual functioning ability.

Questions 1-4 are general information questions inquiring into the specialist's personal and professional knowledge. The vocational specialist must have expertise in the utilization of many sources of occupational information and experience in job analysis to answer questions 1-5. Application of such techniques to local industry will fulfill question 6.

Question 5 requires knowledge of:

A. The client's work history – a profile of all previous jobs held by the client and their relation to the Dictionary of Occupational Titles (DOT), worker trait arrangements, physical demands, working conditions, general educational development (GED), specific vocational preparation, aptitudes, interests, and temperaments.

B. Significant characteristics of the job. Are the characteristics unique to one job?

C. Utilization of tools by the client – the specific training required, if any, to use the tools.

D. The client's responsibilities while on the job. Did the client supervise anyone? If so, outline those specific responsibilities. What was the appraisal of the client's work performance as reported by his supervisor?

E. Essential communication requirements of the job. Was talking, hearing, reading, or writing essential to the client's job? If so, what level and type of communication skills were required?

F. The client's temperament. Are the temperaments exhibited in previous employment commensurate to temperaments exhibited by the client's preference and evaluation results? A major cause of job failure lies with the incompatibility between the client's preference of temperaments and the temperaments required to perform the job.

G. The client's interests. What are the client's stated interests as well as those interests demonstrated during previous employment? Differences (if any) should be explained.

H. The average or median salary for such jobs.

I. The physical demands placed on the client. What would be the magnitude, frequency and duration of any or all of the following: lifting, pushing, pulling, carrying, climbing, balancing, stooping, kneeling, bending, crouching, crawling, reaching, handling, fingering, or feeling? Could the client function on the job without vision? What were the environmental conditions? Was the client exposed to extremes of cold and/or heat; wet and/or humid conditions; noise and/or vibrations; hazards and/or fumes, including explosives, toxic chemicals, moving parts, radiant energy, electrical shock?

J. The client's educational and vocational preparation. What were the General Educational Development (GED) and Specific Vocational Preparation (SVP) levels demonstrated by the client? The level of functional ability for mathematics, reasoning, and language as demonstrated on the job is often more valid than the formal educational level attained by the client. The SVP assigned to a job is similar to the probationary period. Therefore, only those jobs in which the client has demonstrated appropriate longevity should be used.

K. The aptitude level exhibited by the client. What is the correlation between the client's demonstrated functioning ability in aptitudes (e.g., intelligence, form perception, numerical aptitudes) and the working population as a whole?

L. Testing and/or interviewing procedures undergone by the client in obtaining previous jobs. Such information provides the vocational specialist with information regarding the client's job seeking skills.

M. Amount of average daily and weekly hours worked and the number of days worked. Long hours, swing shifts, and uncertain schedules require varying degrees of physical and/or frustration tolerance.

N. Transportation utilized to and from work.

Question 6 requires examination of the client's physical (or mental) conditions as defined by the physician to determine the physical demands, working conditions, GED, SVP, aptitudes, interests, and temperaments in which the client still possesses functional ability.

Question 7 lists some social, recreational, and avocational activities in which the client may engage on a daily basis. This question could be answered through observation and/or questioning of the client. Such activities may be indicative of traits or characteristics the client could transfer to other vocations.

Question 8 assumes an understanding of questions 1-9 with the specialist relating the client's specific disabling condition to all aspects of previous jobs.

Question 9 requires the vocational specialist to have possession of a job market survey that is applicable to the client's living area. If jobs do exist, as outlined in this question, the specialist would answer appropriately.

Questions 10-13 are self-explanatory by their nature.

Question 14 would require essentially the same type of preparation as question 11; however, in this instance attention must be given to prospective jobs and their training requirements, licensing, and/or certification procedures.

Questions 15-19 are self-explanatory as they relate to the training of the client for a specific vocation.

Question 20 is basically self-explanatory; however, sections "d" through "h" require that the specialist expound on the following:

A. The work-samples approach is an evaluation technique designed to assess a client's ability to function within specific areas of work.

B. The work sample is designed to assess the entire behavior of a client, which relates to the basic duties, equipment, and tools of a particular occupational area within a controlled environment.

C. The validity of most current work samples is dependent upon the ability of the evaluator to observe and interpret behavior.

D. The work sample approach assesses many basic traits and characteristics common to various worker trait factors. The skills exhibited by a client in completing a work sample can be linked to industrial norms that are utilized by many work samples, thus comparing performance on the work sample to competitive industrial requirements.

E. The vocational evaluation process examines the client's previous and present skills to determine which skills are transferable to other vocations.

Questions 21 and 22 address the issue of admissible testimony in the event your report is subject to a presentation and defense in a deposition or trial. For an expanded discussion of the "admissibility" issue, refer to the next section of this chapter or Chapter 12 of this text.

The topics and questions presented above are suggestive of the type of preparation required of a vocational specialist to testify in court. It is our opinion that both the attorney and the vocational specialist would benefit from a process in which questions were prepared and reviewed prior to the court appearance. This planning and participation would hopefully result in mutual understanding and respect by both the vocational specialist and the attorney.

Admissible Testimony

The U.S. Supreme Court rulings on the admissibility of expert testimony in *Daubert v. Merrill Dow Pharmaceuticals* (92-102, US Sp Ct, 1993), *Kumho Tire Company v. Carmichael* (526 US Sp Ct 137, 1999), and *Joiner v. General Electric* (96-188, US Sp Ct, 1997) are very critical and important cases for any professional aspiring to be an expert testifying in federal and state courts. For a comprehensive discussion of this topic, review *A Resource for the Rehabilitation Consultant on the Daubert and Kumho Rulings* (Field, et al, 2000; see also Chapter 12 of this text). This resource includes a considerable amount of information including the review and discussion of expert testimony beginning with *Frye v. United States* (No. 3968, 293 F. 1013), the *Federal Rules of Evidence* (2000), *the Federal Rules of Civil Procedure* (2010), a review of Daubert and Kumho rulings with case law studies, a summary of each state's position on Daubert and Kumho (Field, 2010), and professional guidelines (documents from the professional associations) for the rehabilitation consultant who would be testifying in federal and state cases. All of the above documents and federal cases may be retrieved in full by accessing the web and searching through a standard search engine (i.e. Google). The most relevant rules of the FRE and the FRCP are included in the Appendix D of this text.

The VE in Litigation

The vocational expert should be able to provide analysis of an individual's loss of power to earn money as a result of injury or death. Power to earn money is a function of an individual's capacity to perform work. The capacity to perform work is predicated upon a series of quantifiable factors that include age, aptitude, general educational development level, previous work experience, special vocational training, and physical capabilities.

The U.S. Department of Labor (DOT, 1991) identifies and classifies 12,741 occupational titles by a series of worker trait characteristics. These characteristics include physical demands, working conditions, aptitudes, and the general educational development levels needed to perform each of the occupations satisfactorily. The 12,000-plus titles are grouped into a series of over 501 separate occupational categories (the Labor Market Access approach) that include the worker trait factors, wage information, and the number of employed workers. Either national or local labor market data is used to compute an individual loss of capacity to work and earn money as a result of injury or death. Computerization may result in an assessment of an individual's median or midpoint power to earn money. There are several commercial programs available in this area and any program should be used with caution with respect to the outcome of an analysis. Specifically, any outcome report should be viewed by the resource as a general estimate of functioning and job accessibility, and must be tempered with professional clinical judgment by the consultant (see Chapter 12 for a discussion of clinical judgment).

The general rule of thumb is that a loss of capacity to perform labor and earn money will result if an individual has sustained a permanent loss of exertional capacity. The general exception to this rule includes those individuals who are involved in skilled work of a professional, technical, and managerial nature. Such work is typically involved in sedentary or sit-down types of jobs. Therefore, in order for an exertional restriction to affect their skilled capacity to labor and earn money, the degree of injury typically must be one of catastrophic proportions. However, the typical unskilled or semi-skilled worker who experiences a reduced ability to engage in various types of exertional activities will incur a loss of power to earn money as a result of restriction.

In gathering medical proof of both permanency and exertional impairment, it is essential that the physician be asked questions regarding reduced exertional capability from a vocational perspective. Appendix C contains a series of definitions that define the way in which work is classified by the U.S. Department of Labor Employment and Training Administration. When a physician is deposed, there is enormous advantage to asking questions from the perspective of the criteria also listed in the Appendix C. By way of example, in the case of back injury, it would seem reasonable to begin asking the physician questions regarding the work capacity level of the injured worker, beginning with sedentary work. Hence the questioning begins with the least arduous definition of lifting, carrying, pushing, and pulling and ends with the most physically arduous definition of very heavy work. Any individual who has undergone any type of back surgery would, in all probability, be restricted to work of a sedentary to light nature and in some instances work of a medium nature.

The procedure followed in determining loss of earnings capacity involves a wide range of vocational information from consulting sources and labor market databases developed and provided by local, state, and federal governments. In particular, the process involves vocational assessment of the injured worker's level of functioning, both prior to injury as well as his or her current level of functioning. This information is then paired with vocational information that is germane to the worker's local geographical area.

Tools/Graphics

Presentation of the Rehabilitation Expert

The following represents suggestions for the use of aids in the courtroom to display and clarify the opinion. (See also Chapter 11, Forensic Rehabilitation). These suggestions are not appropriate for Social Security. This part of the testimony by the expert in a court hearing utilizes various graphic-type presentations to the jury. Graphics that are carefully done and effectively presented can be a very influential tool in educating the jury about the issues involved in the case. There are four basic types of presentations that the rehabilitation expert can make in using media in this way:

1. PowerPoint is a common and useful method of presenting information. PowerPoint presentations are easy to develop and can be very effective in presenting technical information that is both pleasing and informative. A precaution with this resource, however, is not to appear too "slick" or "fancy." There is no substitute for well-developed information that is accurate and fair, no matter the mode of presentation.

2. Charts are also very common. The chart should be of approximately two by four feet and will be placed on the easel before the jury. The chart should be developed to the most relevant points of the case and should present both employment information as well as wage information in the format of a bar graph or similar type of presentation.

3. Enlargements of related documents or referral information can be very effective in a presentation. The enlargements can be made in a local copying center that has the capability to blow up documents to the approximate size of a chart. Some of these enlargements will contain very detailed information that can be useful in referencing someone else's information as a basis of formulating an opinion. Examples of the types of enlargements that can be made include sections of the medical report, employment and wage survey information, etc.

4. The videotape is a very useful presentation that can show more than just static information about some aspect of the case. A videotape showing the client's/evaluee's range of motion can be made of the behavioral capacities of a client following an injury. An example of this would be a video scene of the person in a wheel chair to emphasize the physical functional limitations of the client as a result of the injury. Another useful practice would be to videotape the client's previous job by showing another person performing the various aspects of that job. A contrast with the client's physical functioning at its current level may dramatically show that the client can no longer perform that job or any other job of a similar nature. Generally, a video longer than 15 minutes will lose its impact (Hunt, 2010).

Characteristics of an Effective Presentation

There are a few basic rules to follow in the development of a graphic presentation to a jury. The points to consider are as follows:

1. The graphic presentation should be basic, simple, and directly related to the issue involved in the case (according to the Rules of Evidence, the testimony must be "relevant" to the question before the court).

As a general rule, only three basic points should be made on the chart so as not to run the risk of complicating the presentation.

2.   The graphic should be easy to read from a distance of approximately ten to fifteen feet. The lines' colors, letters' color, and the figures and characters on the chart should be displayed in an uncomplicated and clear manner.

3.   The presentation should be short, concise, and to the point. In explaining the chart, the rehabilitation expert should remember to present the points in a basic and non-confusing manner. It is important to keep in mind as well that the presentation is by the rehabilitation expert to the jury. There will be no opportunity for discussion between the expert and the jury.

Characteristics to Avoid

The graphic should not be complicated, confusing, or difficult to read and understand. With this in mind, it is important to emphasize a couple of particular points about the presentation.

1.   The presentation should not reflect a slick "Fifth Avenue" approach that appears as though it were done by an expensive firm in graphic artistry. Perhaps the most effective graphic presentations are those that are developed with felt tip pens in a clean and clear fashion on simple white poster board. The point of the exercise is to present the information in a clear and concise manner.

2.   It cannot be overemphasized that the presentation must be done in a simple and straightforward manner. Any presentation that becomes too complicated with redundant or overly detailed explanations runs the risk of not only boring the jury but completely confusing them in terms of understanding the points and issues involved in the case. Keep the presentation basic.

Selected Issues

The vocational expert, at one time or another, is confronted with several different issues that will have some bearing on the development of his or her consultation and testimony. Each of the following issues should be considered carefully.

The rehabilitation expert should be familiar with the "federal rules" relative to the content and process by which testimony is developed and presented. This document (for *Federal Rules of Evidence* and the *Federal Rules of Civil Procedure*, see Appendix D) is a most important resource and guideline, especially for testimony in the areas of personal injury and liability. Note that Rule 702 has been amended (2000).

Fee Setting

It is generally conceded that there are three specific ways in which expert witnesses might establish fees for their work in the preparation and delivery of testimony. The three specific approaches to fee setting include contract agreements, hourly fee standards, and contingency fees.

Contract Payments

In many cases, the expert may contract with an attorney or other party to the adjudication process and establish a fee for services for the entire work that will be done in the particular case. As a means of setting a fee according to this method, estimate the number of days that would be required to complete the work, including the presentation at a judicial hearing, if such a hearing is (or may be) scheduled. It is estimated that the fee would be for x number of days at so much per day for the entire payment.

The Social Security Administration, Bureau of Hearings and Appeals, has established set fees for the payment of VEs in this program. The vocational expert is paid on a structured fee schedule. The fee schedule is based on study/examination and court appearance. As of 2012, for court appearance the VE is paid $110 for the first appearance and $75 for each additional appearance in the same day, whether the contractor does or does not testify. Examination and study of cases are paid according to the following:

a.   Remand case

b.   Other cases

    c.   Response to specific questions in writing vs. personal court appearance

    d.   Written comments on cases previously charged

Hourly Wage

The expert witness may choose to receive payment based upon the number of hours that are involved in any particular case. The work of the expert witness may include preliminary review of the case, preparation of the case, and court presentation including the waiting time for turn on the stand. Many consultants charge different rates for case management, depositions, trial testimony, and travel time.

Contingency Fees

The contingency fee is defined as the receipt of payment for services dependent upon the amount of money that is either saved or earned as a result of the adjudication. This is by far the most controversial method of fee setting as it raises some serious questions about the ethics of such an approach on the receipt of money for services. Perhaps the two greatest counter-indicators of contingency fee setting are that (1) it suggests a bias or special interest in presenting testimony that will obviously benefit the expert in terms of his/her own remuneration, and (2) the issue of venality must be considered (Graham, 1978). The Britannica World Dictionary (1963) defines venality as:

> *the state or character of being improperly influenced by sordid considerations; prostitution, as of talents, office, etc., for gain or reward; willingness to accept bribes.*

This is very strong language with respect to assessing the receipt of fees on a contingency basis; undoubtedly there are some expert witnesses who serve and present testimony primarily for personal financial gain. In cases such as these, we subtly, or perhaps not so subtly, drift into the third major area of concern, which is quite blatantly called corruption. In cases of corruption, the expert witness has moved beyond mere violation of ethics with respect to one's profession and has clearly moved within the fraudulent activity of presenting any testimony that would result in greater financial gain. Perhaps the greatest indicator of this particular activity is the constant and extensive employment of an expert witness by the same attorney to offer testimony in the same or similar cases.

With respect to ethics, the American Bar Association (ABA) has clearly established an ethical and professional standard for the setting of contingency fees:

> *A lawyer shall not pay, or acquiesce in the payment of, compensation to a witness contingent upon the content of his testimony or the outcome of the case. But a lawyer may advance, guarantee, or acquiesce in the payment of . . . a reasonable fee for the professional services of any expert witness.*

Schaper (1977) has argued that the ABA code for ethical practice is probably the best guideline to follow in avoiding contingency fees to expert witnesses. Obviously, the overriding rationale for this guideline is to prevent biased findings that will obviously result in increased financial gain to the expert witness (See Federal Rules in Appendix). In conclusion, the rehabilitation expert must not engage in contingency fee arrangements.

Guidelines for Setting Fees

Irrespective of the method followed in the establishment of a fair and equitable fee for the expert witness, Richardson (1979) has identified several factors that seem to have a great deal of relevance in fee setting. These factors are as follows:

1. The qualifications of the expert witness, including knowledge, skills and experiences, and levels and degrees of learning and training.

2. The usefulness and adequacy of the testimony as presented.

3. The amount of time and services expended by the expert witness in the preparation and presentation of the testimony.

4. The amount of time spent in actually testifying, including waiting time for a hearing in the judicial process.

5. The loss of revenue by the expert witness while away from other employment activities.

6. The generally "accepted" rates for expert testimony work by other professionals in the same geographical area.

7. The awards or fees paid in similar cases to other expert witnesses.

Depositions

In cases involving worker/personal injury, the rehabilitation expert can be very useful to the attorney(s) involved by assisting in depositions. The most obvious way the rehabilitation expert can help is to provide guidance on the kinds of questions that should be asked. The most compelling, single criterion for "good" questions is whether or not the questions are vocationally relevant. The rehabilitation expert should be guided by the following:

1. The laws and regulations appropriate to the program (e.g., Social Security).

2. The "questions" as outlined in this chapter.

3. Vocational assessment and testing information in Chapter 5.

4. The deposition checklist (see Appendix F).

Salary Projections/Wage

In cases of personal injury in particular, a financial award will be contingent in part on the projected loss of income over the worker's estimated years of work lost. Although this type of information may not always be within the VE's area of expertise, the information is of such a "common sense" nature that the testimony may be allowed in some cases.

Determining Disability

One of the most critical issues in the adjudication process with the injured worker is the extent (percentage) of the disability. Historically, judges have relied upon the physician to give a "percentage rating" of an injured back or hand. In addition, the American Medical Association has attempted to standardize the process.

The real issue, however, is the question of the worker's ability to return to his/her previous job, a related or similar job, a markedly reduced job, or no job at all. In order to make a more realistic "disability determination", a process referred to as Labor Market Access (Vander Vegt, Summitt, & Field, 1981; Field, Choppa, & Shaffer, 1984; Field, 1985;Field, 1988; Field, 1993; Weed, 1987) was developed to ascertain the potential for employment of the injured worker. The process involves these simple steps:

1. Complete a pre-injury assessment.

2. Complete a post-injury assessment.

3. Determine the worker's access to jobs in the economy (both pre- and post-injury).

4. Determine the percentage of disability by calculating the difference between the pre- and post-injury assessment.

The original LMA rationale (Field, 1985) draws upon national and state labor market job information. This information is available by state, metropolitan statistical area, city, and county. Each survey includes information on the 501 representative job categories (census codes). Percentages are provided for each title in terms of their frequency within a given economy. The percentage access to jobs prior to injury, less a percentage access to jobs post-injury, results in the reduced employability of the worker. This loss of employability access represents the percentage of disability for the worker.

Do's and Don

While the following is not an all-inclusive list of things to do or not do in court testimony, there are several situations that warrant careful consideration and preparation. First and foremost, the expert should be knowledgeable about the laws, regulations, and/or restrictions governing the case in which testimony is being provided (e.g., Workers' Compensation, Social Security). The second most critical factor is preparation and methodology. The expert should be very thorough in the collection and evaluation of information. When information is not attainable, the expert should be aware of its absence and prepare to offer an opinion regarding its need. The witness chair is always more comfortable for the expert who has over-prepared than it is for the one who is minimally prepared. A discussion of the most common do's and don'ts will help the reader in preparation.

Do's

1. Develop two resumes that describe your educational and vocational experiences. The first resume is a complete listing of personal biographical data (e.g., date of birth, address, marriage status), each educational degree, relevant courses in academic curriculum and brief descriptions of each job held, publications, references, and areas of special expertise and interests. The resume should be used as a thorough listing of all information documenting expertise. The second resume should be a one-page summary of experiences. It should be written in the third person and should sound appropriate to be used as an introduction of the expert to its reader. It should be used for marketing expertise and submitting to attorneys as a summary of experiences relating to vocational expertise.

2. Determine what the person requesting the service expects when asked to serve as an expert witness. Sometimes the person requesting the service has formed conclusions and assumes that the expert will corroborate the conclusions.

   Referral sources sometimes have a propensity for convincing themselves, as well as others, that imaginations are truths. The authors once worked with a defense attorney who was convinced that a client (who claimed total and permanent disability from an industrial accident) was working full-time as a used car salesman and real estate agent. It was later learned that the client had sold his second car and one of the two houses he owned in order to have enough money to support his family.

   Frequently, expert witnesses are hired because opposing counsel has employed a similar expert. In such cases, the second expert is sometimes hired with the assumption that testimony will be provided that will conflict that of the first expert. In other cases, the second expert is hired to offer advice, evaluate the need for more information, proffer cross-examination questions, or to make the attorney feel better.

   Obviously the expert should always evaluate the expectations and assumptions of the person(s) requesting the services. If the expert is uncomfortable with the theories from which conclusions are drawn and can do little to change either, he or she should not agree to serve. On the other hand, many attorneys welcome education. Many do not know how to best use the expert who can testify to damages.

3. Identify the questions that are vocationally relevant to the case. Identification of the vocationally relevant questions is frequently the most important role of the expert. Although the expert may be provided with extensive medical, psychological, educational, social, and vocational reports, the measurable vocationally relevant information is usually absent or at best minimal.

   Most frequently, medical and psychological information is reported in diagnostic terms. For example, a physician may report that the client has "moderately severe degenerative discs at the third and fourth lumbar levels." While such a statement may have medical significance, it has little vocational meaning. The vocational expert would have questions regarding vocationally significant functional limitations (bending, stooping, sitting, walking, etc.) resulting from the condition. A pre-hearing settlement is the most frequent outcome of those cases in which the appropriate vocationally relevant questions have been asked and answered. Therefore, one may conclude that identification of the significant questions is the most critical role of the vocational expert.

4. Meet with the attorney to prepare strategy. This meeting is designed to inform the attorney of the questions and answers that are vocationally important and to inform the expert of the types of questions that may be asked by the opposing attorney.

   The inexperienced vocational expert frequently questions the ethics of such a meeting. However, it has been the writers' experience that these concerns have resulted from fear that an attempt would be made to convince the expert to change opinions. While such attempts may be made, they occur infrequently.

   Expert opinions may be expressed (at such a meeting) that are considered by the attorney to be harmful to his efforts. In these instances, the attorney often decides that the expert will not be asked to testify or that certain questions will not be asked unless done so by the opposition.

Finally, the meeting serves as an excellent opportunity for the attorney to assume the role of the attorney for the opposition. Such practice is helpful for both the expert and attorney.

5. Be prepared to follow expert opinions with supporting rationale. Although an opinion may appear to the expert to have been derived from logical deduction, it is often unclear to the person who hears it. The rationale may be considered as a summary of the critical conditions, which then lead to the logical concluding opinion. For example, the expert may say, "Each of the three jobs held by Mr. Client required that he lift more than 50 pounds both frequently and for long durations. Medical evidence, as the record now stands, prohibits Mr. Client from lifting more than 20 pounds infrequently. Therefore, Mr. Client can do none of his previous jobs."

6. Evaluate all medical, psychological, social, vocational, and educational data. If there are differing opinions, be prepared to give testimony based on each opinion. Differing opinions between and among the medical and psychological professions are common. In such instances, the vocational expert should not attempt to evaluate which is right or wrong. The expert should carefully identify the differences and be prepared to give opinions based on each. Needless to say, the client frequently claims limitations not confirmed by the physician or psychologist. In such cases, the vocational expert should be prepared to provide opinions based on the assumption that such limitations are also accurate.

7. Briefly summarize the vocationally relevant information found in each exhibit and/or report in the file. Such information should be recorded in a manner that may be used as a quick reference. The notes should be brief and, in most cases, chronologically ordered by date. The purpose is not to record extensive or comprehensive information but to outline a reference list of where such information may be found.

    The expert should remember that any notes taken to a deposition or trial may become part of the evidence to be reviewed by both plaintiff and defense. Therefore, care should be taken to note only factual information or notes of opinions based on certain assumptions.

8. Be prepared to cite supporting literature or similar cases of other experts. Information regarding the outcome of similar cases, information from associations formed to serve persons with similar disabilities, experiences of public and private agencies, and policies of employers are all examples of supporting information. While it is not always necessary to cite such information, the expert should be prepared to do so.

9. Answer only those questions that you are qualified (by expertise) to answer. A frequently attempted method of discrediting a witness is solicitation of opinions on topics that are not in the realm of expertise of the witness. Since vocational experts usually utilize data from other professional sources, they should be particularly alert to this downfall. If asked a question about conditions that are medically or psychologically diagnostic in nature, the expert should answer by saying "those clients with whom I have worked and who were diagnosed as having anxiety neurosis (or whatever the diagnosis) have demonstrated. . . . (behaviors)." The expert should never attempt to apply additional meaning to the opinions of an expert in another field. For example if a physician should report that a client was able to do light work, the expert should not interpret "light" to mean 20 pounds occasionally and 10 pounds frequently. In the case of Duncan vs. Moser Leather Company (Ind. App., 408 N.E. 2d 1332, 1980), the judge ruled that at trial, an expert in one field cannot be a conduit for the opinions of an expert in another field. In this case, a rehabilitation counselor interpreted medical and psychological reports to form vocational opinions. The vocational expert's interpretation of meaning of these reports resulted in disqualification. (See also Rule 703 in Appendix D.)

10. Refrain from giving lengthy answers to questions. Answer only what is asked (see "How to give a deposition" in Appendix C. To offer more may open a "can of worms" with which the attorney may fish in otherwise calm waters. Questions should be carefully evaluated, and answers that are brief but complete should be given.

11. Be prepared to change expert opinion based on new evidence. Updated information is frequently introduced at the hearing. Such information often sheds new light on the condition of the client. Therefore, the expert should anticipate questions based on assumptions possibly not previously considered.

    The request for answers based on assumptions can be used to determine the rigidity and/or bias of the expert. All assumptions should be individually analyzed and answered.

12. Be deliberate with answers. If there is need to analyze a question and its answer, do so. Even though the question, or portions of it, has been discussed with the attorney, be deliberate and thoughtful. Two questions may sound similar but can be very different. Therefore, meanings of questions may need clarification.

There are several ways of insuring additional time to consider a question:

   a.   the expert may simply say "let me think about that for a moment";
   b.   the attorney may be asked to repeat the question;
   c.   the expert may restate the question;
   d.   the expert may refer to notes; and
   e.   others may simply be deliberate in their speech.

Finally, the expert should be deliberate, but not reluctant. If the jury or judge perceives that the expert is reluctant, opinions may be suspect by the judge and/or jury.

13. Ask for clarification. If the expert thinks a question has no relevance to the case, clarification on whether it should be answered should be obtained from the judge. When the expert seeks such clarification, the attorney in a jury trial case should use the request as a clue to object. In Administrative Law Judge Hearings, the judge is usually very helpful in such situations. In depositions, the expert should ask for similar clarification from the attorney. The expert should remember that everyone in the courtroom, except one attorney, has empathy for the witness. The judge will usually protect the friendly witness and the jury members will project themselves into the witness stand.

14. Dress appropriately. Although this suggestion may seem to be unnecessary, it should be remembered. A rehabilitation expert was once dressed in a very nice leisure suit. At a pre-hearing lunch, the attorney asked, "Do you think that suit is appropriate for an expert witness to wear at a hearing?" If the question was asked, the answer was obviously "no." It is always appropriate for the vocational expert to dress conservatively. Lapel pins, slogans, or other items that may give an appearance that the expert is biased should not be worn.

It might be appropriate to inquire of the retaining attorney what is appropriate for the venue. Dress relating to federal court in a metropolitan can be very different than a state court in a small city.

15. Consider all resources. Some states have laws that require the expert to consider collateral resources. For example, rehabilitation services may be available through Medicaid, education laws (IDEA), or insurance. This could have a significant impact on bottom line of damages. Be sure to discuss this issue with the attorney.

16. Be prepared to have limited client access. In personal injury litigation, if you are retained by the defense, you may not have access to the client. The writer's experience is that the court may order the plaintiff to be available for an independent medical (related) evaluation, so do not automatically assume you will not have access. Many counselors will provide an opinion based on records. *Generally* it is appropriate to assume the client is telling the truth and the plaintiff's medical expert is the most accurate. It is also appropriate to admit that interviewing the client could have a substantial impact on your opinion. If you have the opportunity, you may obtain information that you would normally require by seeking the attorney's help by providing questions to be asked during a discovery deposition. (A discovery deposition is a legal term for asking witnesses, under oath, questions that are recorded verbatim by a certified court reporter – see Forensic Chapter.)

17. Ask the attorney to tell you about the members of the jury. In one case for the writer, it was comforting to know that the jury member in the back row on the right hand side had slept through most of the trial and it was not related to the testimony style.

18. Look over the courtroom before you testify. This will help with orientation and exhibit locations before you are expected to "perform" and provide the jury with the image of professionalism and competence when you appear to know what to do.

Don'ts

1. Do not allow yourself to be provoked to counterattack by an attorney. Remember the judge and jury side with the person who retains composure. If a question is of a type that is anger provoking, count to ten be-

fore answering, and then concentrate on speaking slowly. If an opportunity occurs to "turn the table" on an aggressive cross-examiner, one may wish to take advantage of it. For example, the expert may be asked, "Since you obviously disagree with Dr. Doe's classification of lifting forty pounds as light work, do you think that anyone would agree with you that the appropriate weight should be no more than 20 pounds?" The expert could answer, "the U.S. Department of Labor and I agree."

Related to the above is the occasional expert who becomes the advocate for the side that has retained him or her. Acting as an advocate may damage the expert's credibility before the jury. Generally speaking, the jury will not remember what exactly the expert said but they are left with an impression. The impression, hopefully, will be a favorable one.

2. Do not answer a question until you understand it. As stated before, some questions may sound similar but have totally different legal implications; for example, a question relating to how many jobs exist in the labor market vs. how many are vacant in the labor market. When the expert does not understand a question, the expert may make a request for clarification. The expert may restate the question, or the judge may be asked to clarify it.

3. Avoid opinions on the "average man" concept. Since much of the vocational expert's testimony is comparisons of an individual's skills with those of the average population, it is easy for the jury, attorney, and/or judge to think the testimony is based on the "average man." The expert needs to remember that there is no average individual, but there are individuals who have one or more skills at levels equal to the average population.

4. Do not state that payment is to be received for testimony. The expert witness is *retained* to provide a professional opinion. Amount of payment varies greatly, but such payment is not for the testimony. The payment is for the expert's knowledge gained through experience as well as for the time involved in studying, analyzing, synthesizing, and preparing. Testimony cannot be purchased, but time can.

5. Do not become lulled into non-preparedness by an ingratiating, mild, good humored, relaxed, and friendly cross-examiner. While some attorneys assume the aggressive or hostile role, others assume the "nice guy" role. Some are very astute at both. The expert should not take a defensive role, but should always attempt to evaluate the implications of questions and their answers prior to answering.

6. Do not expect the attorney to know the types of questions that are vocationally relevant. In a single case, an attorney may need to ask questions about the brake system of a truck, the healing process of a bone, the deceleration speed on wet pavement, causes and controls of seizures, the income rates in two different regions of the country, and the measurement of job related traits. Obviously, the attorney cannot be expert in all these fields. Dependence on various experts is necessary. The expert should never hesitate to suggest questions as well as the format of questions. However, such suggestions should be made prior to testimony. Once the expert is in the witness stand, the attorney should have complete control.

7. Do not use the word speculate. This word has special meaning and will tell everyone that you are simply guessing. If you have an opinion, state it. Looking into the future for the long-term vocational and medical outlook is not speculation when based within rehabilitation probability within your area of expertise. Many attorneys will try to infer that your opinions are speculation and therefore should not be considered by a jury.

There are numerous other do's and don'ts that could be identified. However, the intent of those listed is to help the new expert to overcome initial fears by understanding the most common ones. However, some anxiety can be an effective motivator to assure adequate preparation. As in many other endeavors, experience is the best teacher. For more information on how to prepare for a deposition, see the appendices for an extensive checklist.

Summary

This chapter outlines the general requirements for becoming a vocational expert within Social Security as well as the general requirements for trial preparation and evidence presentation for civil litigation, and it applies to a broad range of rehabilitation experts involved in forensic rehabilitation. Offering expert witness or forensic consulting services is one of the most technical and stressful alternatives available and requires extensive knowledge and experience. Individuals who are interested in forensic rehabilitation should accumulate resources to assure that one understands terms, systems, requirements, and the nature of working within the legal system.

Chapter 3   wk 7 ✓
Workers' Compensation

Historical Perspective

The concepts underlying workers' compensation laws in the United States originated from Germany, in 1884, and Austria, in 1887 (Obermann, 1965; Weed & Field, 1990; Wright, 1980). In 1893 the U.S. Commissioner of Labor studied the need for insurance and compensation, which resulted in a cooperative insurance law in Maryland in 1902. The law was declared unconstitutional because, among other reasons, it denied the right of trial by jury (Obermann, 1965). By 1908, the United States had passed a law referred to as "workers' compensation" for federal employees. Maryland tried another approach, which limited coverage to coal and clay miners, but it was repealed in 1914. New York also passed a law for injured workers, part of which was declared unconstitutional. Despite early conflict, workers' compensation laws were slowly enacted, and, by 1911, ten states had some form of workers' compensation laws. By 1921, forty-five states and territories had some form of workers' compensation law. They all varied by scope, benefits, system of benefits, and administration; however, today all fifty states have some type of workers' compensation laws.

Although the laws vary, each state has adopted a similar definition of injury, which describes an injury caused by an accident "arising out of and in the course of employment" (U.S. Chamber of Commerce, 2005). Additionally, a common provision among workers' compensation laws is medical coverage related to the injury and wage benefits/compensation. Many states also provide for vocational rehabilitation to facilitate a return to employment for the injured worker. Although many have lobbied for a federal law to standardize the workers' compensation programs in the United States, existing laws and regulations are mandated by each state separately (Field & Weed, 1988; Obermann, 1965; Weed & Field, 1994).

Workers' Compensation Overview

With workers' compensation laws in place, employers were relieved of liability brought on by a worker injured on the job. In return, the injured worker received necessary medical treatment, lost wages, and, in some states, possibly vocational rehabilitation or retraining if unable to return to his/her regular job. Table 3.1 lists the six objectives of workers' compensation laws common among states (U.S. Chamber of Commerce, 2005).

Table 3.1
Workers' Compensation Objectives Common Among States

1. Providing sure, prompt, reasonable income and medical benefits to injured workers or income benefits to their dependents, regardless of fault

2. Providing a single remedy and reducing court delays, costs, and work loads arising out of personal-injury litigation

3. Relieving public and private charities of financial drains

4. Eliminating payment of fees to lawyers and witnesses as well as time consuming trials and appeals

5. Encouraging maximum employer interest in safety and rehabilitation through appropriate experience-rating mechanisms

6. Promoting frank studies of causes of accidents, rather than concealment of fault, thereby reducing preventable accidents and human suffering

Source: U.S. Chamber of Commerce, annually updated.

While some states have mandatory rehabilitation assessments for injured workers, other states, such as Georgia, Florida, and Washington, have repealed them (U.S. Chamber of Commerce, 2005). These states have passed legislation to eliminate mandatory rehabilitation based on arguments that rehabilitation costs far exceed the benefit to the worker or to the economy as a whole. This observation is not based on fact nor is it the opinion of the authors or of the majority of rehabilitation professionals (Weed & Lewis, 1994). A section summarizing research on the benefits of rehabilitation can be found elsewhere in this book. Nevertheless, some states such as Georgia continue to mandate rehabilitation assessment for "catastrophically injured" workers and have attempted to define those types of workers (State Board of Workers Compensation, 2011).

In spite of the non-mandatory rehabilitation status of many state laws, workers' compensation insurance carriers and others associated with workers' compensation claims continue to offer vocational rehabilitation as a benefit to the injured worker as a cost-effective means to manage the claim to resolution. Research has supported the benefits of rehabilitation, especially in the workers' compensation arena, not only for cost-effective case management but also to facilitate successful return of the injured worker to gainful employment (Weed & Lewis, 1994).

The goal of workers' compensation rehabilitation can be summarized as promoting maximum functioning and returning to productive, suitable employment. It is accomplished by:

- conducting a needs assessment
- coordinating services (medical and others) to assist in recovery and Maximum Medical Improvement (MMI)
- identifying transferable skills based on residual functional capacity
- assisting in return to gainful employment

Unfortunately, work disincentives exist to impact or impede the rehabilitation process outlined above. The success to which an injured worker returns to suitable, gainful employment is dependent not only on his/her medical condition and residual functional limitations, but on other factors as well. Such factors include the amount of benefits the worker receives (workers' compensation and, in some cases, SSDI, Veterans' benefits, etc.), wages and type of available jobs, and relationship between mental and physical requirements of a job and one's capabilities (Berkowitz, 1988). Likewise, the perception of a large lump sum settlement, the length of time a worker remains out of work, and the worker's personal work ethic serve as disincentives to workers' compensation rehabilitation. The injured worker may not view the rehabilitation process as a means to return to work and to earn as much money as possible within his/her aptitudes, skills, and interests (Deneen & Hessellund, 1981). Quite to the contrary, he/she may be bitter over the injury, angry at a system which he/she feels may not have his/her best interests at heart, and afraid of what the future will be in terms of employment opportunities and earnings potential. A competent rehabilitation consultant can identify these situations and provide effective case management to minimize or overcome these disincentives to employment.

A general approach to workers' compensation job placement was cited by Welch (1979) and expanded upon by Matkin (1981). The approach is based upon a hierarchy of steps for the rehabilitation consultant to take to effect a timely and least costly return to work. Most states utilize the approach described in Table 3.2 or slight variations in their workers' compensation rehabilitation.

Indeed, while the goal of workers' compensation rehabilitation is generally the same across all states, specific workers' compensation laws vary by state and jurisdiction. For a summary of workers' compensation laws by state, the reader is referred to the tables available in the U.S. Chamber of Commerce (annual) *Analysis of Workers' Compensation Laws* publication.

Additionally, many employees such as railroad workers, federal employees, longshoremen, and harbor workers each have separate workers' compensation laws which are distinguished from laws governing most private industry and state government entities. Likewise, not all workers are covered by workers' compensation. Some occupations, i.e., domestic, agriculture, religious, and charitable are exempt from workers' compensation coverage. And some employers with less than a specified number of employees (typically 1 to 5 depending on state) are also exempt from providing workers' compensation coverage (U.S. Chamber of Commerce, annual updates).

Table 3.2
Workers' Compensation Return to Work Hierarchy in Order of Priority

1. Return to work same job/same employer
2. Return to work different job/same employer
3. Return to work same job/different employer
4. Return to work different job/different employer
5. Formal training
6. Self-employment

Disability Defined

Workers' compensation coverage provided to persons injured on the job can be divided into five (5) general classifications based on degree of disability (see Table 3.3):

In addition to the definitions of degree of disability, workers' compensation programs also rely upon impairment ratings to determine benefits. The American Medical Association's *Guides to Evaluation of Permanent Impairment* (2008) describes the process by which a percentage of loss is assigned to each area or function of the body that is impaired. This rating – the impairment rating – is distinguished from a disability rating. Whereas impairment rating is determined by a physician and is based on a medical condition, disability rating takes into account the employee's future loss of employment opportunities and/or functioning.

Another important definition to understand within workers' compensation programs is Maximum Medical Improvement (MMI). This determination is made by a physician and refers to the injured worker's having recovered from an injury to his/her maximal extent. In general, the physician has reported that the client will not materially benefit from further medical treatment. It is usually at the point of MMI when a physician is

Table 3.3
Workers' Compensation Disability Definitions

Classification	Definition
Temporary Total Disability (TTD)	Weekly income replacement benefits payable after a brief waiting period if an employee is totally unable to work for a temporary period of time and is ultimately expected to recover and return to work or is in treatment but may be ultimately partially or totally disabled from work.
Temporary Partial Disability (TPD)	Payable if the employee is partially disabled from his/her regular job. In most instances, the employee works part-time or in a lesser paying job while recovering from an injury.
Permanent Partial Disability (PPD)	Lump sum payment paid in many states according to a fixed schedule based on what part of the body is injured (i.e., hand, finger, foot, loss of eye). Non-scheduled injuries (i.e., head, back, heart) are computed based on a wage loss replacement percentage which applies, in many states, to the difference between pre-injury and post-injury earnings.
Permanent Total Disability (PTD)	Payable if the employee is considered totally and permanently unable to perform suitable employment. In many states this is paid throughout one's life; however, other states place limits (either in dollars or time) on the benefits paid.
Survivor	Benefits provided include burial allowance and weekly payments for the deceased's spouse and dependent children based on a portion of the employee's former wages.

able to provide a release to return to work or render an opinion about the permanency of the injury for the worker and/or physical restrictions to consider for re-employment potential. Often the physician will also provide a total body percent rating for the impairment based on the medical guidelines as published in the *AMA Guides*.

Vocational Assessment

Once a physician provides work restrictions and releases the employee to return to work, efforts begin on the part of the rehabilitation consultant to pursue employment options. Virtually all services within workers' compensation rehabilitation focus on return to work as a critical goal following an employee's recovery from illness or injury (Brodwin, 2008; Shrey & LeConte, 1995). According to the return to work hierarchy described earlier in this chapter, employment with the worker's original employer is the most preferred way for the employee to reenter the labor market. However, if return to the original employer is not feasible, the consultant can explore alternate options to evaluate the worker's vocational potential. The author (see Table 3.4) has compiled informal information on predicting the return to work rates of workers' compensation clients. Although unscientific and based on personal experience of over 40 years in the field of rehabilitation, the table is helpful in determining situations that enable a worker to return to work.

The vocational assessment phase of measuring one's likelihood to return to work is an objective way to evaluate the worker's aptitudes, interests, skills, and abilities as they relate to the work force. Determining an injured worker's appropriateness for placement into an alternate job either directly or with training and being restored to suitable, gainful employment "is perhaps the most important part of the vocational rehabilitation counselor's work" (Deneen & Hessellund, 1981).

A common method of evaluating the worker's vocational potential is a comprehensive vocational evaluation. In workers' compensation rehabilitation, a vocational evaluation may be defined as a process to predict or estimate work behaviors and vocational potential through the use of various tests, techniques, and procedures (Nadolsky, 1971). Tests designed to measure the workers' personality, achievement, intelligence level, vocational aptitude, and vocational interests are widely used for diagnostic purposes with injured workers and are invaluable in assessing the feasibility for employment of an injured worker (Rubin & Roessler, 2008; Power, 2006). Table 3.5 describes some of the more common assessment tools used to determine vocational potential (see also the vocational assessment chapter for more listings of tests and their uses). It is noted that most vocational evaluations for workers' compensation clients emphasize an assessment of physical capabilities and de-emphasize personality and interest traits. In the author's opinion this is inadequate for long-term successful placement.

Results obtained through a vocational evaluation can be utilized in a transferable skills analysis. Such analysis, also historically known as VDARE or Vocational Diagnosis and Assessment of Residual Employability, is a systematic and orderly method to evaluate an employee's potential for work (Field & Weed, 1988). It is based not only on the vocational evaluation, but also on the worker's background, including medical, educational, and work history as well as social and psychological information. The reader is referred to Chapter 6 in this book for a comprehensive explanation of the transferable skills analysis.

At the point that the worker's potential is established, the rehabilitation consultant may want to determine the worker's earnings capacity within the vocational alternatives and/or his/her loss of access to the labor market given the particular disability. This procedure is especially prevalent in personal injury cases, and is becoming increasingly common in the workers' compensation arena; specifically with regard to providing testimony (Field & Weed, 1990, Weed & Field, 2001). Various methods are available to the rehabilitation consultant to determine one's access to the labor market. The most common computer program is probably SkillTRAN (see www.skilltran.com) although there are others as well. This program contains computerized job matching software which enables the consultant to enter a worker's transferable skills adjusted according to his/her physical abilities. A "worker profile" is generated based on this information and a computer search conducted to select jobs that match the profile. The computer data contains all 12,741 *Dictionary of Occupational Titles* job titles coded by worker traits (U.S. Department of Labor, 1992). The resultant job matches are a first step for the job search and are expected to be within the worker's transferable skills and physical abilities. These job matches are indicative of appropriate vocational alternatives.

Table 3.4
Guidelines for Assessing Workers' Compensation Client's
Success Rate for Return to Work: One Person's View

Better News ☺	Unsure News ☺	Poor News ☹
Referred within 3 months post-injury.	Referred 3-6 months post-injury.	Referred more than 6 months post-injury.
Rapport easily established.	Rapport slow to build.	Rapport strained even after several interviews.
Willing to take tests, go though interviews, etc.	Cautious at first; may have heard some "war" stories.	Often wants attorney present for interview.
Does more than asked and seeks information.	Has to "check things out," and questions recommendations, e.g., what's the testing for?	Does not want to take tests; not valid or believes they won't help with finding sutable employment.
Has worried about return to work and read books on careers or talked with others. Has supportive family.	Usually has high wages but few skills or is seasonal worker.	Strong non-financial incentives, e.g., hated job, employer didn't like client, becomes addicted to medication, has family problems, or potential for other secondary gains.
Learns how to compensate for disability. e.g., learns to bowl left handed.	Has not compensated for disability but seems receptive to suggestions.	Not receptive to suggestions, or "it won't work because . . . "
Follows through on commitments.	Has to be urged to follow through or may need to be closely "supervised."	Does not follow directions, poor compliance with doctor(s), has excuses.
Asks for help.	May be receptive if help is offered.	Rejects offers for help. Will not see psychologist.
Comp rate is not enough on which to live.	Comp rate is enough to live on.	Client is receiving financial help in addition to comp.
Hides pain or displays "well" behavior.	Pain may be openly acknowledged.	Exhibits pain behavior, doctor shops, wears back brace on outside of clothes.
No other litigation is pending.	May be considering other litigation.	Personal injury suit is filed or likely to be.
Employer likes the client and wants him or her back.	Employer does not have a position for the client and may not show interest in client's well being.	Employer does not like the client and uses comp as a way to get rid of him or her.
Willing to modify job or will "find" their own job with assistance of counselor.	May find their own job but needs structured management by counselor.	Or the client has history of workers' comp injuries with lump sum settlements before returning to work.

Note. No one factor is predictive. The more factors which represent the client in each column, the more likely the case will follow the better, unsure or poor news column.

Table 3.5
Guidelines for Assessing Return to Work

Assessment Tool	Assessment Area
Wechsler Adult Intelligence Scale-Revised (WAIS-R) Slosson Intelligence Test	Intellectual Assessment
Wide Range Achievement Test-3 (WRAT-3) Adult Basic Literacy Test	Achievement or Academic Assessment
Minnesota Multiphasic Personality Inventory (MMPI) 16 PF Myers Briggs Type Indicator (MBTI) Temperament and Values Inventory	Personality Assessment
General Aptitude Test Battery (GATB) Differential Aptitude Test Battery Apticom Armed Services Vocational Aptitude Battery Purdue Pegboard Crawford Small Parts Dexterity	Aptitude Assessment
Holland's Self-Directed Search (SDS) Career Occupational Preference System (COPS) Career Assessment Inventory (CAI) Strong Vocational Interest Inventory	Interest Assessment
VALPAR Work Samples ERGOS	Work simulated tasks

Successful Outcome: Placement

As stated previously, the goal of workers' compensation rehabilitation is return of the injured worker to suitable, gainful employment. Although widely interpreted, most states define suitable employment as an attempt to return the worker to a job which reasonably resembles his/her job at the time of injury in terms of skill required and wage. (State Board of Workers Compensation, July, 2011)

Maryland similarly defines suitable, gainful employment as: " . . . employment, excluding self-employment, that restores the disabled covered employee, to the extent possible, to the level of support at the time that the disability occurred" (Workers' Comp Law, LE, 9-670, p. 212). The law further states that in determining whether employment is suitable, gainful employment, the following shall be considered: (1) the qualifications, interests, incentives, pre-disability earnings, and future earnings capacity of the covered employee; (2) the nature and extent of the disability of the covered employee; and (3) the current and future condition of the labor market.

Florida's workers' compensation law provides a concise definition of suitable, gainful employment as follows:

> "Employment or self-employment which is reasonably attainable in light of the individual's age, education, previous occupation, and injury and which offers an opportunity to restore the individual as soon as practical and nearly as possible to [his] average weekly earnings at the time of injury" (440.49).

Some clients have successfully challenged the assumption that because they are able to perform the physical functions and they possess the aptitude to perform an occupation that it constitutes suitable employment. One case demonstrates the issue. A licensed practical nurse was injured on the job. The employer offered her a clerical position, which she turned down. Although the clerical job was within her physical limitations, it

54

was not considered suitable employment because "Woods is a nurse, and she never expressed any interest in doing clerical work" (Workers' Compensation Law Bulletin, 1992, 15 [10A], p. 7).

Other states including Oregon, California, and Minnesota have also adopted guidelines which include personality and interest factors, which often are over looked by vocational evaluations (Oregon's code OAR 436-120- 005 [6]; California Workers' Compensation Code L.C. 4635 [f]; Minnesota MS 176.102 [13]).

Identifying suitable employment is one way to assist the injured worker to return to work. Another way is actual placement of the worker in a job and "selling" the worker/applicant to employers. The rehabilitation consultant must be able to convince employers that the applicant can do the job and that there are valid reasons for hiring the worker over other applicants (Wright, 1980). One reason to appeal to potential employers is the availability of a second injury or subsequent injury fund for injured workers. Such funds were developed to protect an employer against excessive claims when a pre-existing injury combines with a new injury to produce a disability greater than that caused by the second injury alone. Not all states (Wyoming for example) have a second injury fund, and Alabama repealed its fund as of 5/19/92 (U.S. Chamber of Commerce, 1993). Additionally, provisions of the funds differ by state; however, the main objective is to avoid penalizing the worker or employer who hired him/her in the event the worker sustains a second injury and becomes "totally disabled" (Wright, 1980). The Georgia legislature in 1977 issued the following statement when it created the Georgia Subsequent Injury Trust Fund:

> *It is the purpose of this article to encourage the employment of the handicapped by protecting employers from excess liability for compensation when an injury to a handicapped worker merges with a preexisting permanent impairment to cause a greater disability than would have resulted from the subsequent injury alone.*

In general, second injury employers pay workers' compensation benefits related to the disability caused by the second injury alone; however, the fund pays a benefit related to the combined disability. Second injury funds are advocated to (1) encourage hiring of injured workers and (2) allocate costs of providing benefits more equitably, thereby reducing the burden of total disability costs on an employer who hires a worker with a previous injury (U.S. Chamber of Commerce, 1993).

Workers' Compensation Rehabilitation as a Profession

A chapter on workers' compensation rehabilitation would not be complete if it did not contain a section relative to rehabilitation counseling as a profession. Indeed, more than 70 colleges/universities offer graduate programs in rehabilitation counseling. Professional organizations such as the International Association of Rehabilitation Professionals (IARP), National Rehabilitation Counseling Association (NRCA), and others show strong membership among rehabilitation professionals in the private sector. Among reasons for a resurgence of growth in workers' compensation rehabilitation are:

(1) a clearly defined goal of returning workers to gainful employment;

(2) smaller caseloads, which allow greater concentration of service delivery in a timely manner;

(3) opportunities for rehabilitation consultants to fully use their training; and

(4) economic rewards for rehabilitation consultants who have the temperament for this litigation and insurance-based specialty.

Coupled with training programs and professional organizations is the establishment of a certification or credentialing process for rehabilitation professionals. The Certified Rehabilitation Counselor (CRC) is perhaps the most widely recognized certification among private sector rehabilitationists. Developed in 1974, the national certification is awarded to individuals who meet specific training and experience criteria in rehabilitation and also pass a written exam. The Certified Disability Management Specialist (CDMS) designation was developed in 1984, and other designations, including Certified Vocational Evaluator (CVE) and Certified Work Adjustment and Vocational Evaluator (CWAVE) were developed later. More recently, the Certified Case Manager (CCM) designation was developed and implemented in 1993 for further certification of rehabilitation professionals who specialize in medical related case management. The purpose of certification is to enable the general public (employers, injured workers, insurance claims adjusters, attorneys, etc.) to identify rehabilitation professionals who have met industry standards over and above what is required to obtain a degree (Rubin & Roessler, 2008). In 1996, the Certified Life Care Planner emerged for professionals who prefer to work with employees who experienced catastrophic injuries.

55

The Future of Rehabilitation

With the passage of the Americans with Disabilities Act (ADA) in 1990 and the update in 2008, rehabilitation consultants have greater employment opportunities than before. In workers' compensation rehabilitation, professionals must have a thorough knowledge of the ADA and its implications for employment of persons with a disability. Specifically, knowledge of a job's "essential functions" and possible job modifications or "reasonable accommodations" is necessary to assist an injured worker to obtain suitable employment. (See the rehabilitation technology chapter and the Appendices for more specific information on ADA).

Additionally, the use of a vocational expert as a witness in workers' compensation cases is an area for rehabilitation consultants to work with plaintiff and insurance attorneys alike. Vocational experts are typically rehabilitation professionals with a master's degree in rehabilitation counseling, one or more national certifications, and extensive work experience in the areas of assessment, case management, transferable skills analysis, and job placement. Professionals who have achieved a Ph.D. in rehabilitation or a related specialty are frequently sought to be vocational experts in workers' compensation and, especially, personal injury litigation. It is important to note that the vocational expert is not an expert in all fields and must recognize the limits of his/her expertise. It is the basic responsibility of the vocational expert to use his/her expertise in determining the extent to which an injury affects a worker's ability to do suitable gainful work and to determine the kinds of employment the worker can perform (Deneen & Hessellund, 1986). The ability of a rehabilitation consultant to provide vocational expert testimony should be judged on the merits of his/her training and experience in order to be viewed as credible in a court of law.

Summary

Although not the opportunity that the industry once was, workers' compensation continues to give professionals the ability to demonstrate effective rehabilitation practice. However, those most experienced in this industry will agree that workers' compensation is a challenge. The client often feels abused by the insurance company, adjusters may not understand the medical complexities of the injury, and attorneys advocate for a specific outcome. This area may be a rather stressful arena, and many professionals look for "life after workers' comp." Ethics of compensation practice is a focal point, and at least four articles suggest that rehabilitation counselors return to the basics of good practice (Rice, 1993; Taylor, 1993; Weed & Golem, 1996; Weed, 2000). The CRC ethics revised in 2010 include an enhanced section relating to private practice (CRCC, 2010).

Without a doubt, rehabilitation case managers offer a valuable service. Indeed, elsewhere in this book, a listing of the available literature clearly supports the efficacy of the profession. This profession is one of the few human service outpatient occupations that help clients become productive and/or independent. In general, it seems that this area of specialty will continue to develop and grow just as it has over the past 20-30 years. However, the consultant is urged to offer objective, ethical, and professional services.

Note: The authors gratefully acknowledge the contribution of Debbie Berens, Ph.D., C.R.C., C.C.M., C.L.C.P. to this chapter.

Chapter 4
Preparing the Case

Introduction

Case preparation should be fundamentally similar regardless of the reason. However, it becomes evident very quickly that in some situations, there are disincentives for doing what needs to be accomplished. For example, in Social Security hearings, the vocational expert (VE) is often not able to complete the testing or interviews that he or she believes will be helpful in developing a reasonable position/decision regarding the client's employability. The authors will present various methods in the three areas most likely to be confronted by the VE: Social Security, Workers' Compensation, and Personal Injury. Rehabilitation professionals with a medical orientation should have a general overview of this section. However, more specific topics and issues for this group will be found in Chapter 9.

For practical purposes, most on-the-job injuries will be classified under Workers' Compensation. However, railroad employees generally have retained the right to sue and therefore are more closely related to personal injury cases; persons who are injured while working on the ocean are covered by the Jones Act; and Longshore and Harbor workers have their own rules.

Social Security

Procedures for Becoming a VE with the Social Security Administration

Participating as a vocational expert with the Social Security Administration requires the individual to follow an application approval procedure. Applications can be obtained by either writing the Social Security Administration (SSA) or contacting a district office. (Note: This section relates to vocational experts who are selected by the SSA. Some attorneys and social security representatives retain their own vocational experts who may or may not be designated a VE by the SSA.) For information, contact:

> Social Security Administration
> Vocational Consultant Program
> Office of Hearings & Appeals
> District Office
> Website: www.ssa.gov

Once approval has been processed, the vocational expert operates on an annual renewable contract basis with SSA. The contracts cover a fiscal year basis of October 1 to September 30. Renewal of the contract is not an automatic procedure, and failure to renew by the SSA is generally due to one of the following three reasons:

1. Consensus of the Administrative Law Judges (ALJ) that the expert provides poor or inadequate services on a frequent and continual basis.

2. Chronic unavailability of an expert when requested.

3. A change of employment status by the VE. The SSA requires the individual to have employment that provides them the retention of expertise and skills in vocational decision-making.

Selection of the Vocational Expert

The Office of Hearings and Appeals (OHA) has established specific criteria for the selection and retention of individuals qualifying as a VE in the Social Security program. The VE is expected to possess current and extensive experience in counseling and/or job placement of adults with a work history who have disabilities. This experience should include utilizing standardized occupational materials such as the Dictionary of Occupational Titles (DOT), understanding of the structure and function of work, and understanding the concept of transferability of skills. The ability to evaluate age, education, and prior work experience in light of residual functional capacities (RFC) and specifically related industrial and occupational trends of local labor market is necessary. Persons having employer-employee relationships with the Federal Government are precluded from having contracts. Also, certain employees in government agencies other than Federal may not be offered contracts.

Role of the Vocational Expert

The OHA developed a "grid system" to provide the Administrative Law Judge (ALJ) with a more systematic method of assessing a claimant's employability. This system has, in some areas, changed the frequency and extent of utilization of VEs by OHA. Vocational Experts are generally called when one of the following conditions exists:

1. Claimant cannot do past work, and

2. ALJ believes expert testimony is needed when

    a. the case cannot be decided using rules or "grid" system

    b. the skill level of work has not been established

    c. transferability is critical

    d. non-exertional impairments are combined with exertional impairments

    e. the claimant has non-exertional impairments only

    f. the claimant's job appears to have been performed quite differently from the customary manner.

The VE is expected to provide both factual information and expert opinion. This information should be objective and impartial in nature. To ensure impartiality, OHA indicates the following rules should be carefully followed:

1. There should not be substantive contact between the VE and the ALJ prior to the hearing.

2. There should be no contact between the VE and claimant or his/her representative prior to the hearing, and after the hearing, only if there is prior approval by the ALJ.

3. The VE must disqualify himself/herself when there is prior knowledge of the case, prior contact with the claimant, or the inability to be impartial.

Preparation for Testimony

Due to the implementation of the Social Security Grid, the expert has been utilized less frequently for applicants whose disabilities are primarily physically related. There is considerable disagreement among experts regarding the validity of the Grid as well as its implementation by the ALJ. Since ALJs are not vocational experts there certainly could be questions regarding their qualifications to classify jobs in such categories as "skilled," "semi-skilled," "unskilled," "professional", etc. To make full use of the Grid one must accept the assumption that persons who have worked only in unskilled jobs possess no transferable skills. A thorough review of the Grid will highlight its obvious inadequacy. Due to these inadequacies many ALJs continue to utilize experts for cases which would be obviously determined as either eligible or ineligible through the use of the Grid.

In Social Security cases where the primary disability is in the non-exertional category the expert continues to be used by most ALJs. Most experts would agree that those cases whose primary disability is emotional instead of (or in addition to) physical are the most difficult to assess. It is not surprising then that they present the greatest problem to the development of a sound rationale for a vocational opinion.

The ultimate purpose for the vocational expert in a Social Security hearing is to offer opinions regarding the employability of the Social Security claimant. All vocational experts are evaluated and certified by the Social Security Administration. A review of each certified expert precedes the annual renewal of the contract. An evaluation of the expert's performance is made by the ALJ upon completion of each hearing. It is therefore important that the expert is thoroughly prepared.

Vocational experts who are certified by the Social Security Administration are registered with one or more local Bureau of Hearings and Appeals Offices. As ALJs from those offices schedule claimants for hearings, decisions are made regarding the need for vocational expert testimony. Experts are then identified from the list by a rotation selection process. The identified expert is then called to determine his or her willingness to serve and availability for the date(s) selected. Should the expert be unavailable the expert whose name appears next on the list should be called. The process continues until a suitable expert is found. It is common for ALJs to schedule multiple cases for one day, or for several consecutive days. Therefore, a vocational expert may be requested to testify on as many as six cases per day for four or five consecutive days. The expert may also be asked to serve for only one case. Except in emergency situations (e.g., an expert previously scheduled becomes ill) the expert is notified six to eight weeks prior to the hearing date. The expert, the claimant, and the claimant's legal counsel (when counsel has been retained) are then officially (in writing) notified of the date, time, and location of the hearing.

Once all involved parties have been notified the file is available for review by the expert, legal counsel or representative, and/or claimant. The file is chronologically arranged so as to reflect the sequence of events. All separate documents are marked and numbered as exhibits. The first page of each exhibit will identify the exhibit number as well as the number of pages found in the exhibit.

The file usually includes:

- biographical data (age, education, marital status, number of children, source(s) of income, address, etc.),
- vocational history,
- the date of disability onset,
- the claimant's statement of physical and/or mental problems,
- statements of each denial (with rationale) by the Social Security Administration,
- a list of the lifetime quarterly payments to the Social Security Trust Fund,
- statements of diagnoses and treatment by physicians and copies of hospital records,
- all correspondence between the Social Security Administration and the claimant (or counsel),
- professional resumes of the vocational expert and other professionals whose services were requested and received by the Social Security Administration.
- The files of those claimants who have had previous hearings will include a copy of the ALJ's decision, which always clarifies the rationale leading to the decision.

Other items of information that may occasionally be found in the file include:

- vocational evaluation reports,
- opinion statements by employers,
- Veterans Administration records,
- depositions,
- supporting letters from neighbors, etc.

While every effort is made to discourage the submission of irrelevant information, should the claimant request that a document be added to the file, it will be.

While reviewing the claimant's file, the expert should carefully summarize the vocationally relevant information. Each summary statement should be identified by exhibit number, date, and author. Such documentation serves as a handy reference for sources of information during testimony. Once the expert is totally prepared, the hearing room will appear to be a more comfortable setting.

A functional capacities checklist is found in most files. However, the expert will find that the checklist is frequently completed by an "in-house" physician employed by the Social Security Administration. Most frequently this physician has never had the occasion to examine the claimant but completes the checklist by reading the medical reports found in the file. Careful review often causes one to question the validity of such checklists.

The Hearing

Upon entering the hearing room, the expert should expect to see a formal arrangement of the furniture. There should be two tables arranged in the shape of a T. The judge will sit at the head of the T, and the hearing assistant (that person responsible for recording and documenting the proceedings) will sit on the right of the table forming the body of the T. The claimant, representative, and witnesses most often sit at the left of the judge, also at the table forming the body of the T. The vocational expert generally sits beside and to the right of the hearing assistant.

If the hearing is held at an office of the Bureau of Hearings and Appeals, the expert should anticipate a setting in which the judge is sitting in a chair that is elevated as much as three feet above the other participants. This setting is frequently very similar to the more formal "trial by jury" setting (without the jury box). Regardless of the setting, however, the processes of the hearings are consistently similar.

After asking the hearing assistant if he/she is ready to begin, the judge opens the hearing with a formal statement regarding the purpose of the hearing, the Social Security Regulations governing the hearing, the status of the claimant's application for Social Security benefits, and a disclaimer of any responsibility for the decisions to date. The claimant is then informed that the judge has the power to reverse or confirm previous decisions without threat from the Social Security Administration or Bureau of Hearings and Appeals.

Those claimants who appear without representation are informed of their right of representation. Should the claim of financial inability for such representation be made, the claimant is informed of the availability of legal aid services without cost. In those cases that need further documentation and development, the judge frequently suggests to the claimant that legal representation may be beneficial. Should the unrepresented claimant decide to retain representation, the hearing will be closed and rescheduled at a later date. If not, the hearing will continue. The similarities or dissimilarities of hearings with and without representation, however, have minimal variation.

For those claimants who represent themselves, the judge becomes the attorney for the claimant and defense, as well as judge. In such cases the judge begins by asking if the claimant has reviewed the file and if there are objections to the contents of the file being accepted as evidence. The claimant is then asked if additional information will be submitted. If so, it is received, identified with exhibit numbers and placed in file.

Following the updating of the file, the claimant is asked to identify other witnesses, if any, who will testify. The claimant and other witnesses (if any) are then sworn.

The initial testimony begins with the judge asking the claimant questions regarding biographical data (name, address, age, weight, marital status, etc.). The collection of biographical data is followed by information relating to educational, vocational, medical, and psychological status at the time of disability onset as well as at the time of the hearing. The claimant is asked to identify the restrictions of functional capacities caused by the disabling condition.

Once the claimant has completed testimony, other witnesses are called. Subsequent witnesses usually do little more than corroborate the testimony of the claimant. Occasionally, however, a physician, former employer, or neighbor may provide testimony that is critical to the outcome of the hearing.

The testimony of non-vocational experts called by the Bureau of Hearings and Appeals may also shed light on physical or psychological information critical to vocational potential. Therefore, the testimony of all witnesses precedes that of the vocational expert. The sequence of testimony allows the expert to consider all verbal and written evidence presented at the hearing in the formation of an opinion regarding the claimant's vocational potential.

The judge asks the expert, prior to being sworn, if there are other questions that should be answered by the claimant or other witnesses. Additional information regarding specifics of previous jobs, residual functional capacities, conditions of previous employment, contacts by rehabilitation workers, etc., is frequently helpful. Should the judge fail to ask if there are additional questions, the expert should ask the judge if questions might be asked. After all questions have been answered, the judge administers the oath and the testimony of the expert begins.

The judge begins by confirming the biographical data (name, employment, address, etc.) of the expert and then confirms the expert's resume (which has already been received as evidence) by saying "do you swear to the content of your resume, which is exhibit #_____, as though it were read into the record verbatim?" The judge then asks if the complete file has been available to and reviewed by the expert and if the record as constituted has sufficient evidence on which to form an opinion.

The answer expected is always yes even though conflicting information or minimal information is exhibited. While the expert can form an opinion on available information, it should be recognized that the opinion might change if one report is considered more valid than another, or if additional information is obtained.

Finally, the expert is asked to summarize the parameters of previous employment, classify each job as skilled, semi-skilled, or unskilled, and enumerate the skills demonstrated by the claimant in the performance of each job. The judge may then ask questions based upon hypothetical conditions. At the end of each assumption, the expert is asked to offer an opinion as to whether there are jobs in the labor market that can be performed by the claimant. When the answer is yes, the expert is asked to identify such jobs by titles and examples of employers. Following the testimony, the claimant is offered the opportunity to question the expert regarding any or all opinions.

Often there is conflicting medical or psychological information, and limitations identified by the claimant during the hearing are frequently more severe than those confirmed by the file. In such cases the judge may ask the expert to form an opinion based on the assumption that one or more of the conditions exist.

The hearing in which the claimant is represented varies from the one previously described in the following ways: a) the representative sits at the side of the claimant; b) the judge may collect the initial biographical data and allow the representative to develop the remainder of the case by asking questions of the claimant and other witnesses; c) the representative may cross-examine the expert(s); d) the representative assumes the responsibility for reviewing as well as accepting the contents of the file as evidence; and e) the representative is more likely to ask that the file be left "open" for a period of time so that additional evidence may be obtained.

The Bureau of Hearings and Appeals provides uniform training to all of its ALJs. In addition, all Trust Fund programs are federally controlled. Therefore, one is likely to find that the procedure for Social Security hearings varies minimally from state to state. Such is not the case, however, for workers' compensation hearings.

The nature of providing an expert opinion in Social Security hearings has some significant differences when compared to other arenas. Therefore, the method of preparation may vary. The VE does not have contact with the claimant or any medical professionals, nor does the VE have the opportunity for testing, interviewing, or other traditional means of collecting information prior to the hearing. Thus the analysis and review of records is a primary step in the decision-making process and the foundation of the VE's testimony.

Review of the records provides the VE the opportunity to prepare quality evidence for the ALJ's decision. The ALJ, not the Vocational Expert, determines whether an individual's disability is too severe to allow the individual to be competitively employed. In preparation for testimony there are four significant areas to be evaluated by the VE:

    a) age,

    b) education,

    c) specific job attributes, and

    d) list of occupations for which the claimant is vocationally qualified.

Following is a brief description of each of these variables as defined and discussed by the Social Security Administration:

1.   Age – "Age" refers to an individual's chronological age and the extent to which age affects the ability to adapt to new work situations and to do work in competition with others. Sections 404.1563 and 416.963 of the Regulations specifically identify the following categories.

   Categories of Age

   a.   Younger Person – if an individual is under age 50, the regulations provide that generally an individual's age will not seriously affect the ability to adapt to new work situations.

   b.   Person Approaching Advanced Age – if an individual is closely approaching advanced age (50-54), age along with a severe impairment and limited work experience will be considered as possibly seriously affecting an individual's ability to adapt to a significant number of jobs in the national economy.

c.   Person of Advanced Age – advanced age (55-59) is considered to be the point at which age significantly affects a person's ability to engage in substantial gainful activity. If an individual is severely impaired, is of advanced age, or cannot do at least medium work, he/she may be found to have a disability, unless the individual has skills that can be used in (transferred to) less demanding jobs that exist in significant numbers in the national economy.

d.   Person Close to Retirement – if an individual is close to retirement age (60-64) and has a severe impairment, he/she will be considered unable to adjust to sedentary or light work unless the individual has skills that are highly marketable.

2.   Education – "Education is primarily used to mean formal schooling or other training which contributes to the ability to meet vocational requirements. This term also addresses the individual's ability to communicate in English. Lack of formal school does not mean lack of education. Work history is frequently utilized in determining the person's present level of reasoning, communication, and arithmetic level of education." Sections 404.1564 and 416.964 of the Regulations address this issue.

Categories of Education

a.   Illiteracy means the inability to read or write. A person is considered illiterate if he/she cannot read or write a simple message such as instructions or inventory lists, even though the person can sign his/her name. Generally, an illiterate person has had little or no formal education.

b.   Marginal education means having the ability in reasoning, arithmetic, and language skills to do simple, unskilled types of jobs. Formal schooling at a 6th grade level or less is considered a marginal education.

c.   Limited education means ability in reasoning, arithmetic, and language skills, but not enough to allow a person with these educational qualifications to do most of the more complex job duties needed in semi-skilled or skilled jobs. A 7th grade through the 11th grade level of formal education is considered a limited education.

d.   High school education and above means abilities in reasoning, arithmetic, and language skills acquired in formal schooling at a 12th grade level or above. Someone with these educational abilities can do semi-skilled through skilled work. High school education includes a General Equivalency Diploma (GED). The criterion of "high school graduate or more" provides for direct entry into skilled work when there is little time lapse between the completion of formal education and the date of adjudication and where the content of the education would enable individuals, with a minimal degree of job orientation, to begin performing the skilled job duties of certain identifiable occupations with their residual functioning capacities (RFC).

3.   Specific Job Attributes – When evaluating the individual in terms of past work history, the VE will assess two factors:

•   exertional level of work and

•   skill level of the occupations.

a.   Exertional characteristics refer to an individual's physical abilities (strength) of walking, standing, lifting, carrying, pushing, pulling, reaching, etc. Determination of physical exertional characteristics is made by using the categories of "sedentary", "light", "medium", "heavy", and "very heavy." For OHA purposes, these terms have the same meaning as used in the Dictionary of Occupational Titles and are discussed in sections 404.1567 and 416.967 of the Regulations.

i.   The regulations define sedentary work as involving lifting no more than 10 pounds at a time and occasionally lifting or carrying articles like dockets, files, ledgers, and small tools. Although sitting is involved, a certain amount of walking and standing are occasionally required and other sedentary criteria are met. By its very nature, work performed primarily in a seated position entails no significant stooping. Most unskilled sedentary jobs require good use of the hands and fingers for repetitive hand-finger actions. "Occasionally" means occurring from very little up to one-third of the time. Since being on one's feet is required "occasionally" at the sedentary level of exertion, periods of standing or walking should generally total no more than about 2 hours of an 8-hour workday.

ii.   The regulations define light work as lifting no more than 20 pounds at a time with frequent lifting or carrying of objects weighing up to 10 pounds. Even though the weight lifted in a particular light job may be very little, a job is in this category when it requires a good deal of walking or standing – the primary difference between sedentary and most light jobs. A job is also in this category when it involves sitting most of the time but with some pushing and pulling of arm/hand or leg/foot controls, which require greater exertion than in sedentary work; e.g., mattress sewing machine operator, motor-grader operator, and road-roller operator (skilled and semi-skilled jobs in these particular instances). Relatively few unskilled light jobs are performed in a seated position. "Frequent" means occurring from one-third to two-thirds of the time. Since frequent lifting or carrying requires being on one's feet up to two-thirds of a workday, the full range of light work requires standing or walking, off and on, for a total of approximately 6 hours of an 8-hour workday. Sitting may occur intermittently during the remaining time. The lifting requirements for the majority of light jobs can be accomplished with occasional, rather than frequent, stooping. Many unskilled light jobs are performed primarily in one location, with the ability to stand being more critical than the ability to walk. They require use of arms and hands to grasp and to hold and turn objects, and they generally do not require use of the fingers for fine activities to the extent required in much sedentary work.

iii. The regulations define medium work as lifting no more than 50 pounds at a time with frequent lifting or carrying of objects weighing up to 25 pounds. A full range of medium work requires standing or walking off and on, for a total of approximately 6 hours in an 8-hour workday in order to meet the requirements of frequent lifting or carrying objects weighing up to 25 pounds. As in light work, sitting may occur intermittently during the remaining time. Use of the arms and hands is necessary to grasp, hold, and turn objects, as opposed to the finer activities in much sedentary work, which require precision use of the fingers as well as use of the hands and arms. The considerable lifting required for the full range of medium work usually requires frequent bending/stooping. (Stooping is a type of bending in which a person bends his or her body downward and forward by bending both the legs and spine in order to bend the body downward and forward). However, there are a relatively few occupations in the national economy that require exertion in terms of weights that must be lifted at times (or involve equivalent exertion in pushing or pulling) but are performed primarily in a sitting position, e.g., taxi driver, bus driver, and tank-truck driver (semi-skilled jobs). In most medium jobs, being on one's feet for most of the workday is critical. Being able to do frequent lifting or carrying of objects weighing up to 25 pounds is often more critical than being able to lift up to 50 pounds at a time.

iv. Heavy work involves lifting no more than 100 pounds at a time with frequent lifting or carrying of objects weighing up to 50 pounds. If someone can do heavy work, OHA determines that he or she can also do medium, light, and sedentary work.

v. Very heavy work involves lifting objects weighing more than 100 pounds at a time with frequent lifting or carrying of objects weighing 50 pounds or more. If someone can do very heavy work, it is assumed he/she can also do heavy, medium, light, and sedentary work. See Table 4.1 for summary table of strength definitions.

b. Sections 404.1568 and 416.968 of the regulations define skill and the three skill categories into which occupations are classified (Table 4.2). A skill is knowledge of a work activity that requires the exercise of significant judgment going beyond the carrying out of simple job duties and is acquired through performance of an occupation that is above the unskilled level (requires more than 30 days to learn). It is practical and familiar knowledge of the principles and processes of an art, science, or trade combined with the ability to apply them in practice in a proper and approved manner. This includes activities such as precise measurements, reading blueprints, and setting up and operating complex machinery. A skill gives a person a special advantage over unskilled workers in the labor market. Skills are not gained by doing unskilled jobs, and a person has no special advantage if he or she is skilled or semi-skilled but can qualify only for an unskilled job because his or her skills cannot be used to any significant degree in other jobs.

Based on the specific vocational preparation levels (SVP), the definitions are coded as follows:

i. Unskilled Work – Unskilled work is work that requires little or no judgment to do simple duties that can be learned on the job in a short period of time. The job may or may not require considerable strength. For example, we consider jobs unskilled if the primary work duties are handling, feeding, offbearing (that is, placing or removing materials from machines that are automatic or operated by others), or machine tending, and a person can usually learn to do the

Table 4.1
Weights Lifted and Carried or Force Exerted

Category	Occasionally	Frequently	Constantly	Comments
Sedentary	0-10 lbs	Negligible	—	Involves sitting with occasional standing or walking
Light	0-20 lbs	0-10 lbs	Negligible	Requires significant walking or standing. Or may require sitting with pushing/pulling of control
Medium	20-50 lbs	10-25 lbs.	0-10 lbs.	
Heavy	50-100 lbs	25-50 lbs	10-20 lbs.	
Very Heavy	100+ lbs	50+ lbs.	20+ lbs.	

The terms occasionally, frequently, constantly are defined as follows:

0%	means the value is not present (NP).
1% - 33%	means the value is rated as occasionally (O).
34% - 67%	means the value is rated as frequently (F).
68% - 100%	means the value is rated as constantly (C).

Table 4.2
SVP Definitions

SVP Level	Defined As	Coded As
1	Short Demonstration	Unskilled
2	Up to 30 days	Unskilled
3	30 days to 3 months	Semiskilled
4	3 - 6 months	Semiskilled
5	6 months - 1 year	Skilled
6	1 - 2 years	Skilled
7	2 - 4 years	Skilled
8	4 - 10 years	Highly skilled
9	Over 10 years	Highly skilled

job in 30 days since little specific vocational preparation and judgment are needed. A person is not considered to gain work skills by doing unskilled work.

ii. Semi-Skilled – Semi-skilled work is work that needs some skills but does not require doing the more complex work duties. Semi-skilled jobs may require alertness and close attention, such as watching machine processes; inspecting, testing, or otherwise looking for irregularities; tending or guarding equipment, property, material, or persons against loss, damage, or injury; or other types of activities that are similarly less complex than skilled work but more complex than unskilled work. A job may be classified as semi-skilled where coordination and dexterity are necessary, as when hands or feet must be moved quickly to do repetitive tasks.

iii. Skilled Work – Skilled work requires qualifications in which a person used judgment to determine the machine and manual operations to be performed in order to obtain the proper form, quality, or quantity of material to be produced. Skilled work may require laying out work, estimating quality, determining the suitability and needed qualities of materials, making precise measurements, reading blueprints or other specifications, or making necessary computations or mechanical adjustments to control or regulate the work. Other skilled jobs may require dealing with people, facts or figures, or abstract ideas at a high level of complexity.

    iv. Highly Skilled – Highly skilled work requires the person to demonstrate leadership and creative qualities, which generally is supported by graduate education, including Ph.D. and M.D. The worker may supervise and coordinate many other workers, fabricate electrical equipment, provide leadership of professional staff, direct editorial activities of a newspaper, direct trusts, and plan or administrate policies of an organization.

4. Vocationally Qualified Occupations – The VE should prepare a list of occupations for which he/she believes the claimant may be vocationally qualified. In this process, the VE should recall the law states in which, to be found disabled, "a worker must have a medically determinable physical or mental impairment(s) of such severity that he or she is not only unable to do previous work, but cannot, considering age, education, and work experience, engage in any other kind of substantial gainful work which exists in the national economy." With this in mind, there are some significant factors relating to the SS hearings with which the VE must be familiar. Following is a brief list:

    a. transferability of skills – when an individual has a work history of semi-skilled or skilled nature, some work activities can be used to meet the requirements of other skilled or unskilled work activities. Transferability is most probable among jobs in which:

        1) the same or lesser degree of skill is required;

        2) the same or similar tools and machines are used; and

        3) the same or similar raw materials, products, processes, or services are involved.

    b. substantial gainful activity (SGA) – sections 404.1572 and 416.972 define SGA as work activity that is both substantial and gainful.

        Substantial work activity is work activity that involves doing significant physical or mental activities. Work may be substantial even if it is done on a part-time basis or if an individual has less responsibility than he or she had before. Gainful work activity is work activity that an individual does for pay or profit. Work activity is gainful if it is the kind of work usually done for pay or profit, whether or not a profit is realized. Generally we do not consider activities like self-care, household tasks, hobbies, therapy, school attendance, club activities, or social programs to be substantial gainful activity.

    c. incidence of jobs – significant in the SS procedure is the test for disability that addresses work that exists rather than job openings that exist. Regulations indicate the following are NOT factors in determining the existence of work: a) inability to get work; b) lack of work in local area; c) hiring practices of employers; and d) technological changes in the industry in which the claimant has worked.

        In July of 1982, OHA provided all vocational experts with a list of unskilled sedentary and light occupations.

    d. non-exertional impairments – sections 404.1545 (c & d) and 416.945 (c & d) of the Regulations state that non-exertional impairment does not limit physical exertion and is any impairment that does not directly affect the ability to sit, stand, walk, lift, carry, push, or pull. This includes impairments that affect the mind, vision, hearing, speech, use of the fingers for fine activities, or use of the body to climb, balance, stoop, kneel, crouch, crawl, reach, or handle. The following are some examples of non-exertional impairments:

        i.   mental impairment

        ii. skin impairment

        iii. seizure disorder (epilepsy)

        iv. vision, hearing, or other sense impairments

        v. postural and manipulative limitations

        vi. environmental restrictions (sensitivity to temperature, dust, fumes, etc.)

Each of the non-exertional impairments has a specific impact upon the person's ability to work. SSA publication No. 70-009 gives a more thorough examination of the categories listed above.

The DOT and the O*NET Database

Effective in 1998, the O*NET database officially replaced the 1991 Edition of the *Dictionary of Occupational Titles* – at least according to the U.S. Department of Labor. As noted above, the Federal Regulations related to the SSA program for disability determination are directly related to the DOT. The regulations make it clear that jobs and job recommendations would be presented within the content of the DOT and its language. It was and is the intent of DOL that the O*NET would replace the DOT of the occupational classification system for the future. However, the nomenclature of the O*NET is very different from that of the DOT. In addition, the worker trait factors (variables that were so critical to the transferable skills process) are replaced by 200+ elements – all of which are very qualitative in nature. This new format makes it virtually impossible to complete a TSA in the way VEs have done for decades. Research and development is currently underway that will remedy this situation, but it will take years to complete this task. Perhaps the most formidable task is to revise the regulations of the federal code pertaining to the determination of disability within the SSA program. The revision process of any federal regulation is oftentimes a "political process" and no less so than with something as politically sacred as the Social Security Program. The process will take sub-committee work in the U.S. Congress, public readings, more revisions, and debates before it is finally brought to the floors of the House and Senate. Following final passage, the "new" regulations will than require an orientation and training period of all consumers of the SSDI process (ALJs, VEs, Disability Determination Examiners, and the public). Concurrent to this effort is a revision of a section (a sub-set of elements) of the O*NET that will eventually provide for a means to completing TSAs with the O*NET alone. This step is essential since the DOT is no longer supported and maintained by the Department of Labor.

In the meantime, there are two possibly short-term remedies that are at the disposal of the rehabilitation consultant with respect to the TSA and job selection process.

1. Review Chapter 6 on Transferable Skills for a suggested alternative. One solution, as discussed in this chapter, is the continued use of the 1991 Edition of the DOT along with the O*NET database. Simply put, continue doing as usual with the utilization of the worker trait factors and then crossing to job possibilities. The only difference is that new titles may be selected from the O*NET database (with some extrapolation) and the new developed on-line job databases (America's Job Bank, and America's Career Information System). This approach employs the DOT (for the worker trait information) and the O*NET database (which cross-references to current occupational information).

2. The second remedy involves a legal solution. A Policy Interpretation Ruling (SSR 00-4p) titled "Use of Vocational Expert and Vocational Specialist Evidence, and Other Reliable Occupational Information in Disability Decisions" addresses the issue of any conflict that might arise between information contained in the DOT and any other occupational source (i.e., the O*NET). Since this is a ruling directly related to the SSA program, the rule may or may not apply to other venues. The ruling reads:

    In making disability determinations, we rely primarily on the DOT for information about the requirements of work in the national economy. We use this publication at Steps 4 and 5 of the sequential evaluation process. We may also use VEs at these steps to resolve complex vocational issues. Occupational evidence provided by a VE generally should be consistent with the occupational information supplied by the DOT. When there is an apparent unresolved conflict between VE evidence and the DOT, the adjudicator must elicit a reasonable explanation for the conflict before relying on the VE evidence to support a determination or decision about whether the claimant is disabled.

Workers' Compensation

First and foremost, the laws vary between States as clearly evidenced from the various state requirements published in Chapter 3. A few states have mandatory rehabilitation laws and others do not. However, the following case preparation guidelines should be appropriate regardless of the location in which one practices.

1. Receive a referral. Generally, the VE receives cases from established referral sources so that they will have a system for review of the case and assignment for counseling. Unlike Social Security and most personal injury cases, workers' compensation cases usually are referred for counseling and job placement in addition to case review, evaluation, case management, labor market surveys, job analysis, wage loss, etc. In most instances, the case will not require testifying in a courtroom. However, the prudent counselor will prepare each case in the same way since it is not uncommon to testify before the workers' compensation board.

2. Review the record. The case record should be thoroughly reviewed, and missing information should be requested (such as medical reports, insurance records, transcribed accident statement, school records, previous rehabilitation efforts, vocational evaluations, and others, depending on the individual situation). Any requests should be noted in the record with the dates requested and a diary date set for follow-up.

3. Schedule the interview. Concurrent with information gathering, the initial interview should be arranged. Note that it is typical for the claimant to have an attorney. If this information is available to the counselor before the initial interview, in most circumstances permission must be received from the attorney before meeting the client. If the counselor discovers this during the interview, it may be appropriate to discontinue the interview until permission is granted. In some cases the attorney may want to sit in on the interview and/or testing. The authors' practice is to allow an observer in the interview but not in the testing.

4. Conduct the initial interview. Depending on the philosophy of the VE, there are two approaches for the initial interview. The authors encourage the use of employment application forms found in most business supply stores. This will help to evaluate the capabilities of the claimant for filling out employment forms as well as his/her attitude toward rehabilitation. It also places into the record, usually in the claimant's handwriting, what they claim to be important history. This, of course, avoids some of the complaints that the counselor did not accurately record the information. The second method is to obtain this information from the initial interview by means of a more unstructured approach.

The interview should be an extensive review of the above form, if used, and other significant information. A suggested form for use is located in the Appendices, and additional details are presented later in this chapter. Of particular importance is the vocational history and current medical status. Other valuable information includes social information, financial status, past legal history including drugs and alcohol, daily activity schedule, activities of daily living, educational history including job training, military history, leisure time activities before and after the incident, and the claimant's view of his or her functional limitations. Depending on the expertise of the counselor, one should consider conducting the interview with two people: a "vocational" expert, such as a Certified Rehabilitation Counselor, and a "medical" expert, such as a nurse. In the authors' experience, it is rare that one person possesses both skills to the degree to be highly effective. It also helps to keep the counselor objective and the occasional recalcitrant claimant from making unfounded accusations about the interview.

5. Cross check the interview information with records. The work history should be in significant detail for purposes of crosschecking the information in the *Dictionary of Occupational Titles* and for work skill transferability. Many times claimants will dwell upon details about the work place that make it impossible for them to return to work, even with modification. This generally means that regardless of the number of years of experience that the VE has, it still is recommended for him or her to personally review the worksite and talk with the employer or their representative.

The following example will illustrate the point: A railroad machinist suffered a knee injury that restricted his mobility in a shop. Although the claimant received medical treatment, he stayed off work partially because the physician was under the impression the shop floor was dirty and greasy and that the machinery was fast and dangerous. A review of the work site revealed clean floors (a person was assigned for the sole purpose of keeping the floors clean and uncluttered) and generally relatively slow-moving machines. For example, a wheel-truing machine actually revolved about one revolution per minute. Most workers sat on a stool through most of their work shift. A photographic and specific work site evaluation was completed and presented to the physician for review. This resulted in a modified job description that the physician approved.

6. Analyze transferability of skills. In addition, the residual employability for an injured worker often rests on the VE's understanding and ability to assess the skills that can be transferred to another job (see chapter on this topic for details). Transferability requires the understanding of the *Dictionary of Occupational Titles* (DOL, 1991), the individual's work history, and the worker traits as listed in the *Transitional COJ* (Field & Field, 2005).

The claimant's medical status should be clearly understood based on subjective (interview) as well as objective (medical records) information. The counselor ought to pay close attention to tests that are less likely to be altered by patient influence such as nerve conduction studies. Asking a claimant what he/she believes his/her limitations to be generally gives the counselor a good estimation as to the likelihood of re-employment, regardless of the medical information (see chart in chapter 3).

7. Develop an action plan. The interview should not be terminated until a plan of action, including time frames, is agreed upon. In most cases, when vocational testing is appropriate, an authorization for release of information needs to be completed, a schedule for additional interviews arranged, and so forth. It is important to be as specific as possible, and the action plan probably should be summarized in writing and a copy given to the client.

8. Schedule appropriate testing. If testing is indicated, it should be arranged as quickly as possible to avoid having people "fall through the cracks." Many complaints seem to center around the length of time it takes from time of referral to the time of a plan. Generally, if the claimant is faced with a change in jobs or retraining, it is advisable to supplement the information with tests. The authors generally recommend an intelligence test (preferably the Wechsler), an academic screening test (such as the Wide Range Achievement Test), an aptitude test (such as Apticom, SAGE or similar), an interest inventory (generally the Career Assessment Inventory or the Strong Vocational Interest Inventory, depending on the level of anticipated training or education), and a personality measure (such as the California Personality Inventory, Minnesota Multiphasic Personality Inventory-2, 16 PF, or Myers Briggs Type Indicator). These are considered a minimum. Depending on the individual situation, several other tests can be used, such as neuropsychological, projective tests, dexterity measures, etc.

9. Contact the health care provider. In addition to the tests and medical records, the primary physician should be contacted. It is helpful for the physician to complete a checklist that will allow the counselor to directly translate any restrictions by the doctor to the worker traits of various jobs (see example physician questions located in the Appendices). The physician should be asked about the physical restrictions, any medical treatment that may be expected in the future, and, for those less versed in the medical aspects of disabilities, a brief education on the disability. Most physicians are well aware of the impact of workers' compensation and other disability insurance programs on the length of time between injury and a return to work. The willingness for the sharing of information depends on several unspecified factors. Some physicians, it seems, are patient advocates and will produce a medical report that favors the patient. Others are reputed to be "insurance doctors." In the authors' experience, most are willing to be as objective as possible, especially if the counselor has accumulated a reputation of fairness.

10. Develop a plan. When the tests are completed and information gathered, the counselor should survey all of the information and look for discrepancies and hidden agendas. For example, the claimant may score very low in aptitudes but have held skilled or sophisticated positions with very good recommendations from a former employer. He or she may present him or herself as unable to sit for more than 15 minutes but will sit in the interview apparently without significant discomfort for 1 1/2 hours, or his or her portrayal of functional limitations may be distinctly different from the physician's. Any inconsistencies should be recorded and resolved. The counselor should have a global view of the client and resist preconceived biases.

Based on the assessment and the client's vocational assets, a plan should be developed. At this point, it is important to obtain the client's endorsement and active participation. The writers base the tasks on observable behavior and measurable goals. The principles are similar to the Job Club (Azrin & Besalel, 1980). This requires accountability from both counselor and client. When the goals are reduced to writing it also tends to help overcome conflict between the counselor and client.

For discussion purposes, we will presume that the case has been scheduled for a workers' compensation board hearing. The reasons can be many, but likely, benefits have not been paid as expected or the client is not participating satisfactorily according to the counselor and/or the insurance company. Satisfactory participation by the client is usually defined by the regulations of the individual state. Unlike Social Security and personal injury cases, the counselor has usually been able to work with the client and has ample opportunity to observe behavior. Somewhere the words "client motivation" will appear. This often is turned into the "counselor's motivation." It is essential that the counselor maintain as much objectivity as possible. Most assuredly there will be pressures to please the person or company who pays the bill. However, the counselor must remain as professional as possible.

11. Maintain objective records. It is important to maintain excellent records, with entries that are behaviorally based and with as little editorial comment as possible. It is one thing to record a statement such as, "The client has failed to contact 8 of 9 employers during the five-day period agreed upon in our interview of ___." And another to say, "The client is unmotivated and didn't do what I asked him to do." Obviously the former is more objective, defensible, and understandable.

When appearing for the Board hearing, bring only the records necessary unless they have been subpoenaed. It is important to be able to provide the following:

- How the referral was made.

- The date of each of the interviews.

- Time spent in each interview.

- Which tests were administered and the results.

- The precise events throughout the course of rehabilitation.

- All written agreements.

- The behavioral responses for both the counselor and client on the tasks.

Although a board hearing is less formal than a court action, it usually is attended by one or more attorneys. If the case is appealed through the system, it could be reviewed in an appeals court by a judge who will most likely have a significantly more "legal" approach to the resolution of the case. This means the counselor should be an excellent rehabilitationist and know the law as well. This can be a challenge because different states have different requirements, and federal workers have different benefits than harbor workers, etc. The better the two skills (rehabilitation/legal) can be blended, the more likely the counselor will have a good result.

Workers' Compensation Hearings

Since the Federal mandate for states to have workers' compensation laws is little more than a requirement for states to have such laws, it is not surprising that benefits, training, and background of judges, hearing procedures, and utilization of expert witnesses varies greatly. It is beyond the intent of this book to discuss all the differences and their assets or limitations. Therefore, the reader should be aware that the description that follows is a generic one that may vary from one setting to another.

The WC hearing differs little from that of the Social Security hearing. The structure of the hearing room is the same. The seating arrangements are very similar, except for the presence of the attorney for the employer. While the Social Security ALJ serves as judge and counsel for defense, the ALJ in the WC hearing is more likely to serve only as judge. In addition, the board will usually have three members: one who acts as the chair and is theoretically impartial, one who represents management, and another who represents labor. The WC insurance carrier (insurance company or self-insured employer) is the usual defendant, while the injured worker is the plaintiff. It is very unlikely that the insurance carrier will be without representation.

The hearing begins with a review of its purpose by the judge. Counsels for plaintiff and defense are then allowed to provide opening statements and additional evidence. The counsel for plaintiff provides direct examination of the plaintiff and plaintiff's witnesses, and counsel for the defense cross-examines. Once all of the plaintiff's witnesses have provided testimony, witnesses for the defense are called to undergo direct and cross-examination by the representatives of the defense and plaintiff, respectively. In those hearings where there is no representation for the plaintiff, the judge has the responsibility for development of the case. The judge may also interrupt with questions or comments.

Finally, the purposes of WC hearings vary. The following are examples of the most common purposes:

1. To determine the potential for employment

    a. In the previous job without modification.

    b. In the previous job with modification.

    c. In other jobs with equal income.

    d. In other jobs for which training is needed.

2. To determine the percentage of lost vocational potential resulting from injury.

3. To determine the appropriateness of a rehabilitation plan.

4. To determine the amount of current wage loss.

5. To evaluate a change of condition.

Employment Potential

Determination of employment potential is the most critical involvement by the vocational expert. Returning to a job previously held is the least disruptive to lifestyle, least expensive, and, therefore, the most desirable objective (may be same occupation with a different employer). The second priority is placement in jobs previously done but for which modifications (jigs, fixtures, accessibility, flex schedule, etc.) may be necessary. If placement into previously held jobs is not possible, the identification of transferable skills applicable to jobs not previously held is critical. Another option is the provision of job-related training, which may not only be expensive but also questionable regarding successful outcome. One problem with training programs is that the person with work experience who earns an income that is consistent with experience will begin at the entry income level at the completion of training for a new occupation. This "demotion" in income is often untenable for the injured worker; therefore, building on previous skills and experience is more important than it might appear at first blush. The last option, self-employment, has only been approved on rare occasions by workers' compensation boards.

The vocational expert is frequently asked to determine lost vocational potential. Such requests should not be mistaken to mean an assessment of financial loss. The vocational expert should limit testimony to job potential changes and resulting anticipated salaries. Testimony regarding the long-range economic results should be the responsibility of the economist.

The appropriateness of the rehabilitation plan is a professional opinion regarding the best method for regaining vocational independence. The major disagreements most frequently encountered are questions of the existence of vocational potential and/or whether training is necessary to guarantee re-employment potential.

"Changes of condition" hearings result from unanticipated progression or improvement of physical or psychological illnesses. Such hearings may also result from change in a local labor market, completion of a training program, change in family support, etc. The vocational expert provides testimony in cases where such changes may affect the vocational potential of the client. Such testimony may also be provided by deposition.

Types of Hearings

Background

In 1965, few people (including clients) ever questioned the decision of the counselor. Decisions regarding eligibility, type, or quality of services were considered to be the "domain" of the rehabilitation counselor. But shortly thereafter, a number of events changed that domain.

1) First, Public Law 89-333 (a rehabilitation act in 1965) was enacted, and for the first time rehabilitation counselors were required to notify their clients of their rights to appeal ineligibility decisions.

2) Second, during the same time (the late 60s), demonstrations for civil rights, educational rights, social rights, the right to a civilian life, and the right to die were common throughout the country.

3) Changes were made in laws governing the diversification of insurance companies' operations.

4) State Workers' Compensation Laws were changed from simple "payoffs" to guaranteed rehabilitation services for people who met certain qualifications.

5) The supply of attorneys began to exceed the demand.

6) State and Federal funds became available to support legal aid societies and services.

7) Private-for-profit rehabilitation programs came on the scene.

8) The 1973 Rehabilitation Act required the involvement of the client and/or his representative in the planning and provision of rehabilitation services.

9) Public Law 94-142 and the more current Individuals with Disabilities Education Act (IDEA) required equal education for all "handicapped," including vocational education.

10) Rehabilitation professionals (evaluators, counselors, psychologists, etc.) learned that they could make more money by appearing in court.

11) Attorneys learned that they had a better chance to win their cases, and make more money, by using vocational specialists.

12) The ADA contributes to the conflict since more than 12,000 complaints were filed during the first year.

Regardless of the cause for the expanded use of vocational specialists in court, the major problem area appears to revolve around the preparation necessary for "expert testimony."

Due Process Settings

While due process settings are commonly defined as formal adversary settings that involve a plaintiff, defender, and referee (or judge), many disagreements in social and educational settings are settled in less formal hearings. The most common is where the plaintiff meets with an administrative representative of the agency against which the complaint is lodged. The process is known as the administrative hearing.

Administrative Hearings

Disagreements regarding eligibility, type of service, quality of service, timeliness, placement within a system, etc. are often settled without the need for a formal judicial hearing. Since many such disagreements are the results of misunderstandings regarding the purpose of programs or regulations governing programs, a clarification by a third party will frequently resolve misunderstandings and prevent the need for further action.

In the administrative hearing, the service provider (rehabilitation counselor, teacher, rehabilitation nurse, physician, etc.) and the client are joined by a program administrator (school principal, hospital administrator, program director, etc.) to discuss and attempt to settle their differences. In such hearings, either party may be represented by someone of their choice. Since this initial hearing is usually for the purpose of clarification and discussion rather than legal "right or wrong," it is not necessary that representatives be attorneys. Other professionals or friends often accompany the client to the hearing. The purpose of representation is to evaluate, clarify, and interpret. Those representing both sides should make every effort to resolve their differences at this initial step. The settings that follow the administrative hearing become purposely more lengthy and uncomfortable for both sides.

Pre-Hearing Conference

In many ways, the pre-hearing conference is very similar to the administrative review. Both may be requested by either side; they are usually held in a setting provided by the agency; they are without judge or jury; both sides may be represented by persons of their choice; both are relatively informal in comparison to other proceedings; the contents of the total file are available for review and copy; and both are usually conducted by an official representative of the agency.

The pre-hearing conference is more commonly used to resolve differences evolving from the educational placement of students with disabilities. (However, it is not limited to educational settings). Since many such differences relate to the evaluation and placement of students, the vocational expert may offer critical recommendations on the adequacy of the educational program to prepare a student for the vocational world. The expert may be requested to comment on the need for vocational skills training, the peer appropriateness of the placement, the anticipated vocational potential of the student, and other relationships between curriculum and job potential.

The role of the expert in non-educational pre-hearing conferences is very similar. The expert may be asked to offer opinions concerning the relationship between the rehabilitation plan and vocational potential, the ability of the worker to return to previous jobs, the potential of the worker to do other jobs with or without training, the availability of such jobs, and/or the levels of pay for the various jobs recommended. It is possible that the greatest service offered by the vocational expert at the pre-hearing conference is the interpretation of information found in the file or presented at the hearing.

The pre-hearing conference is usually recorded. It is most frequently chaired by a representative of the agency. The conference is begun by summarizing the events leading to the disagreements between the two sides. The person(s) who requested the conference is (are) then asked to state the disagreement with the service provided. The disagreement(s) may be enumerated, in full or in part, by the dissatisfied person or by one or more representatives. The vocational expert is asked to offer opinions regarding the adequacy or inadequacy of the planned services. An opinion regarding the most appropriate program of services, as well as its cost and time requirement, may also be given.

Following the more formal statements, an informal discussion usually occurs. During this discussion, both sides attempt to negotiate an agreement. A successful conference always results in mutual agreement or structured settlement. As one may expect, all such conferences are not successful. Regardless of the outcome, the agreements or disagreements are committed to writing. When the conference is unsuccessful, the next meeting is usually in a formal legal setting, which is controlled by a non-biased referee or judge.

Government agencies having responsibility for administering federal and state service programs may employ judges (ALJ) to preside over hearings where disagreements are presented. The U.S. Department of Labor and the Social Security Administration are examples of federal programs that hire judges, whereas a state Workers' Compensation board is most common employer on the state level.

The ALJ hearing is the most common judicial setting for the vocational expert. Historically, the expert's role evolved from and developed through hearings to determine eligibility for Social Security Disability Insurance (SSDI). That determination continues to be the major use of the expert's time, but similar hearings to determine eligibility for Workers' Compensation benefits are at least a close second. Both processes and settings warrant separate discussions.

The Social Security hearing results from a formal appeal by an applicant who has been denied SSDI and/or Supplemental Security Income (SSI) benefits. Most appeals are settled without the involvement of the expert. The expert will be involved only in those cases for which there may be some question of the existence of transferable skills and their relationship to employability.

It may be that a labor market access survey or wage loss survey is indicated. Whether a claimant is referred for rehabilitation or not, a survey can be completed based on available records, personal contacts, and published data. Based on past experience and information from appealed cases, the following is suggested.

The claimant should be interviewed, testing as appropriate should be accomplished, and other appropriate records should be obtained as previously noted. The history information should be recorded, the jobs located in the *Dictionary of Occupational Titles*, and the worker traits listed, such as available from the COJ. It is helpful to use a form such as the Transferability Worksheet (previously known as the VDARE) available from Elliott & Fitzpatrick, Inc., the publisher of this text. The worker traits can be adjusted for test results and physical limitations. The results should provide the residual functional capacity. This can be submitted to a computer based vocational software firm for processing and matching against other jobs listed in the *Dictionary of Occupational Titles*. (Again, see chapter of transferable skills for step-by-step procedures.)

Once various jobs are identified, a specific survey by the counselor in the local economy should be completed (also see chapter on labor market surveys). This is completed by contacting employers, using Department of Labor research, using the network established by most counselors, reading the classified ads, contacting the job service, researching the Career Information Systems if available, obtaining economic outlook publications, and so forth. When contacting employers, it is important to go beyond available jobs in that category and specifically determine if the employer has had experience with employees with a disability (similar to the claimant's is best). In some instances, attorneys have taken the position that the counselor must also ask the employer if they had two people of similar capabilities but one was disabled, who would they hire? In at least one appealed case, the court felt the last step was not justified.

Once the survey is complete, the report should contain an introduction that provides the basic information about the claimant, including type of injury, limitations, work, social, education, and medical history, test results, and other pertinent information.

The methods used to obtain the information, such as transferability worksheets, newspaper ads, personal network, yellow pages, Career Information System, Department of Labor research, etc., are listed. The results of the survey will include the employers contacted (10 should suffice), job availability, wages, training needed, willingness to hire people with disabilities, etc. (see chapter on labor market surveys for checklist). The counselor's conclusion about the claimant's employability, expected range of income, other related comments, and perhaps a labor market loss profile report should also be included.

As one can ascertain, good rehabilitation efforts are included in the suggested course of action for preparing the case for a hearing. More emphasis is placed on documentation than many counselors are accustomed to. The use of preprinted forms, checklists, diaries, and other personal methods for effective rehabilitation and follow-up are strongly encouraged. Several proven forms are located in Appendix K of this handbook as examples. Interview notes should be dictated within 24 hours of the interview to avoid loss or distortion of information. If the counselor keeps only the handwritten notes for a record, they should review them for errors, poor writing, etc., on the same day. It can be embarrassing to be unable to explain your notes in a hearing.

Preparing the Case - Details

Whether the case is associated with social security, workers' compensation, long-term disability, personal injury, or other disability systems, the way in which the professional prepares the case can determine the quality and defensibility of the conclusion and opinion. It is very important to do a thorough review of all applicable records in order to lay the foundation for the casework model. Suggested minimum records to review include the following:

- Medical records
- School records
- Prior vocational testing
- Rehabilitation and medical records from other sources
- Records from allied health professionals

In addition, in personal injury litigation there may very well be depositions by physicians, the client, and others who will have an impact on the course of action taken by the rehabilitation professional. With regard to medical depositions, it is helpful to review these records in order to understand the chronological aspect of the disability, to understand the treatment, and to gain a firm understanding of the medical condition. In most depositions, the attorney will ask the physician to describe the injuries and how the disability impacts the client's functioning. The treatment is often described in great detail. This can be particularly helpful to rehabilitation professionals who have a weak foundation in medical aspects of disability. Also, it is not uncommon for mistakes in the medical records to be revealed in the deposition.

On occasion, it may be helpful to obtain employer evaluations in order to determine the client's capability of performing on the job. It is clear that the number one factor is the human factor, rather than skills or worker traits. That is, the individual may be very bright and have substantial education with a high level of skills, only to have his or her job in jeopardy due to personality traits. One case that comes to mind was the railroad disability dispute where the injured worker from a small community had experienced a back injury. During the course of the evaluation, it was revealed that the client had engaged in wife swapping activities and had advertised in one of the magazines, complete with a picture. Although the magazine was not distributed in the local area, one of the co-workers discovered the picture and posted it on the bulletin board in the railroad maintenance office. This, of course, subjected the employee to considerable ridicule. When the rehabilitation counselor was able to develop a job that was within the claimant's physical limitations, he was not willing to return to that job site, which resulted in a dispute between the claimant and the employer.

When a rehabilitation professional offers an opinion that an individual may have certain work skills but psychologically is unable to return to work in a particular occupation, it is not unusual for the professional to be asked about success stories of people who have overcome much greater obstacles than the client. For an example, one state has a triple amputee who was in high-level politics. Another state boasted that a high-level tetraplegic, who was on a ventilator, was active in rehabilitation efforts. He was also the director of a rehabilitation agency for a few years.

It is the rehabilitation professional's duty to review the individual client for his or her potential for based on all factors. All factors are intended to include the personality traits the client possesses and not the personality traits possessed by the counselor. Clearly, people who are suffering from various disabilities could do something different, if only they were someone else. For example, at one extreme, a schizophrenic could be successful in a much broader range of job opportunities than he is while undergoing treatment for schizophrenia, "if only he would take control of his life." Although the example is an extreme one, it applies generally to the individual with whom the professional works. That is, the individual comes to you with his or her own worker traits, skills, abilities, personality traits, and other factors. That has to be the prime focus in determining the person's vocational potential. For example, a woman was assaulted while working late at night by herself as a hotel clerk and refused to return to that occupation following such a traumatic event. In some instances this individual did not want to work with the public at all. This, of course, will limit the occupational choices, even though worker traits would suggest that the individual is fully capable of functioning in a variety of occupations.

Work Disincentives

There are a number of work disincentives, such as social security disability insurance benefits, workers' compensation benefits or, in some cases, the promise of a large settlement from a personal injury lawsuit. In addition, many employees are angry with the employer or may be having domestic problems. Having a client state that he or she is "not interested" in a particular occupation must be viewed critically. The above discussion simply underscores the need to review the client's past history through documents, records, interviews with family members, co-workers, employers, and others to determine the most feasible course of action for this client.

Another example case includes an individual who had an employment arrangement with a small gas station to work as an "independent contractor." He was a qualified mechanic with two years of technical training and certification as a mechanic. His work history was primarily independent solo work activity with a time of self-employment as an auto mechanic. After eighteen months, he gave up the business and went back to work as an independent contractor because he was unable to "deal with the public and business details." A review of the records and interviews with family members revealed that he worked up to eighteen hours per day and would often provide his services at no charge. He also avoided conflict with his customers by understating his time or by not aggressively pursuing unpaid bills. In this individual's ten-year work history there was not one occasion where he supervised others or was successful at selling to the public.

He, unfortunately, was injured when a wheel exploded, causing injury to both his arms and face. He was transported to the hospital with a two-inch hole in the middle of his forehead, which was leaking cerebral spinal fluid. He had damage to one eye, which was permanent and irreversible. The most significant long-term injury was to his dominant arm. After a long period of recovery and several operations, his dominant arm was permanently impaired to the extent that he had plates in his forearm and the radial head in the forearm was removed. His strength was significantly reduced, and he had a number of psychological problems due to the disfigurement of his face. One rehabilitation professional, who was involved in the defense portion of the case, gave vocational testing that indicated poor interest and aptitude in management and sales. In spite of the history, as well as her own testing, the rehabilitation professional provided an opinion that he would be "perfect" in a sales job or suggested employment that required management and supervision of others. In this example it appears that the rehabilitation professional was exhibiting extraordinary optimism in light of the records and history.

Interviews

Once the records have been thoroughly reviewed, it will be appropriate to initiate an interview. It should be noted that some professionals prefer to do the interview prior to reading records in order to avoid any bias that may come across in the written documentation; nevertheless, it may prompt other questions that should be asked during the interview. As a general rule, the authors are suggesting that the records be reviewed prior to the interview.

Typically, the interview will consist of a standardized approach to obtaining information relative to this person's history and background, including other family members, in an attempt to identify, as best as possible, this person's vocational potential.

An example interview form will be found in Appendix K and provides an overall structure for a general interview to be conducted with most people. There are some variations, depending on the person's circumstances. In some instances the individual may be catastrophically injured, and a life care plan may be conducted (see Chapter 10), at which time it is appropriate to ask a variety of other questions that might not be included in a standard vocational interview. Catastrophic injury and rehabilitation technology appraisal interviews will utilize a somewhat different format.

Assuming a straightforward vocational interview, the most obvious areas of interest will include:

- Social history
- Educational history
- Employment interests
- Medical history

- Employment history
- Current medical treatment
- Medications
- Subjective complaints
- Client's view of limitations/capabilities
- Leisure time activities
- Military experience
- Effects on daily living activities

Of the above, two deserve special focus.

Employment History

Employment history is probably the most critical. Essentially, the person's work history, assuming that they have one, is a demonstration to the rehabilitation professional of the person's worker traits, interests, temperaments, and existing skills. Part of these data can certainly be surveyed by virtue of the interview. Detailed questioning about the person's work environment, job tasks, skills, tools, and other factors can be revealing. In a sense, the client will contribute the information that is uppermost in his or her mind. Experience has shown, however, that most people overlook a majority of the details of a job. In some cases, an individual focuses on those tasks which they cannot do rather than those which they can do. This indicates to the professional that the individual may be a problem with regard to "motivation." Certainly, people who have practiced rehabilitation in the workers' compensation arena have found that the majority of their cases are low back injuries, which constitute the majority of the professional headaches as well. Chronic pain programs sprang up across the country in the 80s and 90s in an attempt to intervene in some of these self-destructive behavioral patterns exhibited by the injured employee. Although there are chronic pain programs still available, the goal of a return to work now seems more in line with ameliorating pain.

In one case, an individual who explained that he was unable to continue working at his job due to "dangerous machinery" received support from his physician who refused to provide a "return to work release" because of this equipment. The rehabilitation professional conducted an on-site job analysis and found that the piece of machinery referred to by the client was, in fact, a large machine which rotated an object once every sixty seconds (previously mentioned in this chapter). Clearly, the client was distorting the information to the physician. The rehabilitation counselor completed a listing of the various tasks, including all machines used and the amount of time the worker was at each machine. Photographs of the machine were also provided to the physician for his review. Based on all of the information, it became clear that 98% of the tasks could easily be accomplished by the employee, and the other 2% could be picked up by helpers who were already in the area. The job was modified to recognize the client's limitations, and a "release to work" was issued.

On the other side of the coin are those people who are optimistic about their capabilities and continually put themselves in jeopardy of having another injury. For example, one case was a client with a brain injury who believed he was fully capable of returning to work but was considered incapable of driving a vehicle by the physician. His cognitive abilities, judgment, stamina, and other factors were significantly affected. In this particular case, the client was a federal aviation administration certified aircraft mechanic and, according to the employer, needed exceptional judgment.

The above illustrations represent, once again, that each client/evaluee must be considered individually. Certainly there are generalities that are consistent among various disability groups. However, the professional must avoid the jaded stereotype view in order to accurately access each individual's vocational potential.

Subjective Complaints

Another area of special emphasis to survey in great detail is the individual's subjective complaints. In many instances, the individual may be much more focused on limitations that can be objectively supported. On the other hand, the individual may claim to have better physical capabilities than the physician supports. It is also important to survey the record for discrepancies. In some events the client may reveal different information to different professionals, which may reveal certain pathology that may interfere with job placement.

Limitations in lifting, standing, walking, and so forth will clearly have an impact on the range of job alternatives available to the client. Generally, the most successful rehabilitation counselor is one who thoughtfully considers the claimant's perception of the disability.

It is important to reveal information that can be related to functional capabilities. In order to reduce the amount of distortion, questions asked of the client may be appropriately couched in forms that may more accurately reveal the individual's capabilities. For example, asking a client how long they can sit may reveal an answer of fifteen minutes, when you noticed that they were able to sit comfortably in the interview for forty-five minutes or longer. Another way of asking a question may be related to certain activities that the individual engages in. For an example, the client may watch a particular television program and be able to sit comfortably. This certainly indicates a sitting tolerance of at least one-half hour. Questions in regard to standing in line at the check-out counter, lifting bags of groceries, walking through a mall, and watching a movie are other ways that may gauge how much weight can be handled, the length of time an activity can be performed, or how often an activity can be engaged in before discomfort results.

Miscellaneous

In general, the authors endorse the concept that the initial interview should take place in the individual's home or place of residence. The environment provides clues as to the claimant's lifestyle, interests, and other "human factors" that may affect the professional's opinion.

Life Care Plans

In the event of a catastrophic injury, the professional may write a life care plan that will delineate the services and products that the claimant may likely use over their lifetime. This topic has become more important and accepted since it was introduced in the rehabilitation literature in 1985 by Deutsch & Sawyer. Chapter 10 in this text comprehensively details the requirements for completing a future care plan. (See also the section on Hedonics in Chapter 12).

Vocational Assessment

Assessment of vocational potential can take at least two paths (Havranek, Field & Grimes, 2005). The first is to survey the person's work history in detail. This can be a review of the job with the claimant, as well as cross-referencing to the *Dictionary of Occupational Titles* (USDOL, 1991), the *Transitional COJ* (Field & Field, 2005), and/or *Work Fields: Codes and Definitions* (Field & Field, 1993). In most cases, the person's demonstrated capabilities are more representative, if not more accurate, than tested capabilities.

On the other hand, vocational evaluations will allow the rehabilitation professional to assess areas that may not have been demonstrated on the job (particularly important for a younger person), as well as to identify capabilities that perhaps have been undiscovered. For an example, one of the clients was a carpenter who suffered a back injury. A review of the work history indicated some ten years of working in construction labor and most recently as a carpenter. However, a vocational evaluation revealed intelligence in the upper 5% of the population. During counseling it became evident that the client indeed possessed superior intelligence but was interested in a "self sufficient" lifestyle. He had engaged in carpentry to be able to live in the rural coastal area and make enough money to "get along." Based on a variety of vocational tests, including intelligence testing, a rehabilitation program was devised that allowed him to obtain training in a higher technical but lower strength job (marine mechanics), which at the same time endorsed his chosen lifestyle.

Chapter 5 provides a more detailed description of the vocational assessment process. The following is a general outline of areas to be included. The vocational assessment should generally consist of measures of intelligence, personality factors, interests, work values, educational achievement level, and perhaps, work samples in appropriate areas. After the paper and pencil testing and work sample testing is complete, it may be appropriate to obtain a situational assessment where the client can attempt a no risk trial at a work area of his choice that is compatible with the worker traits, skill levels, and other factors. This usually is feasible in the various worker compensation programs, but unlikely in personal injury cases.

For examples of various ways to measure worker traits, the reader is referred to the vocational assessment chapter, *Measuring Worker Traits* (Field & Orgar, 1983), *Measuring Physical Capacities* (Field & Pettit, 1985), *Handbook of Measurement and Evaluation in Rehabilitation* (Bolton, 1987), *A Counselor's Guide to*

Career Assessment Instruments (Kapes & Mastie, 1988), *A Guide to Vocational Assessment* (Power, 2006), and *Computer Applications in Rehabilitation* (Weed, 1987d).

In addition to the vocational testing, a measure of functional capacities may be appropriate. There are a number of companies that specialize in measuring physical capacities, which will measure a person's capability of standing, walking, sitting, lifting, climbing, and a variety of other physical functioning capabilities. For more detailed information with regard to physical capacity assessment and work hardening therapy, the reader is referred to *Physical Capacity Assessment and Work Hardening Therapy: Procedures and Applications* (Havranek, 1988; also Havranek, Field, & Grimes, 2005).

Transferability of Skills

Transferability of skills (see Chapter 6 for an expansive discussion of this topic) is defined as those skills that can be used in one job and then interchanged or substituted into another job (Boles, 1988; Field & Weed, 1988). Skills are learned by doing. Generally worker traits and skills are different, though related. For an example, a worker trait includes the person's capability of learning. Skills make use of the worker traits. The client must be capable of learning the skill, say, typing. The client may only have the skill of typing at 10 words per minute but the ability to type 60. After several weeks of training, she may possess the skill of typing 60 words per minute, which can be utilized in a variety of jobs. Worker traits are included in the federal Department of Labor's publications.

Of the 12,741 job titles listed in the *Dictionary of Occupational Titles* (1991), one or more job analyses (about 75,000 total) were conducted in order to provide a foundation for determining levels of capability, physical demands, working conditions, interests, and temperaments that a worker must possess in order to work within the various job alternatives (Miller, Treiman, Cain, & Roos, 1980). Examples of aptitudes include general learning ability, verbal ability, spatial perception, form perception, finger dexterity, manual dexterity, eye-hand-foot coordination, color discrimination, and others.

Obviously, in order for an individual to possess a skill, he or she must have the capabilities of learning. An individual who has an intellectual disability will not learn the skills necessary to be a heart surgeon, but an individual who is very bright may. In a sense, the skills that one learns are somewhat predicated on the worker traits that the person brings with him or her when he or she is exposed to training or work. In summary, the term skill refers to what one learns by doing. As noted above, someone who possesses the skill to type is usually described in terms of the number of words typed per minute. People who learn to type build their skill by practice and education. For all practical purposes, transferability of skills must begin with understanding worker traits.

Further explanation with regard to how a job analysis is conducted by the federal government is important. When one reviews worker traits for persons with a disability, it is not uncommon for certain worker traits that appear at first blush to be appropriate are not included as part of the worker traits as published in the *Transitional COJ* (Field & Field, 2005). For example, the worker traits for an attorney do not have vision listed. On the surface this seems incorrect. However, after reviewing the *Revised Handbook for Analyzing Jobs* (USDOL, 1991), which is the publication that lists the criteria for completion of job analysis, the mystery is solved. The jobs that will have vision as a listed worker trait are those which require attention to visual detail, such as an aircraft pilot or a barber. It is also necessary for this trait to be required for a substantial portion of the job.

One of the reasons to have a complete understanding of the way a job analysis is conducted has to do with job matching computer programs. Most rehabilitation professionals routinely have the experience of inappropriate job matches based solely on worker trait searches. Generally speaking, the worker trait approach to identifying job titles is a good first cut. Once the range has been narrowed to represent the individual's selected industries (as demonstrated by work history), the authors recommend cross-referencing to the work fields (WF) that can be found in the *Transitional COJ* (Field & Field, 2005). The WF code is more representative of the skills needed to perform work in related job titles. Another approach is to utilize the O*NET database and Census codes as representative of the person's skills which can be transferred to other employment.

Estimating Loss of Earnings and Worklife

For a detailed review of issues related to lost wages and earnings, loss of future earnings, and worklife expectancy, please refer to the content in Chapters 6 and 11.

Summary

This chapter summarizes a suggested methodology by which to prepare a case for a variety of settings. Not included is the Labor Market Access/Wage Loss, Life Care Plan, nor transferable work skills analysis procedures, which are located in separate chapters. After the case is prepared, the rehabilitation professional will be challenged to present the information in a clear and defensible manner. All professionals are advised to develop written formats, which are organized with topic headings and clearly convey their opinions.

Chapter 5
Vocational Assessment

Introduction

First, it is assumed that a rehabilitation counselor who has an interest in becoming an evaluator will obtain training that far exceeds the content of this chapter. The chapter is designed to provide the "big picture" overview of comprehensive assessment. For details regarding typical assessments for vocational planning, see Power (2006).

Vocational assessment is an essential part of vocational rehabilitation. In cases of personal injury, vocational assessment determines the loss of power to earn money; for others with a disability, assessment determines successful return-to-work strategies. The ultimate decision rests upon the determination of the worker's pre-injury vocational functioning as compared to post-injury vocational functioning. For adults, the analysis should include information and procedures related to the following specific areas (See separate section in the Forensic Chapter for personal injury opinions regarding children. Prior to initiating the evaluation or interview, for adults or children, a professional disclosure form should be completed [see examples at CRCC, 2011]):

1. Information about vocational functioning of the worker (educational, social, work history, medical, and psychological reports).

2. Information about the characteristics of jobs and their requirements (physical demands, working conditions, educational and training, aptitudes, interests, and temperaments).

3. Information about national, state, and local labor markets (jobs in a geographical area, numbers of people employed, and wage information).

This chapter reviews the information available in the vocational assessment area. Following an overview of the types of information utilized in the vocational assessment process, brief information is provided, which identifies the measures most often utilized.

Vocational History

As noted in the previous chapter, the vocational skills of the person with a work history are obviously one of the more important sources of information in determining current vocational functioning. All rehabilitation experts should be able to systematically assess vocational functioning by studying the worker's job history. The process is a relatively elemental one and will include the following basic steps:

1. Receive information from the worker (or other related sources, e.g., family, former employers) about the specific jobs previously held.

2. Confirm the accuracy of the jobs held, including job title, and a description of the work performed.

3. Complete a job analysis of the job(s) either through observation, interviews, or consultation of standardized published resources, such as the O*Net, *Dictionary of Occupational Titles*, and the *Classification of Jobs* (see References).

4. Summarize the level(s) of worker functioning according to the worker trait characteristics of all previously held jobs. (Note: The worker traits consist of physical demands, working conditions, education and training, aptitudes, interests, and temperaments). See Appendix E for complete listing of worker traits and definitions.

5. Review consultants' and other reports to identify the disabling conditions and their corresponding functional limitations, e.g., a reduced exertional capacity in lifting due to back strain. Include pertinent records, such as medical, psychological, neuropsychological, occupational therapy, physical therapy, speech language therapy, school, available work history, and others. A detailed analysis is strongly suggested.

6. Determine a "revised" level of vocational functioning by "transferring" the residual vocational skills, or identify what the worker can do now (across the worker traits) following injury.

In summary, this process represents an analysis based upon previous work history. This determination is accurate only insofar as the information is reliable from the job history. For complete details of the transferability process, see Chapter 6.

Vocational Referral

Sometimes a client will possess no significant work history. This may be due to having held a series of very short-term jobs or having no work history at all (e.g., an injury to a child). To compensate for the lack of employment history, it may be essential to rely upon additional evaluation and testing in the vocational potential area. At this point, referral to educational, vocational, and psychological testing specialists would be appropriate. Following the receipt of these test data, the rehabilitation specialist can then determine the level of vocational functioning according to the worker traits. Once a determination is made of the worker's levels of vocational functioning (e.g., the worker traits), the next step is to make recommendations for future employment (if possible) that is consistent with the worker's current level of functioning.

Vocational Information

When selecting an occupation, the person is not just choosing a way to make a living. Jobs are more critical to our lives than just a type of activity or a salary. A job determines, to a great extent, our life style. It determines the kind of people with whom we socialize, the type of clothing we wear, the type of car we drive, the location of residence, the time of day we sleep and eat, the amount of traveling we do, and many other aspects of our lives that reveal our beliefs and affect our attitudes.

With so much at stake, one might expect job selection to be based on carefully planned comparisons of job personalities and individual personalities. But we know that such is not the case. Although counselors are employed in nearly every high school across the country and "career education" is common to most junior high and high schools, assistance to students seeking job information is scarce. Those students requesting job information are usually referred to the library. Those who seek help from the U.S. Labor Department Employment Services Counselors are referred to databases on the internet. It's little wonder that Terkel (1972) found, in his interview of persons across the country, so many people were unhappy with their jobs.

The problem confronting persons with mental or physical disabilities is even greater. Oftentimes their life-styles have been vastly modified through the limitations imposed by their disabilities. The 20,000 job titles (12,741 coded titles) identified in the *Dictionary of Occupational Titles* (1991) are assumed to be equally available to all. However, not all people are created equal, and those who have a disability at birth and/or those who acquire a disability after birth are even less equal when competing for employment (Bureau of Labor Statistics, 2001). There are both physical and mental requirements for all jobs, so the process of comparing and matching the abilities and personalities of people with disabilities to the aptitude and personality requirements of the job or occupation is more limiting and therefore more difficult. Jobs have requirements for physical, educational, social, psychological, and vocational aptitudes. If, due to a disabling condition, a person's ability is limited in one or more of these five areas, his ability for successful employment is limited. In such cases special help may be required to analyze residual physical, psychological, social, educational, and/or vocational functioning abilities, and to synthesize the abilities into a viable vocational profile (or plan). Only through such a process can a person who has lost a portion of his ability be placed into jobs that relate to his ability. Such a process is known as vocational evaluation.

Vocational Evaluation Process

There are four general steps in the evaluation process: information gathering, analysis, synthesis, and interpretation (Vocational assessment: Evaluating employment potential, Havranek, Grimes, Field, & Sink, 1994).While the steps are sequential, their uses are not independent. For example, the evaluator doesn't gather all information to be used in an orderly fashion and then analyze, synthesize, and interpret it. Rather, the various items of information are analyzed, synthesized, and interpreted as they are collected. This process identifies the need for additional information as well as the method by which it may be obtained.

An example of such a process has been identified by Nadolsky (1971) as a Model for Vocational Evaluation of the Disadvantaged. A modification of the steps included in his model will be helpful to understand the four general steps of vocational evaluation. The steps in his model, with modifications, suggest that information should be gathered through the following order:

1. Biographical Data
2. Vocational Interview
3. Psychological Tests
4. Occupational Information and Exploration
5. Work Samples
6. Situational or Sheltered Tasks
7. On-the-Job Evaluation

Biographical Data

Biographical data consists of medical, psychological, social, vocational, and educational history. Nadolsky (1971) suggests that "The various types of biographical data are designed to identify the individual in his present situation by discovering the events and experiences in his past history that have served to create and mold his individuality." The major purpose initially is to begin the elimination of certain jobs that are unreasonable due to the individual's residual abilities. The second purpose is to identify additional questions that need to be answered in the ensuing evaluation process. For example, available medical information may indicate past surgery to repair a slipped disc but not contain the specific limitations for lifting, pushing, pulling, bending, etc., resulting from the disability.

Another example may be the non-specific information about previous employment. The written vocational history may list "machine operator", "welder", or "painter", which are generic titles for many different occupations. A man who had entered an alcoholic treatment program listed his previous employment as "Bell Air Farm and Equipment Company." He also indicated that upon discharge he could return to employment in the same job. He gave approval to the evaluator's request for permission to call his employer to confirm the possibility of return to work. The evaluator called the farm and equipment company, identified himself and his client, and asked if it was true that the client could return to his previous job after discharge. The answer was "I suppose if [the client] wishes to come back, he can; he owns the damned place." Needless to say, specific measurable information in all areas is important if the evaluator is to develop appropriate questions to be clarified in the first meeting with the client.

Vocational Interview

The vocational interview (see Appendix K for an example form) is used by the evaluator to both verify and clarify biographical data, as well as to collect additional information. As with medical evaluations where the physician often says that the patient's history is the most important information leading to a diagnosis (T. Musser, MD, personal communication, September 22, 2011; K. Raziano, MD, personal communication, October 27, 2011), the detailed gathering of vocational history is likewise of value. In addition to collecting information, the evaluator imparts information. The client is informed of the additional questions that need to be answered and the techniques to be used in answering. Through this interchange, the client learns both the purpose and the process of the evaluation. With such an understanding, the client is more inclined to be committed to the process. It is recommended that counselors use a specific format to assure that the same information topics are collected every time. This may be even more important in forensic (litigation related) rehabilitation.

Psychological Testing

Psychological testing usually precedes other types of testing because it provides information that may eliminate the need for collecting certain additional data. For example, if a psychological device measures the client's reading level at the fourth grade with the absence of an ability to improve, there would be no need to evaluate for additional aptitudes relating to a job of "editing." Psychological testing in the vocational process usually covers the following categories:

1. Intelligence

2. Educational Achievement

3. Aptitude

4. Vocational Interest

5. Personality and Temperament

The traits measured by psychological tests are abstract in nature but help the evaluator to identify vocational assets and limitations. Intelligence tests most highly respected are the Wechsler Adult Intelligence Scale and the Stanford-Binet. However, the Slosson Intelligence Test and the Revised Beta Examination are frequently used to measure intelligence and do not require as much time to administer. It should be noted that the gold standard test, the Wechsler, requires extensive training and typically requires a doctorate whereas the Slosson may be administered by a master's degree in vocational rehabilitation or evaluation. The Slosson is adequate for a generalized assessment but the Wechlser yields significantly more information (see Power, 2006). The developers of the Culture Fair Intelligence Test claim their test is relatively independent of academic achievement and environmental influences. Personality and temperament tests are too often used only for the purpose of identifying a diagnosis of mental illness. Their purpose in the vocational evaluation process is to identify and/or predict behaviors that strengthen or weaken an individual's potential for employment. Too often the results of personality tests are stated in terms that are of little use to the vocational specialist. For example, frequently the final impression of a psychological examination is "paranoid schizophrenia, chronic undifferentiated type; he can manage his own funds." Such a statement allows the user to classify the examinee as having a disability but doesn't help identify the functional disabilities and abilities that may be a barrier to or assistance with employment.

Some examples of non-projective personality and temperament tests are the Minnesota Multiphasic Personality Inventory (which is the most widely administered diagnostic personality test in the United States, Power 2006), the Edwards Personal Preference Schedule, the Myers-Briggs Type Indicator, 16 PF, and the California Psychological Inventory. Projective tests that are common (but used less frequently in vocational evaluation) are the Rorschach Psychodiagnostic Test, the Bender-Gestalt Test, the Thematic Apperception Test, and the House-Tree-Person Test.

Since there are so many personal and situational factors that may influence tests, results are used to assess the level of a person's behavior at the time the tests were administered, to measure changes in behavior, and to predict potential for changed levels of behavior. The results of tests should never solely be used as the ultimate or final diagnosis. In addition, testing circumstances can interfere with best efforts, e.g., forgetting to bring glasses to the testing, using pain medications, environmental distractions like noise and activity.

Educational achievement tests that measure a variety of areas are preferred. One of the most commonly used is the Wide Range Achievement Test (WRAT) (as revised). The WRAT measures basic mathematics, word recognition, and spelling levels for children and adults. The WRAT is a screening test, but if detailed assessment is desirable, an instrument like the Woodcock Johnson Tests of Achievement is recommended, although, like the Wechsler, it requires extensive training to be administered. The Adult Basic Learning Examination may be used with persons who have completed grades 1-9. It measures three verbal skills (vocabulary, reading, and spelling) and three arithmetic skills (computation, problem solving, and total). Many other achievement tests are available as well.

Shertzer and Linden (1979) state that aptitude tests measure the individual's potential for further success. The General Aptitude Test Battery (GATB), developed by the United States Department of Labor is probably the best known and was the most widely used aptitude test but has fallen out of favor due to validity questions. It measures nine aptitudes, which are cross referenced to the *Dictionary of Occupational Titles*. A sixth grade reading knowledge is needed for valid results. The Differential Aptitude Test also measures nine aptitudes and requires a sixth grade reading knowledge. There are numerous aptitude tests (i.e., Purdue Pegboard, Crawford Small Parts Dexterity, Minnesota Paper Form Board, General Clerical) that measure specific aptitude areas such as manual dexterity, motor coordination, general clerical. The Differential Aptitude Test is useful for skilled trades assessment. For clients who may have been in the military prior to the disability, obtaining a copy of the Armed Services Vocational Aptitude Battery (ASVAB) is useful.

Interest inventories generally compare the interests of the subject to those of persons satisfactorily employed in jobs. These inventories are designed to assess a person's interests and temperaments that relate to jobs rather than the ability for jobs. The Career Assessment Inventory, the Self Directed Search, the

Strong-Campbell Interest Blank, and the online O*Net based Interest Profiler (see http://www.onetcenter. org/IP.html) are commonly used to measure interest. All utilize Holland Typologies for vocational satisfaction (see Table below), which is the most widely accepted theory relating to interest factors and work. There are also interest tests available for the non-reader. Two such tests are the Wide Range Interest and Opinion Tests and the Picture Interest Inventory. Interest inventories can be easily accessed for client use. A summary of Holland Themes is located in Table 5.1.

Occupational Information and Exploration

Occupational information and exploration is a major weakness in the vocational evaluation process. It is too often assumed that the client is familiar with, and aware of, the requirements for being successful in many jobs. It is also assumed that the client should be aware of the relationship between skills utilized on jobs previously held, including those with alternate titles.

One of the first questions common to the vocational interview is "what kind of job would you like to do?" The question assumes that the client has extensive knowledge of jobs and their requirements. Since most people do not have such knowledge, we know that occupational information is necessary to assure client involvement and commitment to vocational selection. The analysis, synthesis, and interpretation of biographical data; the information collected through the vocational interview; and psychological, educational and vocational tests results appears to be the most logical method of increasing the client's knowledge of alternate jobs and their requirements.

By thoroughly analyzing previous vocations (biographical data), the evaluator is able to identify the demonstrated and tested interests, temperaments, aptitudes, physical demands, and educational requirements.

Through the vocational interview, the evaluator clarifies those variables of the job that the client liked the greatest or least. For example, the client may express a dislike for a given job that he/she has held, but further clarification may identify the attitude of a supervisor as the reason for not liking it. There are many other variables that may result in disinterest for the job (environment, physical requirements, shift, stress, repetitiousness, etc.). The evaluator must then identify, with the client, those traits demonstrated in previous jobs that were "pluses" and those that were "minuses." The more "pluses" an employee finds in a job, the more likely he/she is to be successful.

The client may possess interests that are demonstrated only through avocational activities. Therefore, it is imperative that the evaluator clarify traits demonstrated in the avocational as well as the vocational lives of the clients.

Once previous experiences have been analyzed, it is often desirable to identify additional interests and temperaments, as well as additional levels of aptitude, education, and intelligence. If so, psychological tests are administered. However, questions that need to be answered through testing are first identified. For example, the evaluator may find that the client completed the 6th grade in school and that previous jobs required the use of mathematics at only the 3rd grade level. By determining that the client's actual achievement is at the 6th grade level, many additional jobs (for which the client is otherwise capable) may be reasonable options. In such a case a mathematics achievement test may be the only test administered. Depending upon the vocational and educational background of the client, tests may not be used at all, or entire batteries of tests may be used.

Once the levels of a person's intelligence, interests, temperaments, aptitudes, and education have been identified, the information may be synthesized into potential for various worker trait groups or job clusters: i.e., those groups of jobs that require the same interests, temperaments, and levels of intelligence and aptitude. Once the groups or clusters of jobs have been identified, the evaluator should educate the client regarding job availability and requirements. There are numerous audio-visual materials available to provide such information (Gould Inc., Educational Systems Div., Occupational Learning and Career Exploration Systems, Acoustifone Corp., Career Explorational Learning and Career Exploration Programs, SRA Career Information and Occupational Kits). The evaluator may also verbally inform the client about the jobs. Finally, the evaluator may accompany the client to a job site to actually observe the job. Regardless of the source of information, many persons who aren't working, because of a disabling condition, would be working if they were better informed of job requirements and availability.

Table 5.1
Holland Themes

Realistic (R)

- Usually has mechanical and athletic abilities, and likes to work outdoors and with tools and machines.
- Generally likes to work with things more than with people.
- Described as conforming, frank, genuine, hardheaded, honest, humble, materialistic, modest, natural, normal, persistent, practical, shy, and thrifty.
- Examples: auto mechanic, aircraft controller, surveyor, electrician, and farmer.

Investigative (I)

- Usually has math and science abilities, and likes to work alone and to solve problems.
- Generally likes to explore and understand things or events, rather than persuade others or sell them things.
- Is described as analytical, cautious, complex, critical, curious, independent, intellectual, introverted, methodical, modest, pessimistic, precise, rational, and reserved.
- Examples: biologist, chemist, physicist, geologist, anthropologist, laboratory assistant, and medical technician.

Artistic (A)

- Usually has artistic skills, enjoys creating original work, and has a good imagination.
- Generally likes to work with creative ideas and self-expression more than routines and rules.
- Is described as complicated, disorderly, emotional, expressive, idealistic, imaginative, impractical, impulsive, independent, introspective, intuitive, nonconforming, open, and original.
- Examples: composer, musician, stage director, dancer, interior decorator, actor, and writer.

Social (S)

- Usually likes to be around other people, is interested in how people get along, and likes to help other people with their problems.
- Generally likes to help, teach, and counsel people more than mechanical or technical activity.
- Is described as convincing, cooperative, friendly, generous, helpful, idealistic, kind, patient, responsible, social, sympathetic, tactful, understanding, and warm.
- Examples: teacher, speech therapist, religious worker, counselor, clinical psychologist, and nurse.

Enterprising (E)

- Usually has leadership and public speaking abilities, is interested in money and politics, and likes to influence people.
- Generally likes to persuade or direct others more than work on scientific or complicated topics.
- Is described as acquisitive, adventurous, agreeable, ambitious, attention-getting, domineering, energetic, extroverted, impulsive, optimistic, pleasure-seeking, popular, self-confident, and sociable.
- Examples: buyer, sports promoter, television producer, business executive, salesperson, travel agent, supervisor, and manager.

Conventional (C)

- Generally likes to follow orderly routines and meet clear standards, avoiding work that does not have clear directions.
- Is described as conforming, conscientious, careful, efficient, inhibited, obedient, orderly, persistent, practical, thrifty, and unimaginative.

Physical Capacity Evaluation

In the 1980s, there was a growing interest in physical capacity evaluation (sometimes referred to as functional capacity evaluations) and work hardening approaches. This development has evolved as a result of the inadequacy of the DOT database on physical demand characteristics, and the irrelevancy of some vocational evaluation methods of the assessment of work behaviors. Although theses assessments have fallen from favor, they are still useful for a more objective measure of functional capability.

Havranek (1988) discusses many of the issues related to these developments, and provides some good illustrations of work hardening approaches. Len Mathison (of Roy Mathison & Associates of California) was involved in the initial development of the W.E.S.T. and subsequent work of physical capacity evaluation. Contributions of Valpar (of Tucson) have been evident in the development of the MESA (now Joule) (Valpar, 2011). Perhaps the most contemporary new product in this area is ERGOS developed primarily by New Concepts and Tom Brandon of Tucson under the business name of Work Recovery, Inc. (now known as Ergos™ II and owned by Simwork). This product utilizes modules for physical capacity assessment with a wide range of tasks for physical and cognitive evaluation. The unit employs computer systems for comprehensive monitoring of performance and report generation, which are then cross-referenced to government data and the DOT (Simwork, 2011).

Work Samples

For many clients, there is a need to extend the evaluation process beyond the occupational information and exploration stage. For those persons whose vocational history is minimal, or whose disabilities may have eliminated most of their previously demonstrated transferable skills, work samples become a viable method of assessing vocational potential. Work samples usually emphasize psychomotor skills rather than verbal abilities. They produce feedback from hands-on activities experienced by the client. A work sample may take as little as a few minutes, or as many as eight hours to complete.

Since work samples are simulations or "mock-ups" of jobs (or various traits common to jobs), it is easy for the client to understand their relationships to jobs. The actual validity of evaluation systems is the major question confronting their users. While many apparently have face validity, the manufacturer of only one system has reported the results of predictive validity studies.

Work samples can represent an important component of the vocational evaluation process. They allow clients to experience activities that are obviously (to the client) work related. They provide the evaluator an opportunity to observe the behaviors of clients in job related situations, as well as to measure the clients' physical tolerance, frustration tolerance, interests, temperaments, and aptitudes for jobs and groups of jobs. They provide clients with an opportunity to experience work and to relate worker traits to actual jobs. Most companies have reduced their support for such assessments (Vocational Research Institute, 2011); however, some existing facilities may still have in use the following:

1. JEVS Work Sample System, which was streamlined and transformed into the VITAS Assessment System

   The JEVS Work Sample System is designed to measure work performance and behaviors related to ten worker trait groups of the DOT (1965). Subsequent development relates performance on the work samples to the DOT-related Guide to Occupational Exploration. The system consists of 28 work samples that are arranged into the ten worker trait groups. The recommended client group is persons who are disabled or have special needs.

2. VALPAR Component Work Samples

   The VALPAR Component Work Sample series is a collection of 18 work samples and functional capacity evaluations designed to measure worker characteristics. The 18 work samples meet such criteria as universality, efficiency, durability, marketability, flexibility, and mobility. Designed for optimum evaluator efficiency, each work sample is recyclable, scored with ease, equipped for 100 administrations, uses a minimum of consumable supplies, is portable, and is easily stored. The work samples are also designed so that the evaluee's language and reading skills do not present barriers to vocational assessment. All groups are recommended for these samples, including hearing and visually impaired.

3. VIEWS

   The Vocational Information and Evaluation Work Samples (VIEWS) is a system designed for persons with minimal skills for employment. Sixteen work samples evaluate worker activities in four areas and six worker trait groups of the DOT (1965). Work performance factors and behaviors are carefully defined and evaluated. The recommended client group is individuals who have mental disabilities.

Situational Assessment

While work samples may be used to assess for aptitudes, interests, and temperaments, most are minimally useful in determining a client's physical tolerance and frustration tolerance. Actual jobs are utilized in the situational assessment approach. The major difference in situational assessment and an actual job tryout is the work environment. Situational assessment is provided most frequently in a sheltered workshop or work activities center, although employer based assessments are becoming more common. The type of supervision used, the level of production required, the modification of tools and equipment, the structure of the workday, and peer relationships are all controlled by the evaluator.

For example, a supervisor may be asked to "push" one client, but to offer minimal supervision to the next. The purpose is to determine the effects of supervision on the work personality of the client. In another case, the magnitude of physical ability for lifting may be determined by the physician while the frequency and duration of the lifting would be determined through situational assessment.

On-The-Job Evaluation (OJT)

 Until the mid to late 50's, OJT was the most common form of vocational evaluation. The client was moved from one job to the other until one was found that matched the client's skills.

The purpose is to evaluate the client on those job characteristics that can only be determined on an actual job. For example, it may be determined that a client has ability as a gasoline station attendant, but the evaluator (and client) may be uncertain of the client's ability to deal with the many personalities of customers. Therefore, the client would be placed on OJT as an attendant at a service station. No alterations would be made to the work environment.

As may be expected, OJT is more commonly used with those persons who have little or no vocational experience. Those clients whose emotional stability presents challenges may also benefit from OJT. Regardless of the client, OJT should take no longer than 5 days, except, perhaps, in cases of clients with brain injury, special needs, or emotional disabilities. It is common practice to leave clients in the "status" of OJT for longer than 5 days. However, in such cases the true purpose is training rather than evaluation.

There is a variation of OJT related to supported employment. There are two models. Each has four components listed.

1. Train-Place-Train-Follow-up. Components are:

   "(1) surveying potential employers to determine important vocational and social survival skills that need to be trained,

   (2) training individuals to perform such skills,

   (3) placing training clients into competitive employment, and

   (4) providing long-term follow-up training" (Lagomarcino, 1986 as cited in Rubin & Roessler, 2008, p. 415).

2. Place-Train-Follow-up. Components are:

   "(1) job placement,

   (2) job-site training [and advocacy],

   (3) on-going assessment, and

   (4) job retention" (Wehman, 1986 as cited in Rubin & Roessler, 2008, p. 415).

Vocational Counseling

While vocational counseling is not used for the purpose of evaluation, it is imperative to the utilization of vocational evaluation results. Vocational Counseling is more than an interpretation of the evaluation results. It is a process of helping the client analyze and synthesize the evaluation results; of assisting the client to understand the relationship of evaluation data to real jobs; and of aiding the client with clarifying feelings about these assets and liabilities as they relate to potential for vocational independence.

Job Analysis

Several different approaches can be employed in answering the questions posed above. (Also see Job Analysis chapter for detailed information.)

First, standards of measurement are essential with respect to the exertional requirements of a job. Aerobic capacity can be measured by physiotherapists. If the professional knows the behavioral/physical requirements of the job, these data can be applied to the work place. For instance, if three miles of running is required on a daily basis, physiotherapists can measure, through aerobic capacity, the exertion expended in such an activity.

Second, it would be important to identify the behaviors of "reasonable necessity" required in the performance of a job, e.g., a job with the State Patrol. Such physical behaviors might include running, long hours of standing and walking, exertional strength, hand grip, climbing, crawling, balancing, and so forth. Work conditions such as working in cold or hot weather, in humid or wet areas, outside, and around hazards (e.g., dangerous machinery) can also be included.

This discussion will center upon the elements, factors, behaviors, and activities required to perform a job. As noted above, several approaches can be employed in developing an understanding of a job. Each is discussed briefly:

1. The Job Description

    Most organizations, state agencies included, are required to develop job descriptions for positions within the work place. The job description is usually just that: a narrative description of the activities and requirements of the job. Some discussion is usually made of the job tasks or elements, although most descriptions are general and "generic" in nature. With the ADA, more emphasis on the job description development prior to hire has become essential.

    The disadvantage of this method is that often the job description does not accurately reflect what the worker will actually do in that job. In addition, there are frequently a number of variations in the way the job is practiced based on hidden norms (behavioral expectations).

2. Worker Qualifications

    It is common practice for employers to list particular qualifications that the worker or potential worker must possess in order to be hired and actually perform the job. Qualifications have included everything from physical requirements of the worker to educational and experiential achievements.

    The fallacy of this approach is that, many times, persons may or may not be able to perform a certain job independent of the stated and/or required qualifications.

3. Department of Labor

    The Department of Labor has generated information on almost all job titles that exist within the U.S. economy (*Dictionary of Occupational Titles*, 1991; *Classification of Jobs*, 2000). These data identify more than 70 worker trait factors common to most jobs, and they serve as a means of comparison between jobs. The job analyses were completed on the basis of sampling a number of people in these titles from various sections of the country. These data represent large-scale information about people in jobs that approximate what people actually do in each of the job titles. However, the O*Net has accumulated about 10% of the data for occupations as the DOT.

    While these data serve as very useful beginning information about a large number of jobs, the worker trait information is only an approximation of what a single person may actually do within a particular job. The information is particularly useful in describing the general characteristics of a particular job or cluster of jobs.

4. On-Site Job Analysis

A most useful approach in understanding the requirements and parameters of a job is the completion of an on-site job analysis. This approach requires a trained job specialist to observe a person or persons actually performing a job in the job's natural setting. The specialist would use some standard format or criteria (see Chapter 8 for an example) in evaluating the different elements of a job (again, the Worker Traits would serve as a useful beginning point). This approach also allows for several analyses of several different workers in several different locations of the same job. Multiple analyses would provide a more accurate assessment of the general requirements of the job.

The limitation of this approach is that some jobs do not always lend themselves readily to analysis. For instance, an on-site analysis of a person performing a "bench" type job would be relatively easy to complete, while analyzing what is required to be a police officer would be more difficult (due to the mobility required of the job).

5. The Job Interview

To supplement the analysis of a job, interviewing a worker about the job requirements can be a valuable source of information, especially in jobs that may be difficult to analyze in one setting. Likewise, interviewing several persons with the same job title can contribute to a more accurate profile of what a particular job actually requires.

The disadvantage of this approach is the dubious accuracy of the worker's self-report regarding what is actually performed on the job. In cases involving litigation, the literature clearly shows that workers often report job behaviors that favor their position (Weed & Field, 2001). However, people can be expected to report behaviors, incidents, and requirements with a large measure of accuracy. Furthermore, conducting several interviews and involving persons not part of the litigation tends to minimize "extreme" descriptions.

Summary

This chapter outlines the various ways in which the rehabilitation expert can assess a client's potential for work. Some methods utilize vocational testing and work history; others depend on observing clients perform work samples or actual jobs within their expected capabilities. Generally, testing is a sample of behavior over a very brief period of time. Therefore, actual demonstrated performance will usually more accurately estimate work capabilities. Indeed, in some situations the test may not last long enough to assess effects of fatigue or personality attributes. The counselor should be attuned to effects that could adversely affect testing such as:

pain,

medication,

not wearing glasses,

hearing impairments,

language of origin, and

performance disincentives.

Although many experts will rely upon vocational evaluators for conducting tests, the consultant is advised to ascertain the evaluator's competence. Does the test administrator have the qualifications to give the tests? Is he or she a certified vocational evaluator? Many persons who do testing have little or no experience in placement and often identify jobs that are not reasonable or available. For example, a client may have the capabilities to be a union business agent, but these jobs are dependent on experience and membership in the union and election or political appointment. The consultant who can effectively utilize test results will accurately identify potential employment.

Chapter 6
Transferable Skills Analysis

Background

Transferability of skills analysis (generally referred to as TSAs or transferable work skills [TWS] analysis) has been a procedure utilized by rehabilitation and job specialists in one form or another for decades. The 1977 version of the *Dictionary of Occupational Titles* incorporated the arrangement of the "worker traits" as a means of identifying both the capacities of the worker (implied) and the characteristics of a job. While the DOT (a product of the U.S. Department of Labor) was intended for a wide assortment of occupational uses, much of the information especially served those who needed to routinely complete TSAs as an integral part of developing a case. Perhaps the single largest user of the DOT was the Social Security Administration in the determination of disability under the Social Security Disability Insurance (SSDI) program.

Transferability of skills can be defined in a variety of ways. State and federal programs addressing issues related to disability, work, and the return to work, have approached the issue in different ways. For instance, the state-federal vocational rehabilitation program has traditionally required an individualized rehabilitation plan (in current law, referred to as an individual plan for employment) that considers any and all information related to a person's ability to engage in a variety of life activities, including work. In many cases, the goal of the state-federal program is to help the person with a disability achieve an optimal level of functioning with major life activities, including the return to the most appropriate level of work.

In the arena of workers' compensation, an insurance program administered by individual states, there are up to 50 different approaches (plus a few federal compensation programs) with the goal of returning persons who have been injured to the world of work. The issue of transferability takes on many forms across these state programs since individual state legislatures have defined the return-to-work process differently.

Transferability, when applied to legal cases, takes on an even broader application, depending largely on the inclinations of the court, the judge or hearing officer, and the attorneys managing the case. Forensic rehabilitation professionals have used a variety of individualistic methods and procedures in the development of a case for either deposition or trial.

For purposes of this discussion, the "Social Security model" will serve as the standard (or benchmark) frame-of-reference for both the definition of transferability and how the process can be applied to most cases. The reasons for selecting the Social Security program as a major referent are several. First, the social security program has a rich and long history of addressing disability issues, including the consideration of whether or not a person can work with or following injury. Second, the amount of people who have been "processed" through the SSDI program now numbers in the millions. A very substantial process for determining disability and the capacity of a person to be able to work has been implemented for over forty years. Third, the Code of Federal Regulations (Part 404, in particular) defines in great detail issues related to disability, and the disability determination process. The language is exact and provides a well-defined guideline in arriving at the outcome of the process. The SSA program is generally considered the "granddaddy" of many rehabilitation (or return-to-work) programs and has served as a benchmark from which other related state and federal programs have been developed. For these reasons, the SSA regulations for the SSDI and SSI (supplemental security income) programs will be a major referent for this discussion on transferability.

Social Security Disability Law and Disability Insurance (SSDI)

Title II of the Social Security Act (42 C.R.F.) covers old age, survivors, and disability insurance benefits for wage earners and their dependants. For the Social Security representative (a person, often an attorney, who acts as the advocate for the person claiming disability in Social Security hearings), disability benefits will generate most if not all of the opportunities for representation under Title II. With that in mind, only Social Security Disability Insurance (SSDI) will be discussed. Representing a claimant seeking other benefits under Title II, such as retirement or survivors' benefits, requires an understanding of much of the same terminology and procedures, but also involves many unique aspects, which the representative would need to carefully consider before undertaking such a claim.

While the Social Security Act offers the framework for consideration of a claimant's disability, the regulations provide a detailed interpretation of the law, and the Social Security representative will find most of what he/she needs to assist a claimant on obtaining benefits within the regulations. The regulations pertaining to SSDI may be found in Title 20 of the Code of Federal Regulations, part 404. A copy of the regulations are an essential part of the representative's resources and may be obtained from the Government Printing Office or online at http://www.ssa.gov/OP_Home/cfr20/404/404-0000.htm.

The Social Security Administration's Rulings also provide an important source of information. The Rulings offer interpretations of the regulations and are binding on the Social Security Administration (SSA). Cumulative editions of rulings are available from the Government Printing Office, but because of the rather convoluted nature of the rulings, the representative would be advised to refer to one of the various publications available on Social Security representation for a list of important rulings. Eligibility for Social Security Disability Insurance benefits is dependent on the claimant meeting two basic requirements:

(1) Sufficient earnings with payments into social security to be insured for disability; and

(2) A finding of disability (42 C.F.R.).

Of course, the claimant also must apply for benefits. Unlike the Supplemental Security Income (SSI) program, a needs based program that does not require a work history (see below), SSDI is not a federal welfare system where eligibility is based in part on need. SSDI is a part of Social Security's insurance system, and, like private insurance programs, requires a claimant to have paid into the system to be entitled to benefits. If the claimant has made sufficient contributions to Social Security and has a disability, eligibility generally is established. The determination of whether or not the claimant has a disability usually represents the more important and difficult issue of SSDI eligibility.

Supplemental Security Income (SSI)

Title XVI of the Social Security Act (42, 1381-1383d), commonly known as the Supplemental Security Income (SSI) program, is a federal welfare program that provides financial assistance to the elderly, blind, and people with disabilities based on need. In most cases, if a claimant is over 65, blind, or has a disability and meets certain income and resource limits, he/she will be eligible for cash and other forms of assistance such as Medicaid. As mentioned in the section discussing SSDI, while the statute establishes the basic tenets of the law, the federal regulations are of primary importance in implementing the statute. Anyone who intends to provide representation to a SSI claimant would be advised to become familiar with the regulations, which may be found in title 20 of the code of Federal Regulations, part 416. Ready access to a copy of the regulations is a must for the Social Security representative. And as with SSDI, the rulings concerning SSI are an important source of information.

The basic eligibility requirements for SSI can be summarized as follows:

(a) The claimant is

(1) Age 65 or older;

(2) Blind; or

(3) Has a disability.

(b) The claimant is a resident of the United States, and is

(1) A citizen or national of the US;

(2) An alien lawfully admitted for permanent residence in the US;

(3) An alien permanently residing in the U.S, under color of law; or

(4) A child or armed forces personnel living overseas.

(c) The claimant's income does not exceed the permitted limits;

(d) The claimant's resources do not exceed the permitted limits;

(e) When drug addiction or alcoholism is a contributing factor to the claimant's disability, the claimant has not previously received a total of 36 months of SS benefits when appropriate treatment was available or 36 months of SSI benefits on the basis of disability where drug addiction or alcohol was a contributing factor material to the determination of disability;

(f) The claimant files an application for SSI benefits (20, 416.202).

Basic Definition of Disability

The disability standard for Social Security Disability Insurance (SSDI) benefits and Supplemental Security Income (SSI) benefits (where disability is the basis for eligibility) is the same. Parallel citations for both programs are provided for the reader's reference. To be eligible for SSDI or SSI benefits, the claimant must meet the statutory definition for disability.

The claimant shall be determined to be under a disability only if his/her physical or mental impairment or impairments are of such severity that he/she is not only unable to do his/her previous work but cannot, considering his/her age, education, and work experience, engage in any other kind of substantial gainful work which exists in the national economy, regardless of whether such work exists in the immediate area in which he/she lives or whether a specific job vacancy exists for him/her, or whether he/she would be hired if he applied for work. For purposes of the preceding sentence (with respect to any individual), "work which exists in the national economy" means work which exists in significant numbers either in the region where such individual lives or in several regions in the country (42, 423(d)(2)(a), 1382c(a)(3)(B)).

The regulations further define disability as the inability to do substantial gainful activity by reason of any medically determinable physical or mental impairment that can be expected to result in death or that has lasted or can be expected to last for a continuous period of not less than 12 months. The impairment must be severe, which means the claimant cannot do his/her previous work or any other substantial gainful activity in the national economy (20, 404.1505).

The meaning of each of the relevant terms in the definition of disability is discussed infra, in conjunction with a discussion of the five steps in the evaluation process. Meeting the definition of disability can be very easy for some claimants and extremely difficult or impossible for other claimants.

Steps In Disability Determination

The regulations establish a five-step process to determine whether or not a claimant has a disability and is thus eligible for SSDI or SSI benefits (if other relevant requirements are met). It is important for the vocational expert to learn this five-step evaluation:

(1) The disability evaluation begins by determining whether the claimant is presently performing substantial gainful activity. If the claimant is doing substantial gainful activity, he/she does not have a disability.

(2) If the claimant is not engaged in substantial gainful activity, the SSA will consider the effect of the claimant's mental or physical impairment, or, if the claimant has more than one impairment, the combined effect of the claimant's impairments. The impairment must be severe and meet the duration requirement before the individual will be found to have a disability. Impairment is severe if it significantly limits the individual's physical or mental ability to do basic work activities. Age, education, and work experience are not considered at this step. If the impairment is not severe or does not meet the duration requirement, the claimant does not have a disability.

(3) If the claimant's impairment is severe and meets the durational requirement, the claimant will be found to have a disability if the impairment(s) is (are) listed in Appendix 1 of part 404 or is (are) equal to a listed impairment. Again, age, education, and work experience are not considered. If the impairment does not meet or equal a listed impairment, the claimant may still be considered to have a disability if he/she passes the next steps.

(4) If the claimant's impairment is severe and meets the duration requirement, the SSA will then review the claimant's residual functional capacity and the physical and mental demands of the claimant's past work. If the claimant can still do the work he/she did in the past, the claimant does not have a disability.

(5) If the claimant cannot perform any work he/she has done in the past, the SSA will evaluate the claimant's residual work capacity and the claimant's age, education, and past work experience to determine if the

claimant can perform other work. If the SSA decides the claimant cannot perform any other work, the claimant has a disability (20, 404.1520).

1. Is the Claimant Engaged in Substantial Gainful Activity?

Substantial gainful activity (SGA) is defined as work that

> (a) Involves doing significant and productive physical or mental duties; and

> (b) Is done (or intended) for pay or profit (20,404.1510).

Work may be "substantial" even if it is only part-time, the pay is less, or the claimant works fewer hours or has less responsibility than before the onset of the impairment. "Gainful" activity merely includes work activity if it would normally result in pay or profit, even if it does not (20,404.1572). Earnings may also show that the claimant is currently engaged in SGA (20,404.1574).

Issues concerning Substantial Gainful Activity usually involve whether the claimant is able to engage in SGA, not whether he/she is currently performing SGA. While the determination of the claimant's ability to perform Substantial Gainful Activity does not really become an issue until step four in the process, a full discussion of the issue is presented here in the interest of clarity.

If the individual is able to engage in SGA, he/she will be found not to have a disability. Work that by itself may not be SGA nevertheless may be evidence of the ability to perform SGA. All medical and vocational evidence will be used to determine if the claimant is able to engage in SGA (20,404.1571). When determining whether a claimant is able to engage in SGA, the agency will consider:

> (a) The nature of the claimant's work- the use of experience and skills, supervision, responsibility, or substantial contribution to the business all tend to show the ability to perform SGA.

> (b) How well the claimant performs - satisfactory work usually is evidence of the ability to do SGA, unless the claimant requires supervision or assistance above that of other employees in order to perform simple or ordinary tasks. Doing simple, undemanding tasks, which are of little use to an employer does not show the ability to perform SGA.

> (c) Work done under special conditions- if a claimant is working in a sheltered workshop or hospital, the work may be SGA even though the work takes into account the impairment.

> (d) Self-employment- supervising, managing, advising, or other significant personal services may show the ability to do SGA.

> (e) Time spent in work- The SSA evaluates the work done, regardless of whether or not the claimant spends more or less time at work than others who are not impaired (20,404.1573).

Earnings are another way the SSA determines whether the claimant may perform SGA. Substantial earnings usually equate to SGA, but the converse is not always true. If the claimant is forced to stop work after a short period, which would be labeled an unsuccessful work attempt, those earnings generally will not be evidence of the ability to perform SGA. The SSA only considers earnings from work activity. The regulations establish certain dollar amounts, which ordinarily show either that the individual has or has not engaged in SGA (20.404.1574).

2. Is the Claimant's Impairment Severe and Is the Duration Requirement Met?

Severe Impairment— If the claimant has an impairment that significantly limits the ability to perform basic work activities, the impairment is severe (20,404.1521). Generally, only impairments that are slight and only have a minor impact on the claimant's ability to work will be labeled non-severe. A reduction in the claimant's residual functional capacity, discussed infra, is usually sufficient to show severity. No separate proof is required.

Duration Requirements—Generally, unless the impairment is expected to result in death, it must have lasted or be expected to last for a continuous period of at least 12 months (20,404.1509). The duration requirement cannot be met by combining the duration of two or more unrelated severe impairments that by themselves do not meet the 12 month requirement. If the severity of the impairment is dependent upon the combined effect of two or more concurrent impairments, the combined effect must last for 12 months; if one or more impairments end or improve making the combined effect non-severe, then the duration requirement will not be met (20,404.1522).

3. Does the Claimant's Impairment Meet or Equal a Listed Impairment?

A disabling impairment is an impairment (or combination of impairments) that, in and of itself, is so severe that it meets or equals a set of criteria in the Listings of Impairments in Appendix 1 of Subpart P of Part 404 of Chapter 20 of the C.F.R. or that, when considered with the claimant's age, education, and work experience, would result in a finding that the claimant otherwise has a disability (20,404.1511).

Showing an impairment—If the claimant is not performing substantial gainful activity, the agency will always look first at the physical or mental impairment(s) to determine if the individual has a disability. The impairment must result from anatomical, physiological, or psychological abnormalities, which can be shown by medically acceptable clinical and laboratory diagnostic techniques. A physical or mental impairment must be established by medical evidence consisting of signs, symptoms, and laboratory findings, not just by the claimant's statement of symptoms (20,404.1508).

Evidence of Impairment—The agency requires the claimant to prove that he/she has a disability (or blindness). This is done through medical and other evidence. Evidence includes medical signs and laboratory findings, medical history and opinions, the claimant's own statements, the decisions of other agencies, and other information. The claimant must furnish any information requested to assist in the determination. The SSA will develop a complete medical history (going back at least 12 months) for the claimant from information provided from the claimant and by making its own contacts.

The agency may have difficulty obtaining information from certain sources and is not obligated to even try to obtain information from sources it has had trouble with in the past. Therefore, it is advisable for the representative and claimant to work with the agency adjudicator handling the case to be sure all information is made available to the decision maker. Failure to cooperate with the agency means they will make their decision based on the available information (20.404.1516).

4. Can the Claimant Perform Past Work?

If the claimant's impairment(s) does not meet or equal a listed impairment, the disability determination agency will then determine if the claimant can perform any work which he/she has done in the past when the claimant's Residual Functional Capacity is taken into account. If the claimant can perform the work he/she has done in the past despite his/her impairment, the claimant will be found not to have a disability (20.404.1520e). Age, education, and work experience are not considered when the question is whether the claimant can do his/her past work. The only issue is whether the claimant has retained the ability to do his/her past work (20,404.1560b).

Residual Functional Capacity—The claimant's Residual Functional Capacity (RFC) is assessed to determine if the claimant has a disability based on vocational standards. RFC refers to what the claimant can still do despite his/her limitations. All relevant evidence will be considered when determining a claimant's RFC. Besides the claimant's impairment, the agency will look at any related symptoms, such as pain, which may impose physical or mental limitations on the claimant's ability in the work setting. Observations and descriptions by physicians, family, friends, the claimant, and other persons may also be used. The RFC assessment is used to determine both whether the claimant can perform past work and what types of work the claimant may be able to do despite his/her impairment(s). Only after the claimant's RFC is analyzed in combination with the claimant's vocational background is the disability determination made (20,404.1545a).

5. Can the Claimant Perform Other Work?

If the agency finds that the claimant cannot do the work he/she has done in the past, the claimant's Residual Functional Capacity will be considered in conjunction with the claimant's age, education, and work experience to determine if the claimant can do other work. Other work refers to jobs that exist in significant numbers in the national economy (20,404.1560c). The claimant's age, education, and work experience are extremely important at this step in the disability determination; each variable is discussed in the regulations (20,404.1563). Generally, older claimants and those with less education will be likely to be incapable of performing other work in the national economy. Work experience, which involves unskilled labor and nontransferable skills, will also increase the likelihood that the claimant will be unable to do other work.

In deciding whether a claimant has a disability, the disability determination agency will use the Medical-Vocational Guidelines as set in Appendix 2 of Part 404 of the regulations. The Guidelines, commonly referred to as the grids, establish a framework for the decision makers when presented with a claimant. The grids reflect three levels of RFC- the ability to perform sedentary, light, or medium work. Age, education and work experience are incorporated into the grids to guide the agency in its determination. While the grids are useful for the decision makers and for the representative, they do not work for all claimants. If the circumstances of a particular claimant do not fit the grids, the rules will not be used. Instead, all relevant factors will be considered in determining if the claimant has a disability (20,404.1569).

The skill level of the claimant may influence a claimant's ability to perform other work. The main concern is the transferability of skills. The more skills held by a claimant, the more likely there would be other work he/she can perform (20,404.1568).

Physical exertional limitations, which impact a claimant's ability to perform work, are considered in regard to the strength demands of a job. The grids will be the initial source of guidance for exertional limitations and will dictate a decision if the claimant fits a grid profile. A claimant may also have nonexertional limitations, which impact the claimant's ability to work. Such nonexertional limitations will take a claimant out of the grids and require a more thorough analysis of the claimant's ability to perform other work by using other sections of the regulations (20,404.1569a).

SSDI - The Work Requirement

Besides having a disability, a claimant for SSDI benefits must be insured for disability benefits and be "fully insured." The claimant's work history generally will determine whether or not the claimant is properly insured to be eligible for SSDI benefits.

A claimant is fully insured if he/she has acquired a sufficient number of quarters of coverage (QCs). QCs are credited to a claimant for periods of work in which the claimant paid Social Security taxes. The calculation of QCs varies depending on whether the work period was before or after 1978 (20,404.140-146). A claimant needs a minimum of six QCs but not more than forty QCs to be fully insured (20.404.110b). Generally, if the claimant has one QC for each year after the claimant's 21st birthday, he/she is fully insured.

To be insured for the purpose of establishing a period of disability or becoming entitled to disability insurance benefits, the claimant must meet one of four rules, which may be summarized as follows:

(1) The 20/40 requirement – The claimant must have 20 quarters of coverage in the 40-quarter period ending with the quarter in which the claimant acquired the disability. This basically means the claimant must have worked for a total of five years in the last ten years prior to the quarter in which he/she acquired the disability. This rule is the most frequently utilized to establish disability insured status.

(2) Acquired a disability before age 31– The claimant must have quarters of coverage in at least one-half of the quarters between age twenty-one and the quarter he/she acquired the disability, or a minimum of six quarters of coverage.

(3) Period of disability before age 31 – The claimant acquired the disability at age 31 or later after having a previous period of disability before age 31 for which the claimant was only insured under Rule number 2 above.

(4) Statutorily blind – the claimant's vision is impaired so as to meet the regulatory standards (20,404.130).

While a dispute may arise as to whether the claimant is fully insured or whether he/she fits within one of the above rules for disability insured status, the determination of disability is usually the heart and soul of the issue of eligibility. If a claim is denied because the SSA determines the claimant lacks fully insured or disability insured status, the representative should be prepared to fully analyze the claimant's work history and the relevant regulations and rulings to determine the propriety of the SSA's determination.

Waiting Period

An additional requirement for SSDI benefits is that the claimant must have had a disability for five full consecutive months before he/she is eligible. The five months begin in the first month in which the claimant is both insured for disability and fully insured (20,404.315a). By requiring five "full" months, the regulations extend most waiting periods for more than five months. If the claim is filed on a day other than the first day of the month, the waiting period will include the days left in the month of application plus five full months.

No benefits will be paid during the waiting period. However, SSDI benefits may be paid to a claimant for the 12 months preceding the filing of the claim. The waiting period may begin up to 17 months before the date of the application, but no earlier. While the SSI program does not require a waiting period, SSI benefits are only payable from the first day of the month following the date of application (20,416.501), as opposed to SSDI's possibility for 12 months of retroactive payments.

Blindness

A claimant will be eligible for SSDI benefits if he/she is statutorily blind, which means the claimant's vision is 20/200 or less in the better eye with the use of corrective lenses, or the claimant's field of vision is no greater the 20 degrees (20,404.1581). A claimant under the age 55 must be unable to perform substantial gainful activity (20,404,1581). A claimant over age 55 who is engaged in substantial gainful activity may still be eligible for SSDI benefits (but not cash benefits) if he/she is blind and unable to use skills acquired in previous work activity (20,404.1582-3). Even if a claimant is not statutorily blind, the claimant's visual impairment(s) may be adverse enough for the claimant to be found to have a disability under the regular disability requirements.

Transferability

The most prominent user of TSAs have been professionals related to SSDI (Blackwell, Field, & Field, 1992; Field, & Weed, 1988; Hannings, Ash, & Sinick, 1972). Transferable skills analysis, or transferability, is the process by which similar, related, or new jobs are identified for a person following injury or disability. These jobs are both consistent and compatible with previous work experience and fall within the range of residual post-injury functioning of the claimant. The return-to-work movement of the 1980s (mostly through state legislatively mandated rehabilitation programs) also utilized various notions of transferability for the injured worker. A natural extension of these legal mandates was the utilization of TSA procedures in the determination of reduced and/or lost employment and the diminution of wages in cases involving personal injury cases. In this author's opinion, the main referent and foundation of the transferability process has always been and will continue to be the disability determination program (SSDI) of the Social Security Administration. Before the central issue of transferability is addressed, consideration and review must be directed to information related to the disability determination process, the legal basis for transferability, and relevant sources of occupational and employment information.

SSDI and Transferability (Definition)

Reference Part 404 of the Code of Federal Regulations, 20: 1995.

> *(d) [Transferability refers to] the skills that can be used in other jobs, when the skilled and semi-skilled work activity you did in past work can be used to meet the requirements of skilled work semi-skilled work activities of other jobs or kinds of work. Transferability is the most . . . meaningful among jobs in which (I) the same or a lesser degree of skill is required; (ii) the same or similar tools and machines are used; and (iii) the same or similar raw materials, products, processes, or services are involved."* (Part 404.1568, p. 341).

Part 404.1566 provides administrative notice (d) of the *Dictionary of Occupational Titles* and the *Occupational Outlook Handbook*, both Department of Labor publications as *"reliable job information"* to be used in the determination process. (p. 340).

Part 404.1566 also establishes the use of a vocational expert *(e) "if the issue in determining whether....your work skills can be used in other work and the specific occupations in which they can be used."* (p. 340).

Compensation and Legal Cases (Moving Toward the O*NET)

In the arena of worker's compensation, usually an insurance program administered by individual states, there are up to 50 different approaches (plus a few federal compensation programs) with the goal of returning persons who have been injured to the world of work. The issue of transferability takes on many forms across these state programs since individual state legislatures have defined the return-to-work process differently. In the area of long-term disability, perhaps there is a greater emphasis on employability – or just being able to return to employment. With that objective, the O*NET occupational resources becomes much more relevant – such as finding occupations and viewing labor and wage surveys.

Transferability when applied to legal cases takes on an even broader application – depending largely on the inclinations of the court, the judge or hearing officer, and the attorneys managing the case. The variety of cases may include situations involving children, catastrophic injury, household issues, future lost earnings and evaluating employment potential (or the loss thereof). Forensic rehabilitation professionals have used TSA and employability methods and procedures in the development of a cases for either deposition or trial.

Occupational information is needed in a variety of settings, depending on the client situation and the laws or regulations that govern the case. It cannot be assumed that transferability, for instance, needs to be applied in every case, or in the same manner for those cases requiring job selection. The table below summarizes the various programs and their respective requirements in order to illustrate this point. The Social Security Disability Insurance program generally requires a TSA related to the determination of disability, and those decisions are almost always predicated on the DOT database (the SSA 00-4p ruling not withstanding).

Often when assisting a worker/client with an acquired disability, (whether from the state/federal vocational rehabilitation agency, an SSDI applicant, the workers' compensation system, or referrals from the VA), the most appropriate place to start the vocational exploration process may be with a transferable skills analysis. If the worker has employable skills that have been previously demonstrated, the chances of getting the worker back to work are greatly enhanced. The worker will most likely be able to start to work at a much higher wage than if they were required to undergo retraining. Many workers like the idea of retraining but are unwilling to return to work at a wage that is lower than what they had previously enjoyed prior to the onset of their disability. Again referring to the table, some programs could be well served by using both the DOT and O*NET. The requirement of developing a TSA clearly depends upon the type of case and the desired or expected outcome.

The TSA process is a highly effective tool in establishing if the worker has skills that can be transferred to another position resulting in quicker placements and the return to self-sufficiency for the worker. The TSA will also be very useful in assisting those workers who have exited the workforce and have been drawing social security disability income. Now that the Ticket to Work program has been enacted (see Chapter 1), there are tens of thousands of potential client/workers who may be helped to return to productivity and good wages. The vocational consultant who overlooks the potential of TSAs in these return-to-work programs will be doing a disservice to the clients. Likewise, the vocational consultant who ignores the resources available through the O*NET may be bypassing some very valuable and relevant information on occupations that could prove to be helpful to the client. On the other hand, cases involving children or clients with a catastrophic and/or long-term disability would not as likely benefit from a TSA analysis. The experience and judgment of the consultant should prevail in this decision-making process. For a more complete discussion of these and related forensic issues, see the chapters in this text on these issues.

America's Job Bank and America's Career Information Network

Along with the development of the O*NET, the federal government has also developed two online resources that are consistent with the fluid and dynamic rational for future development in occupational information.

Table 6.1
The Application of Occupational Information in Rehabilitation Settings

Setting/Program	Requirement	TSA	Occ. Database
Social Security/SSDI	Past relevant work or other work	Yes	DOT/other
Workers' Compensation	Return-to-Work (Job Placement)	Yes	DOT
Long Term Disability	Employability	Y/N	DOT/O*NET
Personal Injury Cases			
Injury to Children	Evaluating Potential	No	DOT/O*NET
Work Place Injury	RTW/Employability	Yes	DOT/O*NET
Catastrophic Injury	RTW/Employability	Y/N	DOT/O*NET
Wrongful Death	Future Lost Earnings	No	O*NET
Divorce Proceedings	Evaluating Employment Potential	Y/N	DOT/O*NET

The AJB is a listing of jobs that are available for workers in all geographical areas of the nation. Employers (those who list job openings), as well as potential employees (job seekers), have free and easy access to this ever-expanding database. The ACINET contains a wealth of information about existing jobs, wage surveys by geographical areas, and demand and trend information.

Vocational Expert Testimony: DOT vs. O*Net

The work activity of the vocational expert has been obscured with confusion over continued use of the DOT versus the switch to the O*NET. The transition between the old to the new has not been as smooth as administrators had hoped; furthermore, it appears that will take a few years before there is a satisfactory solution to the issue. (Table 6.2).

The Social Security Administration, which administers the vocational expert program under the Bureau of Hearings and Appeals, has relied heavily on the *Dictionary of Occupational Titles* (the resource is even listed in the *Federal Regulations* as a resource in determining SSDI cases). With the growing obsolescence of the DOT, and a corresponding article in the *Occupational Outlook Quarterly* (latest printing), DOL has announced that the "O*NET replaces the *Dictionary of Occupational Titles*" (M. Mariani, personal communication, 1999). This announcement has created somewhat of a quandary for the SSA disability determination program. Since the new O*NET really did not provide a database that would effectively replace the old DOT, especially within the legal restraints of the regulations for transferability, what was SSA to do? Some vocational experts (VEs) began to offer testimony that was not always related to the constructs and language of the DOT. As a result, several Administrative Law Judges (ALJs) in various federal circuits issued rulings – sometimes allowing departures from the DOT, and sometimes not. In those cases where the DOT was allowed to be "rebutted," the rulings were generally referred to a "acquiescence rulings" (ARs), which were binding in only that particular circuit. The most clearly stated AR was the case of vocational expert testimony and the *Dictionary of Occupational Titles* (*Haddock v. Apfe*l, 1998). The court held that the:

> DOT {does not} trump a VE's testimony when there is a conflict about the nature of a job. Rather, the court explained that it was merely holding that the ALJ must investigate and obtain a reasonable explanation for any conflicts found.

Table 6.2
Comparison of DOT vs. O*NET

Item	DOT	O*NET
12,741	Titles	@1,000
72 Worker Traits	Factors	@450 Elements
Scaled Ratings Generally Quantitative	Measures	Some Scaled Ratings Very Qualitative
General Testing Applies	Vocational Assessment	Testing/Assessment Somewhat Impossible
Assessment, Evaluation, Transferability, Job Matching, Guidance	Applications	Guidance & Counseling America's Job Bank America's Career InfoNet
GOE, WF, SIC, SOC, Census	Linked Codes	SOC, MO, Census, AJB, ACINET
Growing Obsolescence	The Future	Dynamic, Revision in Progress

Note. Adapted from Weed & Field (2001), p. 105.

In other words, the SSA will continue to expect VE's to use the 1991 Edition of the DOT in determining testimony, unless an ALJ is satisfied that any alternative system (e.g,. O*NET) used by the VE is satisfactorily explained. The situation is best explained as follows:

> *The only good, reliable information upon which the vocational expert could rely in describing jobs that exist in the local economy as they are generally performed is a vocational analysis performed by the expert by on-the-job inspection and observation of the job. The Dictionary of Occupational Titles is developed from 50,000 such analyses. The expert should be asked to produce the job analysis for the job about which he or she is testifying if the testimony conflicts with the description of that job as found in the Dictionary of Occupational Titles. The Appeals Council has stated that if an expert is not relying on the Dictionary of Occupational Titles, he/she must be able to show that the opinion is derived from onsite work analysis or other reliable information and testify as to the source of that information.* (Social Security Practice Guide at 15.05[3][I].

In a more recent ruling (SSR 00-4p), the Administration addressed the issue of resolving conflicts in the use of occupational information by the vocational expert. The DOT, which has been the standard bearer for occupational information in cases that require a determination by the Office of Hearings and Appeals (primarily in SSDI cases), the VE may use other occupational information – other than that information supplied by the DOT. However, when the VE's information is in conflict with the DOT, the adjudicator must elicit a reasonable explanation for the conflict before relying on the VE's evidence to support a determination or decision about whether the claimant has a disability. Reasonable explanations for the conflict might include any of the following: (a) information about a particular occupation may not be included in the DOT, (b) information about a particular job's requirements may not be included in the DOT, (c) requirements for a job may differ from workplace to workplace and among geographical regions, and (d) other occupational data sources may provide more specific or complete information about a job. Other sources of information do not automatically "trump" the information in the DOT. On the contrary, when conflicting information is provided, the adjudicator must question the VE for a reasonable explanation for the alternate occupational information. A case in point might be the use of the O*NET database which provides occupational information quite differently when compared to the DOT. While the O*Net database does not lend itself easily to the process of transferable skills analysis (as has been traditionally processed with DOT data), it was assumed that the O*NET would eventually replace the DOT.

The continued use of the DOT is best legitimized as a result of this ruling. SSA clearly supports the revision and/or further development of sections of the O*NET database which will permit a complete switch from the DOT to the O*NET. In the meantime, research is under way (involving both SSA and DOL) to resolve the problem of identifying selected factors from the O*NET that could be operationally defined and measured for the purpose of transferable skills analysis. This research endeavor will probably be completed within the next three to five years (Cannelongo, 2001). At the time of this updated text (2012), little of practical value has been accomplished. Until such time, however, rehabilitation consultants and other professionals will need to continue using the DOT while drawing from the useful sections of the O*NET database. As in the past, and in view of the Daubert and Kumho rulings (Field et al., 2000; Field & Stein, 2002), rehabilitation professionals will still be required to follow some methodological approach on transferability when preparing testimony.

The Dictionary of Occupational Titles

The DOT was last published in 1991 in the form of a 4th revision, although only about 20% of the titles were updated from the 1977 edition of the DOT. The publication (two volumes) consists of 1404 pages containing job listings (a specific DOT title and code for each job) and descriptions with only a few defined characteristics for each title. Specifically, the DOT contains:

1. 12,741 coded titles and descriptions.

2. An organizational format for jobs according to categories (from the general), divisions, and groups (to the specific) as identified by the first three digits of the DOT code.

3. A job title cross reference to the Guide to Occupational Titles (GOE) and selected worker traits (strength, reasoning-math-language of the GED, and specific vocational training).

4. Information of the Date of Last Update (DLU) for each job title and description.

5. A set of appendices including information on Data-People-Things arrangement, definitions of strength, GED and SVP, and an explanation of the revisions that were contained in the 4th edition.

6. An alphabetical index of all job titles.

7. A coding of all jobs arranged by Industrial Designation.

A major problem and concern related to the DOT (1991) is the growing obsolescence of the occupational information. Unfortunately, this "static" (i.e., non-changing) database is no longer being developed, enhanced or supported by the U.S. Department of Labor. Over time this has created a serious problem for practicing rehabilitation professional, especially those who are involved in forensic cases in such areas as social security, workers' compensation programs, and legal cases representing clients involved in personal injury, re-employment, wrongful discharge, and the like. A near crisis situation exists with the Social Security Administration where more that one million SSDI cases alone are adjudicated each year – each case under the federal regulations requiring an analysis of the claimant's transferable skills.

The Classification of Jobs (COJ)

The *COJ 2000* (5th ed., 1999) was based upon data and information contained in the 1991 *Dictionary of Occupational Titles* and the released *O*NET* database (Occupational Information Network, 1998). *The Transitional COJ* (2004) is an extension of the *COJ 2000* in that the same 1991 DOT database is referenced along with a current version the O*NET database. This resource is particularly useful for rehabilitation and career guidance professionals who work with persons with disabilities and/or persons attempting to narrow a career choice. With respect to rehabilitation issues, such as transferability, job matching, estimating loss of employment, and estimating lost earnings capacity, this resource can prove invaluable to the professional making these kinds of judgments. The following pages will provide additional information about the databases and their arrangements and, in particular, a suggested format and guide on "how" this resource can be utilized in resolving issues related to forensic rehabilitation.

The Occupational Network Service (O*NET)

During the last two decades, the federal government, primarily the U.S Department of Labor, decided not to create a fifth edition of the DOT. As an alternative, a new format of occupational information was planned and developed through a contractual arrangement primarily with the Utah Department of Economic Security.

The O*NET Database was developed with a "content model" (see Appendix H) that arranges occupational information into one of six groups. Of the approximamately 1000 occupations listed in the O*NET database, each occupation has the potential to be rated on approximately 450 "elements" (depending on how one counts), which are scattered across the six groups. Each element, which is roughly equivalent to the old worker traits, is generally rated on the level of ability to perform (0 - 7); the importance of the ability (0 - 5), and how frequent the activity is performed (1 - 4). This general structure and the high number of elements make it somewhat impossible for the rehabilitation consultant to complete a transferable skills analysis by using the O*NET, that is, in the manner that has been used with the DOT. The format does provide a considerable amount of information, however, and can be very useful in finding occupations. Such an approach will require some innovative strategies and "out-of-the-box" thinking in order to benefit from what the O*NET offers. In the meantime, SSA, in cooperation with DOL, is proceeding to address the issues related to transferability and the O*NET. This proposed research will address such issues as identifying the requirements of jobs, the development of job analyses instruments designed to measure job requirements, the gathering of occupational information about jobs in the U.S. economy, and the analysis of the results that will classify occupations into a database that can be used with and for people with disabilities – especially in the area of transferable skills analysis. Another issue to be addressed is to redefine and quantify the O*NET occupational elements more closely with the older worker trait factors of the DOT. This step would allow for more accurate determination of employment disabilities usually associated with SSA's regulatory language utilized in matching jobs to persons with disabilities.

Occupational Information Development Advisory Panel

In 2008, the Office of Program Development and Research (OPDR) established the Occupational Information Development Advisory Panel (OIDAP) for the purpose of developing an Occupational Information

System (OIS) under the direction of the Office of Vocational Resources Development (OVRD) which would eventually replace the *Dictionary of Occupational Titles* (DOT). Since the Department of Labor (DOL) had decided not to update the *DOT* from the 1991 version, and replaced the *DOT* with the *O*Net* system, the Social Security Administration has embarked upon and sponsored the pending development of the OIS. The projected date for the completion of the OIS is not clear (at this date), but has already created a significant amount of study and subsequent research on the project. Eventually, the OIS will replace the *DOT* as the essential occupational data source to be used in steps four and five of the disability determination process.

How to Use the O*NET Database

With a little practice, the O*NET is relatively easy to use. In fact, the information about the O*NET contained in this publication is minimal since O*NET Online is so easy to use. It will take several hours initially to work through the multiple screens in order to get a feel of the O*NET's capacities and resources. Further time will be required in order to understand how the program works and what information can be retrieved from the system. Information about the O*NET model and its structure can be found at http://online.ONETcenter.org. It is a good idea to click on the available tabs and scroll through the many screens and get a general notion about how O*NET is structured, including the many linked resources

The next step is to study the structure for identifying, evaluating, and selecting jobs, including survey and wage data. This webpage is divided by three different options: Find Occupations, Skills Search, and Crosswalk. There is a link to these functions from the main menu, or go to http://online.ONETcenter.org

The Transitional COJ (2004)

For the rehabilitation professional, especially one who is involved in forensic issues, it is imperative that access to all current, reliable, and relevant information be available for the formulation and development of opinions related to a case in question. One of the most critical issues confronting a forensic rehabilitation professional is the issue of a person's transferable skills analysis following an injury or disability. Historically, the rehabilitation professional has relied heavily on previous editions of the DOT (including the worker trait data) to formulate an opinion of a claimant's ability to return to work and earn wages. Unfortunately, the 1998 release of the O*NET database does not permit an easy and logical way to determine the TSA of a person. As noted above, the O*NET contains about 450 "elements" potentially related to a particular job. Furthermore, many of the factors have no rating, either quantitatively or qualitatively, thus making it virtually impossible to utilize these factors in the traditional sense with respect to Transferable Skills Analysis (TSA).

It is the opinion of the authors, and the primary reason for the publication of this resource, that the 1991 DOT database and the full range of the worker trait factors as presented in the 1992 edition of the Classification of Jobs are still useful (and sometimes required) in order for the rehabilitation professional to address issues related to job choice, transferable skills analysis, and estimation of earnings capacity. In one sense, it is unfortunate that the DOT is now somewhat dated, and secondly, that the O*NET database fails to provide the essential information needed to assist in making proper decisions. The future potential and utility of the O*NET database is becoming more apparent as further development and subsequent releases are achieved. In the meantime it seems essential that the O*NET database must be recognized for its officially sanctioned presence (by the federal government) and may be expected (and/or required) to be utilized in any work product by a rehabilitation professional. As a minimum, it is imperative that a rehabilitation professional know about and employ the O*NET database as expeditiously as possible. The *Transitional COJ* presents two methods that achieve two objectives: (1) the professional can use the O*NET database to identify jobs, and (2) the professional still has access to the DOT database that has direct applicability to such issues as transferable skills analysis and job matching. Two different methods (or approaches) will be discussed, which highlight the options for finding occupations.

The primary characteristics of *The Transitional COJ* are best represented as outlined in the "contents" page of this resource.

Section 1 contains much of the same information as in previous editions of the COJ and is formatted to match-up with the TSA worksheet. The final two columns contain a crosswalk to the O*NET code and title.

Section 2 provides a crosswalk of DOT codes to multiple O*NET codes, and light and sedentary titles by work fields, and also a listing of light and sedentary unskilled DOT titles.

Section 3 consists of several appendices containing more descriptive information on the worker traits, the arrangement of work field and SOC codes, two case illustrations on how to find occupations using both databases (DOT and the O*NET), and a comprehensive summary of the O*NET database.

Explanation of Codes

The four occupational codes described below are the codes that are linked to one another in this resource. The codes are:

Dictionary of Occupational Titles

The nine-digit code is assigned to each of the 12,741 titles contained in the 1991 edition of the DOT. A detailed explanation of this code is presented on pages xvii to xxxvii of Vol. 1 of the DOT (4th edition). The *Dictionary* consists of two volumes of narrative descriptions of each of the titles along with the strength, GED (math, reasoning, language), and SVP of the worker traits.

Work Fields

All DOT titles are clustered within one of the 100 work fields. The work field code is discussed in the *Revised Handbook for Analyzing Jobs* (1992) and displays an arrangement for grouping similar jobs by work tools, materials, aides, and behaviors. A more detailed presentation of the Work Fields, plus a listing of sedentary and lights jobs, can be found in *Work Fields: Codes and Definitions* (1993). This code is considered (Field, 2002) as the most valuable and useful code for transferable skills analysis since the jobs are essentially clustered by work skills.

O*NET Database

The O*NET code consists of 8 digits for approximately 1000 titles in the database. The federal government (DOL) did not publish this database as it is considered a "dynamic" file of occupational information. Access to this and related databases are available on the website free to any needing or wanting occupational information.

Standard Occupational Classification

The SOC (revised in 1998) corresponds directly to the new O*NET database. In fact, the SOC title code is the same as the O*NET code. The arrangement of this code is found in Appendix C of this book. The SOC code clusters information about the presence and availability of jobs in the U.S. economy. Labor market surveys and labor projections will be completed by the government using this code and arrangement.

Transferable Skills Analysis

The Traditional TSA vs. the O*NET Attempt

Like the two databases, the method of completing a "transferable skills analysis" is also in transition. The **first method** is basically one that has been used by professionals for the last three decades in a variety of settings. This basic "equal to or less than" rationale has been incorporated into many of the commercial job matching computer programs, which have been marketed to the rehabilitation community for over two decades. However, in a research report, Kontosh and Wheaton (2003) surveyed over 13,000 cases in which vocational experts did not use any of the software programs in 56% of these cases. While the "software" approach has proven useful in many cases, computerized printouts are apparently not essential in order to complete TSAs. This first method is basically a "manual" approach for completing the analysis (although the discontinued Labor Market Access program was a computerized version of this method). This method incorporated labor market information from the Bureau of Census and the Bureau of Labor Statistics. The only variation suggested in this resource is to rely more on labor market and wage information found in the online websites. Field (1999) always emphasized that the use of a computer program should be viewed as providing "benchmark" information and that counselor judgment should always supersede any computer output in the final determination of recommended jobs for a client.

The **second method** is an attempt to address transferability in a new light – namely, by using the O*NET database. This approach requires much more judgment on the part of the professional since quantifiable data are not yet available for the O*NET database (Truthan & Karman, 2003). This new database does provide a significant amount of information on occupations, which allows for a carefully reasoned approach for finding and describing reasonable occupations for a client. Clearly this method and approach will involve more information of a descriptive and qualitative nature rather than measurable results. The clinical judgment of the rehabilitation consultant will be paramount throughout the process.

Method #1: The Traditional DOT Approach

Transferability of work skills is the foundation of any attempt to identify similar or related jobs that are consistent with or equal to the functional skill levels of a worker. The process of TSA is important to career counseling and to issues related to finding jobs for people within the U.S. economy. Job matching requirements are essential in government-sponsored programs such as Social Security Disability Insurance, workers' compensation program within each state, and cases involving personal injury and/or product liability.

The transferable skills analysis is essentially a process by which jobs that are consistent with the worker's capabilities and functional restrictions (the worker's capacity to perform work may be reduced by limitations imposed from the results of a disease or injury) are identified. The TSA process, however, does not have to be complicated; in fact, following the seven basic steps listed below, while learning how to use this and other resources, will result in a quick and reasonably accurate analysis for matching jobs to a worker. The steps need to be followed in order:

Step 1: Identifying Jobs in a Person's Work History

Using the Transferable Work Skills Worksheet (published by E & F, Inc., Ref. W601), identify all the jobs that are relevant and meet at least the SVP level for each job (frivolous or short-term jobs should be ignored).

Step 2: Select an Occupational Code and Title

Using the DOT (Vols. 1 & 2), or the O*NET system from the government website (http://www.onetcenter.org), select a code and title for each job. A "base" or beginning code allows the user to now select a secondary code (for transferability and/or labor survey data). Using the alphabetical index in the DOT, look up the appropriate code and enter onto the Worksheet.

When using the O*NET database titles or codes, it is imperative to cross-reference back to the DOT database. This step is necessary since the worker trait information is required in order to complete a transferable skills analysis.

Step 3: Profile the Jobs

Fill in the appropriate columns of the worker trait factors by looking up the DOT code in Section 1 of *The Transitional COJ* and profile out the desired worker traits onto the work sheet. At the same time, enter the Work Field code since this code will be useful during the TSA process.

Step 4: Create an Unadjusted Vocational Profile (UVP)

Assuming that there are two or more jobs in the worker's job history, identify the highest level of demonstrated functioning from the work history profiles. For instance, if three different jobs had a strength rating of sedentary, light, and medium, the letter "M" would be entered in the "UVP" line on the worksheet. The same procedure would be used for all the worker traits.

Step 5: Creating the Residual Functional Capacity Profile (RFC)

Table 6.3
Suggested Use of Codes and Arrangements

Code/Arrangement	Primary Use	Secondary Use
DOT	Job definitions	Base Code
O*NET	Job definitions	Base Code
Work Fields	Transferability	Guidance/Counseling
SOC	Labor Surveys	Labor Projections

102

The RFC is merely an adjustment of the UVP line, taking into consideration any restrictions imposed by disease or injury. For instance, a worker who has been able to work at medium jobs pre-jury (an L 4-5 accident) now might be able to work at sedentary jobs only. Accordingly, the "M" factor would be adjusted to an "S" on the worksheet. The same procedure would be used in adjusting any or all of the other worker traits. Sources of information that would help decide any adjustment include medical or psychological reports and/or vocational evaluations.

Step 6: Finding Related or Similar Jobs

Finding similar or related job titles for a worker following disease or injury is not an exact science. Rather, the TSA process can result in the selection of some reasonable and common-sense selections that would be appropriate for the worker. Finding a job title "that make sense" can be achieved by following these three logical steps:

First, stay within the same occupational area that represents the primary job history of the worker. This is accomplished by simply looking for a job title by the first digit of the DOT code. For example, if the worker has held 2 or 3 jobs in the "machine trades" (Area 06), then it makes sense to attempt to find similar or related titles in the same "machine trades" area. This is a critical first step in assuring that new jobs will have the same general work requirements (aptitudes, knowledge, and capacities) as previous jobs. It does not make good sense, for example, to place a person in the "service" industry who has had 30 years of experience in the "machine trades."

Second, stay within the same work field, or one closely related. This step will ensure that a person with a good work history in machining (WF 057), for instance, will be able to transfer to similar or related job titles with the same or similar work skills (e.g., method or active verbs, machines, tools, equipment, and work aids). Remember, work skills are best represented by aptitudes, knowledge, and capacities related to a specific area of work. Identifying a job or jobs for a person with the same work skills as previously demonstrated makes good sense.

Third, identify a job title within the same occupational area and then the same work field that is equal to or less than the requirements of the various worker trait factors in the adjusted RFC profile.

By way of an **example**, assume that the worker has worked in a machine shop for the last thirty years and has sustained a back injury that has prevented him from doing any work requiring exertion other than sedentary or light work. Proceed to the listing of Light and Sedentary jobs as arranged by the Work Fields in Section 2. Notice that the first column is the Work Field code (WF) arranged chronologically. Proceed through the pages until the "057" jobs appear on page 2-11. There are exactly 52 job titles that fall within the 057 Work Field. Next identify the job title that begin with the digit "6" which represents the machine trades; there are exactly 38 job titles. Next, identify jobs that fall within the RFC restrictions for this worker, namely, the "light" exertional range. Note that all 38 job titles in this listing are "light."

This procedural approach quickly permits the user to move from all 12,741 job titles listed in the DOT to 38 job titles that fall within the worker's range of experience, skills, capacities, and functional restrictions. From these 38 job titles, the user would select the most appropriate by taking into account other relevant worker trait data and the preferences of the worker (if possible).

Step 7: Finding Jobs in the Local Labor Market

At this point in the process, regarding the job titles that are identified as job matches from the previous steps, 1-6 above are possibilities only and should be evaluated using common sense and good judgment, taking into account the appropriateness for the worker. Of special concern is the process of identifying a job title that actually exists within the local labor market and meets the transferability requirement for the worker. Assume that the job of "model maker" (DOT #693.680.010) was selected. In order to find this job title in a particular labor market, go to Section 1, pages 1–152 in order to obtain the corresponding O*NET code and title (O*NET #51406100, model maker, metal & plastic). Next, go to http://online. onetcenter.org for wage and employment information, or to the www.careeronestop.org website to check for occupations with this title, a full narrative description of the occupation, jobs in a particular geographical location, numbers of workers, and wages. Proceeding to the America's Job Bank (www.ajb.org) will provide information on employers for a particular occupation within a geographical area (state, city, zip).

Finally, the References listed in Section 3 of this resource provide the reader with additional sources on the topic of transferability, labor market information, and how decision-making can be applied in various settings.

Method #2: The O*NET Approach (Employability)

The general approach discussed above is still the most commonly used approach by rehabilitation professionals today. In this context, TSAs are usually based still on the 1991 version of the DOT and may be analyzed with any one of the commercial software programs – all of which are based on the 1991 DOT database. As discussed earlier in this chapter, the DOT has become obsolete with its credibility propped up by such legal rulings at the SSA Policy Interpretation (00-4p). A second major consideration for the continued use of the DOT is the recognition that the O*NET, while still under construction and revision, is not yet fully usable in its current form in legal settings. Consequently, the DOT has been and continues to be used due to a lack of what some view as a reasonable alternative.

Work on the O*NET database, however, has made significant strides toward the O*NET becoming fully usable for the rehabilitation professional in forensic settings. The basic structure of the database is in place, including many useful constructs, which serve to define work and work behaviors and their requirements. The remaining area of concern is to identify and quantify selected elements that can easily be employed in the TSA process (this research and development is well under way with support from both DOL and SSA). Since the O*NET does not lend itself readily to a traditional TSA process, another consideration is to view the O*NET resource as an "employability" tool. Through a process of relying on information about the client that is decidedly of a more subjective nature, the counselor would place greater emphasis on finding occupations (employability) that would be suitable for the client. This approach does require more clinical judgment on the part of the counselor. Decisions would be based on information from client interviews, employment history, client preferences, and the availability for particular occupations within a local economy. In the interim (until the O*NET is revised to accommodate TSAs), the professional might consider the "best of both worlds" by using both the DOT (Traditional Method #1) and the proposed O*NET format (Method #2 - O*NET Employability) as suggested below. Given the deficiencies of both databases, a more reasonable approach is to use both methods: the DOT for transferability, and the O*NET for employability.

Step 1: Find Occupations

The O*NET database is an online website database and program. One of the essential characteristics of the O*NET is that it is "dynamic" and ever changing. One of the most encouraging aspects of the program is that it is easy to use – with a little practice. *But practice is important.* The more you use the O*NET Online programs, the easier and faster it gets. The first step is to find the appropriate website in order to get started. Go to http://online.onetcenter.org

Notice that the user has three options to follow in generating information about an occupation:

Find Occupations – type a key word or phrase, an O*NET code, or a job family.

Skills Search - identify the various skills possessed by the worker,

Crosswalk- type in one of the following codes: DOT, military, apprenticeship, or SOC.

For instance, if the title "machinist" was the key search word, a list of titles would appear, each with a relevance score in the left hand column. The higher the score on relevance, the most closely related was the job to the title that was typed into the system.

Step 2: Reports - Find Occupations

Following a review of the list, select the title that is closest to what you want to review. Notice also that there are three columns to the right of the titles list with the captions of "summary," "details," and "custom" under **Reports.**

The **Summary Report** provides an overall, descriptive summary on the following: tasks, knowledge, skills, abilities, work activities, work context, job zone components, interests, work values, related occupations, and a wages and employment link. It is possible to print any and all of the screens of these areas.

The **Details Report** is basically the same structure as the Summary Report except that the report content has far more detail. The report includes information on tasks, knowledge, skills, and so forth. However, each of the items is rated from high to low culminating in a list of occupations for further consideration. The items at the top of the list for each of the areas are the more important items for that occupation. This report also provides a short list of related occupations.

The **Custom Report** permits the user to find occupations at a particular cut-off score by either "level" or "importance" in areas. For instance, a cut-off score of "80" can be set for the area of "knowledge" for "importance." This filtering procedure will result in short list of occupations that match this filter. Filtering can include any of the other areas, set at a particular cut-off score, and can sort by either importance or level. For an explanation of the scales, ratings and scores, review Appendix E.

Step 3: Skills Search

With the Skills Search feature, the user is able to identify occupations by tagging the skills possessed by the client. The skill areas are basic skills, social skills, complex solving skills, technical skills, troubleshooting skills, system skills, and resource management skills. Simply tagging those skills that are of interest or are relevant to the client will result in a **Skills Report**. This report will include in the left-side column a total of the number of skills matched for each occupation, which is listed in the report. The job zone is identified for each occupation, and it is possible to review and/or print each of the three reports (summary, details, custom) for each of the occupations. Likewise, a link to wage and employment information is also available.

Step 4: Crosswalk Search

The last search option allows one to search for occupations by one of four search modes. By entering either a code or a title within one of the crosswalks, it is possible to find occupations. The same standard reports (summary, details, custom) are available. The crosswalks are:

- *Dictionary of Occupational Titles (DOT)*
- *Military Occupational Classification (MOC)*
- *Registered Apprenticeship Information System (RAIS)*
- *Standard Occupational Classification (SOC)*

Step 5: Occupation Report

The Occupation Report is a summary of wage and employment information for a specific occupation. The report contains two tables: one for wages and one for trends in employment. A left-hand column addresses a variety of very relevant information for the one occupation, including general outlook, wages and trends, What it Takes (skills and abilities, etc.), state information, jobs and employers, and career tools. The information (and links to other data sources) is excellent and can prove to be very useful in making determinations for future employment of a client.

In summary, Method #2 represents a whole new approach to finding occupations for a client. The rehabilitation professional should be expected to employ a significant amount of time in making judgments on various pieces of data and information. The approach is very different from the large data searches of a computerized approach as depicted in Method #1. Each may have their place during this transition period, but even with the growing demise of the DOT, the O*NET represents considerable promise for professionals involved in forensic the field.

The DOT and the O*NET

Given the deficiencies of both occupational databases, a more reasonable approach is to use both methods: the DOT for *transferability*, and the O*NET for *employability*.

Future Options

As indicated earlier, the Social Security Administration has not committed to the recommended format as presented by the AIR report. It is quite possible that SSA will take quite a different tact, although other options are in the discussion stage only. One possibility, however, is to revise and/or update selected portions on the 1991 DOT by addressing only those titles that would appear to be relevant to the disability determination process. The format of the occupational database would remain essentially the same, including the worker trait arrangement, except that titles and job analysis data would be revised to reflect today's labor market. Another possibility could be to develop a totally new database that would address the specific needs of SSA. Either one of these strategies would preclude the necessity of revising the regulations for determination of a proposal that AIR has suggested on more than one occasion.

For the Present: A "Merged Option"

The most reasonable approach, at least for this interim period while this issue is being resolved, is to use a "merged" approach as was suggested by Field and Field (1999) in the revised *Classification of Jobs* 2000 with an O*NET Crosswalk. Considering the implications of SSR 00-4p (see page 106) that may require the VE to explain to the court's satisfaction any deviation from the ratings in the DOT (1991), one should proceed with caution while using the O*NET for transferability especially until SSA has time to decide exactly what the preference will be regarding an occupational database. The steps to follow for this traditional approach are listed on pages 111–114 along with suggestions (p. 105–106) for crossing to O*NET related databases.

Occupational Information Development Advisory Panel (OIDAP)

As noted on the website (http://www.ssa.gov/oidap/), "On December 9, 2008, Michael J. Astrue, Commissioner of Social Security, established the Occupational Information Development Advisory Panel (OIDAP) under the Federal Advisory Committee Act. This discretionary panel will provide independent advice and recommendations to rehabilitation professionals on the creation of an occupational information system (OIS) for use in our disability programs and for our adjudicative needs. We require advice on the research design of the OIS, including the development and testing of a content model and taxonomy, work analysis instrumentation, sampling, and data collection and analysis" (para 1).

The above announcement established an effort to provide a new occupational format and database, which would eventually replace of aging *Dictionary of Occupational Titles* as the primary source for SSA. While the final product may still be years away, there is hope that this new resource would be available to the entire rehabilitation community with the kind of utility needed to make reasonable analyses with transferable skills.

Commercial Software Programs

The software programs listed below are potentially excellent resources (depending on how used) for the vocational expert in SSDI and SSI hearings. These commercial programs should be considered as another resource from which the professional can draw information in the development of a vocational opinion. Like any other resource, the programs should not be used as the "answer-provider" for decisions regarding the potential for return to work of a person with residual functional job skills. The author does not endorse any particular program; conversely, all the programs enjoy a good reputation in the field.

SEER (Software for Employment, Education and Rehabilitation)
Developer: Robert Hall
www.seersoftware.net

Skill*TRAN* (Software for Rehabilitation, Forensic and Career Services)
Developer: Jeff Truthan
www.SkillTran.com

MVQS (The McCroskey Vocational Quotient System)
Developer: Billy Joe McCroskey
www.vocationology.com

OASYS (Rehabilitation Applications)
Developer: Gale Gibson
www.SkillTran.com

Meeting the Daubert-Kumho Challenge

Admissibility

The admissibility of testimony by experts (including rehabilitation professionals) has become an important consideration in the formulation of opinion involving litigated cases. Renewed emphasis is placed on reliable and relevant methodology as the basis for developing and offering expert opinion in legal settings. Taking into account the criteria, as set forth in *Daubert v. Merrill Dow Pharmaceutical*, and further discussed in *Kumho v. Carmichael* and the Federal Rules of Evidence (i.e., Rule 702), a rehabilitation professional should be very cognizant of these rulings when developing testimony (Field et al., 2000). In this context, the following observations are presented as a guideline when employing transferable skills analysis as a method or approach to casework.

Standards of Practice—Transferability is a time-honored and generally accepted approach with roots established by decades of rules, regulations, and practice of the Social Security Administration disability program. The same general method is also used by professionals in state VR agencies, in workers' compensation programs, and in legal cases (Weed, & Field, 2001). This approach, as outlined in the seven steps discussed earlier, enjoys general and widespread acceptance in the broad rehabilitation community.

Specialized Knowledge—While TSAs cannot meet the strict requirements of scientific method and statistical error, the method does require technical and other specialized knowledge on the part of the rehabilitation professional. In light of *General Electric Company v. Joine*r (1997), and *Kumho v. Carmichael* (1998), the Court held that the Daubert standards apply flexibly to all expert testimony – at the discretion of the trier of fact. Adopting and utilizing an accepted method for TSAs is critical to the development of expert testimony.

Peer Review—Countless papers, technical manuals, government guidelines, and journal articles have been published since the 1950s on both general and specific topics related to the transferable process. Both the degree of use and wealth of publications serve to substantiate the efficacy of methodologies related to transferable skills analysis.

Reliability and Validity—Reliability is established by the degree of consistency that is inherent in any method; any of the computer programs (consisting basically of algorithms) can easily demonstrate reliability. The issue of validity is basically established by the nature and content of the resources that are used in the TSA process. The method or approach in finding similar or new jobs for a person following illness or injury, when accommodating previous work experiences and skills, is referred to as transferable skills analysis. This method is a process, requiring technical and specialized knowledge on the part of the professional. The process requires the review, organization, and synthesis of much information as a means to arrive at a conclusion. The *Dictionary of Occupational Titles* is the primary source of information used in the TSA process, including any of the computer job-matching programs. The concern about the DOT being obsolete (Mariani, 1999) or inadequate (A critical review of the DOT, 1980) certainly raises questions regarding its validity. However, the SSA Policy Interpretation (SSR 00-4p), at least for the near future, seems to suspend or neutralize this concern. In either case, clinical judgment of the professional should prevail in all decisions regarding TSAs. (Also see Chapter 12).

Conclusion

Transferable skills analysis is a time-honored method for reasonably selecting similar or new jobs for people following illness or disability. The most critical ingredient in the determination process is the activity of the rehabilitation counselor (Field, 2006). In cases where the online O*NET or a commercial computer program is used, information that is inputted to the program is basically determined by the counselor. Likewise, any report, including job recommendations, generated from the computer process needs to be carefully scrutinized for relevancy and appropriateness. Ultimately, the TSA process is a method utilized by the professional for purposes of processing occupational information resulting in a reasonable conclusion.

Figure 6.1
Example Transferability Worksheet

TRANSFERABILITY OF WORK SKILLS WORKSHEET

Date _June 1993_ Phone # _____

Name of Client/Student _Joe Example_

Address _123 Main Street_

City/State/Zip _Anytown, USA 01234_

SS# _006-52-4447_ Age _46_ Height _6'_ Weight _185_

Level of Education Completed _H.S._ Date _____

Special Training _____ Date _____

Counselor _Jim Helper_

Step #1

Previous Work History

1. _Wood Machinist, Apprentice_ From _'65_ To _66_
2. _Wood Machinist_ From _66_ To _75_
3. _Machine Setter_ From _75_ To _81_
4. _Patternmaker_ From _81_ To _92_
5. _____ From _____ To _____
6. _____ From _____ To _____
7. _____ From _____ To _____

Notes:

Client's Name _____

Step #2

	D.O.T. Code #	D.O.T. TITLE	SIC	Census Code	Work Field Code	SVP (1-9) Duration D	GED (1-6) Reasoning R	Math M	Language L
WORK HISTORY	669.380-010	Wood Machinist, Apprentice	292	657	057	6	3	3	3
	669.380-014	Wood Machinist	292	657	057	6	3	3	3
	669.280-010	Machine Setter	292	733	057	7	3	3	3
	661.281-022	Patternmaker	332	656	102	8	4	4	3
	5								
	6								
	7								
	Pre-Vocational Profile (Summary Of Job History)					8	4	4	3
	Worker Traits To Be Evaluated (check)								
	Residual Functional Capacity (Transferability To Current Level Of Functioning)					7	4	4	3
	Consultants Reports & Vocational/Assessment Procedures Utilized (footnote)					1			

Step #3, Step #4, Step #5

JOB POSSIBILITIES	615.130-010	Press Head Supervisor			057	7	4	3	3
	693.130-014	Finishing Supervisor			057	7	4	3	3
	693.281-022	Patternmaker, Sample			102	7	4	4	4
	4								
	5								
	6								
	7								

Step #6

VOCATIONAL OUTCOME	1						
	2						
	3						
	4						
	5						
	6						
	7						

Step #7

FOOTNOTES on Consultant's Reports & Vocational/Assessment Procedures

1 Allows orientation to next job.

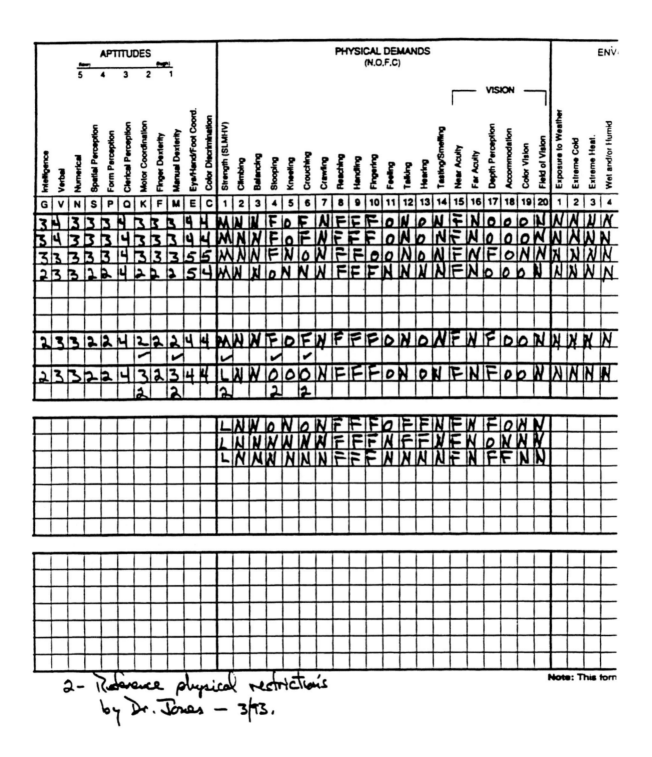

APTITUDES												PHYSICAL DEMANDS (N.O.F.C)																VISION						ENV
Intelligence	Verbal	Numerical	Spatial Perception	Form Perception	Clerical Perception	Motor Coordination	Finger Dexterity	Manual Dexterity	Eye/Hand/Foot Coord.	Color Discrimination	Strength (SLMHV)	Climbing	Balancing	Stooping	Kneeling	Crouching	Crawling	Reaching	Handling	Fingering	Feeling	Talking	Hearing	Tasting/Smelling	Near Acuity	Far Acuity	Depth Perception	Accommodation	Color Vision	Field of Vision	Exposure to Weather	Extreme Cold	Extreme Heat.	Wet and/or Humid	
G	V	N	S	P	Q	K	F	M	E	C	1	2	3	4	5	6	7	8	9	10	11	12	13	14	15	16	17	18	19	20	1	2	3	4	
3	4	3	3	3	4	3	3	3		4	M	N	N	F	O	F	N	F	F	F	O	N	O	N	F	N	O	O	O	N	N	N	N	N	
3	4	3	3	3	4	3	3	3	4	4	M	N	N	F	O	F	N	F	F	F	O	N	O	N	F	N	O	O	O	N	N	N	N	N	
3	3	3	3	3	4	3	3	3	5	5	M	N	N	F	N	O	N	F	F	O	O	N	O	N	F	N	F	O	N	N	N	N	N	N	
2	3	3	2	2	4	2	2	2	5	4	M	N	N	O	N	N	N	F	F	N	N	N	N	F	N	O	O	O	N	N	N	N	N	
2	3	3	2	2	4	2	2	3	4	4	M	N	N	F	O	F	N	F	F	F	O	N	O	N	F	N	F	O	O	N	N	N	N	
						✓		✓			✓			✓		✓																			
2	3	3	2	2	4	3	3	3	4	4	L	N	N	O	O	O	N	F	F	F	O	N	O	N	F	N	F	O	O	N	N	N	N	N	
						2		2			2			2		2																			
											L	N	N	O	N	O	N	F	F	F	O	F	N	F	N	F	O	N	N					
											L	N	N	N	N	N	N	F	F	N	F	F	N	F	N	O	N	N					
											L	N	N	N	N	N	N	F	F	N	N	N	N	F	N	F	F	N	N					

2- Reference physical restrictions
by Dr. Jones — 3/93.

Note: This form

*Noise Intensity Rated 1-5

ENVIRONMENTAL CONDITIONS (N,O,F,C)*											TEMPERAMENTS (Y,N)											GOE INTEREST AREAS (Y,N)											
			HAZARDS																														
Noise (1-5)	Vibration	Atmospheric Conditions	Moving Parts	Electrical Shock	High, Exposed Places	Radiant Energy	Explosives	Toxic Chemicals	Other Hazards		Working Alone	Directing Others	Expressing Personal Feelings	Influencing People	Making Judgments	Dealing With People	Performing Repetitive Work	Performing Under Stress	Attaining Tolerance	Working Under Instructions	Performing a Variety of Duties	Artistic	Scientific	Plant & Animal	Protective	Mechanical	Industrial	Administrative	Selling	Accommodating	Humanitarian	Leading	Sports
5	6	7	8	9	10	11	12	13	14	A	D	E	I	J	P	R	S	T	U	V	1	2	3	4	5	6	7	8	9	10	11	12
4	N	F	F	N	N	N		O	O					1				3		2					✓							
4	N	F	F	N	N	N		O	O					1				3		2					✓							
4	N	F	F	N	N	N	N	N	N					1				3		2					Y							
4	N	N	N	N	N	N	N	N	N					1				2							✓							
4	N	F	F	N	N	N		O	O					1				3		2					1	2						
		✓																														
4	N	F	O	N	N	N		O	O					1				3		2					1	2						
		2																														

...to be used with the **Dictionary of Occupational Titles** (1991), and the **Classification of Jobs** (1992 revised edition)

111

Chapter 7
Labor Market Survey

Introduction

What most people know as a labor market survey is sometimes referred to as labor market search (Neulicht, Gann, Berg, & Taylor, 2007). An argument can be made that a better umbrella term is "labor market research" because employer sampling, reviews of the literature, and the obtaining of published labor data are all related to the broad term "research" (Cambridge on-line dictionary, 2003, as cited in University of Idaho, 2011; Experimental-resources.com, 2011). However, for purposes of this chapter, the authors have selected to retain the more familiar term because (1) the term "survey" is descriptive of the process, (2) most professionals are familiar with the concept by that name, and (3) many workers' compensation laws include the term "labor market survey" for activities associated with this chapter (Barros-Bailey, in press; Ford & Jensen 2003; Gilbride & Burr, 1993; Weed & Taylor, 1990; Washington State Department of Labor and Industries, 2011). For practitioners, particularly in private practice, the labor market survey seems like such a basic part of rehabilitation that it is easy to assume one only needs access to a pencil, a pad of blank paper, and a telephone in order to conduct such research. Used to justify plans in both the public and private sectors, as well as in both personal injury cases and selected workers' compensation cases mandated by some states (Ford & Jensen, 2003), a labor market survey is sometimes seen as "grunt" work, which is often passed on for support staff personnel to conduct. At the other extreme, rehabilitation professionals sometimes use biased labor market information to justify an opinion (B. Taylor, personal communication, January 16, 2000).

However, as one of the cornerstones to building appropriate rehabilitation opportunities, a labor market survey can carry significant impact on the life and future of the individual being served. As such, it deserves to be conducted in a methodical, standardized, and objective manner that replaces personal bias on the part of the rehabilitation professional with clear data to support realistic placement opportunities.

Farrell, Knowlton, and Taylor (1989) emphasize the necessity of a well-organized rehabilitation process in highlighting the savings that result from an individualized case management approach in long-term disability cases. Although successful return to work can sometimes be achieved through short cuts, "rehabilitation must be viewed as a dynamic process requiring direct involvement and personal attention . . . . The effective rehabilitation program strives to objectify and measure disability. Methods include medical management, functional capacity assessments, job analysis, transferable skills analysis, job modification, vocational testing, job placement assistance, labor market surveys, and retraining" (p. 113).

Clearly, rehabilitation is a multi-step procedure, and the negligent omission of any one of those steps can weaken the entire process, thus negatively affecting the outcome.

The unexpected results of a comparative study of placement techniques, subject demographics, and rehabilitation outcomes by Seyler and Chauvina (1989) demonstrate the benefit of taking an analytical approach to as many aspects of rehabilitation as possible. Of the 142 cases reviewed, almost one-third evidenced successful client rehabilitation. Of the positive outcome cases, 78% had job analyses (see next chapter for details about job analysis) included in the rehabilitation process, compared to only 58% from the total sample. To take job analysis one step further, instead of simply determining how closely a job might match a client's residual capabilities, use of labor market analysis can help determine how readily available such jobs will be to the client in question. In determining the probability for placement following vocational rehabilitation, there is little reason to suspect the impact of a labor market survey would be any less than that demonstrated for job analysis.

The multi-faceted process of rehabilitation often requires us to look to other specialists for information in determining the most appropriate direction for a client. Rehabilitation plans depend on documentation from doctors and therapists (physical, occupational, and/or psychological) for the limitations within which a client and his counselor must operate. These professionals prescribe how much weight a client can lift, how many hours a client can stand, how much strength a client has retained, how much stress a client can endure, and so forth. (The reader is referred to a sample Physician Form located in the appendices.) Frequently, these data are then incorporated by a vocational evaluator into an assessment of how employable the client is, given his or her documented limitations. Unfortunately, answering the question of employability does not resolve the question of placeability.

Placeability

The issue of placeability revolves around how difficult it may be for a client to obtain employment (Weed & Field, 1990). Many jobs exist in the national economy, but the availability of those jobs varies day-by-day and hour-by-hour. A properly executed labor market survey report will establish the frequency of availability of certain jobs, not as a general rule of thumb, but for a particular client in question. It serves little purpose to conduct a labor market survey that demonstrates significant availability of jobs for which a client is well suited if the study does not take into consideration the qualifications and limitations of the individual for whom the job is being investigated. If a vocational consultant cannot find employers who are willing to hire previously injured workers under any circumstances, then the jobs these employers may have available in general are not in actuality available to a rehabilitation client. "Employable" does not automatically translate into "placeable," if jobs exist that are unavailable to a client. Only well-done labor market related research could resolve this issue.

For example, one client suffered a significant injury to both arms and hands as well as to his head. At the time of the incident, the client, a mechanic, was changing a tire when the rim "blew up", rendering him unconscious. He had a two-inch gash in his forehead with air and cerebral spinal fluid leaking from the hole. His face was "rearranged," but cosmetic surgery successfully repaired much of the damage. His right dominant arm was severely damaged, and bone was removed and was replaced with a metal rod. Because of a poor driving record due to the injury, he had lost his driver's license and walked to work. The small town did not have public transportation.

A defense rehabilitation expert was hired to conduct a labor market study to see what jobs the client could do. She contacted a number of employers and concluded there were a number of jobs available to this client. It was soon discovered, however, that she had failed to disclose to the employer that the client's dominant arm was functionally impaired and that he had no driver's license, which was a requirement for most of the jobs surveyed. This, of course, totally changed the validity of the opinion and cast doubt about the consultant's ethics.

Labor Market Survey Checklist

The Labor Market Survey (LMS) Checklist was developed to insure that important information is not overlooked in gathering occupational data. Other formats are available and worthy of consideration (See Barros-Bailey, in press). The format described below has been successfully used by one of the authors in workers compensation and forensic cases on numerous occasions. By categorizing the segments of the survey, the two-page LMS Checklist provides a quick reference for both the novice and the seasoned professional regarding points significant to the search. Obviously, omissions can result in faulty documentation of a client's placeability. Using the Checklist prevents "reinventing the wheel" each time the counselor must conduct a survey. It also insures that the person conducting the survey will not ignore standards of the industry that dictate the use of thorough, objective data to support recommendations for rehabilitation. (See Figure 7.1)

1. Introduction Section

The Introduction contains general case history information on the client/evaluee, particularly as it relates to employability. Each subheading within the Introduction (i.e., age, date of injury, type of injury, medical limitations, work experience, education, other historical information, vocational test results, etc.) serves as a reminder of a particular point to be covered prior to beginning a survey. To the experienced professional it may seem unnecessary to include such references; however, it is often easy to overlook what seems to be common sense information. Since each point within the Introduction can have a direct bearing on placeability, failing to consider any one of these items can result in a survey that is not fully applicable to the client in question.

Figure 7.1
Labor Market Survey Checklist

Labor market research (LMR) specifically examines the availability of employment for adult clients. This study addresses the question of placeability rather than employability. A job analysis, following the LMR, will help determine if the probable occupation is within the client's capabilities (see also job analysis checklist). In order to standardize the information and assure obtaining respectable data, the following checklist is recommended.

INTRODUCTION (include the following identifying information for report.)
_____ Name
_____ Age
_____ Date of injury
_____ Type of injury
_____ Functional limitations
_____ Work experience
_____ Education
_____ Other historical information
_____ Vocational test results
_____ Other

METHODS USED (What method(s) was (were) used to obtain the information? Suggest starting with residual employability profile by VDARE for worker traits.)
  Personal contacts (as appropriate) with
_____ Personal network
_____ Chamber of Commerce
_____ Professional and trade associations
_____ Employment services (private and public)
_____ Vocational rehabilitation
_____ Other

  Publications/On-line Resources
_____ O*Net
_____ Occupational Outlook Handbook (on-line)
_____ State career information systems (or similar)
_____ City directory or Haynes directory
_____ Occupational supply and demand (state Dept. of Industry and Trade or Labor)
_____ Wage rates for selected occupations (state)
_____ Manufacturing directories (SIC codes)
_____ Bureau of Labor Statistics, e.g. Area Wage Survey (federal)
_____ Census Bureau (federal) and Current Population Surveys (CPS)
_____ Classified ads
_____ Identified discreet jobs related to client's experience
_____ Job flyers
_____ Other

RESULTS
_____ Employer's contacted – approximately 10
_____ Jobs(s) available (last 3 months, now and future expectations - within next 3-6 months)
_____ Wages
_____ Training/education needed
_____ Benefits (holidays, vacation, sick, medical, dental, personal leave, etc.)
_____ Willingness to work with disabled
_____ Accessibility/architectural barriers
_____ Willingness to participate in job analysis if appropriate
_____ Other

CONCLUSIONS (professional's opinion)
  Placeability
  Expected outcome
  Other related comments

Copyrighted by Dr. Roger Weed, 2001 (rev. 2011). Published by E & F, Inc., Athens, GA.

Labor Market Survey Summary
Employer Sampling Results

Client/Evaluee: _____

Employer/Contact Name	Job avail (A) Job exist (E) Both (B)	Job Title	Wages High	Wages Low	Wages Ave	Required Educ/Training	Benefits	History of work with person with dis? (Y, N, ?)	Accessible? (Y, N, ?)	Other (e.g., shift work, special tools, etc.)
1.										
2.										
3.										
4.										
5.										
6.										
7.										
8.										
9.										
10.										

Conclusions

Employment potential estimate	Expected income range
Percent access to labor market (document method)	Other

2. Methods Section

There are two separate categories under the section for Method(s) Used. The first concerns contacts made directly by either the client/evaluee or the counselor. The most significant of these elements is the personal network of those family members and friends who can report on job openings in their own work settings. Likewise, they can recommend that their employers give consideration to the client in question, should an appropriate job become available. This avenue is the most productive for client and counselor alike since the general impression is that no one is going to recommend another person for hire unless there is a likelihood that the employer would be pleased with that individual's performance.

Other sources of contact for job leads include the Yellow Pages, or equivalent, for listings of local business addresses and telephone numbers. Likewise, the R.L. Polk City Directory can provide a cross reference for names and addresses to go with telephone numbers that appear in blind ads for "help wanted." The primary shortcoming of both the Yellow Pages and the City Directory is in the timeliness of the information contained in each. Publication deadlines require that information be submitted well in advance of release dates, so even a new directory will contain information that is several months old. As the year progresses, the information continues to age. Businesses come and go, and the older the directory is, the less complete its information is assumed to be. That is why the next item on the LMS Checklist, the Chamber of Commerce, is an appropriate contact to make in following up on new businesses and services developing within a community. In addition to having brochures about the community itself, the Chamber also has information on the number of citizens and schools in the area as well as the major sources of employment. Both the telephone directory and the Chamber of Commerce can provide information on professional and trade associations, which often have their own job referral systems for qualified members. Most professional and trade associations have internet sites that may facilitate information gathering.

Public agencies that offer access to the private enterprise arena include local employment or job service offices, which maintain information on jobs available in the general vicinity of the agency. A majority of jobs listed with employment service offices are unskilled or semi-skilled positions, requiring a limited amount of training or education. Thus, the number of appropriate jobs likely to be found in such agencies will be in reverse proportion to the amount of education and experience a client may have had.

Occupational trends for the state, and perhaps even for areas within the state, can be obtained through the state employment development division (or its counterpart). Unlike employment service offices, the employment development division is often a singular agency centrally located in the state capitol or some other metropolitan area of the state. Although this makes direct personal contact more difficult, general information gleaned from this commission regarding employment trends within a geographical location can be invaluable in searching out viable work opportunities for a client.

The state/federal rehabilitation services agency has long been the backbone of the rehabilitation movement, and as such it can serve an important role in a labor market survey. Local vocational rehabilitation offices stay in touch with the business community on a regular basis and their counselors can offer an accurate overview of what to expect in searching for jobs. However, it is unrealistic to believe that an already overworked rehabilitation counselor from the state agency can find the time to respond to the myriad questions that arise when a new community is encountered. Developing a personal network by joining professional associations that are attractive to public section rehabilitation counselors, like the National Rehabilitation Association, can prove useful.

A more workable alternative to achieving "personal contact" without necessarily going into the community oneself is contracting with a local rehabilitation specialist whose services can be retained on a per-case basis. For personal injury casework, it is of key importance that the local expert be under the direction and supervision of the professional who is expected to testify (for further information refer to the Rules of Evidence). For example, when a client's/evaluee's location is not in close proximity to the rehabilitation supplier's home base, this alternative can be routinely accomplished. As long as the principal counselor maintains control of all casework and as long as services are provided in a manner that adheres to appropriate legal and ethical standards, "personal" contacts can be increased significantly by retaining the services of a local rehabilitation professional.

Personal contact is the primary method used in determining the current *availability* of jobs for a particular client/evaluee. A second method involves the use of publications that provide data on a number of items including wage rates, occupational supply and demand, and industrial sources, to name a few. Although the LMS Checklist does not presume to include reference to all such publications, it lists a cross-section of those thought to be most representative of the "real" work world. Table 7.1 presents published items highlighted on the LMS Checklist, with a resource listing and a brief explanation of the type of information such publications may contain.

3. Results Section

The Results section of the LMS Checklist outlines standard information needed on jobs and/or employers in determining a particular client's/evaluee's placeability. Results of counselor inquiry are recorded on the LMS Summary found on the reverse side of the LMS Checklist. A major advantage to listing job data in the format found in the LMS Checklist lies in the ability to view, almost at a glance, whether jobs being investigated require more education of a client, provide enough income, or are available at all. This can be especially advantageous when a staff person has conducted a telephone survey for the vocational consultant. Rather than having to wade through several pages of material, only to discover that none of the employers contacted are hiring at the moment, the counselor could simply look down the column titled "Jobs Available/Jobs Exist" and learn in a matter of seconds that his/her worst fears have been confirmed for this client. Or, on the optimistic side, that his/her best hopes have been realized!

4. Conclusions Section

The final category in the LMS Checklist is the Conclusions section. This is the critical point where the professional arrives at a decision regarding a person's placeability. If the information obtained in a labor market survey has been gathered in an objective, well organized, and clearly structured manner, the results should be the same, regardless of who has requested the information. Whether plaintiff or defense, Social Security or rehabilitation services, administrative law judge or insurance adjuster, professional ethics demand that labor market data be presented in a way that will not skew the outcome of a case. Limiting or editing information in any way is a breech of ethical responsibility, even if that omission is an innocent oversight. By following a prescribed format in conducting labor market surveys, the rehabilitation professional can be assured that stated opinions represent a true and fair analysis of the client's placeability.

With regard to ethics and competency, personal loss of access to the labor market and employment-potential opinions should have a proper foundation. It is no longer adequate for the rehabilitation expert to offer an opinion based on "education and experience." Although the topics of transferable work skills, case preparation, loss of access to the labor market, and employment-potential assessments are located in other chapters, be advised that standardized procedures and generally accepted methods of each exist. The report should document the source or method on which the opinion is founded.

Applications of the Labor Market Survey Checklist

Though time-consuming and tedious, research into the needs of the local labor market is an essential step in marketing any product, be that hardware, software, or adult humanware. In general, the "labor market" is determined by a geographical configuration, which allows for job opportunities without requiring a change of residence (National Occupational Information Coordinating Committee, 1984). A blend of industries and occupations in a central community and surrounding area, the labor market can be very unique in what it has to offer, as well as in what it expects. Ignoring this uniqueness can result in wasted effort, if one is not careful (Boles, 2012).

The Career Services for the Handicapped in Albuquerque, New Mexico, has incorporated the labor market survey into its regular program. Long identified as providing a model job development and placement program for its clients, CSH supports through its philosophy of operation the belief that " . . . by understanding [the labor market] one can exercise better judgment in carrying out an effective marketing plan" (Rehab Brief, 1985, p. 3). The pitfalls of failing to adequately investigate labor market needs are inevitable.

O'Brien (1987) outlines a number of these pitfalls in his discussion of placement attitudes. He demonstrates how a systemized approach to knowing both the offerings and demands of the labor market can expedite job placement by reducing the necessity of covering territory already explored. In line with this idea, the LMS Checklist allows for the establishment of an information base, which can be updated or altered on any given industry or job area without requiring the vocational consultant to repeat a study in its entirety. Such cost-saving steps can increase a consultant's efficiency in serving the client by decreasing delays that are often erroneously deemed "inevitable" in the rehabilitation profession.

Table 7.1
Example Uses and Resources for Labor Market Surveys

AREA WAGE SURVEY

USE: To estimate potential earnings.

RESOURCE: U.S. Government, U.S. Dept. of Labor, Bureau of Labor Statistics (Bulletin # 3050-16)

OCCUPATIONAL SUPPLY AND DEMAND

USE: To evaluate level of competition for jobs and future outlook for various occupations.

RESOURCE: State Departments of Labor or Departments of Industry and Trade

STATE CAREER INFORMATION SYSTEMS

USE: To explore local career options, wages and outlook in most states.

RESOURCE: Local Departments of Labor, University of Oregon (Eugene, Oregon)

MANUFACTURING DIRECTORY/MANUFACTURING WAGE SURVEY

USE: To access information about wages, business names and industries within a state

RESOURCE: State Dept. of Industry and Trade or Dept. of Labor

BUREAU OF LABOR STATISTICS

USE: To determine level of unemployment in specific geographical areas. Also source for wages which are cross referenced to Census codes.

RESOURCE: U.S. Dept. of Labor, Bureau of Labor Statistics.

CENSUS BUREAU

USE: Research for numbers of jobs in local, state or national areas. Listed in 503 Census codes

RESOURCE: Money Income & Poverty Status in the U.S. (Series P-60, # 161) and Money Income of Households, Families & Persons in the U.S. (Series P-60, # 162): U.S. Government, U.S. Department of Commerce, Bureau of Census. Also E&F Inc. (1-800-843-4977). www.census.gov

JOB SERVICE MICROFICHE/POSTED JOBS

USE: To identify availability of jobs listed through employment service.

RESOURCE: State Job Service Office. See State Government listings in phone book. www.acinet.org

CLASSIFIED ADS

USE: To identify availability of jobs listed through newspaper advertisements

RESOURCE: Local newspapers, Wall Street Journal.

IDENTIFIED DISCRETE JOBS

USE: Jobs that are available now.

RESOURCE: Personal network.

JOB FLYERS

USE: To identify availability of jobs not listed elsewhere.

RESOURCE: Larger businesses, governments and educational institutions.

MISCELLANEOUS

USE: General employment patterns for local area. Also provides specific contacts to start survey.

RESOURCE: Chamber of Commerce, R.L. Polk City Directory, Job Service, Careers and the Handicapped (516-261-8899), Business Week's Careers (800-635-1200), American Almanac of Jobs and Salaries (212-399-1357), CapCo (800-541-5006). Also see Job Placement Basics chapter for on-line resources.

NOTE: Some states have more resources than others. The above provides a sample of typical resources.

The LMS Checklist has multiple applications. As an aid in conducting a standard labor market survey study for placement purposes, the LMS Checklist can organize and structure the information-gathering process to ensure that all necessary data has been obtained. A further application is in evaluating loss of access to the labor market for clients who will be unable to return to previous work. There are several established methods for determining loss of labor market access following an injury, a consideration that is of paramount importance in many personal injury litigation cases (Cutler & Ramm, 1987; Field & Weed, 1987; Weed & Field, 1990; Weed, 1986; Weed, 1999). Of critical interest is the percentage of jobs lost in estimating the economic ramification of injury as it relates to employment.

In profiling a case study, Hughes (1988) clearly establishes the lack of utility in determining loss of access to jobs in the national labor market without carrying it one step further to determine placeability. Access to nationally listed jobs through residual capabilities is of little use to person with a disability when those jobs are not readily available in the local labor market. One of the ways to establish that availability is through a labor market survey.

Summary

This chapter has summarized the importance of conducting a labor market survey before implementing a rehabilitation plan, particularly if the program entails training or education. With regard to the value of this chapter, critical questions that can be answered by a labor market survey are:

1) Do jobs of a particular nature exist in the economy?

2) If these jobs exist, are they available locally?

3) If available locally, are these jobs open to my client or the evaluee?

4) If not available now, were they available within the last three months? Or are they expected to be available (say three-to-six months) in the future?

5) What do these jobs pay (including benefits)?

To answer these questions, one must investigate not only sources of possible jobs, but also sources of statistical information about jobs. These two entities are different, yet connected, and a labor market survey without both is incomplete. The standardized format suggested in this chapter was based on a peer-reviewed article and ensures adequate information based on objective methods to collecting data for the adult client. The format is intended to catch people doing things right as well as assure professional quality work. This will, in the authors' opinion, help the entire profession progress to a higher level of achievement and reduce criticism for biased and unethical behavior.

Chapter 8
Job Analysis

Introduction

Job analysis has been important for understanding the essential elements of jobs since the 1930's with the first edition of the *Handbook for Analyzing Jobs*, published in 1944 (U.S. Department of Labor, 1991). Indeed, in order to compile the job definitions listed in the fourth edition of the *Dictionary of Occupational Titles* (DOT, 1991), the U.S. Department of Labor set out criteria for worker traits that were considered important for on-the-job success. These worker traits were published in the *Revised Handbook for Analyzing Jobs* (U.S. Department of Labor) and were used by Department of Labor analysts who assigned specific criteria to each of the jobs included in the DOT.

Categorized by government analysts, these worker traits included the following factors:

- physical demands
- working conditions
- general educational development level
- specific vocational preparation
- aptitudes
- interests
- temperaments

Approximately ten years after the original *Handbook for Analyzing Jobs* (1972) was published, the Materials Development Center at the University of Wisconsin reissued these criteria with the federal government updates in their publication, *A Guide to Job Analysis* (MDC, 1982).

Other vocationally related publications, such as the *Guide for Occupational Exploration* (USDOL, 1979), *Occupational Outlook Handbook* (USDOL, 1990 – 1991 with updates), *Selected Characteristics of Occupations Defined in the Dictionary of Occupational Titles* (DOL, 1981), *Work Fields: Codes and Definitions* (Field & Field, 1993), *Job Analysis for the Private Sector* (Blackwell & Conrad, 1990*), On-site Job Analysis Training Manual* (Donham, 1990), *Job Analysis and the ADA: A Step by Step Guide* (Blackwell, Conrad, & Weed, 1992), and *Transitional Classification of Jobs* (Field & Field, 2004), also have direct relevance to the job analysis procedures outlined by the Department of Labor. In fact, job analysis might be viewed by some experts as being at the very core of the vocational rehabilitation process. If we don't know the requirements of a given job, how can we be certain that it is suitable for a particular client?

The importance of job analysis cannot be overestimated. Research has demonstrated that when persons with disabilities are properly placed, they have greater chances for success (Field & Weed, 1988; Weed & Field, 1990; Wright, 1980). Some states, such as California, actually require that a job analysis be conducted for Workers' Compensation clients prior to direct placement (A. Johnson, personal communication, October 24, 1990). By enforcing this requirement, it would appear that such states are increasing the likelihood of a successful return to work for many of their industrially injured clients, as attested to by reports that people with a disability, when properly placed, experience long-term successful returns to work (Dupont, 1981; Seyler & Chauvin, 1989). One study revealed that 78% of successfully rehabilitated clients had job analysis performed compared to 58% in the sample as a whole (Seyler & Chauvin, 1989).

In recent times, it has become evident that job analysis standards need to be upgraded especially for use in the private sector. In fact, the *Dictionary of Occupational Titles* (DOL, 1991) has been replaced by the O*Net online career planning process, but there are shortcomings. One of the needs for determining pre- vs. post-injury work capabilities is a hierarchical assessment of workers' traits and skills. The O*Net does not offer a way to enter data which will sort through worker traits in the way that the DOT did. This is mostly relevant for personal injury litigation, medical malpractice, workers' compensation, and social security disability applications. As a remedy, especially in recognition of the aging DOT, the Commissioner of Social

Security established the Occupational Information Development Advisory Panel (OIDAP) in 2008 (OIDAP, 2011). "This discretionary panel will provide independent advice and recommendations to us on the creation of an occupational information system (OIS) for use in our disability programs and for our adjudicative needs" (para. 2). However, at the time of this revision there has been no alternative, and rehabilitation counselors still need to conduct transferrable work skill and job analysis with the DOT as a part of the process.

With regard to rehabilitation, certain procedural deficiencies seem evident. For example, a physician might more easily determine the appropriateness of a job's physical demands if photographs or a videotape of the job are made available, along with a full explanation of the job. Of course, this will not guarantee cooperation from physicians who have little time to look at a job that closely or decline to make such specific recommendations.

As a significant plus for positive rehabilitation, job analysis can be viewed from several different vantage points. This chapter will highlight job analysis information that is, in the authors' view, appropriate for private sector rehabilitation. A summary checklist is also offered as an overview of the process itself.

Relevance of Job Analysis to Labor Market Surveys

Labor market surveys are often conducted to determine the employability and placeability of adults with disabilities. If an individual with a back injury is referred to a rehabilitation counselor for placement, it may be appropriate to determine the efficacy of the proposed rehabilitation plan with regard to employment before funds are expended. In the past, it has been evident that many rehabilitation clients have been trained for a specific job, only to find that there was no market for such job skills, or that the pay was inadequate, and that money spent for training had been wasted.

In addition, there are occasions when some rehabilitation clients, particularly in the workers' compensation arena, do not wish to participate in vocational rehabilitation efforts. A labor market survey is often conducted as a prelude to settling the case between the client and the insurance company. The ethics of this use of labor market surveys, except in occasional circumstances, has been questioned (Weed & Taylor, 1990). Indeed, in some situations, labor market surveys specifically leave out significant placeability factors, including interests and personality factors, as criteria in job selection in order to de-emphasize the human element or so-called subjective factors.

In an attempt to avoid misplacement or forced-fit placement, job analysis is recommended for adult clients to enhance the results of a labor market survey. Unfortunately, labor market surveys are occasionally conducted based solely on the client's physical limitations and his or her work history, with little apparent regard for the accuracy of an opinion regarding the person's ability to be employed (Weed, 1990). In such instances, it is imperative that a match first be made between job requirements and client abilities before limiting the analysis to physical demands only.

As a process, the labor market survey can lead the rehabilitation professional to an employer who may be an appropriate target for client placement. Once such an employer is identified, a job analysis should be conducted to determine the compatibility of the worker's traits with the factors of a particular job. The job analysis might further reveal to what extent the employer may be willing to modify the job or accommodate the worker.

Such information is particularly important considering the changes implemented in the Americans with Disabilities Act of 1990 (ADA) and the update of 2008, which has had a significant impact on all employers. The ADA extends equal employment opportunity requirements to most employers, not just those working with the federal government. In addition, the idea of reasonable accommodations is based on what the ADA describes as "essential functions" of the job, which can be identified with accuracy and (hopefully) with objectivity through a job analysis (see the chapter on rehabilitation technology for more information on this topic). Thus, the completeness of any job analysis becomes an essential element not only in providing truly professional rehabilitation services, but also in meeting the letter of the law.

To summarize the above, some of the applications for job analysis are:

1.   To identify the worker traits within a job.

2.   To identify the "essential functions" of a job for ADA compliance and job accommodation issues.

3.   To develop a comprehensive job description.

Table 8.1
Summary of Suggested Worker Traits for Job Analysis

Physical Demands	Comments
Lifting/strength	Include freq. and duration
Sit	Include freq. and duration
Stand	Include freq. and duration
Walk	Include distance and duration
Climb	Include type and frequency
Balance	Include examples
Stoop	Include examples
Bend	Include examples
Reach	Include unilateral/bilateral and feeling
Handle	Include unilateral/bilateral and feeling
Finger	Include unilateral/bilateral and feeling
Feel	Include sensation requirements
Talk	Include examples
Hear	Include example
Vision	Include near, far and depth
Eye/hand/foot	Include examples

Working Conditions	
Inside, outside	Both or unusual details
Cold/Changes	Include protective gear
Heat/changes	Include protective gear
Wet	Include hazards
Humid	Include examples
Noise	Include decibels and frequency
Vibrations	Include examples
Hazards	Include examples of risk of injury
Fumes/odors/dust	Include hazardous materials

General Educational Development Levels	Comments
Reasoning	Vocational relevant info
Math	Include practical examples
Language	Include practical examples
Reading	Include practical examples

Job Training Time	Education and training requirements

Aptitudes	
Intelligence	General learning ability
Verbal	Vocabulary needs
Numerical	Concrete examples
Spatial	Vocationally relevant
Form perception	Vocationally relevant
Clerical perception	Vocationally relevant
Motor coordination	Give examples
Finger dexterity	Bilateral/unilateral
Manual dexterity	Bilateral/unilateral
Eye/hand/foot coordination	Give examples
Color discrimin.	Give examples

Interests	Relate to Guide to Occupational Exploration

Personality Factors	Include reward values and personal characteristics

Job Description	Include special clothing and tool requirements

DOT Definition	Compare to job description and Classification of Jobs

Work Hours/ Overtime	Also note seasonal employment

4. To educate a physician about the details of a client's potential job and provide a formal method for review and approval/modification.

5. To avoid unnecessary risk by hiring appropriate persons for the job based on a detailed review of the job.

Suggested Outline of Worker Traits Contained in a Job Analysis

The traits as listed in Table 8.1 are consistent with the federal government's approach to job analysis. Recommended expansion to several of the categories have also been included. (See also Appendices for sample job analysis forms.)

General Requirements of a Job Analysis

Several years ago, one of the authors conducted a straw poll among employees and supervisors who were asked to spontaneously describe their job. Without observing the position and making note of its specifics, the respondents were unable to supply most of the details about the job. This illustrates how people who work in a particular job will tend to remember certain tasks that stand out in their minds, thereby biasing their opinions about the details of that job. The same holds true for supervisors.

Often, an "unmotivated" client, when asked about the specifics of his or her job, will be biased to remember those tasks that he or she no longer can do. Conversely, if an individual is highly motivated to work, that worker may recall those tasks he or she can still perform. Thus, the first and perhaps most important general rule about job analysis is that unless the job is specifically observed by a trained rater, an accurate listing of the requirements of the job cannot be obtained. Even then, in many instances, the job analysis will not precisely match those definitions as published in the *Revised Handbook for Analyzing Jobs* (DOL, 1991) nor the worker traits research by the federal government and published in the COJ 2000 (Field & Field, 1999).

A detailed job analysis requires an educated rater who observes the job long enough to be able to answer detailed questions about that position. Since it is widely acknowledged that a picture is worth a thousand words, it is also advisable to have photographs or a videotape of sample job duties. For practical purposes, still pictures would be more appropriate for a physician's review since most doctors would balk at being asked to view a 10-20 minute videotape of a person working in a job.

If aptitudes and interests of the client match those of the job, then the job analyst should identify those areas that the physician needs to address. While workers' compensation case disposition often places more importance on the physical demands of a job, the concept of "suitable employment" (discussed in an earlier chapter) is defined quite differently among the various sectors in rehabilitation. Such definitions are usually found as statements of individual law within the separate areas of workers' compensation, personal injury, and public sector rehabilitation. Therefore, it is erroneous to assume that a job analysis should only address physical demands when in reality those physical demands are only one segment of a much broader picture.

Other points to be considered in conducting a job analysis include discussing in detail with the employer what "essential functions" constitute a given job. Although the ADA will require most employers to extend employment by reasonable accommodation to qualified persons with disabilities, it also allows the employer to determine which factors in a job are essential and therefore unmodifiable. Failure to fully explore such information with a prospective employer may negate the results of a job analysis.

For example, in one case, a rehabilitation nurse conducted job analyses for a client with a 40-pound limitation on lifting. Although she concluded that he had access to a variety of high-paying jobs, another professional refuted this contention with a follow-up inquiry to many of the same employers. Through this investigation, it became clear that the client was not placeable because an essential function of the job, in addition to lifting up to 40 pounds, was to be able to perform unrestricted duties in cases of emergency. Because action had to be taken immediately in such instances, the employers determined these duties were not modifiable due to the safety factors involved. However, the original, incomplete job analysis failed to detect this very important discrepancy.

In exploring areas of question with employers, it is important for the job analyst to determine to what extent the employer is willing to restructure a job, to provide flextime, or to make other reasonable accommodations. Within the area of accommodations, one must also consider whether the use of technology might open job opportunities to the client by making the job or job site more accessible. Cost factors cannot be ignored in the issue of placement, however, and so it is important to learn ahead of time whether special tools or clothing are required by the employer.

Cost also enters into the consideration of architectural barriers on the job site. If such barriers exist, it must be decided whether they can be eliminated and what the costs might be to do so. Some barriers are simple to eliminate, such as in rearranging furniture to allow a wheelchair to pass. Others, such as stairs, may be more difficult and more expensive to overcome.

Once a job analysis has been completed, it is important for the employer and/or a supervisor to approve the job as analyzed. This will allow such persons to bring to the attention of the job analyst any details that may have been unusual at the time of the observation, or to mention any details that may have been overlooked. If the job analysis is being conducted with a particular client in mind who may have personal knowledge of the job, he or she should also have an opportunity to comment. For example, an injured employee may have minor restrictions at maximum medical improvement but is expected to return to his or her regular job. The rehabilitation professional may submit the job analysis of the client's regular job to his or her physician for approval only to learn that a critical detail was omitted when the client is informed about a release to work.

This point was made clear in a job analysis completed for a railroad engineer who was a below-knee amputee who also had a back injury with a 25 pound lifting limitation. Initially, it appeared he could perform all of the duties of railroad engineer. However, in discussion with the employee and observation of the required task, it was learned that he had to, on occasion, carry 50-pound bags of sand to the top of the locomotive to the sander, a device which dropped sand onto the track when the train goes up hills. After hearing this, the job analyst realized that his client would be unable to complete this task, thereby making a return to work unsuitable.

After the employer, supervisor, and, if appropriate, the client/employee have approved the job as analyzed, it is then appropriate to provide the job description, job analysis, and supporting data to the physician for his or her approval. If the physician requires certain modifications, the rehabilitation professional can return to the employer and client to negotiate changes. At that point, the results of the job analysis will become uniquely applicable to the client in question, allowing the rehabilitation client to proceed toward placement or settlement.

Selected topics to be included in a job analysis can be found in Table 8.2. In addition, the reader is encouraged to consult the references in this article for more information about the details of how to perform a job analysis, especially those focusing on the private sector.

As a final note, it must be stressed that ethical considerations apply to the job analysis process as much as they do to any area of rehabilitation. One ethical consideration is competence. The rehabilitation counselor should use published methodology so that results are valid. In *Drury v. Corvel* (1993), a nurse completed a job analysis based on the company's one page report form. She had no knowledge of the government publications related to this topic. The person was released to work by his physician on the basis of the report and was reinjured as a result. The case went to trail, and the jury awarded $261,400. Also, the rehabilitation professional must guard against conducting a job analysis with preconceived notions that might bias the outcome of that analysis. As mentioned in the above examples, even the most innocent assumption about a job must be confirmed with objective, accurate data. Otherwise, the client can be made to suffer as a result of an analysis performed in a slipshod manner (as in the Drury case). A job analysis should produce the same results on a given job by any number of experienced raters, provided the same criteria are followed during observation and exploration. It is only if modifications are made that the job description might vary from one individual to another. Regardless, objectivity and accuracy remain critical elements throughout the process.

Summary

Job analysis is an important part of the private sector rehabilitation process. In addition to using job analysis to develop descriptions and ADA/Equal Employment Opportunity criteria, job analysis can be the final step toward placement of an adult client with a disability or a prelude to job accommodation. Through communication, cooperation, and coordination of efforts, clients can be properly placed, enhancing the potential for long-term employment success and promoting the image of rehabilitation as a valuable profession. For more detailed information, see *Job Analysis and the ADA: A Step by Step Guide* (Blackwell, Conrad, & Weed, 1992). Sample forms are located in Appendices.

Table 8.2
Job Analysis Checklist

✔ Have you included all physical demands of the job? (Strength, sit, stand, walk, lift, carry, push, pull, climb, balance, stoop, kneel crouch, crawl, bend, reach, handle, finger, feel, talk, hear, smell/taste, right & left hand, and near, far, depth, color, accommodated vision requirements.)

✔ Have you included the environmental conditions? (Inside, outside, cold, heat, wet, humid, noise, vibrations, hazards, fumes, odors, and dust, exposure to electric shock, radiation, and toxic chemicals.)

✔ What are the general educational development levels? (reasoning, math and language.)

✔ What are the entry level training requirements? (High-school, vocational school, on-the-job, college, etc.)

✔ What aptitudes are required? (General learning ability, verbal, numerical, spatial, form perception, clerical perception, motor coordination, finger dexterity, manual dexterity, eye-hand-foot coordination, and color discrimination.)

✔ What interests are appropriate? (Refer to the Guide for Occupational Exploration)

✔ What personality factors (temperaments) are important? (Directing, repetitive, influencing others, variety, expressing feelings, work alone, stress, precise tolerances, under instructions, dealing with people, judgments.)

✔ Have you obtained the employer's job description?

✔ Have you compared the description with the Dictionary of Occupational Titles definition?

✔ What are the normal work hours?

✔ Is overtime likely?

✔ Did you observe the job long enough to fully understand all of the details and requirements?

✔ Would pictures or a video of the job be appropriate to describe the job?

✔ Will the employer modify the job? (Flex time, restructure, job share, etc.)

✔ Special clothing or tools required?

✔ Will job accommodation (or rehab tech) make the job more accessible to the client?

✔ What architectural barriers exist? Can they be eliminated?

✔ Did the employer approve the job as analyzed?

✔ Did the client approve the job as analyzed?

✔ Did the client's physician approve the job as analyzed?

Reference: *Handbook for Analyzing Jobs-Revised* (1991), U.S. Dept. of Labor.

JOB ANALYSIS NARRATIVE REPORT

Position: Scaleperson

DOT#:   920.685-090

Date of Job Analysis: 3/6/92

Location: Union Camp Paper Mill
                                     Franklin, Virginia

People Present:

H. S. (personnel department), C. S. (union representative and co-worker), J. C. (shift supervisor), J. J. (day supervisor), S. R., RN; C. G., rehabilitation counselor, Learning Services Corporation, R.W., rehabilitation consultant

General Job Description: (Source: Union Camp Paper Mill)

The scaleperson job has two primary functions: 1) to properly identify all first quality, offgrade, reject, and downgrade rolls coming from the paper machine winder; to generate and apply proper core tags and bar codes for rolls produced and to enter the required information into the computer; and 2) to move these rolls from the scale table onto the roll handling system and operate that portion of the roll handling system which serves the scale table. Additionally, the scaleperson is responsible for maintaining a neat and orderly scale table.

Communication and cooperation with other mill employees are required to facilitate the filling of orders. The scaleperson is responsible for informing the supervisor of potential backlogs or problems to prevent winder shutdown. When necessary, the scaleperson directs the activities of the scaleperson helper.

Salary and Benefits:

As of the date of this report, the Scaleperson position paid $15.27 per hour (approximately $32,000 for 2,080 hours of work). Occasionally, income can vary with increased duties. Overtime opportunities are often available.

In addition to wages, comprehensive benefits are included. Employees receive two weeks of vacation after three years, three weeks after eight years, four weeks after 12 years, five weeks after 18 years, and six weeks after 25 years.

Work Hours and Schedule:

Shifts are not routine. A general schedule is as follows:

> 11:00 p.m. to 7:00 a.m., 7 straight days with 2 days off
> 3:00 p.m. to 11:00 p.m., 7 straight days with 1 day off
> 7:00 a.m. to 3:00 p.m., 7 straight days with 5 days off

Essential Functions:

1. Measure diameter of new set and enter into computer with order information previously entered (see photos).

2. Stencil ends of rolls as required.

3. Print proper core tags and bar codes and apply them to corresponding rolls.

4. Move rolls from scale table to roll handling system. (Push pressure is approximately 25 pounds due to floor slant.)

5. Operate portion of roll handling system serving Scaleperson's table. (Power assisted.)

6. Communicate with mill personnel to find out about offgrade, reject, and downgrade rolls and reasons. Enter order numbers and reason codes in computer system.

7.   Keep work area (scale table) clean and orderly.

This scope of work is not an all-inclusive listing of the duties for this position. Non-routine duties are not included in the list of essential functions; additional duties may be assigned as circumstances dictate.

Qualifications:

The position requires a high school diploma or general equivalency diploma. As computerized equipment is added to the paper mill, more cognitive skills and increased judgment are required; however, the computerized equipment is not considered complex. No specific certifications or licenses are required. The employee learns on-the-job and works up the ladder and through various job stations as he or she is competent to do so and as positions become available. A check-off system conducted by supervisors will certify the work capabilities of the employee.

General Educational Development:

No specific math level requirements were identified. However, the employer reports that math requirements have become increasingly more important. Presently, skill to perform the four basic mathematical functions (add, subtract, multiply, divide) is adequate.

Practical communication language is required. Hand signals, because of the noisy environment, are often used. Listening and understanding what is being said and being able to follow written directions are required. Although computers are likely used to compile reports, occasionally written communication for reports is required. Little writing is required as the computer compiles the information and the employee enters the data via computer screen and keyboard. Paperwork consists of orders for rolls and sets of paper.

Aptitudes:

When working at the scale, rapid decision making and stress is not critical. However, operating the paper machine requires rapid decision making and good judgment when paper breaks occur.

No general testing was conducted. No job description in the Dictionary of Occupational Titles precisely fits the job observed. The closest title, Roll Finisher (920.685-090) appears to generally fit the requirements of the position.

Aptitude	Explanation
Intelligence	Below Average
Verbal	Below Average
Numerical	Negligible
Spatial	Below Average
Form Perception	Below Average
Clerical Perception	Below Average
Motor Coordination	Below Average
Finger Dexterity	Below Average
Manual Dexterity	Average
Eye/Hand/Foot	Negligible
Color	Negligible

Temperaments:

This position involves frequent repetitive work. When working at the scale, rapid decision making and stress are not critical; however, the paper machine can be dangerous and requires rapid decision making and good judgment when paper breaks. Although not normally a job task, the scaleperson helps others with paper breaks.

Reportedly no specific production quotas are required and the amount of stress one feels is reported to be dependent upon the individual's perception. The employer reports there is "generally a fair amount of pressure."

The scaleperson works on his own but not alone. Other people with different responsibilities are in the immediate area. Communication and cooperation with other mill employees (including supervision, other scalepersons, quality control staff, planning personnel, and office clerk) are required. When necessary, the scaleperson directs the activities of the scaleperson helper.

Environmental Conditions:

The scaleperson works at the end of a line where paper is made, processed, rolled, and cut. The job is performed entirely indoors and, therefore, not subject to extremes of temperature. The environment is that of a large warehouse that is generally noisy and requires ear protection. Occasionally, periods of loud or shrill noises are accented by a variety of bells, whistles, horns, and other alerting mechanisms.

No significant fumes or odors were noted. The employer reports that TRS gases pass through the area once per month, when vented from the pulp mill. No known health or medical problems result from this brief exposure.

Operating the paper machine can be dangerous due to high speed rollers and cramped location. Water and other apparent non-toxic chemicals were in the area. Contact with toxic chemicals is rare.

No exposure to electrical shock, unprotected heights, radiation, explosives.

The worker must wear safety shoes, helmet, ear protection, and eye protection. No uniforms are worn.

Exertional Physical Demands:

The employer states that standing varies depending on the duties and the size of the rolls of paper. Larger rolls of paper allow more rest and sitting, although sitting is allowed less than 30 minutes per shift. Smaller rolls require standing and moving around. On average, approximately two-thirds of the time during a work day involves standing. Walking is described as a minor part of the job. General walking involves an approximately 30 foot square area with occasional walking to the paper machine to help clean up a paper break. Walking to the work site from the parking lot, estimated to be about one-fourth mile, is the most significant walking requirement.

According to the employer, the maximum amount of lifting is generally 10 to 15 pounds. Occasionally, rolls of paper weighing 2,000 pounds or more may need to be pushed with the aid of a pry bar. The work area observed during this job analysis rarely required pushing of rolls due to the angle of incline of the floor. There is overhead pulling of 20 to 30 feet of wrapper paper off an overhead spool 20 to 30 times per month. There is also above-the-head pulling of a cord that controls a conveyor belt.

Non-Exertional Physical Demands:

No significant climbing was observed, although stairs to and from the work site and climbing into and around the paper machine are required. Stooping and/or bending is not a significant part of the job. The worker must be able to bend over to place plugs into the center of a roll of paper and to apply stenciling and bar code labels. General body functioning is required, however, excellent physical conditioning is not necessary. Crawling is not a significant part of the job.

The position requires data entry into a computer, handling bar code labels (peeling them from paper and placing them on the plugs of a set of paper). A control panel with dials ranging from one-half to two inches in diameter is used. Fine finger dexterity is not generally required. The worker must use hands and arms to reach and handle the plugs for the rolls of paper, apply stenciled lettering and numbers, and utilize wood mallets and pry bars. Use of both hands appears to be important. Accommodation may be possible.

The scaleperson must be able to answer a telephone several times each day in a noisy environment to receive and pass along instructions.

Near vision is required to the extent that the scaleperson needs to be able to read a computer screen, bar codes, and small numbers associated with bar codes. This task is required 20 to 30 times per day for a period of about five minutes each time. Depth perception and far vision are not a significant part of the position.

Field of vision is not generally significant, although the loss of one eye may pose safety problems due to moving machinery and rolls of paper.

Balancing, kneeling, crouching, feeling, and smelling are not generally required in the position.

Work Area

The mill has six scales. The job observed was scale number one, reportedly the easiest of the scale positions.

Promotion Prospects

Within the job category, the Scaleperson is next to the top job. The top step is termed Global Control which pays $16.74 per hour. The Scaleperson occasionally fills in for the Global Control person. Supervisory work is also available, and the salary is negotiated once the supervisor is accepted for management on a permanent basis. In order to be considered for management, the employee may be temporarily appointed to the position. As a temporary, the employee receives the highest pay in the category plus 10%. For example, a Global position paying $16.74 per hour plus 10% would be the rate for the temporary foreman. The wage rate for managers was not available.

The workers often have overtime opportunities.

Union

The plant is approximately 90% union for hourly employees.

Machines, Tools, Equipment, and Work Aids

No specific tools are required, and those which are utilized are provided by the company, for example, wooden mallets, stencil and brushes, pencils/pens, pry bar, tape measure, and paper. Machines and equipment include the use of computer terminal and printer, ramp lifts, stencil machine, and hydraulic control panel. One scaleperson's position requires the operation of a clamp truck (see photo).

Miscellaneous

The union rules state that an injured employee has one year to recover and return to work. He or she must work for an additional two weeks before their eligibility for another year absence is established. If the employee is unable to return to work within that time frame, they will lose their benefits and seniority position. If the employee attempts to return to work after the one year period he or she would have to reapply as a new worker and begin from the bottom.

If conditions warranted job coaching, the employer is willing to consider having an outside professional assist in an employee's return to work.

The employer indicates that employees routinely work overtime, estimated to average 56 hours per week.

Union Camp is located in a town of approximately 8,000 persons. It is located in a rural area of Virginia close to the North Carolina border.

The fine paper division has approximately 1,261 hourly employees with a total of 1,634 employees.

See following pages for photographs of Scaleperson and Global Control areas.

Photograph of the Scaleperson work area.

Photo depicts a "set" of paper that is delivered to the Scaleperson for processing and tagging. Depending on the size of the paper, the expectation that 20 or more sets per shift are processed. The sets of paper will come in different widths and heights depending on the order.

The Scaleperson measures the paper rolls in and enters the data into the computer to produce bar codes and ordering information.

Butt rolls, which are excess paper, are rolled to the side, banded, and removed. The round brown objects (also may be metal) on the floor are plugs for the center of the rolls of paper (see below).

The set of paper is released from a ramp stop and rolls, due to a slight incline in the floor, to another position where tagging and plugging takes place. The ramps drop to allow the paper to roll to the conveyor belt. Occasionally, the Scaleperson must assist in "breaking" the set or moving the rolls of paper. He or she may occasionally use a pry bar to initiate rolling. The rolls must be separated in order to plug the ends and affix the bar codes.

One of the control panels used by a Scaleperson for paper and conveyor belt control. The ramp stops are controlled from this position.

Rolls of paper are shown ready for metal or wood plugs to be placed into each roll.

Photo of the stencil machine where stencils are produced that will identify the order. The employee will use a brush to apply the identification data on the side of the roll of paper.

The operator enters the ordering information into the computer, and the printer (left) prints bar code tags, cart tag, and order information.

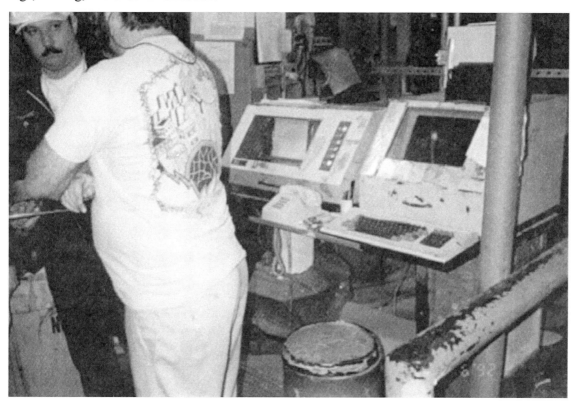

A clipboard is used to hold the report after being processed through the computer.

The Scaleperson or a helper uses a wood mallet to plug each of the rolls. The bar code labels are affixed to the plug.

The Scaleperson uses a brush to stencil the rolls. He or she also affixes bar code tags to the plug.

Photo shows a conveyor belt which moves rolls of paper out of the Scaleperson area. The device in the background on the left is a mechanical assist for rolling paper to another conveyor.

The Scaleperson pulls cords to start and stop the conveyor and ramp stops.

This clamp truck is located at scale number 2. The truck is used to move rolls of paper to the "Global" area.

Prepared by,

Roger Weed, Ph.D., Certified Rehabilitation Counselor, Certified Insurance Rehabilitation Specialist, Fellow, National Rehabilitation Counseling Association.

I have reviewed the job analysis and agree that it reasonably summarizes the requirements of the job.

_____   _____
Union Camp Representative   Date

Chapter 9
Job Placement Basics

Introduction

According to the 2010 U.S. Census, nearly 309 million people (50.8% female) live in the United States, an increase of 9.7% from 2000, and the number one goal with regard to economic stability is to be employed. In 2010 approximately 139 million people were employed, which is a decline from 2009 (Bureau of Labor Statistics [BLS], 2010a). Of that number, approximately 66 million were females (Bureau of Labor Statistics, 2010b). With regard to race, 72.4% were white, 12.6 were African-American, 16.3% were Hispanic (although the definition of Hispanic includes people of any other race), with the remaining including Asian, Native Americans, and others.

It is of interest to note that there has been a significant shift in labor force participation by gender. In 1960, 83.3% of the male population was employed, whereas in 1995 only 75% were employed. However, in 1960, 37.7% of women in working age were employed, and in 1995 this number rose to 58.9% (Farley, 1995). Of the total work force, 47% are women (BLS, 2010b) Thus, it is evident that women are clearly having a significant effect on labor force patterns.

Having a disability continues to be a detriment to employment. In 2010, the employment-population ratio was 18.6% for persons with a disability. Among those with no disability, the ratio was much higher at 63.5% (BLS, 2011). Interestingly, little change has been noted over the past 10 or so years. Men with a work disability working full and part time were employed at an approximate rate of 35.7% (with full time only being 23.4%). This compares to 88.9% of men without a work disability who are employed full and part time and 74.8% for men without a work disability working full time (U.S. Department of Commerce, 1989, p. 4). For women with a work disability, working full and part time, the rate was approximately 27.5%, whereas women without a work disability was 69.5%. However, when working full time only, the percent of participation was 13.1% compared to full time working women without a work disability of 47.1%. For all worker with a disability, 32% usually worked part time in 2010, compared with 19% of workers without a disability (BLS, 2011)

Based on the data, and as expected, it appears that work is an extremely important goal for the vast majority of the people and that there is a significant difference between people with a disability and without a disability with regard to their labor force participation rate (BLS, 2011; Pope & Tarlov, 1991). It is obvious that people with a disability have difficulty obtaining a job, and many are simply unemployed because they are unable to find suitable employment. Research consistently shows that approximately 67% of people with a work disability who claim that they want to work are unable to secure employment even if they have the job skills (Stoddard, Jans & Kraus, 1998; U.S. Census Bureau data as cited in Farley, 1996). Another reference states that about three out of four people with severe disabilities do not have jobs (Thornburgh & Fine, 2000). In general, people with a disability have difficulty obtaining suitable employment because of employer attitudes (Brown & McDaniel, 1987; Havranek, 1991; Thornburgh & Fine, 2000; Weed & Field, 1994) and because of the practical aspects of the limitations that people with disabilities possess. For example, it is well known that people with emotional disabilities and significant brain injuries have the greatest difficulty in finding and keeping jobs (Lewis & Bitter, 1991; McMahon & Shaw, 1991).

Another disability related issue that affects employment is appearance (Arokiasamy, Rubin, & Rossler, 1995). One study measured the general effects of appearance on income for the general population and found that people who are considered "lesser attractive" earned from 5-10% less than the average-looking person (Hammermesh & Biddle, 1993). Consistent with research regarding people without a disability, those who have an obvious disability and/or are aesthetically disfigured are more likely to be unemployed or have the most difficulty locating suitable employment and may be relegated to jobs that do not deal with the public or have much face-to-face interaction. Examples include people with scars from severe burns (especially facial), people with cerebral palsy, and people with extremity deformities or amputations. The Veterans Administration has developed a table of estimated economic losses associated with head, face, and neck disfigurement that can be found in the Veterans Administration (VA) Schedule for Rating Disabilities (as cited in Johnson, Ley, & Benshoof, 1993). In the VA table, economic losses associated with disfigurement range from 0% if disfigurement is considered slight/negligible to 50% if considered complete, which is defined as exceptionally repugnant deformity of one or both sides of face. The losses increase within the category of moderate, severe, or complete disfigurement if there is marked discoloration or color contrast associated with the disfigurement. On the other hand, many people have "hidden" disabilities and are commonly able to avoid disclosure to employers, thereby making them much more likely to obtain employment. Examples of "invisible" or hidden disabilities include people with back injuries, well-controlled seizure disorders (epilepsy), heart disease, cancer, HIV, and others. Another problem many people encounter is the combination of disability and minority status. In this context, minority status includes immigrants as well as individuals of minority status who are born in America. With regard to State rehabilitation services, people of ethnic and racial minorities who have a disability have a disproportionately higher rate of rejection for services, are less likely to complete a rehabilitation program, and have less effective or satisfying vocational outcome (Moore et al., 2009; Arokiasamy, Rubin, & Rossler, 1995).

The Value of Rehabilitation Counseling

As can be concluded from the available data on employment rate of people with disabilities, it should be no surprise that rehabilitation counselors are a valuable asset in assisting people with disabilities to overcome many of the obstacles to successful employment. Clearly, the efforts of rehabilitation have been successful in a variety of settings, including workers' compensation, state rehabilitation services, mental health, and the like (Pope & Tarlov, 1991; Rubin & Rossler, 1995; Weed & Field, 1994). In addition, studies have demonstrated that once employed in an appropriate position, people with disabilities perform as well as people without disabilities (Dupont, 1982; Weed & Lewis, 1994).

Therefore, the bottom line is that rehabilitation counselors are in a unique position to spur change and influence the ability of people with disabilities to obtain and maintain satisfying employment. However, it takes effort, focus, and commitment on the part of the client as well as the rehabilitation counselor to arrive at the point where the client can be successfully employed. The rehabilitation counselor must be adequately educated in job placement procedures and methods to facilitate research into the labor market and help to structure, guide, and counsel clients with regard to job-seeking skills and ultimate job placement (see Bolles & Brown, 2000). This chapter will outline some of the basic steps the rehabilitation counselor can utilize with regard to job placement. A list of Internet resources as well as a reference list is included at the end of the chapter for suggested reading of other publications that go into much more detail with regard to various disability groups and specialty areas.

Client Preparation

Although it seems obvious that clients need to have various job skills in order to be attractive to employers, many rehabilitation counselors seem to take the approach that employers can do their "humanistic duty" by hiring people with disabilities. It is this author's contention that that is absolutely the wrong way to approach job placement. One anecdotal story from an employer is that a rehabilitation counselor approached him with the idea that it would be part of his civic duty if he could assist a client in returning to work. He agreed to work with the rehabilitation counselor and offer the client (who had a back injury) a job. However, rather than employing an individual who could contribute to the employer's overall productivity and financial success based on appropriate work skills, the employer was under the impression that he could arrange his business around the client's disability. Initially all seemed to go well, and the client was oriented to the job for one month and then placed with co-workers who assisted in the tasks that the client was limited in performing. As can be expected, within about six months, co-workers' attitudes went from being interested in helping the client to resenting the fact that they now had to do their work as well as assist this other person to do his work. Less than one year later, the client had to be "let go" in order to save the morale of the business in general. This story also underscores the value of performing a job analysis prior to placement to assure that the client can perform the essential functions of the job, even if reasonable accommodations are necessary.

In job placement, a basic premise is that the client, in order to be successfully placed, must have job skills that enhance the employer's business and that the match is "a good business deal." Studies show that when properly evaluated and placed, clients will perform at levels consistent with people without disabilities (Du Pont, 1982; McCray, 1994). In a previous chapter of this book, the reader was provided the basic information for conducting *labor market survey* to identify various job opportunities that exist in the labor market and would be consistent with the client's skills, abilities, aptitudes, interests, and temperaments. Once a potential job is identified, it is appropriate to obtain a detailed and specific *job analysis* (see appropriate chapter elsewhere in this book for procedures) that identifies the worker traits required of the job and compares them with the work characteristics of the individual to ensure a successful match.

To accomplish this task, the rehabilitation counselor can help prepare the client in a variety of ways. One of the author's presumptions, based on years of job placement experience, is to be sure that the client is psychologically ready for employment (e.g., they have the right attitude). It is the author's opinion that a client, who is otherwise not expected to go back to work for one to two years following the injury, should be contacted by the rehabilitation counselor as early as possible after the injury in order to keep them motivated and focused on the ultimate goal of returning to work. This client contact also allows the counselor to develop a relationship with the client over a period of time, and it helps prevent the client from feeling pushed or prodded in areas or ways contrary to what they perceive as in their best interest or financial well being. Having ongoing discussions with clients regarding their attitudes toward work, engaging in some sort of educational, volunteer, or work related venture if possible, and otherwise focusing on the intended goal of enhancing their economic well being by being employed is a good start for the rehabilitation counselor's work with the client. In some cases, clients are seen in the hospital while still recovering from such injuries as traumatic amputation or severe burns where it is not expected they would return to work anytime within the near future. The rehabilitation counselor's counseling skills are quite useful at the outset to lay the foundation for future rehabilitation activities and enhance successful job placement.

One of the other options available to rehabilitation counselors is to assist clients in attaining a more positive approach to life. Suggested readings in this area include books such as *Think and Grow Rich* by Napoleon Hill (1960), *In Search of Excellence* (Peters & Waterman, 1982), and *What Color is Your Parachute?* (Bolles, 2012) and video series on *YouTube* (Bolles, 2009). Coupling these readings with discussions and vocational exploration sessions with the client may prove to be useful. Obviously if the client has a mental or cognitive/intellectual disability to the extent that they are unable to adequately participate in reading or performing these kinds of exercises, a very different approach, suitable to the individual client, must be considered.

In the event that the client has a mental incompetency (a brain injury, emotional disorder, autism, or other mental challenge), it is important to include the family and/or guardian/legal representative in the job placement planning. Behavior therapy techniques are also effective with this group of clients. Perceived "reinforcers," such as tokens that can be exchanged for a valued commodity, can be useful in enhancing the client's participation. In addition, it may be necessary to develop a "work readiness" program that includes training in proper personal hygiene, behavior skills, time management techniques, and public transportation usage. If work readiness is needed, it is recommended that the client be referred to the appropriate community resource for evaluation and training.

Historically, rehabilitation counselors who work within the workers' compensation system have attempted to place clients in jobs that are within their capabilities regardless of whether the job matches their temperament or interest areas, as long as the client has the physical capabilities of working (Weed & Taylor, 1990). One argument is that interests can be very subjective in nature; for example, a client could simply say, "I don't want to do that" and opt not to accept employment that on the surface seems reasonable. An example where this method of job placement backfired was described earlier in this book in the case of the client who had been working as a nurse and was physically restricted from lifting patients due to a work related injury. The client reportedly was ordered to accept a job with the employer that was clerical in nature (and within her physical capabilities). However, because the job did not match her interests, she did not enjoy the work and ultimately quit. Although her workers' compensation benefits were terminated, they were reinstated after she appealed through the court system since the job was considered "not suitable" based on her specific history and traits. In general, regardless of the jurisdiction, it is this author's opinion that it is reasonable and prudent to consider the "entire person" and not just physical functional capabilities, when developing job placement plans. In fact, this approach is mandated by federal law for people seeking assistance through the state-federal public agency program (U.S. Department of Education, 2001). Indeed, probably the most important factor for successful job performance is the personality fit. People who have the social skills and communication capability, who are dependable and responsible, and who possess good worker traits are more likely to continue employment than workers who do not have these "people skills." In at least one publication, it was determined that most people did not lose a job as a result of their inability to do the work; rather, they lose a job because of personal skills such as dishonesty, not getting along well with people, failing to show up for work, having a "different" personality from the employer, using forbidden or illegal substances, etc. (Cohen, 1984). In the event that a client subjectively disregards employment opportunities because of a claimed lack of interest, the rehabilitation counselor should closely review the client's past work history (if they have work history) in order to identify appropriate temperament and interests for use as demonstrated personality factors.

In addition, the rehabilitation counselor has available to them the option of referring the client for a vocational evaluation, which includes formal testing in the areas of aptitude, interests, and temperament/personality and can be very beneficial in rehabilitation and job placement planning. However, anecdotally reviewing the results of the evaluation in conjunction with listening to the client's expressed interests probably is the most effective job placement approach. Sometimes clients will add objections because they are fearful, unsure, or suspicious of the counselor's motives. Taking the time to develop a relationship that works toward achieving common goals will help reduce or eliminate objections. Obtaining a commitment from the client to work with the counselor is also recommended. For example, the rehabilitation counselor could say, "If I work with you to assist you in achieving your vocational goals, will you work with me?" If the client hesitates or fails to offer an affirmative answer, it may be useful to explore underlying concerns and find a forum where a clear "yes" commitment can be obtained. Otherwise, the client may very well not work with the counselor, which then adversely affects the entire job placement process as well as the professional reputation of the rehabilitation counselor.

Probably one of the most important elements of successful job placement is having the client be involved in achieving their own "destiny" and actively participating in the process of gathering information for the foundation of their efforts. Perhaps an analogy of cooking is helpful to describe the process. For example, before one shops for ingredients, one should have an idea of what it is they want to cook. In essence, the client, too, needs to know what it is they want to do. Part of gathering occupational information is to look through "cookbooks" to get an idea as to which jobs look or sound good. The client may want to check out a new cookbook and try to determine what the current trends are, such as job shortages or other information found in periodicals or through employer contacts, informational interviewing (see Porot, 1995), networking, etc. The rehabilitation counselor also must help determine if the "ingredients" are available. That is, does the client have the intelligence, interest, aptitude, and personality to be able to "cook this gourmet meal" (i.e., find the right job)?

Once the client knows what they want to "cook" and they have the ingredients, they also need to have the tools that are necessary such as stove, pots, pans, utensils, etc., which, from an analogy point of view, are training sites and employers in a geographical area who offer the kind of job opportunities for which the person is looking (think of trying to find Italian food in a rural village in China). It may be that a client must be willing to consider moving to a location that would maximize their successful placement and therefore satisfy their palate. For example, living in a rural area in Colorado probably is not a good location if one wants to work on a shrimp boat. Also, a job title may not really describe what is actually involved in a job; for example, working in the oil fields also requires workers being apart from their families for extended periods of time. Tractor-trailer truck drivers experience similar kinds of family separation and stresses. There are also elements within a job that may be very unpleasant. For example, rehabilitation counselors may find the amount of paperwork, forms, procedures, and such to be much more than they had intended when they decided to work with people with disabilities. Indeed, when this author began his first professional rehabilitation counseling job for a state agency, he was handed a 3-ring binder filled with forms that had to be learned. It took the better part of one year just to accommodate to all of the job requirements of being a rehabilitation counselor that were not included as part of the master's program in rehabilitation counseling.

In order for a client to fully understand what is included in a job, it will take much more than looking through brochures or reading job titles on the O*NET or the career information system available in most states. The client also needs to understand that job titles may be consistent but have very different requirements within the job itself. For example, a secretary position entails certain duties and tasks in a legal office and other tasks in a medical office and still other tasks in an accounting or other business office. Requirements of the job (i.e., the sophistication needed and the job duties and tasks) can vary dramatically from location to location. In some situations, a person may not have all the required skills that are needed, or some elements of the job may need to be accommodated. Using the cooking analogy, this is similar to locating almost all of the ingredients for the gourmet dinner but having to substitute for something that was not available in the store or in the person's kitchen. Having the ability to be somewhat flexible is a useful trait to possess. In some occasions, people who have a significant enough disability that they have little flexibility or choice will likely be willing to accept jobs that are not exactly what they want. In other cases, it may be that there are numerous opportunities available and several jobs have all the work characteristics the client is seeking. The latter, of course, is ideal though seldom achieved, especially during the national economic challenges at the time of this revision (BLS, 2010a).

Some clients prefer to seek employment by developing their own business. While this may be an appropriate option for some clients, efforts for placement with an employer generally are explored first before self-employment is pursued. It is widely known that most businesses fail within the first five years, and it is necessary to build a solid business foundation before undertaking this extraordinary effort. However, persons with a disability are more likely to be self-employed than those without a disability (BLS, 2011). This chapter does not include the details for starting a business and for the rare client who may be a candidate for self-employment, the rehabilitation counselor is advised to direct them to the local office of the Small Business Administration (SBA) or on-line at www.sbaonline.sba.gov and the local SCORE resource (Service Corps of Retired Executives), which can be located through the SBA or on-line at www.score.org.

The Resume

There are several good reasons to help a client develop a resume, even if the job that they apply for or company that they apply to does not require or want a resume. Reasons include the following:

1. Requires the client to review their skills (skills are work related talents and abilities that are learned by doing). Generally, many clients have not taken the time to identify their skills. For example, a client may think that word processing 45 words per minute (wpm) is really not much of a skill because "anybody can do it" when, in fact, most people cannot. Additionally, if a job requires typing 45 wpm, then having this skill may make the difference between potential employment or not. The rehabilitation counselor may need to help "massage" the client's view of their own capabilities and identify those skills, interests, and abilities that the client does well and that may enhance their successful job placement.

2. Organizes the client. Many people have a difficult time organizing their thoughts or their lives. This is an opportunity to spend time trying to put job related information in an order that will assist the client in answering various questions that may be asked on job interviews.

3. Can be used to sell themselves. Even for employers who do not accept resumes, they can be used as a foundation to educate clients to "sell" themselves, particularly when clients are uncomfortable talking to others. The rehabilitation counselor can assist clients in developing their resume to help highlight abilities, accomplishments, and topics that may be of interest to perspective employers. Additionally, having an opportunity to practice discussing their accomplishments in advance should reduce the client's anxiety and stress when meeting with prospective employers.

4.   Focuses attention on work. Unless people actually set time aside to discuss work options and to develop work related vocational goals and plans, it probably will not happen. A resume helps develop this foundation.

On the other side of the coin, it is very important to understand that resumes are most often used to screen people out, not in (Bolles, 2012). This is particularly justifiable for businesses that may have an opening for which numerous people apply. The person who scans resumes essentially will be looking for ways to eliminate people from consideration. This underscores the need to conscientiously develop resumes for those businesses that seek them. Certainly, a poorly written resume which also is not well organized or has misspelled words is likely to work against the client. Likewise, many resumes include a generic job objective statement that does not specifically relate to the job opening or business, and this, too, will probably quickly eliminate them from consideration. In other words, do not write a job objective statement unless it directly relates to the company's hiring goal! The statement should be written to reflect that the client has capabilities that are directly in line with what the employer is looking for. (Use key words that are listed in the ad so that electronic word scanning software will retain the resume for closer inspection.) Having statements such as "interested in a work site that utilizes my skills and allows for upward mobility" is too broad and will not impress an employer. A job objective statement should be left off if it is necessary to take a resume to an interview when enough information is not available. However, it is recommended that a client not provide a resume at the first interview unless they have conducted enough research to know about the job requirements and what traits and skills the employer is seeking. Furthermore, the resume should be written so that it matches the client's personal goals with those of the employer. In his book, *What Color is your Parachute?*, Richard Bolles, an international expert on job hunting skills, writes, "an employer is going through a whole stack of resumes, and on average he or she is giving each resume about eight seconds of their time... Then that resume goes either into a pile we might call 'Forgeddit,' or a pile we might call 'Bears further investigation'" (as cited in Terrell & Richards, 2011, para. 4) so the client and counselor will need to pay attention to details of the resume.

In instances where a client has a strong interest in working for a particular employer and their skills are directly in line with what the employer states that they are seeking, the job objective statement can be a way to quickly identify the client as a qualified applicant. For example, let us assume that a private rehabilitation company is looking for an individual who would like to work with clients who have been injured while working and are involved in insurance rehabilitation. Let us further assume that the position is one for job placement of such clients. In this case, the job objective on the resume could state something along the lines of "Seeking a private rehabilitation firm that can utilize my skills as a job placement specialist for people who are involved in disability insurance rehabilitation programs."

There are several books and on-line resources that are available with regard to writing resumes (e.g., Parker, 2002; Schultze, 2012; Mesmer, n.d.; and other resources located at the end of this chapter.)

The type of resume that the client should develop will depend on their skills, traits, education, and work experience. For example, clients who may have little or no work history, such as those with mental challenges, people who were injured prior to entering the work force, people on welfare assistance, etc. may need to survey what they do to run their home, as well as any voluntary activities, to determine what their skills are. For example, babysitting entails certain capabilities, as does maintaining a household, participating in church activities, raising a family, preparing meals, and performing other similar activities. In this instance, it is useful to try to identify skills that can be listed rather than focus on paid employment where there really is not adequate employment history.

A special note: Many employers have become quite savvy with regard to the accuracy of resumes. Several studies have indicated that resumes commonly falsify information. One study revealed that 71% of the people lied on their resume, 40% left something off of the resume that probably was relevant, and 80% of the people thought it was a common practice to falsify resumes in one way or another (Atlanta Journal and Constitution, 1999). Another study in 1992 of 6,873 high school and college students revealed that one-third of students thought it was okay to lie on resumes (Bolles, 2000). The rehabilitation counselor should endeavor to verify as much as possible the client's skills, abilities, and work history in order to accurately reflect the information. Indeed, the author's own experience reveals that one rehabilitation consultant practiced for several years claiming he had a master's degree in rehabilitation when, in fact, he did not. Another claimed that his degree came through a medical school when, in fact, it was his internship site that was at a medical school. Some of these items are flat falsifications and others may be a twist of the truth. Nevertheless, for the longevity of successful employment, it is recommended that accurate information always be provided.

Effective Job Placement Techniques

In general, the three best approaches to finding employment are networking, networking, and networking (Bolles, 2012). The vast majority of people who find jobs, particularly those who work in areas of high competition or who perhaps are not "cream of the crop," do so through contacting people such as friends, relatives, past co-workers, teachers, casual acquaintances, volunteer activity contacts, church members, neighbors, ex-classmates, family friends, and acquaintances (Azrin & Besalel, 1980). In order to get started, it also is recommended that the job developer join local business clubs such as Rotary Club, Chamber of Commerce, Lion's Club, and others.

Another obvious alternative to locating potential employers is to look at the on-line Yellow Pages. The various job possibilities are arranged by category and the client can make calls directly to businesses of interest even if there are no known openings. One disadvantage is that the manager or owner's name is not listed so it may be difficult to speak with the person in charge of hiring and applications. An option is to go to the public library or a Chamber of Commerce office in larger cities and ask to use the R. L. Polk City Directory (although the directory is not online, the resource is available online at www.polk.com). The Directory is organized in several ways, including name, type of business, and location. Most businesses also have key people's names listed, and, even if the key person has left the business, just knowing a name will help get past secretaries and others who screen out "cold callers." In smaller cities, the Chamber of Commerce is still a reasonable point of contact, since their mission is to sell the location to potential businesses and residents. Larger businesses and industries generally are well known, and the people who work as staff for the Chamber can be outstanding sources of information about the local economy, labor market trends, and people. Additional resources include job services (for online versions, see resources at end of chapter), "headhunters" if the client possesses the skills for primarily skilled or professional work settings (companies usually specialize in a particular industry, so some investigation may be required to find the "right" one), and the local Division of Rehabilitation Services counselor or placement specialist (see Table 9.1).

In general, it is not a good idea to simply "apply" for jobs. It is usually preferred to initiate the "informational interview" approach (see resource at the end of this chapter). An informational interview for a client who is cognitively and temperamentally capable of using this method, means that they would approach the employer with the attitude that they are not looking for a job as such, but rather gathering information with regard to the work force:

- what is required (education, skills, tools, etc.)
- what is the pay
- what are the benefits
- what are the job opportunities within a particular industry.

Following the informational interview, it may very well be that a job that a client truly would like to pursue exists with that employer. In this example situation, a resume with a properly worded job objective should then be sent back to the prospective employer along with a thank you note for the amount of time that was spent answering questions or providing information. Sometimes it is difficult to get an appointment with an employer (as opposed to personnel department or someone who is not in a position to hire), and it is useful to be able to reference a referral from someone who knows the individual. For example, think of the impact it might have if you were able to contact an employer and say "President Barack Obama suggested that I con-

---

Table 9.1
A Checklist For Starting A Job Search

✔ Make lists of people who can help with networking. Include family, friends, past co-workers, church contacts, recreational pursuit peers, neighbors, past teachers, social clubs, and personal physician.

✔ Review yellow pages (online or paper) in the category of job of interest.

✔ Go to local Chamber of Commerce office to review their directories for company names, phone numbers and executive's names.

✔ If in a larger community, go to library or Chamber of Commerce and ask to review the Polk City Directory. Be sure to list manager names and phone numbers.

✔ If the occupation has a trade association or union, contact them.

✔ Call to talk with supervisors or managers (people in a position to hire).

✔ Go to larger organizations and review job listings (e.g., government or Fortune 500 businesses). Many have openings online.

✔ Review job openings listed online (see Internet resources at end of chapter).

✔ Consider job placement firm if they do NOT require fees unless placement is achieved.

✔ If the client is a skilled worker or professional, consider "head hunters" who specialize in the field of choice.

✔ Check out the local government job service office and/or review America's Job Bank online (see resources).

✔ Contact the State rehabilitation office to network with the job developer.

✔ Perhaps review want ads (last resort unless skills are esoteric or rare).

---

tact you, because you are quite knowledgeable in this area of employment." In order to ask for a person by name, networking with others in the same industry is fruitful. For example, if one contact is asked to offer the names of two employers/managers, each of whom is then asked for two names, it will not take long to have an extensive list of contacts. Also, one can call the company and simply ask for the name of the manager or supervisor, or use the Polk Directory or other similar resources if the client's geographical area is large enough to warrant having the directory.

As referenced above, it is very important to send thank you notes (hand written, not emailed) to all people who assist in providing job-planning information, regardless of the client's interest in jobs associated with the employer who was interviewed. Also, in the event that the client would like to work for the employer but no position is available, it is especially important to leave a good impression and leave the door open, so to speak. In some situations, a job may be strongly pursued by the client but a competitor may be offered the position. A thank you note may very well prove to be a positive influence, particularly if the person to whom the job was offered either rejects it or stays for a very short period of time, therefore creating another opening for the job (something that happens more frequently than many people may realize). In this example, even though the client may have been number two at the initial interview, he or she may become number one by virtue of some of the extra effort that they have expended in order to leave a positive image in a prospective employer's mind.

During the job placement process, it is important that the client attempt to identify people who are in a position to hire, rather than network through individuals who are not in a position to hire. Larger businesses usually have personnel departments, and, in general, supervisors are not always impressed with the personnel department. In fact, sometimes supervisors actually have strong negative opinions regarding personnel departments. Typically, the personnel department's role is to make sure that the supervisor in charge of hiring meets various rules (e.g., diversity hiring), laws (e.g., equal employment opportunity), and that there is a position that is available based on company budget. A supervisor may very well indicate that, prior to hiring, the client would have to submit an application to be reviewed by the personnel department to make sure they meet whatever the requirements are; however, the supervisor probably is able to significantly influence the selection and hiring process. It also should be noted that most supervisors are not trained, or at least adequately trained, in the hiring process and probably resent the amount of time it takes to interview people. Anything one can do to facilitate the process or to reduce the supervisor's time and effort may be useful. For example, most supervisors will be positively influenced by having individuals referred to them by co-workers or someone that they know (Bolles, 2012). Having an individual come in "cold" off of the street gives supervisors no basis on which to make decisions other than limited paper review (i.e., resume or application) and a short interview. However, if it is known that this individual is well liked by co-workers in another setting or that they have a good reputation, etc., the decision maker may be influenced to the extent that they will overlook limitations in the client's work capability.

Other approaches to finding employment include reviewing the classified ads in newspapers. Most clients and job seekers spend copious amounts of time reviewing want ads when this is probably the least effective way to actually find employment. Most applicants looking for jobs through the classified ads fail (Bolles, 2012). In addition, approximately 85% of prospective employees will review job ads which only represent 15% of the available job openings. That means that most job openings are not being advertised in the newspaper and the competition for those jobs is substantially reduced. Certainly people do obtain jobs through the classified ads in the newspaper, but those usually are people who are either "cream of the crop" or the job that is advertised is so widely available that one would not need the ad to find it in the first place. For example, a fast food worker could probably go to the nearest fast food restaurant or a nurse could probably contact health care organizations to be able to find employment and would not need to see the ad in the newspaper. Another opportunity to be employed through the want ads is if the job is very esoteric or specific in nature. In those situations, there are so few people who are capable of performing a certain job that a want ad would be a good way to find that one applicant (such as a certified mechanic for General Electric rocket engine model number 1302).

Another option is to approach an employment agency. Many employment agencies do provide job opportunities, however, there are some pitfalls. Some employment agencies require that the client or job seeker pay a substantial fee for either job assistance or actual job placement. Of course, there are also bogus job search organizations that will take an individual's money and then not provide any satisfactory service. If the employment agency charges their fee only if a job is secured, it may be an option since no fees are incurred unless the goal is achieved. In some cases, legitimate employment agencies have their fees paid by the employer if they are in jobs that are either hard to fill or are white-collar or skilled type jobs. Organizations that charge fees in advance of employment should raise the "red flag" and be avoided.

The rehabilitation counselor should also be aware that there are companies that will place ads in the newspaper which do not provide information that will allow the job seeker to contact them. Sometimes these are noted as "key box" or "blind ads" where the job seeker sends information typically to a post office box location or online that does not identify the employer. This is often a tactic for legitimate employment firms in order to avoid writing rejection letters to unsuccessful applicants. Also, in some situations, the business may be a company that sells products and people who are rejected for employment may very well stop buying their products. Therefore they do not want to disclose that information to a large number of people in order to reduce the potential for losing customers.

Another reason for an employment agency to have a key box or solicit online applications and resumes is to collect information in advance of having a job opening. For example, an employer may very well be willing to employ somebody from an employment agency, but they may also place an ad in the newspaper. If the employment agency waited to place the ad at the time the employer needed the person, several days would be lost. However, if they have been collecting resumes they could potentially provide top notch candidates to the employer the same day that a job became available, because they had been collecting the information in anticipation of some job openings such as secretarial, warehousing, drivers, and so forth. In most instances the job seeker simply will not receive any kind of contact from the "key box" holders unless they are a potential candidate. In this event, the vast majority of the applicants are screened out without any feedback to the client. A special alert! Some online, key, or blind box ads are placed by criminals who are seeking personal information, especially social security and driver's license numbers, to commit fraud against the "job applicant." In summary, it is recommended that clients avoid sending applications to key boxes or employers whose identity is unknown.

Employer Issues

Most employers are not interested in employee turnover. It is an added pressure to have to advertise openings, sort through applications, interview people, train new workers, and hope they have found the right match. In addition, most people who are in a position of hiring do not represent the owner or the CEO of a business, particularly when it is a larger company, and people who are supervised by others will be much less likely to take chances with the unknown. In essence, they play the game so that they do not "lose" rather than play the game in order to "win." In order to not lose, it is important for the supervisor to take whatever has been used as the standard practice within the company and try to replicate it. This includes everything from cultural, ethnic, religious, and, of course, disability related information. Some employers also perceive themselves as being "hampered" by the Americans with Disabilities Act (ADA) and other local, regional, or federal laws associated with hiring practices. Clients need to be educated and proactive with regard to developing a way to address any of these issues. Employers also may need to be educated with regard to the client's functional limitations and capabilities. In discussing abilities, it is best to avoid using diagnoses as a way to describe a person's limitations. Indeed, many people have a different view of what emotional illness might mean based on their personal experiences. In addition, a diagnosis does not automatically educate an individual with regard to limitations. For example, a client who has a seizure disorder (aka epilepsy) can be described in more than one way. The seizures may be uncontrolled or it could be that this person has taken medication for several years and has not had a seizure while on medication. Some experience a warning before having a seizure and others do not. Clearly, concerns with regard to employment would vary dramatically, depending on the actual capabilities and limitations associated with the disability. For example, many years ago a government entity issued a memo asking supervisors to identify "jobs that people with disabilities can do." It was quickly retracted when an individual indicated that a person with a disability could do any job within the government and it would depend on what the disability was and what their limitations, skills, and abilities were as to what could be expected. Indeed, several presidents of the United States have had disabilities, including paralysis, back injuries, and hearing loss. Under the ADA, employers cannot ask if a potential applicant has a disability, only if the applicant can perform the essential functions of the job (see chapter elsewhere in this book on the ADA). Also, pre-employment medical exams can only be ordered after an offer has been made.

Another employer issue is related to social networking sites. First, it is common for employers to Google the applicant to see what is easily available on the Internet (Fisher, 2011). The rehabilitation counselor also should Google the client in the event that certain information may need addressing prior to an interview. Furthermore, the client should be educated about appropriate and inappropriate content on such sites as Facebook, Twitter, and other social networking outlets.

Job Placement Myths

Employers, in general, are under-educated and/or misinformed with regard to hiring people with disabilities. For this reason, several "myths" surround the employment of people with disabilities that will be discussed in this section.

1. Some employers have a mistaken impression that if they hire people with disabilities, the company's workers' compensation rates will go up. The actual reason for a rise in workers' compensation rates is related to the risk associated with a job (a roofer has a much more dangerous job than a secretary) and the injury record or history of the business (i.e., the number of workers' compensation injuries reported), rather than by the individuals actually performing the job.

2. People with disabilities miss more work than the average employee. Several studies, most notably the Du Pont study (1981), indicate that this is not the case.

3. People with disabilities are injured or re-injured easier. As noted in the Du Pont study and others, this is not the case. Indeed, one of the roles of the rehabilitation counselor is to make sure that the client is properly placed, taking into account functional capabilities, limitations, and work tasks, so that a appropriate employment match is achieved.

4. People with disabilities are more sick than average. The evidence also does not support this myth.

5. People with disabilities have a lower productivity and are slower on the job. Another finding in Du Pont and other studies is that the productivity of people with disabilities is equal to other employees. In fact, some may say that people with disabilities actually work harder to be a good employee and are more appreciative of their job and the ability to be employed than people without disabilities.

One legitimate concern of people with disabilities who are seeking employment is the difficulty they may have with obtaining appropriate health insurance, particularly if working for smaller companies. Many people with disabilities have been "locked into" jobs in the past because they did not believe they could change jobs and were afraid to risk losing their health insurance. Although large companies with a major medical insurance program generally do not present this problem because of the large risk pool, some smaller companies are not in a position to adequately fund a potential increase in health insurance premiums, which may be a detractor. Some clients may lose their health coverage (.e., Medicaid/Medicare) if they find employment and are able to earn wages above the cutoff level, and this certainly is a disincentive. However, the reader is referred to Chapter 1 in this book - Public Law 106-170 - for a potential solution to this significant problem. (Note: The effects of the Affordable Care Act of 2010 are not known at the time of this revision.)

Accommodations

Many people with disabilities require job modifications which can range from flex time to part time hours to rehabilitation technology assistance. Understandably, some employers are quite concerned that this could be very expensive; however, several studies have indicated that most accommodations do not cost much, if anything (McMahon, 2010). In 1995, a Sears study indicated that 69% of their accommodations cost nothing, 28% cost less than $1,000, and 3% cost more than $1,000 [ADA Pipeline 4(3), 1995, p. 24]. The job accommodation network in 1995 reported that 31% of accommodations cost nothing, 50% cost less than $50, 69% cost less than $500, and 88% cost less than $1,000. (No author, 1995). Another study reported that, on average, accommodations for workers with disabilities cost employers less than $100 for each such worker (Thornburgh & Fine, 2000). For suggestions on job accommodation, please refer to the chapter on ADA and reasonable accommodation elsewhere in this book.

Considerations for Adverse Work History

Sometimes rehabilitation counselors may be utilized to assist clients

- who have spent time in prison,
- undergone significant physical rehabilitation and have been out of the work force,

- have not participated in the work force at all due to their disability (such as severe mental challenges or emotional illness),
- have been a homemaker and have no work history, and
- have been fired from previous jobs.

Historically, the latter one was more of an issue than it has been in the last decade, based on "downsizing" and the rapid turnover of people within the employment world. The stigma for switching jobs or not being employed for some period of time may be somewhat reduced as a result of the experiences of the economic decline in the United States. However, it is important to address these concerns with the client at the outset. Some individuals who have been laid off or fired from jobs may very well have a reduced "self-esteem" with regard to their capabilities and have a difficult time explaining, at least in rational terms, what happened. In general, it is strongly advised that the client not "bad mouth" a previous employer. There are almost always two sides to a story, and it may be that an employee simply did not have the personality that matched with the employer. Individuals who have taken the Myers-Briggs Type Indicator may have some experience or understanding of how someone could be effective on the job but still have difficulty working with colleagues based on differences in the way they approach the work world. In this event, it may be a "no fault" ending to a job, where both employer and employee may be effective in their own ways, and it would be a matter of arranging the workplace to accommodate the individuals' personalities such that employment can be successful. There are, of course, occasions where clients simply do not have the personal skills, or they may have impaired judgment, such that this could be a consistent ongoing problem and result in several job terminations or job changes. Nonetheless, the rehabilitation counselor is urged to individually evaluate each client's strengths and weaknesses and the decisions that will be developed based on the available data. If a client feels "destroyed" by being fired from a job, certain personality related interventions would be necessary. In other cases, weaknesses in a client's skill level may need additional support, training, or education.

Summary

A significant amount of commitment and effort is required in order for a client to find a job. Diligence is a virtue in finding a job as well as in the work force. Table 9.2 summarizes some of the necessary topics and issues to be considered in the job search. Having the attitude that a client will bring something to the work force and will economically and psychologically benefit is of course a primary need. Trying to find a job is a job in itself, and clients who plan to spend an hour or two a day are not likely to be successful, at least not in any kind of reasonable time frame. Clients should expect to spend full-time developing relationships, working on leads, networking, developing their resume, writing letters and thank you notes, and conducting all other efforts that are associated with finding employment. One research study based on welfare clients indicated that the key, particularly for people who have little employment history, was the number of interviews they arranged. (Azrin & Besalel, 1980). Obviously, the more interviews in which a client participates, the greater their chances of employment.

In addition to job placement activities, rehabilitation counselors may very well be educating or working with clients on areas that are not directly related to employment. For example, transportation arrangements, grooming and hygiene, proper attire, reactions or attitudes toward work, family support or interference, and other challenges that impede the client's ability or interest in seeking employment are areas the rehabilitation counselor must address with the client. In addition, of course, are disincentives such as health insurance, disability insurance, and pending litigation that may interfere with an enthusiastic job search. Not to be underestimated may be prospective reactions that employers have toward hiring clients with obvious or visible disabilities. It is also important to understand that employer bias that is not so obvious will affect successful placement as well. Nonetheless, the proficient rehabilitation counselor can make a huge difference in the work and life satisfaction of their clients.

Table 9.2
Checklist of Job Placement Topics

✔ Do you have the necessary medical/physician restrictions (if any)?

✔ Are there any other medical considerations (such as need for medication at work, flex time schedule, accommodations, etc.)?

✔ Do you need to include family members or a legal representative/guardian in the process?

✔ Does the client have a *clear* vocational goal?

✔ Is vocational testing needed (aptitude, intelligence, interests, temperaments, achievement, etc.)?

✔ Is the client "ready" for employment (attitude, interpersonal skills, hygiene, transportation, work skills, etc.)?

✔ Is the client willing to commit to seeking employment?

✔ Has the client agreed to a daily/weekly job search schedule?

✔ Can the client adequately present themselves on the telephone?

✔ Can the client fill out an application accurately, cleanly, and with correct spelling?

✔ Is there a need for additional training or education?

✔ Is there a need for labor market research to determine feasibility of job placement?

✔ Has there been a job analysis or is there an adequate job description to identify essential functions of the job?

✔ Is there a need for a job analysis?

✔ Has a resume been completed (recommended even if the employer does not accept resumes)? If little or no work history, is the resume based on skills learned by life experiences (child care, volunteer work) rather than work experience based?

✔ Has the client developed a list of networking contacts?

✔ Does the client have a telephone (cell or wired) with answering machine to take messages? Or an alternative number where there is one?

✔ Does the client have thank you notes and stamps?

✔ Can the client adequately answer common interview questions? (e.g., Why work for this company? Why not still working at last company? If no or sporadic work history, why? Where do they see themselves in five years? What can they contribute to the business? How well do you get along with others? How much money do you expect?)

✔ Is there any problem Internet based content about the client? (Google the client's name, discuss Facebook, Twitter and other social networking sites.)

✔ Do you, the rehabilitation consultant, have a way to acknowledge and/or celebrate when the client successfully obtains a suitable job? (Such as bottle of champagne, an award or certificate of achievement.)

Chapter 10
Life Care Planning and Case Management

Introduction

This chapter reviews the history of life care planning, summarizes life care planning and basic case management issues, and offers a step-by-step guide for completing a basic plan. This chapter will emphasize life care planning tenets, processes, and methodology because they apply to catastrophic injury and people with complex health care needs, which encompass the needs of clients/evaluees who are not as impaired but may require case management. Life care planning concepts have been successfully used in a variety of settings for more than thirty years, including workers' compensation, personal injury litigation, medical malpractice cases, long term health care planning, insurance reserves setting, family trust accounts, special needs trusts (Countiss & Deutsch, 2002), elder care planning (McCollom, 2004), mental health care (Hilligoss, 2004), and other venues. Over the years since first being introduced into the rehabilitation literature in the seminal book *Guide to Rehabilitation* (Deutsch & Sawyer, 1985), the process/methodology has been modified, refined, and research enhanced (Weed, 2004a). The benefit of utilizing published life care planning procedures and methodology is to ensure all necessary topics and issues are included in a lifelong plan of care and that plans are reliable (Sutton, Deutsch, Weed, & Berens, 2002; Weed & Berens, 2001).

Life care planning is closely related to "case management" (CM) with some professionals comparing life care planning to a "higher level" of CM, since life care plans are typically developed for people with catastrophic injuries or complex health care needs (see definitions below) (Countiss & Deutsch, 2002; Weed & Riddick, 1992). In today's health care industry, life care planning is a widely used term which continues to gain popularity (Countiss & Deutsch; Weed, 2004a). In the early 1990's, the Individual Case Management Association and a certification as a case manager (Certified Case Manager or CCM) were formed in 1993, and a life care planning-specific certification, Certified Life Care Planner (CLCP) was launched in 1996. For purposes of this text, the author suggests that case management is closely associated with life care planning since both are a problem-solving approach that promotes continuity of care and effective appropriation of services. Anecdotally, it appears that most certified life care planners are also certified case managers. Case management in its broadest scope serves to coordinate and integrate services, resources, communication, and expectations among the patient, family, treatment team, and payer. According to the Commission for Case Manager Certification (CCMC, n.d.), a definition for case management is:

Case management is a collaborative process that assesses, plans, implements, coordinates, monitors, and evaluates the options and services required to meet the client's/evaluee's health and human service needs. It is characterized by advocacy, communication, and resource management and promotes quality and cost-effective interventions and outcomes (para. 1).

Furthermore, the basic philosophy for case management is consistent with life care planning as described by CCMC below (n.d.):

> *Case management facilitates the achievement of client/evaluee wellness and autonomy through advocacy, assessment, planning, communication, education, resource management, and service facilitation. Based on the needs and values of the client/evaluee, and in collaboration with all service providers, the case manager links clients/evaluees with appropriate providers and resources throughout the continuum of health and human services and care settings, while ensuring that the care provided is safe, effective, client-centered, timely, efficient, and equitable. This approach achieves optimum value and desirable outcomes for all—the clients/evaluees, their support systems, the providers, and the payers (para. 3).*

Effective life care planning and case management is interdisciplinary in nature, involving members of the treatment team, the client/evaluee, and, often, family members. The life care planner/case manager often represents the team leader, acting as a liaison between the client/evaluee, physicians, therapists, counselors, equipment vendors, teachers, family members, and others. Consistency, continuity, and communication of shared expectations among the client/evaluee, family, funding source, and treatment team are essential to achieve a successful outcome in case management as well as life care planning. As noted above, utilizing the life care planning process generally means the client/evaluee has experienced a catastrophic injury or has complex medical needs. Catastrophic cases include significant traumatic brain injury, spinal cord injury, amputations, severe burns, premature birth, congenital anomalies, organ failures and transplants, and debilitating diseases such as cancer and HIV/AIDS. Also included as catastrophic in nature can be chronic disabling conditions such as diabetes, multiple sclerosis, stroke, cardiac disease, severe pulmonary conditions, and other diseases. (For detailed information relating to the above topics and more, the reader is referred to Weed, R. & Berens, D. [Eds.]. [2010]. *Life Care Planning and Case Management Handbook* [3rd ed.]. Boca Raton, FL: St. Lucie/CRC Press.)

Life care planning can serve as the core of catastrophic injury case management (Weed, 2004a). This organized and consistent approach, which outlines the short term and long term needs of an individual with a severe disability, can serve as the necessary framework for successful catastrophic injury case management.

Today's life care planners enter into catastrophic injury case management from a variety of disciplines. Occupations common to this group include physicians, nurses, rehabilitation counselors, occupational therapists, speech language pathologists, physical therapists, and psychologists/neuropsychologists. Professional training and experience includes facility based case managers and discharge planners, independent or insurance-based case managers, private sector rehabilitation counselors, and allied health care providers, all of whose tasks involve controlling costs for the insurer, as well as the communication, cooperation, and coordination of services which are essential to the successful outcome of the case management process. Successful outcomes can be measured by the reduction in number of complications associated with the disease, process, expense, product, and level of satisfaction as measured by the client/evaluee.

History

The idea of the life care plan as a specific approach to case management was developed by Paul Deutsch and Frederick Raffa when they published the original format in the legal textbooks *Damages in Tort Action,* volumes 8 and 9 (Deutsch & Raffa, 1981, 1982). Their table format provides an organized, standardized, consistent, time-efficient, and comprehensive method for providing the framework of services. Life care plans address quality of life issues, long term comprehensive needs for patients and family, complications of the conditions, and non-medical categories such as transportation and architectural considerations for home care.

For purposes of this text, a working definition is as follows: A Life Care Plan is a dynamic document based upon published standards of practice, comprehensive assessment, data analysis, and research, which provides an organized, concise plan for current and future needs with associated costs for individuals who have experienced catastrophic injury or have chronic health care needs.

Source: Combined definition of the University of Florida and Intelicus annual life care planning conference and the American Academy of Nurse Life Care Planners (now known as the International Academy of Life Care Planners) presented at the Forensic Section meeting, NARPPS (now known as the International Association of Rehabilitation Professionals) annual conference, Colorado Springs, CO, and agreed upon April 3, 1998 (as cited in Weed & Berens, 2010, p. 3).

As mentioned in the definition, the life care plan is a dynamic document that can be updated and revised as the individual progresses through acute rehabilitation into long-term rehabilitation. The process of obtaining information for all life care plans must be consistent in methodology, and the procedures below will assure a comprehensive approach. It is essential that the life care plan be specific to the individual and not generalized to a type of injury.

Imperative to the development of the life care plan is the understanding of the medical aspects of disability. By developing a firm understanding of a disability and its complexities, the life care planner can design a plan intended to prevent medical complications before they occur. In this way, life care plans can also be an effective form of preventive rehabilitation.

Tenets

The basic tenets were originally developed by Paul Deutsch with participation from Julie Kitchen in the 1980s, updated in the *Guide to Rehabilitation* in 2003 (Deutsch, Allison, & Reid) and further refined as conditions warrant (Weed & Berens, 2004).

1. The first canon is to develop a philosophical approach. Objective, fair, professional, comprehensive, and competent are terms that fit (Weed, 1991). A plan is individualized to the person's needs and not based solely on the disability. For example, a young male with a spinal cord injury living in a rural area where there are no sidewalks or paved roads will have different wheelchair and transportation needs than a young male with a similar disability in metropolitan Atlanta.

2. Inherent in the process is the necessity of learning, knowing, and understanding the disability, terminology, clinical practice guidelines (as appropriate), disability related statistics and research. Not only is the lifelong planning for a health care related disability typically multifaceted and complex, changes in diagnosis and treatment occur regularly, and continuing education will be essential. For example, years ago, this author evaluated a client's/evaluee's plan that recommended extensive rehabilitation treatment for pain control from serious burns. The problem with the pain control plan was that the client/evaluee was spinal cord injured and did not feel pain (which is one of the reasons he was burned). Obviously, the rehabilitation nurse was somewhat embarrassed during her testimony.

3. The life care plan is intended to be proactive in the model of care rather than reactive. Increasing quality of care, reducing overlap, anticipating gaps in care (reducing "falling though the cracks"), and planning for client/evaluee aging-related needs are relevant considerations (Weed, 1998).

4. The life care planner needs to understand the link between the data obtained from interview, evaluations, and records and that which is contained in the life care plan. The author of the plan should carefully connect recommendations in the plan to data that can be double-checked by an independent party (particularly in light of the thorough scrutiny to which most plans will be subjected). Some plan authors footnote various recommendations to show the source on which they rely (be it an individual, research, or clinical practice guideline).

5. The life care plan should assume *probability* of success. If the entries are reliably solicited, quality of care is intended, and a thoughtful plan of care is developed, one should reasonably expect a good outcome.

6. The lifelong plan of care should be well organized and easy to read. One format for accomplishing this goal is the table matrix developed by Drs. Deutsch and Raffa almost 30 years ago. However, no one format is the "right" one. Many experienced professionals have successfully designed their own report format (some using Excel and others Microsoft Word – see example plan based on Microsoft Word developed by Weed & Berens, 2010, at the end of this chapter), and there are a few computer programs available for purchase, such as TecSolution's LCPStat™ (http://www.lcp3.com) and Saddlepoint's PlannerPro™ (http://www. SaddlePoint.net).

7. The plan of care is life-long, and therefore cannot be dependent on deeply discounted negotiated rates, any one source, or region in the country. For entries that constitute a significant part of the plan, such as attendant care, three sources should be surveyed and maybe more if there is a large range of costs. If the life care planner lives in the northeast, and the client/evaluee with the disability lives, or will reside, in the southeast, the product, services, and other research should be conducted in the southeast (location-appropriate research).

8. Plan recommendations may not be available in the local area. Some clients/evaluees live in rural areas where transportation to medical centers may be a part of the care plan. Also, some clients/evaluees may require occasional treatment at Centers of Excellence. For example, for cerebral palsy, an occasional evaluation in St. Louis may be in order. Or, for multiple amputations with complications, Denver might be the resource. Or, for spinal cord injuries, Atlanta. The point is that each disability will have high quality care research centers throughout the country that may be appropriate as a treatment option, and, if so, transportation, lodging, and attendant care will require special attention.

9. Pay attention to details. Plans should not have overlaps, mathematical errors (a common problem) or disconnected recommendations, and the plan entries should be logical in relation to the client's/evaluee's situation. An example past problem is a pediatric case where the child was attending school and the time required for therapies, when combined with school, left inadequate time for sleep.

10. Stay within your area of expertise. As noted above, life care planners come from many professional disciplines. A physician life care planner should be able to develop medical recommendations, but is not usually qualified to offer psychological, home architectural modifications, case management, or vocational opinions (aside from functional limitations). A vocational counselor with specialized training may require the assistance of the physician, nurse, and neuropsychologist to accurately assess needs. It

is unlikely that a single life care planner can address all aspects of future care, and collaboration with others will be the rule. Furthermore, many life care planners are asked to summarize the costs into a "bottom line" figure, and few are educationally equipped to competently do so (see role of economist below).

11. Know the rules associated with the jurisdiction under which a life care plan is being completed. Typically, the plan will only include the costs associated with needs that are related with the disability for which the plan is completed (not pre-existing problems or needs associated with general wellness care). In most cases, the life care plan is intended to differentiate between what clients/evaluees needed before an incident (although there are exceptions like family trusts) and what they need after an injury or illness. For example, people generally need routine health care, dental care, transportation, food, housing, and so forth. Therefore, a life care plan would not typically include the costs of these needs (e.g., an entry might read, routine dental care, two times/year, $0). People may also have a preexisting problem, such as diabetes. Although the needs might be included in the life care plan, only the costs associated with increased care would be recommended. For another example, a young female client/evaluee with a diagnosis of diabetes and paraplegia might have an additional need for vigilance in the event of pregnancy so the recommendations may include the extra medical care costs, but not insulin, blood sugar monitor, or test strips. The same concept applies for transportation and housing, since most clients/evaluees will either be compensated for their loss of earning capacity (e.g., personal injury litigation) or the "rules" do not provide for certain needs (e.g., workers' compensation). Typically, an accessible home or specialized vehicle (like a handicap equipped van) will not be purchased, only the renovations or enhancements associated specifically to the disability or the cost difference between what they have and what they need (see Architectural Considerations and Transportation categories below).

Step-by-Step Procedures

After receiving a referral (documenting the referral information and arranging a contract with the payer of services), one of the first steps is to obtain all relevant medical records and consultations (see Table 10.1 for a summary of the procedures). If the individual is involved in litigation, depositions of health care professionals are often available. If information is unclear, confirmation of a diagnosis is essential, which may require additional medical appointments.

After background information is obtained, an interview with the client/evaluee should be arranged. If the client/evaluee is not capable of participating (such as an impaired child or incompetent adult), then family members should be the point of contact (note: in some litigation cases, the client/evaluee is not available to observe or interview. In these situations one might use medical records, depositions, videos of the client/evaluee, and other sources to comprehend the client's/evaluee's disability and needs). If the client/evaluee resides at home, it is recommended that the interview take place in the residence rather than in a professional office. Observing or interviewing a client/evaluee at their place of residence not only is typically more convenient for the client/evaluee, but also will provide more information. An on-site tour will help identify and inventory equipment, supplies, environmental needs, and transportation needs. For complex medical cases, it is unlikely that the client/evaluee will remember all of the drugs and supplies, and an on-site inventory is the most effective way to determine the client's/evaluee's current needs. A thorough assessment usually requires several hours to complete. (Note: life care plan topics follow the Step-by-Step Procedure section.)

During the initial interview, information is obtained with respect to the client's/evaluee's pre-incident medical and social history, family history, and present physical and emotional status including limitations, medical treatment, socioeconomic status, employment history, and long term plans, as well as current equipment, supplies, and medications (see Sample Interview Form in Appendix K for an overview of recommended topics). The actual content of the interview will vary depending on type of client/evaluee (child vs. adult), type of injury or disability, and whether or not a vocational opinion will also be offered.

Subsequent to the medical records review and the client/evaluee/family interview, the care planner begins the process of identifying long term care needs and options. When possible, the treatment team is consulted and is encouraged to take an active role in identifying client/evaluee needs. The Life Care Plan Checklist (see Table 10.2) becomes a working document that assists in the exploration of long-term planning. The life care planner acts to coordinate and communicate information to all members of the treatment team (when available), to the client/evaluee, and to the family. A primary role of the life care planner is to author the doc-

Table 10.1
Step-by-Step Procedure for Life Care Planning

1. **CASE INTAKE**: When you talked with the referral source, did you record the basic referral information? Time frames discussed? Financial/billing agreement? Retainer received (if appropriate)? Arrange for information release?

2. **MEDICAL RECORDS**: Did you request a **complete** copy of the medical records? Nurses' notes? Doctors' orders? Ambulance report? Emergency room records? Consultants' reports? Admission and discharge reports? Lab/x-ray/etc.?

3. **SUPPORTING DOCUMENTATION**: Are there depositions of the client/evaluee, family, or treatment team that may be useful? "Day in the life of .." video tapes? And, if vocational issues are to be included in report – are there school records (including test scores)? Vocational and employment records? Tax returns?

4. **INITIAL INTERVIEW ARRANGEMENTS**: Is the interview to be held at the client/evaluee's residence? Have you arranged for all appropriate people to attend the initial interview (spouse, parents, siblings)? Did you allow 3 to 5 hours for the initial interview?

5. **INITIAL INTERVIEW MATERIALS**: Do you have the initial interview form for each topic to be covered? Supplemental form for pediatric cases, CP, TBI, SCI as needed? Do you have a copy of the life care plan checklist? Camera or video camcorder to record living situation, medications, supplies, equipment, and other documentation useful for developing a plan?

6. **CONSULTING WITH THERAPEUTIC TEAM MEMBERS**: Have you consulted with and solicited treatment recommendations from appropriate therapeutic team members? If you do not have access to treating professionals, do you have adequate medical foundation for opinions (from records or consulting MD)?

7. **PREPARING PRELIMINARY LIFE CARE PLAN OPINIONS**: Do you have information that can be used to project future care costs? Frequency of service or treatment? Duration? Base cost? Source of information? Vendors?

8. **FILLING IN THE HOLES**: Do you need additional medical or other evaluations to complete the plan? Have you obtained the approval to retain services of additional sources from the referral source? Have you composed a letter outlining the "right" questions to assure you are soliciting the needed information?

9. **RESEARCHING COSTS AND SOURCES**: Have you contacted local sources for costs of treatment, medications, supplies, and equipment? Or do you have catalogs or flyers? For children, are there services that might be covered, in part, through the school system?

10. **FINALIZING THE LIFE CARE PLAN**: Did you confirm your projections with the client/evaluee and/or family? Treatment team members? Can the economist project the costs based on the plan? Do you need to coordinate with a vocational expert? Do you need to determine life expectancy (opinion from MD or someone uniquely qualified)? If "normal" what tables should be used?

11. **LAST BUT NOT LEAST**: Have you distributed the plan to all appropriate parties, (client/evaluee, referral source, attorney, economist, if there is one)?

© 2003 by Roger O. Weed, Ph.D., CLCP, & Susan Grisham, RN, BA, CLCP. Reprinted with permission

ument, although many people, including the client/evaluee, help provide the foundation for professional opinions and recommendations. The life care plan will identify the primary source of recommendations for each of the listed needs.

Once an initial life care plan is developed and, when possible, agreed upon by the client/evaluee, family, and treatment team, investigation into resources, costs, and availability of services begins (in many cases evaluees will not be actively involved due to the nature of litigation). The process of identifying resources can be a long and arduous task, involving research into community and national resources by personal and telephone contacts. If a person has an established record of suppliers, such as pharmacist for medications, obtaining a printout of, say, six months of purchases will reduce the amount of work required. Also, with the advent of the Internet, many resources are available online (however, this resource can also be abused). In order to obtain printouts of purchase history, contact health care providers, or solicit client/evaluee-specific information, a Health Insurance Portability and Accountability Act (HIPAA) compliant information release will need to be obtained from the client/evaluee or legal representative (for more information, see http://www.hhs.gov/ocr/privacy/). In some cases the referring source can obtain records, but contact with health care providers will still require the information release.

Upon a complete and thorough investigation, the life care plan is usually presented and reviewed by the client/evaluee/family and treatment team (if available or appropriate). This document can provide the family and care planners the opportunity to coordinate and execute effective long-term options with a clear understanding of the financial resources necessary for completing the plan.

Life Care Plan Contents

The topics to be covered under a life care plan can only be generalized for purposes of this chapter. The approximately 18 topic headings covered in the life care plan are as follows (Deutsch & Sawyer, 1985; Weed & Field, 2001; Weed, 2004a):

1. **Projected Evaluations.** This topic heading is intended to encompass non-physician periodic evaluations that will occur on a periodic basis, which may include physical therapy, speech therapy, recreational therapy, occupational therapy, music therapy, dietary assessment, audiology, vision screening, swallow studies, and others.

2. **Projected Therapeutic Modalities.** After non-physician evaluations have been completed, recommendations for ongoing treatment will be offered. In most catastrophic injuries and complex health care cases, it is relatively common to see treatment recommendations for physical therapy, speech therapy, and occupational therapy, as well as family education, counseling, and so forth. It is this topic area which identifies which allied health treatment is recommended, over "X" period of time, and at "X" cost. For example, "It is expected that physical therapy will be needed three times per week over the next six months, then one time per week for another six months at the in-home billing rate of $140 per treatment." Obtaining treatment recommendations like "as needed" cannot be priced by an economist (see later in this text for the role of the economist).

3. **Diagnostic Testing/Educational Assessment**. This topic area is intended to estimate educational, vocational, psychological, and neuropsychological diagnostic needs. Laboratory and radiographic requirements are listed elsewhere. Generally speaking, people with catastrophic injuries will undergo a variety of diagnostic testing, including neuropsychological (see sample list of questions to ask a neuropsychologist at end of chapter), psychological, vocational evaluation, and, in the case of children, psycho-educational testing. Evaluations can be one time only or occur at specific points in a client's/evaluee's life which would be identified by listing the years at which the evaluation would take place. For example, a child might be specifically tested psychologically at ages that coincide with certain developmental stages or specific educational milestones such as upon beginning school, at onset of puberty, beginning high school, and post high school.

4. **Wheelchair Needs.** This topic area includes the type and configuration of wheelchairs. For example, a client/evaluee diagnosed as tetraplegic (quadriplegic) often requires a power chair that reclines or is "tilt-in-space" capable. The individual accesses and controls the wheelchair in a variety of ways, including joystick, sip and puff, head tilting, voice control, and others. Specialized seating configurations are often required. The more detailed the specifications the better, since the particulars will allow the life care planner to obtain costs from a variety of vendors. Provision for aging may increase or decrease costs. Many paraplegics after 20+ years of using a manual chair will require a power chair due to shoul-

der injuries and/or a decline in physical functioning (Winkler & Weed, 2004). Many clients/evaluees who are power chair dependent reduce their usage of a chair when they age, so costs may go down. The plan also needs to identify replacement schedules, like every 5 to 7 years, though the actual replacement schedule will depend on many client/evaluee specific factors, and an equipment specialist may be in a better position to offer data on which to rely (Amsterdam, 2004).

5. **Wheelchair Accessories and Maintenance.** Each wheelchair requires certain accessories such as lap tables, carry bags, and other custom features. In addition, wheelchairs require maintenance. Maintenance costs vary depending on amount of use and can be very high for regularly used power wheelchairs or low for wheelchairs that are used only for back-up purposes (e.g., when a power chair is in for maintenance or if the power chair is used on outings and the manual chair is used around a home) (Amsterdam, 2004). It is problematical to utilize averaged costs for maintenance (such as equipment life expectancy data offered by manufacturers). Some clients/evaluees are younger and very active, perhaps even involved in wheelchair sports. Others may be elderly and/or confined to a home or facility. The bottom line, so to speak, is that the maintenance expense should be based on client/evaluee-specific data. Provisions should also be made for aging (see #4), and estimates of need will probably be best offered by the supplier of the client's/evaluee's equipment.

6. **Aids for Independent Function.** Many individuals have restricted functional ability and will benefit from products that improve independence (Watkins, 2004). A common example is the environmental control, which can be relatively inexpensive and purchased from Radio Shack. However, one model, Multimedia Max, is very comprehensive and allows a severely impaired client/evaluee to turn lights on and off, open and close doors, start and stop computers, turn on televisions, radios, fans, adjust room temperature, etc., and costs about $13,000 if all options are selected (for details visit http://www.abilityhub.com/ecu/index.htm). Some less expensive adaptive aids may include reachers, which allow an individual to grasp items on a shelf or pick items off the floor without having to stand up or bend over, or specialized eating utensils, etc. (There are thousands of potential products. Visit http://www.sammonspreston.com/ for examples or see Kitchen & Brown, 2004). An occupational therapist is typically the allied health professional who is skilled at recommending aids for independent living. Speech/language pathologists will assist with communication technology aids.

7. **Orthotics and Prosthetics**. Obviously, most amputees will need at least one prosthesis. Prostheses will need replacement and ongoing maintenance. The cost for all of the items, including the replacement schedule, will be included here. With regard to significant head injury and spinal cord injury, most clients/evaluees will make use of braces or ankle/foot orthosis (AFO), etc. Sometimes these braces, when custom designed, are costly and over an individual's lifetime can add up to a significant amount of money. Although many physicians are skilled at estimating these needs, certified prosthetists (CP) or certified orthotists (CO) are more likely the resource of choice (visit www.oandp.com for additional information).

8. **Home Furnishings and Accessories**. Often a client/evaluee living at home will have need for a specialty bed, portable ramps, patient lifts, and the like. In-home care will require a specific inventory of the client's/evaluee's needs at home. (See http://www.sammonspreston.com/ for many examples.) Specialty contractors or health care professionals will likely participate in the decision process for what is required (also see Architectural Considerations below) (for more details, see Karl & Weed, 2007). There also may be a need for assistive technology (which might also fit with the Aids For Independent Living category).

9. **Drug and Supply Needs.** This topic area includes prescription and non-prescription drugs and supplies. Although some clients/evaluees may have little or no need, other clients/evaluees can have rather complex needs. For example, a spinal cord injured individual will have a lifetime need for a very extensive inventory of bowel and bladder management supplies such as catheters, leg bags, gloves, chux, laxatives, and perhaps prescriptions like anti-spasm medications, etc. Ventilator-dependent tetraplegic clients/evaluees (quadriplegic), obviously, have even greater needs for a variety of drugs, supplies, and medical equipment. As noted in a previous category, a printout of products used over the previous six months is a good starting place for estimating future care needs. The physician will also be instrumental in predicting these needs.

10. **Home Care/Facility Care.** Philosophically, it is more desirable to have a client/evaluee live in the least restrictive environment that is reasonably possible. Sometimes this may not be the most cost-effective. On the other hand, quality of care can significantly affect potential complications and emotional status

of a client/evaluee. Facility care, generally, is not as responsive to an individual as a custom-designed home care program where the caregivers are employed directly by the client/evaluee. On the other hand, some individuals have no capability of living at home or their needs exceed those which can be reasonably provided in a home environment. For example, inpatient facilities may be the most appropriate for ventilator-dependent tetraplegic clients/evaluees or persistent vegetative state traumatic brain injured clients/evaluees. There may also be a need for short-term specialty programs such as a yearly summer camp (clients/evaluees with end-stage renal disease, brain injury, cystic fibrosis, burns, etc.). The level of care should also be identified. For example, some individuals need only occasional home care and others need 24-hour-awake, high-tech nursing care.

In addition, for clients/evaluees who reside in a facility where the "per diem" rate includes attendant care, therapy treatment, food, lodging, laundry, transportation, etc., there may be special rules the economist will need to know about. In some jurisdictions where the client/evaluee receives damages for loss of earnings capacity, the economist should reduce the life care plan related per diem rate by the amount of board, room, and related costs for which the client/evaluee will be compensated through an earnings capacity damage claim (e.g., personal injury litigation). As an example, say the per diem facility rate is $100 per day, and the client/evaluee will be compensated for lost earnings capacity from which one would expect to purchase food, housing, transportation, and other needs. Say the expected expense for these needs would have been about $15 per day if the person had not been injured. Based on this example, the $15 per day would be deducted from the $100 per day charge.

11. **Future Medical Care–Routine.** This topic area is to identify physician-related recommendations (Bonfiglio, 2004; Zasler, 1994). Routine medical care includes routine and annual evaluations by whatever specialty may be appropriate for the disability. For instance, in spinal cord injury cases the client/evaluee may need an annual evaluation which includes X-rays and lab work. Other clients/evaluees may need custom-organized annual evaluations that may include dental care, urology, dermatology, physiatry, orthopedics, neurology, and others. Some clients/evaluees, such ones receiving psychotropic medications, will have follow up by a psychiatrist four or more times per year. The variation in routine medical needs can be almost infinite. (See end of chapter for summary of sample physician questions.)

12. **Transportation.** Transportation needs vary from individual to individual and all specifications for transportation requirements will be included in this category. Some individuals need little or no modification to their vehicles. Others may solve their problem by simply adding hand controls to their present vehicle. However, other individuals may need a custom designed van with lift and wheelchair tie-downs. Typically, only the cost differential between what the client/evaluee had and what they need will be included. For example, a client/evaluee diagnosed as tetraplegic may have owned an average car which was valued at $27,000, but he or she now needs a van with hand controls and side lift that costs about $50,000. In most cases, the economist should be instructed to deduct the value of the existing vehicle from the value of the needed transportation. (For more information, see Weed & Engelhart, 2005.)

13. **Health and Strength Maintenance.** This category, titled Recreation and Leisure Time Activities in the original literature, was designed to identify specialty recreation needs, adaptive games, and devices that would allow clients/evaluees to be as active as possible (Weed, 1991). Specialty wheelchairs (such as basketball, tennis, and other custom designed chairs) should be placed in the Wheelchair category. One argument this author has heard against including these needs is related to an objection to paying for a client's/evaluee's fun. However, activity is very important to the physical and emotional well-being of a client/evaluee, and recreational therapists are trained to develop enjoyment related activities that enhance physical therapy treatment as well as offer cognitive remediation (for people with brain impairments). (For more information, see Support for Recreation and Leisure Time Activities in Life Care Plans, Weed, 1991.)

14. **Architectural Considerations** (also referred to as Architectural Renovations). If the client/evaluee is to be cared for at home, significant and comprehensive architectural accommodations will often be required. In fact, one reason this author has altered the title from "renovations" to "considerations" is that renovations often are either not reasonably possible on the existing structure or cost-prohibitive. Therefore, selling the existing home and building an accessible home based on client/evaluee needs is often the best option (Karl & Weed, 2007). As with transportation, in most situations (and especially personal injury litigation), the costs associated with increased needs will be a part of the plan. For example, a client/evaluee with a spinal cord injury at the paraplegic level will need ramps, preferably at two entries into the home, and may need widened hallways, kitchen modifications, specialized fire or smoke detection, specialized floor coverings, enlarged bathrooms, and added equipment and attendant rooms. How-

ever, the value of the existing home or an "average" home will be deducted. The American National Standard Institute (ANSI) publishes handicap-accessible architectural standards for those uneducated in this area.

15. **Future Medical Care/Surgical Intervention or Aggressive Treatment**. In some situations the client/evaluee will have a known need for care that is one time only or periodic, rather than routine. Phrenic nerve implants for spinal cord injury, time-limited inpatient care for brain injuries, and a series of cosmetic surgeries for burn clients/evaluees are examples for this category.

16. **Orthopedic Equipment Needs.** Some clients/evaluees will need specific orthopedic equipment such as body support, walkers, or standing table. These products are often termed "durable medical equipment." In addition to the initial cost, replacement schedules need to be added so that an economist can factor these expenses into the present value totals.

17. **Vocational/Educational Plan.** This category was not included in the original life care planning literature, probably because the professional involved in the life care plan may not be responsible for this portion of the client's/evaluee's care (such as a registered nurse who is the life care planner). Qualified vocational experts may choose to complete a narrative and offer a specific rehabilitation plan focusing on vocational issues, which is located in a separate document. However, a life care plan is intended to provide a road map of care for the total person, and one element for many clients/evaluees will be related to their vocational needs as assessed by a qualified vocational counselor. Common entries include the cost of job coaching, vocational counseling, tuition/fees, books and supplies, rehabilitation technology, and/or specialized educational programs. (Also see separate section of the role of the vocational expert below.)

18. **Potential Complications**. "Potential complications" is defined to mean "possible" rather than "probable" problems and as such the costs are not typically included in the total cost of the life care plan, presumably because effective life care planning will reduce complications since it provides the structure for quality care. On the other hand, it is important for people to understand what common complications are involved with a particular disability, especially if the client/evaluee is not afforded quality care. In the case of persons with significant brain injuries, individuals often re-injure themselves due to poor balance or poor judgment. Individuals with spinal cord injuries often experience skin breakdowns, cardiovascular difficulty, pulmonary diseases, etc. Individuals on some anti-seizure medications often will have gum disease or other dental problems. An article published in the Rehab Consultant's Newsletter (Weed, 1991) outlines the effects of poor health and strength maintenance on potential complications. An individual's poor psychological adjustment to their disability often is the direct result of poor environment, poor care, or inability to engage in meaningful activities.

The Role of the Vocational Expert in Life Care Planning

As noted above, the life care planner and the vocational expert may not be the same person. However, in most cases where a life care plan is appropriate, vocational recommendations should be included (Berens & Weed, 2004). Table 10.3 summarizes topic areas for the life care planner to ask the vocational expert. Some of the questions are not specific to the life care plan, but will help an author of the life care plan determine the credibility or completeness of vocational opinions. In many instances, a vocational plan may well be underway. If so, then obtaining specific information for future care recommendations is a relatively straightforward process. However, in most litigation and workers' compensation cases, the person with a disability is not working nor is there a plan in place. It is also common to conclude that a client/evaluee is not employable (e.g., a person in a persistent vegetative state).

In order to make a determination of work potential, certain questions should be asked during the interview. Obviously the person's work history will be relevant. Questions specific to the client's/evaluee's education, skills (skills are what people learn by doing, such as computer programming), work tasks, vocational industry, tenure, reason for leaving various jobs, training obtained (formal as well as on-the-job), income earned, vocational interests, and the client's/evaluee's representation of their functional abilities will help form a "picture" or foundation for opinions.

It is important that the vocational expert has access to medical records to understand functional limitations and capabilities (rather than relying totally upon a client's/evaluee's portrayal of his or her condition). Likewise, it is recommended that available vocational documentation be obtained, such as tax returns, job evaluations, school records, and an opinion of a client's/evaluee's functional abilities as projected by a physician.

Table 10.2
Life Care Plan Checklist

Projected Evaluations: Have you planned for different types of non-physician **evaluations** (for example; physical therapy, speech therapy, recreational therapy, occupational therapy, music therapy, dietary assessment, audiology, vision screening, swallow studies, etc.)?

Projected Therapeutic Modalities: What therapies will be needed (based on the evaluations above)? Will a case manager help control costs and reduce complications? Is a behavior management, or rehab psychologist, pastoral counseling or family education appropriate?

Diagnostic Testing/Educational Assessment: What testing is necessary and at what ages? Vocational evaluation? Neuropsychological? Educational levels? Educational consultant to maximize IDEA?

Wheelchair Needs: What types and configuration of wheelchairs will the client/evaluee require: power? shower? manual? specialty? ventilator? reclining? quad pegs? recreational?

Wheelchair Accessories and Maintenance: Has each chair been listed separately for maintenance and accessories (bags, cushions, trays, etc.?) Have you considered the client's/evaluee's activity level?

Aids for Independent Functioning: What can this individual use to help him or herself? environmental controls? adaptive aids? omni-reachers?

Orthotics/Prosthetics: Will the client/evaluee need braces? Have you planned for replacement and maintenance?

Home Furnishings and Accessories: Will the client/evaluee need a specialty bed? portable ramps? Hoyer or other lift?

Drug/Supply Needs: Have prescription and non-prescription drugs been listed including size, quantity, and rate at which to be consumed? All supplies such as bladder and bowel program, skin care, etc.?

Home Care/Facility Care: Is it possible for the client/evaluee to live at home? How about specialty programs such as yearly camps? What level of care will he/she require?

Future Medical Care - Routine: Is there a need for an annual evaluation? Which medical specialties? orthopedics? urology? internist? vision? dental? lab?

Transportation: Are hand controls sufficient or is a specialty van needed? Can local transportation companies be used?

Health and Strength Maintenance: What specialty recreation is needed- blow darts? adapted games? Rowcycle? annual dues for specialty magazines? (Specialty wheelchairs should be placed on wheelchair page.)

Architectural Renovations: Have you considered ramps, hallways, kitchen, fire protection, alternative heating/cooling, floor coverings, bath, attendant room, equipment storage, etc.?

Future Medical Care/Surgical Intervention or Aggressive Treatment: Are there plans for aggressive treatment? Additional surgeries such as reconstruction?

Orthopedic Equipment Needs: Are walkers, standing tables, tilt tables, body support equipment needed?

Vocational/Educational Plan: What are the costs of vocational counseling, job coaching, tuition, fees, books, supplies, technology, etc.?

Potential Complications: Have you included a list of potential complications which can occur such as skin breakdown, infections, psychological trauma, contractures, etc.? (Usually "possible" rather than "probable.")

In the event that adequate information is not available, the vocational expert should arrange for a vocational evaluation (if permissible). The life care planner should understand that not all vocational evaluations are equal. A Slosson IQ test is not as comprehensive as the Wechsler Adult Intelligence Scale and the Wide Range Achievement Test is not as "good" as the Woodcock Johnson Achievement Test (Berens & Weed, 2010). However, most vocational evaluators with a master's degree are not qualified to give tests that are considered the best or "highest power." In addition, some tests can be biased. For example, a client/evaluee has significant motor control problems from a brain injury and is given a test that is speeded or timed. "Speeded" means the client/evaluee is not expected to be able to complete all tasks in the time allotted (e.g., digit span sub test in the Wechsler) and "timed" means that most examinees will be able to complete the tasks within the time allowed (such as most certification examinations). Clearly a speeded test will not offer an accurate estimate of the person's capabilities if the disability interferes with completion of test items. For effective life care planning, vocational entries must be based on reliable opinions. This author has included here some fundamental vocational issues to help the life care planner determine reasonable needs, recommendations, and cost estimates.

Additional work related testing, depending on the disability, may include neuropsychological examination and a physical capacities assessment. (For additional information about this topic, please refer to Berens & Weed, 2010).

When all of the information is available and a vocational plan can be developed, items typically included in the life care plan are vocational counseling, labor market surveys, job analysis, educational costs (tuition, fees, books, and supplies), as well as work-related assistive technology, job placement assistance, attendant care, and transportation needs. The life care planner may need to inquire about how the needs in the life care plan will differ from what would have occurred without a disability in order to avoid duplicitous damages and should be sure to inquire about the potential that a vocational expert will submit their own report, which may encompass the same information. That is, damages may be awarded for future care as well as lost earnings capacity, so coordination of damages valuation should occur since some items could appear in both reports. As with all life care plan entries, the vocational related needs will require frequency, duration, and costs in order to arrive at a "bottom line" (see checklist in Table 10.3).

Working with the Physician or Other Treating Professionals

Although a few certified life care planners are physicians, the vast majority are not. Since most life care planners are not legally allowed to prescribe medical treatment, it is essential to rely on opinions by medical professionals, such as physicians, or medical reports, medical depositions, clinical practice guidelines, medical research, etc. as the foundation for future *medical* care recommendations (Bonfiglio, 2010; Zasler, 1994). It is noted that some care plans, such as for clients/evaluees with cognitive deficits, may have few if any medical recommendations, and life care planners should adjust their resources accordingly (e.g., utilize a neuropsychologist or speech/language pathologist for recommendation foundation).

In addition, life expectancy is an essential element in order to determine the cost of care. Unless designated as "normal" by a physician, the care planner typically should not estimate the client's/evaluee's disability related life span. Except for a few highly qualified life expectancy researchers, physicians are the expected source of a client's/evaluee's life expectancy opinion.

There are many other professionals besides physicians who might be involved in the client's/evaluee's care or consultations. Examples include nurses, nutritionists, recreational therapists, case managers, discharge planners, audiologists, speech and language therapists, occupational therapists, and physical therapists. In most cases, the physician is the hub of the *medical* treatment wheel and will be the person to order the various therapies. For long-term future care recommendations, the MD with the most appropriate training to work with a life care planner is the physical medicine and rehabilitation doctor (also known as a physiatrist). For catastrophic injuries and some complex health care plans, a physiatrist may be willing to organize a comprehensive evaluation by all relevant professionals. In this author's opinion, a comprehensive evaluation is ideal because the purpose is to provide the data needed for a lifelong plan of care, and the life care planner will, in a collaborative way, provide the structure to accomplish the goal.

Occasionally, identifying the lifelong frequency and duration of activities, services, products, and medication can be very a complex task. Pediatric catastrophic cases commonly include needs for periodic speech, occupational, and physical therapy, which may begin and end at specific developmental periods in the child's life. For instance, occupational therapy may be needed for activities of daily living for a six-year-old client/evaluee and then may be discontinued for several years. When the child is ready to enter the work

Table 10.3
Questions The Life Care Planner Should Ask The Vocational Expert

✔ First, determine if vocational aspects have been considered or are already underway. (e.g., already initiated by insurance company or attorney.)

✔ What vocational interview information has been obtained from the client/evaluee? (e.g., work skills, leisure activities, education, work, functional abilities based on O*Net or Department of Labor.)

✔ Have you obtained copies of relevant medical records?

✔ Have you obtained work-related information? (Such as tax returns, job evaluations, school and test records, training history, and treating or consulting MD comments.)

✔ Does the client/evaluee need testing before determining vocational potential? (e.g., vocational evaluation, psychological, neuropsychological, or physical capacities testing. Also, is the evaluation a "quality" and "valid" appraisal?)

✔ If there is work potential, is there a need for justifying a plan by performing a Labor Market Survey? If LMS, which method is used? (e.g., direct contact with employers vs. statistics, computer program, or publications.)

✔ What is the client's/evaluee's expected income including benefits? (If personal injury litigation, then pre vs. post injury <u>capacity</u>.)

✔ If there is an apparent market for the client's/evaluee's labor, is there a need for a job analysis? (And if an analysis was completed, was it done according to the Americans with Disabilities Act guidelines?)

✔ What are the estimated costs of the vocational plan?
  • Counseling, career guidance? (When does it start/stop, frequency and cost? E.g., 30 hrs. over 6 months beginning 6/2013 at $75/hr.)
  • Job placement, job coaching or supported employment costs?
  • Tuition or training, books, supplies? (Include dates for expected costs. E.g. Technical training 2 years, @ $4200/yr., 2014 through 2015)

✔ Rehabilitation or assistive technology, accommodations, or aids, costs for work, education and/or training? (E.g., computer, printer, work station, tools, tape recorder, attendant care, transportation – include costs and replacement schedules.)

✔ What effect, if any, does the injury have on worklife expectancy? (e.g., delayed entry into work force, less than full-time, earlier retirement, expected increased turnover, or time off for medical follow-up or treatment?)

world, occupational therapists may rejoin the client's/evaluee's treatment team in order to supply assistive devices for work-related activity. Sometimes treatment team professionals fail to consider the lifetime needs since they are most often involved in care lasting one to two years. The life care planner must be able to identify long-term needs and consult with the appropriate professionals to identify care for the client's/evaluee's lifetime.

One more point. The competent life care planner will make sure the "right" questions are asked. In other words, when a referral to *any* professional is made for life care planning purposes, the life care planner should provide the framework for completing a comprehensive plan by posing questions and providing information about what needs categories are required. A client/evaluee should not be referred for a generic neuropsychological exam. Rather, questions to be answered should be submitted (see example neuropsychologist questions at end of chapter and in Appendix K). The same concept is true for most treating professionals or consultants who participate. The active participation of a competent life care planner in the process will underscore the value of the specialty practice area, otherwise, continued criticism that the life care planner is simply a secretary, recording someone else's opinions, will be heard (see also Weed, 2002). At the other extreme is the know-it-all who believes that no one is better than they are at predicting future needs. Life care planning is a collaborative process, and it is unlikely that a single individual can accurately or reliably anticipate all future needs of clients/evaluees.

Working with the Economist

The role of the economist is to arrive at a bottom line figure (Deutsch & Raffa, 1981; Deutsch & Raffa, 1982; Dillman, 1987; Dillman, 2010). The life care planner or expert witness, particularly those who offer personal injury expert opinions, will typically work with an economist since there are many areas in which health care professionals do not have the expertise to offer opinions (Weed, August 15, 1992), e.g., regarding inflation rates (medical vs. non-medical), investment strategies, and other economic rules of the profession. The economist will utilize the base cost identified by the life care planner to project the cost of care throughout the client's/evaluee's life expectancy. On occasion, life care plan costs have been summarized by the rehabilitation consultant who does not have an education in economic forecasting with a footnote that an economist should determine present value.

There are a few states which endorse the "Alaska Rule" (Weed & Field, 2001), which assumes that inflation and reasonable investment rates are essentially equal and therefore no economist may needed. However, most jurisdictions expect an accurate prognostication of costs, and the economist will be necessary to provide expertise in inflation and investment strategies. For example, you may have completed a life care plan for a child paraplegic who is expected to have a normal life expectancy. What investments should be picked in order for the client/evaluee to have enough money for his or her life expectancy? Would you invest in a bank money market, bonds, mutual funds, annuities, or stocks? How much financial risk are you willing to undertake? What are the medical and non-medical categories inflation rates? If the life care planner can not answer these questions (and more), or unless he or she has specific training in this specialized practice, it is strongly recommended that the expert defer to an economist for the ultimate value of the life care.

Many health care providers offer opinions that a client/evaluee will require follow-up services for "a long time." It is not possible to identify specific costs in these situations. In order for the economist to accurately estimate the cost for the care plan, the professional must include:

a. intended expected type and amount of treatment

b. date to start

c. date to stop

d. base cost of treatment

e. and in some cases, the replacement schedule of products (vehicles, wheelchairs, durable medical equipment and others)

See checklist in Table 10.4 and the sample case which follows for an example of how this information is utilized.

Table 10.4
Economist Related Requirements

Necessary Minimum Data for Damages

- When does the treatment start?
- When does the treatment stop?
- How long is each session (if charged by the hour)?
- What is the cost for each session?
- Are there ancillary costs like lab, x-ray, radiographics, etc.?
- If medications (in addition to the above), what size and number?

Examples

- Psychological evaluation in June, 2013 at a cost of $1,000
- Psychological counseling beginning July, 2013, one time per week, one hour per session for 6 months, then 2 times per month at one hour per session at a cost of $150/hour.
- Expect group counseling beginning in July 2014 at one time per week for one year at the rate of $50/session
- Expect psychiatric appointments for medication follow-up four times per year for 2 years beginning July 2013, at $150 for the initial session, then $75 each visit thereafter.
- Prozac, one 20mg per day for two years beginning July 2013 at $130 for 30.

Ethical Issues

Professional Preparation

The qualifications of professional rehabilitation practitioners depend on specialty and academic preparation as well as experience. It is imperative that one's credentials be represented accurately, and that current licensure and/or credible credentialing be maintained. For registered nurses, the scope of nursing practice may vary somewhat in different states: be certain that the applicable parameters are observed. Practitioners are held to the ethical standards of their professional discipline(s), and many experts maintain multiple certifications. In addition to one's primary professional identity license or certification, certification as a life care planner is recommended since the credential provides a specific forum for ethical standards (see below for further information).

Who is the Client?

It is important that the agreement (retainer) for services clarify the responsibilities of the life care planner. In this context the client is defined as the person with the disability. However, preparing a life care plan for litigation, especially if one is retained by the defendant, the "client" is likely not the life care planner's client (i.e., no client/counselor or client/case manager relationship exists), and the person will likely be referred to as the evaluee (Barros-Bailey, Carlisle, Graham, Neulicht, & Taylor, 2008). On the other hand, a case manager may also provide some life care planning related services as part of their duties, in which case the relationship will be technically different. In any event, the professional is obligated to provide objective, independent opinions, limited to his or her field of expertise, and demonstrating no conflict of interest (Banja, 1995; Blackwell, 1995; Weed & Berens, 2004). Ultimately, the goal is to provide for the needs of the person with the disability over their life span in a manner that preserves quality of life while remaining at a reasonable cost (i.e., cost-benefit analysis).

Informed Consent

The client's/evaluee's (or their representative's) consent will be required for an in-person interview, obtaining copies of medical and other records, and communicating with providers of health care, goods, and services. For non-litigation cases, the client must understand and consent freely to these services. He or she is free to withdraw consent from any or all portions of services at any time. In personal injury litigation, and sometimes in workers' compensation claims, the client/evaluee will have an attorney who will approve the client's/evaluee's information release. Many life care planners who are retained by the defendant will not be permitted to contact caregivers, and medical and other records obtained will be provided by the client's/evaluee's attorney. Life care planners unfamiliar with litigation rules are urged to seek specialized training in order to assure compliance with the various laws and rules (e.g., Federal Rules of Evidence), which vary from jurisdiction to jurisdiction and from state to state. As a beginning point, professionals interested in litigation related life care planning should obtain the Forensic Series of short and easy-to-read books from Elliott & Fitzpatrick (publisher of this textbook).

Confidentiality

Client/evaluee confidentiality rules are somewhat dependent on the jurisdiction under which the care plan is developed. Within the context of Health Insurance Portability and Accountability Act (HIPAA) of 1996, certain requirements were implemented nationwide. Although intended to be relevant to health care providers who use electronic means to transmit records (of any type), in reality it appears to be the standard of the industry, and life care planners need to become familiar with the regulations (visit http://www.hhs.gov/ocr/privacy/). Additionally, obtaining records or soliciting information from health care providers will not be possible unless proper information release forms are signed. In fact, in this author's experience, some providers will not release information even if the proper forms are submitted (e.g., pharmacists). It may be that the client/evaluee will need to obtain their own records and then forward to the life care planner, or the information source will have their own release form that must be completed. The consultant should take special care when transmitting protected information by e-mail or fax. Anecdotally, it is seems common to accidentally send an e-mail with an attachment to the wrong source, or fax to a location where unauthorized personnel have access to documents. In summary, records should not be distributed to others without prerequisite approvals.

If the life care plan is provided for litigation cases, special requirements are to be observed. In most circumstances a person initiating a personal injury lawsuit by statute has waived their rights to privacy; however, since this event occurs within the legal context, the expert should rely on an attorney's advice (Tyron Elliott, Esq., personal communication, February 17, 2007). Another confidentiality detail is the concept of privileged communication which exists between the life care planner and an attorney who retained them. This means that some documents within an expert's file may not be disclosed to others even at deposition when records are disclosed. Again, rely on the attorney's opinion for a guideline on what is proper.

Summary

Life care plans have emerged as the most comprehensive and widely accepted process for comprehensively identifying needs and the concomitant economic projections associated with complex medical impairments and catastrophic injuries (Weed, 2004a). Life care plans have been used for effective case management of complex medical conditions and in workers' compensation cases to help set reserves for insurance companies, to control costs, and to effectively coordinate care. They have also been used in medical malpractice and personal injury litigation as a method to resolve a case by identifying damages associated with an injury. Pediatric life care plans represent a special challenge since education and family matters are more complex than for adults.

Effective case management for catastrophic care is paramount to quality care. The amount of coordination required when 10 to 15 professionals are involved in a client's/evaluee's life care requires a consistent approach to avoid complications, overlap, conflict, and poor quality of care. Life care plans obviously provide a guide for professionals, family, insurance companies, attorneys, discharge planners, and case managers to follow as a standard of care.

Professionals considering the specialty practice of life care planning should seek additional training. As of this writing, there are at least three online training programs: Kaplan University (http://kaplan.edu/hcp/programs/lcpMain.aspx), University of Florida (http://LCP.dce.ufl.edu), and Capital Law School (http://www .law.capital.edu/LCP/).

In addition, one organization, the International Academy of Life Care Planners (IALCP), has developed a mission specific to this specialized industry and incorporates peer-reviewed standards of practice (http://www.rehabpro.org/sections/ialcp). If the life care planner is interested in certification, information can be obtained from the Commission on Health Care Certification (http://ichcc.org).

Note: This chapter is based in large part on excerpts from the booklet, Weed, R. (2007), Life Care Planning: A Step-by-Step Guide. Athens, GA: Elliott & Fitzpatrick, Inc. Reprinted with permission.

Example Case History

The client/evaluee was allegedly rendered thoracic level 7 spinal cord injured as a result of medical malpractice.

NAME:	Robert "Bobby" Acworth_
AGE:	21 years_
DOB:	3/5/84
DOI:	10/29/01
PRIMARY DIAGNOSIS:	Functional T7, incomplete, spinal cord injury
REPORT DATE:	8/19/04

LIFE CARE PLAN

Note 1: Support for recommendations are based on review of available medical and other records and depositions, research, on-site interview with Bobby Acworth and his parents, consultation with a certified rehabilitation technology specialist, and consultation with Dr. Thomas Wishful, physiatrist and spinal cord injury specialist.

Note 2: For purposes of this life care plan, it is expected Mr. Acworth will have a Baclofen pump implanted within the next three (3) months with successful outcomes, including significant reduction in spasticity and increased function.

Note 3: This preliminary plan may be supplemented upon receipt of additional, relevant information that becomes available, including outcome of Baclofen pump implant.

Note 4: This plan does not include provision for advances in scientific, medical, or rehabilitation technology that may have an effect on his future needs and functional abilities.

Note 5: For purposes of this plan, unless otherwise indicated, the following initials are placed in parentheses according to their respective recommendations:

(TW) = Thomas Wishful, MD, consulting physiatrist

(RW) = Roger Weed, Ph.D., certified life care planner

\multicolumn{4}{c}{**Routine Future Medical Care – Physician Only**}			
Recommendation (by whom)	**Frequency and Duration**	**Purpose**	**Expected Cost**
Physiatrist (TW)	1-2 X year (avg.) to life	Monitor long-term rehabilitation needs and prevent complications	Re-evaluation: $150-300 F/up visits: $35-150 per year @ $35-75 per visit to life expect Mileage: $63 per trip
\multicolumn{4}{l}{**Economist** to reduce one physiatrist visit on years SCI evaluation is done, see next entry.}			
SCI Evaluation at Craig Hospital Rehabilitation Center (TW, RW)	Every 2-3 years to life expectancy	Comprehensive evaluation of needs related to SCI	$1,296-1,471 (est.) (per case documentation in file) Mileage to Denver: $65
\multicolumn{4}{l}{Note: See also Future Aggressive Treatment, page 17, for 1 X inpatient rehabilitation program in 2005.}			
Urologist (TW)	Every 1 X year to life	Monitor urinary function and reduce/ prevent complications, including UTIs	Adult urologist new pt: $150-250 F/up: $150/visit (avg.) Mileage: $65/yr. to life
Urinalysis (TW)	2-4 X yr. (avg.) to life		UA: $21 each
Urine Culture & Sensitivity (TW)	2-4 X yr. (avg.) to life		C&S: $33 each
Renal/bladder ultrasound (TW)	Every other year (avg.)	Monitor kidney and bladder function	Renal US: $1,262 (incls. radiologist fee)
Voiding cystome-trogram/EMG (TW)	Estimate 3-5 over life-time	Monitor urological function	CMG: $350, done in urologist's office
\multicolumn{4}{l}{Note: Given his age, the client/evaluee will soon be transferred from his current urologist at the Children's Urology Group to an adult urologist. Costs above reflect research with adult urologist in his local area.}			
Podiatrist (TW)	3 X year (avg.) to life	Foot care including toe nail cleaning/cutting to prevent complications	$135/year to life expectancy @ $45 per visit Mileage: $21/yr. to life
\multicolumn{4}{l}{Note: Due to instrumentation in the client's/evaluee's spine and spasticity, he reportedly is restricted in his ability to bend over and reach his feet to perform foot care. He has had toenail infections and other foot complications in the past.}			
Neurosurgeon for Baclofen pump (TW)	1 X evaluation	Evaluation prior to Baclofen pump re-implant	$300-517 Mileage to Denver: $47 for 1 X evaluation
\multicolumn{4}{l}{Note: According to the consulting physiatrist, the client/evaluee is expected to be ready for the Baclofen pump implant within the next three months. See also Future Aggressive Treatment.}			

Routine Future Medical Care – Physician Only (con't)			
Recommendation (by whom)	Frequency and Duration	Purpose	Expected Cost
Plastic surgeon (TW)	1 X year to life expectancy	Monitor skin issues	$150/year (avg. est.)
Orthopedist (TW)	1 X year to life expectancy	Monitor orthopedic issues	$150/year (avg. est.) Mileage: $47/year

Note: It is expected Mr. Acworth will be able to schedule some physician appointments on the same day to reduce amount of travel.

Internist/General Practitioner (RW)	As needed	General medical care	No cost over same age population
Blood tests (TW)	1 X year to life expect.	Sequential multiple analysis blood work	SMA: $45 CBC: $32 Lipid panel: $67 Draw fee: $12
Annual influenza vaccination (RW)	1 X year to life expect-ancy	Flu vaccine	$20/yr. (est.) to age 60
EKG (TW)	Begin 2024: Every other year to life expect.	Monitor heart/cardiac problems	$120-150 (est.)
X-s (TW)	1-2 X year to life	Films to include chest, long bones, etc.	$200-400/year (avg. est.) to life expectancy

Note: Cost of flu vaccine after approximately 60 years old to life expectancy is not included in plan as the vaccine commonly is recommended for the "senior" population.

Projected Evaluations – Non Physician (Allied Health Evaluations)			
Recommendation (by whom)	**Year Initiated/ Suspended**	**Frequency/Duration**	**Expected Cost**
Physical Therapy Evaluation (TW)	2005 to life expectancy	Every 2-3 years at time of SCI evaluation, see pg. 1	$0. Included in cost of SCI evaluation, see pg. 1.
Occupational Therapy Evaluation to include equipment assessments (TW)	2005 to life expectancy	Every 2-3 years at time of SCI evaluation, see pg. 1	$0. Included in cost of SCI evaluation, see pg. 1.
Recreation Therapy Evaluation (RW)	2004 to life expectancy	Every 2-3 years at time of SCI evaluation	$0. Included in cost of SCI evaluation, see pg. 1.
Wheelchair Seating Evaluation to assess wheelchair needs (RW)	2004 to life expectancy	At time of wheelchair replacements, see pgs. 5-6	At time of wheelchair replacements, see pgs. 5-6

Note: Wheelchair seating evaluation from one equipment vendor researched in client's/evaluee's local area also is provided at no charge.

Home Accessibility Evaluation, see Architectural Considerations, pg. 15 (RW)	N/A	N/A	N/A. Expected to be included with Architectural Considerations, see pg. 15

Projected Therapeutic Modalities			
Recommendation (by whom)	Year Initiated	Frequency/Duration	Expected Cost
Physical therapy (TW)	2005 - life expectancy	2-4 visits/year (avg.) to life expectancy	$75-160 per visit Mileage: $7-23 miles per trip (depending on facility)
Note 1: See Future Aggressive Treatment, page 16, for expected Physical Therapy following Baclofen pump implant. Note 2: See also Inpatient Rehabilitation Program, for intensive, comprehensive therapy program once recovered from Baclofen pump implant.			
Counseling for adjustment, coping, education, inter-personal relations, etc. (RW, TW)	2005, 2010, 2024, 2039	1 X initial visit then estimate 2-4 X month for 6 months (avg.) at time of life transition stages (serious relationship/marriage, fathering children, work, physical decline, etc.).	Initial visit: $125-175 Follow-up: $125-175 per session
Peer support and mentoring program for individuals with spinal cord injury (RW)	2004 to life expectancy	Variable schedule	$0. Offered through Spinal Cord Injury Research Center located Craig Rehabilitation Center
Note: The client/evaluee disclosed during the interview (and confirmed by his mother) that he is not currently interested in receiving counseling services. The consulting physiatrist report appears to indicate he was taking an antidepressant medication at the time of the medical examination on August 6, 2004; however, there is no record of antidepressant medication in the records and no mention of this during my interview.			
Case Manager (RW, TW)	2004 to life expectancy	2-4 hours per month (avg.) for next 12 months, then 1 hour per month (avg.) to life expectancy, assumes client's/evaluee's complications better controlled and functional capabilities improved to the extent he can coordinate most of his own care.	2004-05: $1,968- 3,936 total @ $82 per hour 2006: 984/year (avg.) to life expectancy
Note: Reduction in case management services beyond the next 12 months assumes the client/evaluee receives a Baclofen pump implant with successful outcomes, completes a comprehensive inpatient rehabilitation program, and has significant reduction in spasticity and an increase in functional abilities.			

Wheelchair Needs			
Recommendation (by whom)	**Year Purchased**	**Replacement Schedule**	**Expected Cost**
Invacare A4 manual wheelchair (per interview and records)	Estimate 2000 (current chair)	Every 7-10 years (avg.) as backup chair to TiLite to 2024 (age 40) then discontinue (assumes power chair, see next page)	$3,000-4,000 (per vendor). See also Note 1 below.
TiLite titanium lightweight, fold-up manual wheelchair (per interview and records reviewed)	Estimate 2002 (current chair)	Every 5 years (avg.) as primary chair to 2024 (age 40) then every 10 years (avg.) to life	$3,400 (est.) + $1,200-1,500 (est.) for customized frame due to size = $4,600-4,900 per chair.
(2) Roho cushions (per interview, records, and TW)	Already has one cushion purchased in 2000 (est.). Current need for 2nd cushion for vehicle (2004).	Every 2 years (avg.) each to life expect.	1) W/C Cushion: $340-450 (dep. on size) 2) Vehicle cushion: $340-450 (dep. on size)
Spare cushion cover for wheelchair (RW)	2004	1 X year (avg.) to life	Cover: $45-70/year to life expectancy for wheelchair only

Note 1: The client/evaluee requires two (2) cushions: 1 for wheelchair and 1 for vehicle

Note 2: A spare cushion cover is recommended in the event the primary cover becomes damaged, gets soiled and requires laundering, or is otherwise unable to be used.

Wheelchair Needs (con't)			
Recommendation (by whom)	Year Purchased	Replacement Schedule	Expected Cost
e.motion™ or other power assist wheels for manual wheelchair (RW)	2014 (age 30)	Begin 2014: Every 5 years (avg.) to 2024 or expected time of power wheelchair use, see next page.	2014-2024: $6,000-7,500 (in addition to cost of manual wheelchair above)
Spare e.motion batteries (RW)	2014 (age 30)	Every 1-1½ years (avg.) to 2024 or expected time of power wheel-chair use	2014: $795 for initial spare pair then $480 per pair (refurbished) to $795/pair every 12-18 months to 2024
Power wheelchair (TW) Examples include: Invacare Freedom or Permobil Street power wheelchair with seat elevator	2024 (age 40)	Begin 2024: Every 5 years (avg.) dep. on wear and tear to life expectancy	Begin 2024: Invacare Freedom: $10,687 Or Permobil Street: $14,167
(2) Gel batteries for power chair (RW)	2026	Begin 2026: Every 2½ - 3 years (avg.) to life expectancy	Begin 2026 to life: Invacare: $363/pair Permobil: $675/pair

Note 1: Due to the client's/evaluee's size, he will require customization to the wheelchair, thereby incurring an increased cost over standard equipment. The above costs are reasonable estimates based on consultation with a certified rehabilitation technology specialist who indicates that the manufacturer of most wheelchairs will have to custom fabricate a wheelchair to adequately accommodate his size.

Note 2: Reduction in frequency of replacement of manual wheelchair after age 40 presumes he begins to utilize a power chair beginning approximately age 40 (such as Invacare "Formula" or Permobil "Street") with the manual wheelchair for backup.

Wheelchair for rural soft dirt (per client's/evaluee's request and supported by TW)	2004	Every 2-5 years (avg.) to life expectancy	$2,000-2,400 (est.)
Activeaid shower/ commode chair, requires roll-in shower (TW)	2004 or when get roll-in shower	Every 5 years (avg.) to life expectancy	$1,600 (est.) + $600 (est.) for customization = $2,200 each

Note: Activeaid chair is expected to replace the client's/evaluee's current shower/tub bench.

Wheelchair Accessories and Maintenance			
Recommendation by whom)	**Year Purchased**	**Maintenance or Replacement Schedule**	**Expected Cost**
Manual wheelchair maintenance to include tires replacement, etc. (RW)	2004	1 X year or as needed after 1 year warranty expires.	**2004-2023** (age 40): $200-500/year (avg.) after warranty. 2024-life: $200-500/ year (avg.) to life as backup chair (assumes power chair is primary).
Power wheelchair maintenance (RW)	2025	1 X year or as needed after 1 year warranty expires.	Beginning 2025: Estimate 10% cost of wheelchair per year to life expectancy after 1 year warranty.
Beach wheelchair maintenance (RW)	2005 or one year after getting chair	1 X year or as needed after 1 year warranty expires.	$100-500/year (avg. est.) to life
Activeaid shower/ commode chair maintenance, requires roll-in shower (RW)	2005 or one year after getting chair	1 X year or as needed after 1 year warranty expires	5% cost of wheelchair per year (avg.) to life
Note to Economist: Do not include maintenance costs on years in which each wheelchair is replaced.			
Allowance for wheelchair carry bag, beverage holder, gloves, tool kit, tire pump, etc. (RW)	2004	1 X year	$50/year (avg.) to life expectancy

Aids for Independent Function			
Recommendation (by whom)	**Year Purchased**	**Replacement Schedule**	**Expected Cost**
Ultra Select sliding transfer board (per interview)	2000 (est.)	Every 10 years (avg.) to life	$30-250 depending on size/length
Allowance for reachers, cordless telephone, hand-held shower, long-handled bath brush, gooseneck mirror, transfer belt, sheepskin, wedges, etc. (RW)	2004	1 X year	$50/year (avg.) to life expectancy
Portable wheelchair ramp for community access (RW)	2003 (already has)	Every 15 years (avg)	$250-850 depending on length and width

Home Furnishings and Accessories			
Recommendation (by whom)	**Year Purchased**	**Replacement Schedule**	**Expected Cost**
Elevated toilet seat/ commode chair (RW)	2004 (following pump implant)	Every 5 years (avg.) to life expectancy	$71 (per case documentation from vendor in file)
Select Comfort Bed with adjustable air mattress, remote control, extension legs for bed foundation, and headboard/footboard brackets (TW)	2004 (current need)	Replace every 20 years (at end of manufacturer's warranty)	Set: $3,750-4,450 (includes mattress, foundation, legs, headboard/footboard brackets, and pump)
Note : Economist deduct avg. cost of standard bed that client/evaluee would have required unrelated to the injury.			
Adjustable overbed table (per interview)	2000 (already has)	Every 10 years (avg.) to life expectancy	$125-200
Begin 2024 (age 40): Hoyer lift for transfers (TW)	Currently has though reportedly not used as able to use sliding board for transfers.	Expect replacement in 2024 (age 40) and ev. 10-15 years (avg.) thereafter to life exp.	2024: $750-1,000 (per local vendor) then ev. 10-15 years thereafter to life
Slings (2) (RW)	2024	Every 1-2 years each to life expectancy	Slings: $240 @ $120 each
			Begin 2049 (age 65): $10,180-10,220 (est.)
Begin 2049 (age 65): Barrier free ceiling or wall-mounted power lift for transfers (TW)	2049	Begin 2049 (age 65): 1 X only (assumes home at that time can accommodate ceiling lift)	
Slings (2) (RW)		1 X year each to life expectancy	Slings: $360-440/yr. @ $180-220 each
Barrier-free lift maintenance (RW)		1 X year after 2 year warranty expires	$300/year (avg.) to include batteries replacement, etc.
Note: The client/evaluee currently transfers using a sliding board and generally is able to transfer by himself with some occasional assistance. It is expected he will be independent in transfers following the Baclofen pump implant and inpatient rehabilitation program. Beginning 2024 (age 40), expect gradual increase in transfer assistance.			

Transportation			
Recommendation (by whom)	**Year Purchased**	**Replacement Schedule**	**Expected Cost**
Hand controls for vehicle, grab handles to assist with transfers, specialty rear view mirror, suspension system for stability, automatic trans-mission, and power package (per interview)	2004 (already has)	Every 5-7 years (avg.) or when vehicle replaced to 2024 (then accessible van at time of power chair acquisition, see next page)	$1,300 for modifications only (per case documentation from vendor in file)
Wheelchair transport in vehicle: Option 1, Able to fold up w/c and put in seat Or Option 2a: Car topper (Braun or other) to transport manual wheelchair or Option 2b: Wheelchair hoist (Bruno or other) (RW) Installation of Roho cushion in driver's seat (TW)	2004	Option 1: N/A. Option 2a & 2b: Every 5-10 years (avg.) per vendor to 2024 (then accessible van at time of power chair acquisi-tion, see next page). Can be reinstalled on different vehicle. Every 2 years (avg.) to life	Option 1, No additional cost, assumes independence. Option 2a, Car topper: $4,450 (does not include potential color match painting) Or Option 2b, Hoist: $2,499 Labor to install cushion: $110 (see pg. 5 for cost of cushion)

Note 1: The client/evaluee states he currently is physically unable to put his manual wheelchair into his vehicle. Following the Baclofen pump implant and inpatient Craig rehabilitation program, it is expected he will be able to accomplish this independently (see Option 1). However, if difficulties continue, a wheelchair car topper or hoist is offered as an alternative to loading the chair into the vehicle.

Note 2: **Note to Economist**: For purposes of this report, include wheelchair car topper or hoist (Opt.2a or 2b) to begin 2014 (age 30) to 2024 (age 40) when van with lift is expected at time of power chair acquisition.

Note 3: One vendor researched in client's/evaluee's area, informed they would provide an Adapted Driver Accessibility Evaluation to best determine the client's/evaluee's capabilities and needs free of charge.

Transportation (con't)			
Recommendation (by whom)	**Year Purchased**	**Replacement Schedule**	**Expected Cost**
Begin 2024 (age 40): Wheelchair accessible van with hand controls, wheelchair lift, tie-downs, 6-way power driver seat, dual battery system, raised roof, raised side door, 6" lowered floor, automatic trans-mission, power package, etc. (RW)	2024 (age 40) or when get power wheelchair, see page 6.	Beginning 2024: Every 5-7 years (avg.) to life	Begin 2024: $25,775 per vendor for modifi-cations only (does not include cost of van) Note: Due to the client's/evaluee's size, a full-size conversion van likely will be needed.
Maintenance for hand controls (RW)	2004 to 2023	Yearly maintenance of accessibility features	2004-2023: $100/yr. (avg.)
Maintenance for hand controls, van lift, and other accessibility features (RW)	2024-life expectancy	Same as above	2024-life: $200/year (avg.) to include van lift maintenance.

Note to Economist: Do not include maintenance on years when equipment is replaced, assuming 1 year warranty on new equipment.

Cellular telephone for emergency communication (RW)	2004 (presume already has)	Every 5-7 years (est.)	No additional cost over general population.

Health and Strength Maintenance			
Recommendation (by whom)	**Year of Purchase or Attendance**	**Replacement or Attendance Sched.**	**Expected Cost**
Easy Stand 6000 Glider (per interview)	2001 (already has)	Every 15 years (est.)	$6,500-7,500 for custom (per case documentation from vendor)
Membership to health club with accessible pool (RW)	2004	Yearly membership to life expectancy	$468/year to life @ $39 per month. Note: Does not include one time $75 enrollment fee at one facility.
Yearly allowance for disability-related leisure and recreational activities (RW)	2004	1 X year to life expectancy	$100-200/year (avg. est.) to life expectancy over and above general population

Home/Facility Care			
Recommendation (by whom)	**Year Initiated/Suspended**	**Hrs/Shifts/Days of Attendance or Care**	**Expected Cost**
Home-related assistance (TW)	2004 to life expectancy	3 hours/day (avg.) to life expectancy	Home assistance: $10-18 per hour (range from privately hired house-keeping to agency personnel) Economist to deduct 4-6 weeks while client/evaluee in inpatient rehabilitation program.
Personal care assistant (PCA) for assistance with activities of daily living/ADLs (TW)	Begin 2021 (age 37)	Begin 2021: 2-4 hours per day (avg.) for 10 years then increase 2-4 hrs/day (avg.) every 10 years thereafter to last 5 years of life expect.	<u>Begin 2021, PCA:</u> $16.95-20 per hour
Live-in caregiver (TW)	Begin last 5 years of life	Begin last 5 yrs. of life: Live-in available 10-12 hrs/day and overnight for emergencies, 7 days/week (generally allow live-ins 8 hrs. for sleep and 4-6 hours for meals and breaks)	Begin last 5 yrs. of life, Live-in: $225/day

<u>Note 1</u>: Home-related services averages for individuals with spinal cord injury who function at the T7 level = three (3) hours per day (Source: Blackwell, T., Krause, J., Wishful, T. & Steins, S. (2001). *Spinal cord injury desk reference: Guidelines for life care planning and case management*. New York, NY: Demos Publishing. Table M, pg. 229.).

<u>Note 2</u>: Expect the addition of personal care assistance (PCA) as he ages (beginning approximately 2021 or age 37) due to factors associated with aging with a spinal cord injury. Gradually increase PCA over time as outlined above. -

<u>Note 3</u>: Cost of home-related and caregiver assistance may be reduced through negotiation with home health agency, private hire, and/or if parents continue to provide assistance. Cost above does not include one time $75 nurse evaluation fee charged at one agency.

<u>Note 4</u>: In-home services would be reduced during times of expected annual hospitalizations, see pg. 16. However, no deduction is able to be made based on available information.

Interior and exterior home maintenance (RW)	2004 to life expectancy	N/A	Defer to **Economist** to add average time spent performing these activities for male.

Drug Needs			
Drugs and costs change over time and are representative of the client's/evaluee's current needs.			
Recommendation (by whom)	**Purpose**	**Cost per Unit**	**Cost per Year**
Detrol, 2 mg, 2 X day (per interview). Note: per Dr. Wishful's IME, freq. is 1 X day.	Bladder management	$62.79 for 30 tablets	$1,528/year to life expectancy
Ditropan XL, 15 mg. (per Dr. Wishful IME)	Bladder management	$117.19 for 30 tablets	$1,426/year to life expectancy
Magic Bullet suppository (per interview)	Bowel management every other day	$40 per box of 100 suppositories	$73/year to life expectancy
Colace, 1 per day (per Dr. Wishful IME)	Bowel management	$12.99 for 30 tablets	$158/year to life expectancy
Senekot, 1 per day (per Dr. Wishful IME)	Bowel management	$18.49 for 30 tablets	$225/year to life expectancy
Remeron, 15 mg, 1-2 at bedtime (per Dr. Wishful IME)	Antidepressant	$62.39-120.49 for 30-60 tablets	$759-1,466/year to 2006
Bactrim DS, 1 X day for 7 days alternate with Macrodantin, 100 mg/day for 7 days then repeat cycle (per interview)	Prophylactic for urinary tract infections	Bactrim: $13.99 for 14 tablets/month alternated with Macrodantin: $21.79 for 14 tablets per month	$429/year (avg.) to life expectancy
Note: Successful implant and outcome from the Baclofen pump (pg. 16) is expected to eliminate the client's/evaluee's reliance on narcotic and pain medication and spasticity medication, including Pepcid which reportedly is related to spasms in lower extremities/abdomen following mealtimes that reportedly have an affect on his stomach and feeling of reflux.			

	Supply Needs		
Supplies and costs change over time and are representative of the client's/evaluee's current needs.			
Recommendation	**Purpose**	**Cost per Unit**	**Cost per Year**
MMG O'Neil catheters (per interview)	Self-catheterization	$5.05 each for 120-150/month (avg.)	$606-758/year to life
Condom catheter (per interview)	Overnight catheter	$1.55 each for 35/month (avg.)	$651/year to life
Leg bags with connector kit, tubing and straps (per interview)	Urological supply	$4.72 each for 2 per month (avg.)	$113/year to life
Reusable leg bags with tubing and straps (per intrvw)	Same as above	$32.71 each for 1 per month (avg.)	$393/year to life
Foley bags (per interview)	Same as above	$3.50 each for 1 per month (avg.)	$42/year to life
Personal hygiene gloves, latex free (per interview)	Personal care and hygiene	$4.99 per box of 100, 3-4 pair (avg.) ev. other day for bowel program	$55-73/year to life
Surgilube lubricant (per interview)	Lubricant for bowel/bladder program	$1.60/tube for 2-3 tubes per month	$38-58/year to life
Chux pads (per interview)	Hygiene and bed linen protector	$36/box of 150, ev. other day for bowel	$44/year to life
Elastikon tape (per interview). Note: Accdg. to vendor, this is discontinued and replaced by Elastiplast	Urological supply	$2.68/roll for 10 rolls of Elastiplast per month (avg.)	$32/year to life
Cleaning solution (per interview)	Supply cleaner	$9.09 per 16 oz. bottle for 1 bottle per month	$109/year to life
Yearly allowance for misc. supplies (RW)	Bunny boots, heel protectors, lotions, urinals, syringes, bowel irrig. kit, etc.	Annual allowance	$100/year (avg.) to life

Architectural Considerations
(List considerations for home accessibility and/or modifications)

The client/evaluee currently lives with his parents in a one-level home. The home has been somewhat modified to include enlarging doorways, modifying master shower, installing taller toilet, and installation of ramp from garage into house. He requires a one-level barrier-free home that is wheelchair accessible and includes covered parking for inclement weather, ramps to front and back doors, hard floors and/or low-knap carpet, widened doorways/hallways, accessible bedroom and bathroom with roll-in shower, grab bars in bathroom, accessible kitchen to include sink and fixtures, lower kitchen cabinets and counters, front load washer and dryer, etc. Given his size, he requires larger equipment and larger living space (i.e., bedroom) to accommodate his oversized bed and other large equipment.

Cost of fully wheelchair accessible home = 8-12% over cost of standard home (Source: Moreo Construction, www.moreoconstruction.com). For purposes of life care planning, **Economist** to include provision for two (2) moves, approximately $5,000 (est.) for each, related to costs associated with packing and moving his equipment due to his reduced ability related to the SCI.

Economist to also deduct value of average home in client's/evaluee's local area.

Vocational/Educational Plan

Recommendation (by whom)	Year Initiated/Suspended	Purpose	Expected Cost
Vocational Evaluation (RW)	2004 (current need)	Assess intelligence, aptitudes, interests, temperaments, and abilities related to work/vocational activity	Private $750 (est.) for report with recommendations Division of Voc. Rehab: $0.
Vocational Rehabilitation Counseling/ Guidance to include labor market surveys, job analysis, selective placement and f/up, etc. (RW)	2005 to 2008	Facilitate educational goals and enhance career selection, problem-solving and placement in appropriate work activity	Private $3,750-7,500 total for 50-100 hours @ $75/hr. Division of Voc. Rehab: $0.
Personal Computer (RW)	Unknown (already has)	Enhance access to work, education, leisure, etc.	No additional cost over general population.

Orthotics

Recommendation	Year Purchased	Replacement	Expected Cost
Not applicable. According to the consulting physiatrist, AFOs (ankle/foot/orthoses) are not expected to be needed.			

Future Medical Care, Surgical Intervention, Aggressive Treatment			
Recommendation (By Whom)	Year Initiated	Frequency	Expected Cost
Data show that expected annual hospitalizations for individuals with spinal cord injury between T1-S5 level cost $4,828 per year in 1992 dollars. [Source: DeVivo, M., Whiteneck, G., & Charles, E. (1995). The economic impact of spinal cord injury. In Stover, S., DeLisa, J., & Whiteneck, G. (Eds.), *Spinal Cord Injury: Clinical outcomes from the model systems.* Aspen Publishers, page 238. Also referenced in Blackwell, Krause, Wishful, & Stiens. (2001). Spinal cord injury desk reference: Guidelines for life care planning and case management. Demos Medical Publishing, Inc. New York: New York, page 146.]. **Economist** to update cost to 2012 dollars.			
Baclofen pump implant (documented in the records, Dr. Wishful consultation, and client/evaluee interview)	2004	1 X only re-implant	Implant: $33,120-33,500 (per case documentation in file) Mileage to Denver: $48
Initial adjustments to pump (per neuro-surgeon's office)	2004-05	2 X month for approx. 6 months following implant	$0. Anticipate initial adjustments included in cost of implant. Mileage: $47 per trip for 12 trips.
Physical therapy following implant surgery (per neuro-surgeon office)	2004-2005	3 X week (avg.) for 6 weeks then re-evaluate	Evaluation: $80-85 Therapy: $75-160 per session for 17 sessions. Mileage: $7-23/trip
Baclofen refills (per neuro-surgeon's office, refills done in office by nurse)	2005 to life expectancy	Every 1-2 months (avg.) to life expectancy	$180-250 per refill depending on Baclofen dosage Mi. to Denver: $47/trip
Replace pump/ battery every 5 years (avg.) to life (per neurosurgeon office)		Every 5 years (avg.) to life expectancy	Replacement: $17,500 (per case documentation in file) Mileage: $48
Note: Cost information from University Hospital regarding Baclofen pump implant is pending, and plan may be updated once received.			

Future Medical Care, Surgical Intervention, Aggressive Treatment (con't)			
Recommendation (By Whom)	Year Initiated	Frequency	Expected Cost
Comprehensive inpatient rehabilitation program (TW as well as Dr. Presser and Dr. Bates, 10/03)	2005, following successful Baclofen pump implant	4-6 weeks (avg.)	Craig SCI Model Systems program: $2,000/day (avg.), incls. therapies and MD plus Travel to Denver for client/evaluee + one: $47 mi. + $400 (avg.) lodging/ meals (see Note 2 & 3)
Male fertility evaluation (TW)	2011 (est.) or when ready to start family	1 X only	$180 Mileage: $63
Semen retrieval (TW)		Expect 1 X only to obtain sufficient specimen	$1,200-1,700 Mileage: $63
Intrauterine insemination (IUI) for female (TW)		Per reproductive specialist, 3 cycles avg. per insemination	$900-3,000 for 3 cycles (range reflects frequency of fertility medications and ultrasounds)
Or In vitro fertilization (IVF) for female (TW)		Or 1 X avg. per IVF	Or $10,000 per cycle Note: For 2 children, double the cost for IUI and IVF.
Note: The client/evaluee expresses an interest in fathering children.			

Potential Complications

Note: Funding for common probable complications requiring hospitalizations has been included in this life care plan (see Future Medical Care, Surgical Intervention, Aggressive Treatment above). Potential complications include the list below (costs not included in plan).

- Orthopedic/Musculoskeletal problems including chronic back pain, problems with spinal instrumentation, traumatic arthritis, contractures, heterotopic ossificans, myosistis ossification, osteoporosis, fractures, overuse/problems with shoulders/wrists/elbows due to manual wheelchair use, etc.

- Neurologic problems including increased or uncontrolled spasticity, pain/burning sensation, syringomyelia, etc., which are not able to be controlled with expected Baclofen pump implant.

- Gastrointestinal and/or metabolic problems including significant weight gain/loss, poor diet/nutrition, chronic constipation, possible dilated colon, reflux, sepsis related to infections, etc., which require additional evaluation, treatment, medication, and/or diagnostic studies.

- Adjustment to disability, including depression, anxiety, withdrawal, decreased coping skills, increased fatigue, poor or loss of self-esteem, interpersonal relationship problems, anger/behavior management, etc. that may require increased psychological intervention and peer support. May also experience increased problems with age, as related to decreased functional abilities.

- Urological problems including recurrent urinary tract infections (UTIs), kidney infections, bladder/kidney stones or blockage, urinary incontinence, renal calculus, autonomic dysreflexia, urethral strictures, effects of long term catheter use, hydronephrosis, etc. that require more extensive and expensive tests, i.e., complex urodynamics @ $2,000-3,000. Reportedly has a history of UTIs for which he takes prophylactic antibiotics.

- Medical and therapeutic care, including lab work and diagnostic tests, which is more frequent and expensive than expected. May require evaluation and/or follow-up by medical specialists, including pulmonologist, gastroenterologist, etc., and intermittent physical and/or occupational therapy, as well as increased case management services and additional adaptive equipment/devices due to complications and as he ages and functional abilities decline. According to documentation in file materials provided for review, reported recommendation from his pediatrician is for an "extra pulmonological visit 1 X year over and above his pre-existing needs." However, the consulting physiatrist, Dr. Wishful, opines this is not necessary based on his evaluation.

- Increased need for homemaker care, up to 6 hours/day (avg.), if less than successful outcomes from Baclofen pump implant and/or other complications.

- Pressure sores/skin breakdown/decubitus ulcers that are non-healing and may require aggressive wound care and/or surgery to repair. As a worst case scenario, if decubitus not healed in approximately 60 days, may need plastic surgery to close wound prior to Baclofen pump implant.

- Circulatory problems including inflammation of veins with clots, deep venous thrombosis, swelling in lower extremities, electrolyte imbalance, feet/leg problems, high blood pressure, etc.

- Cellulitis and/or ingrown toenails.

- Adverse reactions to long-term use of medications

SAMPLE INTERVIEW TOPICS

-CONFIDENTIAL: FOR PROFESSIONAL USE ONLY-

Roger O. Weed, PhD, CRC, CLCP/R, CDMS/R, FNRCA, FIALCP

Note: Many of the interview headings below are not relevant unless the life care planner also prepares a vocational report.

Date: Time Start: Stop:

Location of interview:

Name:

Date of Injury:

Date of Birth:

Social Security #:

Address:

Phone:

Attorney:

Referral Source:

Injury Incurred or Disability:

Employer at Time of Injury: (Complete only if appropriate)

    Occupation:

    Length of Employment:

    Union: Yes (name of union), NO

    Duties:

Social Information: (Include family history, where raised, what the parents did for work, health of family members, location of each and occupation, list of siblings or step-parents/brothers/sisters, family closeness, marital status, children and ages, relationship with spouse, religious orientation, history of illegal activity, etc.)

Military: Branch:

Dates: Duties:

Location: Special training:

Rank at discharge: Honorable?: Y / N

Hobbies/Leisure Time Activities: (Include before injury/illness and compare to post injury/illness, note avocational interests particularly if severe disability, TV program, reading interests and subscription, etc.)

Educational History: (Include high school and other schooling best and worst subjects, likes and dislikes, perceived success, outside activities, sports, vocational training, higher education, short courses, etc.)

Employment History:

Dates|Age|Company |Job Title |Duties (include skills and tools) |Wage

(Also note skills, reason for leaving, likes and dislikes, perceived employee ratings, etc.)

Employment Interests: (What does the client/evaluee want to do?)

Skills/Strengths: (Include tools and expertise from paid and non-paid work.)

Current Financial Status: (Include sources and amounts of income, rent costs, monthly expenses, loans, public assistance, social security, workers' compensation, SSDI, SSI, VA, Soc Sec retirement, food stamps, loans, etc.)

Medical History: (Include childhood diseases and residuals, accidents and residuals, hospitalizations, smoking, drinking and drug history, etc.)

Present Medical Treatment Information: (Information regarding the current treatment, such as the next appointment with the doctors and therapists.)

Medications: (Prescription and nonprescription, size, amount, reason. Include supplies.)

Smoke: Drink: Drug abuse:

Subjective Complaints: (Include the list from head to toe of the perceived current problems due to the accident/illness. Pain, paralysis, lack of feeling, headaches, ringing in the ears, etc.)

Activities: (Include the working conditions and physical demands consistent with the Department of Labor research on worker traits.) For severely impaired clients/evaluees, consider adding the four-page Activities of Daily Living Skills form available from Elliot & Fitzpatrick.

    Lifting/strength limitations:
    Climbing:
    Balancing:
    Walking:
    Standing:
    Sitting:
    Stooping:
    Bending:
    Reaching above head:
    Reaching above waist:
    Finger dexterity:
    Manual dexterity:
    Feeling:
    Talking:
    Vision:
    Hearing:
    Working in/out of doors:
    Working cold
    Working heat:
    Working wet/humid areas:
    Working noise/vibrations:
    Working around hazards:
    Working around fumes/odors/dust:
    Sleeping:
    Stamina:
    Driving:
    Other:

Daily Activity Schedule: (Include time up, eat, who fixes meals and does household duties, yard work, laundry, and what s/he does to keep busy, time to bed, etc. Note if daily routine is established or whether client/evaluee is looking for things to fill in time.)

Motivation/emotional tone/comments regarding the interview: (What was the attitude, how receptive to information, any psychological concerns noted that may require further study.)

Approach to eval: + ± -

Conclusions/Recommendations:

Copyright Roger O. Weed, Ph.D., CLCP. Reprinted with permission

<u>Sample Information Release Form</u>

WEED AND ASSOCIATES, INC.

Roger Weed, Ph.D., CRC, CLCP, LPC, CCM   Debra E. Berens, MS, CRC, CCM, CLCP
P. O. Box 2133, Duluth, Georgia 30096   1156 Masters Lane, Snellville, Georgia 30078
(770) 476-0075   (770) 978-9212   FAX (770) 972-6112

AUTHORIZATION FOR RELEASE OF PERSONAL INFORMATION

For the Use and Disclosure of Personal, Health, Psychological, Academic and Vocational Information

---

Note: Federal law says that Weed and Associates, Inc. and its representatives cannot share your health information without your permission except in certain situations. By signing this form, you are giving Weed & Associates, Inc. and its representatives permission to share the information you indicate below. This does not keep the information from being shared with other individuals or entities once it leaves Weed & Associates, Inc. and is beyond our control. This authorization will remain in effect unless you specify an ending date. If you decide later that you do not want Weed & Associates, Inc. and its representatives to share your information any more, you can sign the REVOCATION SECTION at the end of this form and return it to us.

To whom it may concern:

I hereby request and authorize you to release to Weed & Associates, Inc. and its representatives the following types of information which you may have or may receive pertaining to me. A copy of this form shall have the same effect as the original.

I give permission to _____ **to share the information checked below with Weed & Associates, Inc. and its representatives:**

☐ All information

☐ Information from a certain time period (specify dates):

     From _____ To _____

☐ ll information relating to a certain event or injury – specify a specific event(s) and/or date(s):

     Event _____ Date of event_____

☐ Other (specify): _____

Printed Name:_____ Signature: _____ Date: _____

Date of Birth: _____ SSN: _____

If applicable, client's/evaluee's maiden name or other names used: _____

If client/evaluee is a minor or otherwise incapable of offering consent or making an informed decision, signature of parent or guardian required: _____

If client/evaluee unable to write name use "X" or other mark which will be witnessed by two parties:

_____

_____

REVOCATION SECTION: I no longer want my information shared.

Signature: _____ Date _____

NEUROPSYCHOLOGIST QUESTIONS

In addition to the standard evaluation report, add the following as appropriate.

1. Please describe, in layman terms, the damage to the brain.

2. Please describe the effects of the incident on the client's/evaluee's ability to function.

3. Please provide an opinion to the following topics:

    a. Intelligence level? (include pre- vs. post-incident if able)

    b. Personality style with regard to the workplace and home?

    c. Stamina level?

    d. Functional limitations and assets?

    e. Ability for education/training?

    f. Vocational implications - style of learning?

    g. Level of insight into present functioning?

    h. Ability to compensate for deficits?

    i. Ability to initiate action?

    j. Memory impairments (short-term, long-term, auditory, visual, etc.)?

    k. Ability to identify and correct errors?

    l. Recommendations for compensation strategies?

    m. Need for companion or attendant care both as child and as adult? Include projected # of hours per day as child and adult.

    n. What considerations related to aging with a disability need to be included?

4. What is the proposed treatment plan, including frequency and duration both now and expected over life-time?

    a. Counseling (individual and family)?

    b. Cognitive therapy?

    c. Re-evaluations?

    d. Referral to others? (e.g., physicians)

    e. Other?

5. Include cost per session or hour as well as for any re-evaluations recommended in question #4.

Copyright Roger O. Weed, Ph.D., CLCP (with partial attribution to Robert Fraser, Ph.D.) Reprinted with permission

EXAMPLE QUESTIONS TO ASK THE PHYSICIAN

Purpose: Medical foundation for diagnosis and treatment

Note: The physiatrist is typically team leader for allied health recommendations BUT may not have expertise to cover all needed areas.

1. Future Care (determine what is reasonable and appropriate vs. medically necessary vs. desirable)

    *   How long will the patient need follow-up?
    *   When will the patient reach maximum medical improvement?
    *   How long and how often will treatment be needed? (Be sure to include frequency and duration.)
    *   What treatment is expected? (Follow-up visits, routine evaluations, etc.)
    *   Are x-rays or lab work needed?
    *   Do you anticipate any further surgeries or aggressive medical treatment?
    *   If so, how much will each of these procedures cost?

2. Possible Complications

    *   What complications are possible/expected with poor care, or based on history or disability? Examples:
    *   Traumatic arthritis
    *   Contractures
    *   Skin breakdown
    *   Psychological
    *   Adverse reactions to medications
    *   Respiratory
    *   Etc.

3. Recommended Medical Follow-Up by Other Specialties

    *   Physicians? (Neurology, plastic surgery, orthopedic, urology, internist, etc.)
    *   Therapists? (occupational, speech and physical therapists, dietary, audiology, vision, etc.)
    *   Psychologists?
    *   Vocational?
    *   Etc.

If any of the above are recommended ask for an opinion regarding what treatment will be needed, how often it will be needed and expected cost?

4. Functional Limitations

    *   What functional limitations do you reasonably expect?
    *   Will these limitations require attendant care?
    *   If so, how much? And at what level? (e.g., companion, house keeping, nurse's aide, L.P.N., R.N., High tech)

5. Work related limitations

Note: This chapter is based in large part on excerpts from the booklet, Weed, R. (2007), Life Care Planning: A Step-by-Step Guide. Athens, GA: Elliott & Fitzpatrick, Inc. Reprinted with permission.

Chapter 11
Forensic Rehabilitation

Introduction

According to *Black's Law Dictionary*, forensic rehabilitation refers to the practice of rehabilitation principles in legal settings (1990). This chapter will discuss the relationship between rehabilitation and the courts, expert witness roles, and selected terms that may be important to the rehabilitation consultant within the legal system.

Rehabilitation experts are relatively new to the courtroom. Indeed, historically rehabilitation counselors were trained specifically to work in public agencies and were often shielded from acting as expert witnesses in personal injury litigation. The first entry into the private sector was nursing in the late 1960's when International Rehabilitation Associates, now Intracorp, was formed by an insurance company to help process and manage insurance claims. By the 1990's, private sector rehabilitation has extended into almost all areas of disability care, including workers' compensation, long term disability, Social Security disability insurance, health insurance, railroad (Federal Employers Liability Act), longshore workers, Jones Act, as well as personal injury litigation. Although there is considerable similarity across jurisdictions, there are a number of differences about which the rehabilitation expert should know before stepping into court.

For example, the word disability is defined differently in various systems. In public rehabilitation, disability usually refers to the medical condition which establishes eligibility for services indicating that the client be able to perform work and benefit from rehabilitation services. When Social Security determines a person is disabled, the person is deemed unable to perform "substantial gainful activity" and may qualify for government support for living. In workers' compensation systems, some states have provision for disability which may be permanent or temporary as well as partial or total. As with the word "disability," terminology can make a significant difference and it is important for the rehabilitation expert to understand the words used in the courtroom.

As noted in the chapter on the vocational expert, many jurisdictions require specific education or training in order to be qualified. It may be surprising to learn that it is not necessary for the rehabilitation professional to be certified or possess a certain level of education to be an expert in personal injury litigation. According to *Kim Manufacturing v. Superior Metal Treating* (1976), an "expert witness is one who by reason of education or specialized experience possesses superior knowledge respecting a subject about which persons having no particular training are incapable of forming an accurate opinion or deducing correct conclusions." Therefore, an attorney may offer as an "expert" someone who would not be considered expert in some states for workers' compensation, or as a vocational expert (VE) for the Social Security system.

Roles of the Rehabilitation Expert

There are generally two areas which the attorney must address in litigation: liability and damages. When a party is found liable, that party is determined to be at fault. The next task is to prove damages, or the cost associated with the incident. The rehabilitation expert will generally participate in the damages portion of litigation by assisting in establishing the cost of future care and the significance of the incident with regard to the person's ability to perform work (earnings capacity) by acting as either an expert or as a litigation consultant.

Persons who are disabled as a result of an accident or a disease process, especially in cases involving negligence and/or liability, may have the right to claim a financial award (damages) to offset the costs involved in being victimized. Depending on the degree of accident and/or injury, the costs can be enormous. Cases involving brain injury, tetrapelgia, and burns can lead to astronomical costs in medical expenses, including long-term medical maintenance (see Table 11.1). Based on an extensive review of settlement awards from 1979 to 1983, the average award was $64,000 per case across all classes of injury. The largest award reported in this review was $2.7 million for a brain-injured person. The largest award reported to date (1984) in the State of Florida was for $12 million to a 26-year-old woman who suffered brain injury. A brain injury

Table 11.1
Settlement Awards (1979-1983)

Area Injury	# Cases	Range Low	Range High	Mean
Brain	29	$750	2,744,059	$283, 063
Face & Skull	68	50	1,275,000	50,966
Shoulder	20	250	300,953	38,190
Arm & Elbow	36	50	425,000	44,458
Wrist & Hand	29	2,000	281,000	36,851
Neck & Cervical	120	350	649,481	30,846
General Back	90	500	830,000	44,452
Lumbar & Low Back	63	500	412,000	74,000
Internal Injuries	22	314	800,000	99,631
Hip & Pelvis	10	500	200,000	61,120
Leg & Foot	69	1,000	325,000	72,828
Knee	22	200	250,000	49,686
Loss of Senses	10	10,000	500,000	89,250
Sexual Injuries	5	1,250	250,000	56,950
Burns	18	4,000	1,000,000	326,286
Other	64	300	638,000	30,049

case in which one of the authors participated was $21 million in damages which was settled for $5 million present value. (Present value is an economic term which basically means the client's family was awarded $5 million which is invested to provide far more than $5 million over the client's life time).

The specific areas and reasons for awards of this size are not always delineated in the general literature. However, the two areas which justified the largest amount of cash settlement would be the medical area and the claimant's loss of earnings capacity to earn money. The medical area would obviously include projected medical costs for adequate health maintenance over the expected remaining years of a person's life. Other factors would include current lost wages as a result of lost time from work, the issues involved in pain and suffering, any punitive damages if negligence was involved, and the general loss of opportunity to be employed in the future.

Without a doubt, the rehabilitation professional is the one who is in the best position to testify to damages in personal injury litigation. Future medical care and loss of earnings capacity are directly related to the education and experience of most rehabilitation counselors. Many nurses and rehabilitation psychologists have gained experience in this area as well. It seems clear that attorneys are turning to our professional to help settle cases, provide case management services and assemble the experts to answer critical cases.

For example, one case involves a multiple amputation due to an electrical injury. One of the authors was responsible for setting up medical and psychological evaluations, writing a life care plan, arranging vocational testing, providing the analysis of vocational impact and identifying the economist to opine as to the economic loss bottom line.

In the area of workers' compensation, most states have gone so far as to identify schedules of injuries which establish an actual percentage loss of total functioning of the person, taking into account the area of bodily injury (see Table 11.2 for an example).

The three most critical areas for the rehabilitation professional are the questions involving current lost capacity to earn, the loss of opportunity to be employed and future medical care. As noted above, these issues

Table 11.2
Impairment Schedule

Member	Maximum Whole Body Disability (%)	Member	Maximum Whole Body Disability (%)
Thumb	16	Burns and skin impairments, including disfigurement	70
Index finger	11	Internal organs, excluding brain	85
Middle finger	9		
Ring finger	4	Brain	100
Little finger	2	Stomach	65
Great toe	5	Pancreas	65
Lesser toe	1	Colon	50
Hand	54	Spleen	0
Hand and Wrist	54	Bladder	30
Arm	60	Sexual organs or function	20
Foot	21	Circulatory system	90
Foot and Ankle	28	Heart	85
Leg	40	Lungs	85
Eye	24	Liver	75
Eyes (both)	85	Solitary kidney	10
Hearing loss (both ears)	35	Kidney, excluding solitary kidney	77
Back	71		
Voice	70		

Source: Minnesota Workers' Compensation Laws (1984)

generally represent the most economic impact in a liability case. The ability to address these critical questions will provide valuable and important information to an economist who will project all future lost earnings in the claimant's behalf. The loss of opportunity to be employed is a question which addresses the claimant's reduced employment potential, if any, as defined by his ability to be employed within a particular geographical labor force. This concept will be discussed later in this chapter and referred to as labor market access.

The second issue for the rehabilitation professional is the question of lost earnings capacity. It is generally simple to determine the wages being paid to the claimant at time of injury. This may or may not represent the client's capacity to earn. The next step is to determine the projected earning power of the claimant following the injury and the probable reduced opportunity to be employed. This question does not involve the added issue of future earnings power but rather, what would the claimant be able to be paid if the claimant was to return to work in this calendar year. Approaches and methods of determining wage loss and future wage loss will be discussed in the section titled "Wage Loss Analysis." Table 11.3 outlines several issues that the rehabilitation professional must address in order to arrive at a conclusion.

A third issue may to identify other experts to "fill in the blanks" or consult with an attorney about the work of others. The rehabilitation consultant may also help develop deposition or trial questions since many attorneys can not be educated in all of the medical, vocational and related areas and therefore rely upon professionals who are. In addition, they may have too many irons in the fire and need help managing complex cases.

To ascertain the costs of future care, particularly for serious medical conditions and catastrophic injuries, is the Life Care Plan (see Chapter 10). This method organizes topics according to various categories which

Table 11.3
Earnings Capacity Checklist

Typical Topics

See RAPEL Checklist for reporting format.

- **Earnings v. Earnings Capacity**: Did the individual have an extensive work history? Do the earnings represent the capacity? For example, is the client a housewife, prisoner, farmer, military person or someone who recently changed jobs?

- **Work History**: Have you obtained tax records? Do you have depositions or other records from the employer? Do you have an opinion as to the client's work capability?

- **Industry**: If the person has a work history, did the job have clear advancement potential for career progression? (For example, a union job that begins as a helper, apprentice, them becomes a master.)

- **Transferable Skills**: Does the individual possess work skills that can be transferred to other occupations? Does the individual have the worker traits necessary to be able to learn new skills?

- **Labor Market Survey**: Have you considered a specific labor market survey for the selected industry?

- **Loss of Opportunity**: Does the disability cause a vocational handicap to the labor market? Is there a loss of access to chosen jobs?

- **Vocational Handicaps**: List physical, mental and emotional handicaps that result from the incident.

- **Impact on employability**: Does the disability restrict access to existing jobs?

- **Impact on Placeability**: Will your client have difficulty in finding a job? Will the client need professional rehabilitation services? Will job skills training, employment coaching, etc. help overcome the handicap?

- **Work Life Expectancy**: (labor force participation rate): Will this person be able to work full-time or part-time? Will there be long periods of time that the person will be unable to work due to complications? Will it take longer for this individual to find employment? Will the person "retire" early?

- **Vocational Development Options**: What was the pre-incident level of capability for education or training? Post-incident? Is there a difference?

- **Vocational Alternative**: What were the pre-incident reasonable jobs for the client? Post-incident? Is there a difference?

- **Earnings Capacity**: What is the average wage for jobs available pre-incident compared to jobs available post-incident? Is there a diminution of capacity?

---

outline expected treatment, start and stop dates, costs and other information which will provide the jury with an understanding of the treatment plan. The format is designed to develop a comprehensive rehabilitation plan which includes the necessary information to project the expense, usually with the help of an economist, in order to arrive at a "bottom line figure."

Venues

Estimating earning capacity and related constructs cannot effectively be understand without a knowledge of a particular venue. According to Black's (2000),

> *Venue: The proper or possible place for the trial of a case, usu. because the place has some connection with the events that have given rise to the case (p.1260).*

While venue oftentimes refers to a geographical location, determinations in this broad area of estimating earnings capacity is simply not defined by a location (i.e., state court, federal court), but also the nature and scope of the judicial program. As will be discussed, estimating lost earnings in California or North Carolina can be markedly different in the field of workers' compensation. The same holds true for other settings and programs as well (venues), i.e., the state and federal compensation programs, the Veterans Administration, and state and federal courts in civil disputes. Therefore, the type of program (venue) is perhaps the first consideration in applying a determination regarding lost earnings (five basic venues are discussed).

A more perplexing problem is that terms related to earning capacity may take on different meanings depending on the source of the program. For instance, any discussion of earning capacity and related constructs are usually associated with civil or personal injury litigation. However, the general issue of employability is very germane to the field of workers' compensation and even SSDI (Social Security Disability Insurance). The issue is further compounded by a variety of program requirements as set forth by the many different types of compensation programs (by state, plus federal programs). An additional source of legal definition and constraint is established by case law. This section identifies and presents the most salient sources of definitions and parameters from these sources and/or venues. Therefore, the type of program (venue) is perhaps the first consideration in applying and understanding of the role of the rehabilitation expert (See Table 11.4).

Venue #1: Social Security

Social Security Disability Insurance (SSDI) and Supplemental Social Insurance (SSI) are two of the largest social programs providing safety-net support and services for people who are disabled or disadvantaged and who can no longer work and earn money. SSDI is the larger of the two programs and more directly relates to people with a work history prior to the presence of a disability. The SSDI does not address the issue of earning capacity. However, the language that exists in the federal regulations related to a person with a disability and their potential to return-to-work is significant. SSDI has long been considered the granddaddy of all of the rehabilitation consulting programs. Indeed, the SSA Vocational Expert (VE) program is generally the starting place for many VEs, especially those who expand their practice into the forensic area.

Under SSDI, a person with a disability is evaluated on a variety of factors as defined below:

> *If you can do your previous work, we will determine that you are not disabled. However, if your residual functional capacity (RFC) is not enough to enable you to do any of your previous work, we must still decide if you can do any other work. To do this, we consider your residual functional capacity, and your age, education, and work experience. Any work (jobs) that you can do must exist in significant numbers in the national economy. (20 CFR, 404.1561).*

The work related factors, as defined by the Social Security Administration (SSA), such as age, education, work experience, physical exertion and work skills, including the notion of transferable skills, are all defined and discussed in detail within the federal regulations (20 CFR, 404.1563-65, 404.1567-68).

Substantial gainful activity (SGA) is an important concept as well and is defined in two parts:

> *Substantial work activity is work activity that involves doing significant physical and mental activities. Gainful work activity is work activity that you do for pay or profit. (20 CFR, 404.1572).*

These regulations and definitions are still prominent today in terms of assessing past work while considering residual functional capacity, and the important factors of age, education and experience of people with disabilities. While the SSA does not require any estimations of future lost earnings, the program does require an evaluation and assessment of the capacity to work and earn money. Accordingly, the SSA program has provided a significant foundation for the assessment of work and earning money across the spectrum of earning assessments in all compensation programs and, in particular, cases involving personal injury.

Venue #2: Department of Veteran Affairs

The Department of Veterans Affairs (VA) compensation program was developed to address the issues of loss and disability by veterans. The VA adopted a rating schedule (Halstrom, 2000) in 38 C.F.R.4, as a way to determine the extent of an injured veteran's impairment of earning capacity in civil occupations.

Halstrom illustrates how the VE schedule would be used (even in civil cases) in determining a reduced earnings capacity. A woman was injured on her way to work while riding a city train that collided with another train. The woman suffered multiple injuries, including damage to her spleen, scarring after surgery, depression, and posttraumatic stress disorder. By using the VA rating schedule, a combination of the injuries resulted in a whole-body disability rating of 40%. Multiplying her wage at time of injury ($29,000 annually) by 40% and multiplying by the number of work years remaining (the assumption was that she would work until the retirement age of 65), her future lost earning capacity was estimated at $359,600, not reduced to present value.

This is a rather simplistic approach that would not be allowed in most civil cases (VA cases, maybe). The first serious problem is equating a direct relationship between a disability rating and a loss of earning capacity. Second, assuming one's worklife expectancy would be a retirement at age 65 is not always defensible, especially given the existence of by federal and private tables for estimating worklife.

Venue #3: Workers' Compensation (State)

Programs in the workers' compensation area are as varied as the 50 states and the various federal programs. In the first instance, each state is responsible for developing and administering its own respective program. While there are general themes which are consistent for the state programs, there is also a great deal of variability between the programs on the rules and regulations regarding disability and compensation. The federal employee, depending on the source of employment, is subject to the respective compensation programs as well. Under the Office of Workers' Compensation Programs (OWCP), a number of programs exist: Federal Employee Compensation Act (FECA), the Jones Act and the Longshore and Harbor Workers' Compensation Act (LHWCA). Rather than reviewing the many compensation programs, information is drawn from the LHWCA in order to illustrate common parameters of many compensation programs – either state or federal. Following are selected definitions from the glossary of the LHWCA:

Average Weekly Wage: AWWis set at one fifty-second part of the employee's average annual earnings.

Functional Loss: Describes a situation in which a physiological function can no longer be performed by the individual . . . which should be measured in quantifiable terms.

Impairment: The loss, loss of use, or derangement of any body part, system or function.

Loss of Wage Earning Capacity: A computation of economic loss which takes into consideration a claimant's age, degree of disability, education, work history, training, and the availability of work in which the claimant lives.

Disability: Disability is generally an economic concept, or, more specifically, the inability of an employee because of injury or other factors, to earn the wages which the employee was receiving at the time of the injury in the same or other employment.

Further, consider the North Carolina Workers' Compensation program, in which benefits following injury and disability are designated by a "schedule" . . . whereby compensation is awarded as a percentage of the loss of a body part or function.

Schedule of Injuries: The rate and period of compensation, based on the loss of a body part or function.

The concepts underlying workers' compensation laws in the United States originated from Germany, in 1884 and Austria, in 1887 (Obermann, 1965; Weed & Field, 2001; Wright, 1980). In 1893 the U.S. Commissioner of Labor studied the need for insurance and compensation which led to a cooperative insurance law in Maryland in 1902. The law was declared unconstitutional because, among other reasons, it denied the right of trial by jury (Obermann, 1965). By 1908, the United States had passed a law referred to as "workers' compensation" for federal employees. Maryland tried another approach which limited coverage to coal and clay miners but it was repealed in 1914. New York also passed a law for injured workers, a part of which was declared unconstitutional. In spite of the conflict from the beginning, workers' compensation laws were slowly enacted and, by 1911, ten states had some form of workers' compensation law. By 1921, 45 states and territories had some form of workers' compensation law. The laws all varied by scope, benefits, system of benefits and administration, which continues to exist to this day. However, all 50 states have some type of workers' compensation law/industrial insurance program.

Although the laws vary, each state has adopted a similar definition of injury which describes an injury caused by an accident "arising out of and in the course of employment" (U.S. Chamber of Commerce, 1993). Additionally, a common provision among workers' compensation laws is medical coverage related to the injury and wage benefits/compensation. Many states also provide for vocational rehabilitation to facilitate a return to employment for the injured worker. Although many have lobbied for a federal law to standardize the workers' compensation programs in the United States, vigorous opposition exists from the states.

With workers' compensation laws in place, employers were relieved of liability brought on by a worker injured on the job. In return, the injured worker was to receive necessary medical treatment, lost wages, and in some states, possibly vocational rehabilitation or retraining if unable to return to his/her regular job. For information of state programs, comparisons and a summary of the state laws, visit the AFL/CIO websites listed in the reference section.

North Carolina: For illustrative purposes, the North Carolina Compensation Program (97-29 and 31) describes what is somewhat typical of many other state workers' compensation programs. A "schedule of injuries" provides a formula for the amount of compensation for a specified number of weeks. For example, a worker with a loss of a hand would be compensated at the rate of sixty-six and two-thirds on wage at time of injury for a period of 200 weeks. A loss of a thumb would also be for a pay rate of sixty-six and two-thirds, but for 75 weeks. The schedule lists in detail other body parts lost to injury and their corresponding compensation. In cases of total and permanent disability, compensation, including medical expenses, shall be paid for the remainder of the worker's life. Many states have adopted a similar format for compensating disabilities, although other states have modified their compensation program to recognize the different categories of disabilities: temporary partial, temporary total, permanent partial, and permanent total. States that rely on a schedule of injuries and compensation usually have minimal disputes once the nature and extent of the injury is accurately decided.

Venue #4: Workers' Compensation (Federal)

As noted previously, there are several federal compensation programs (www.dol.gov/esa) that have been developed for various setting and/or occupations. These include:

- Federal Employees' Compensation Act (FECA) (federal and postal workers around the world)
- Longshore and Harbor Workers' Compensation Act (HLWCA) (federal employees on navigational waters around the United States)
- Federal Employees Liability Act (FELA) (railroad workers)
- Merchant Marine Act of 1920 (i.e., The Jones Act) (sailors on American ships and vessels)

Since most of the federal programs have similarities in terms of the definitions and compensation guidelines, the Longshore and Harbor Workers' Compensation Act will be presented. LHWCA provides medical benefits, compensations for lost wages, and rehabilitation services to employees who are injured during the course of employment. LHWCA serves approximately 27,000 cases per year with $747 million dollars expended for medical and rehabilitation services. Relevant terminology is:

Functional loss: Describes a situation in which a physiological function can no longer be performed by the individual. It should be measured in quantifiable terms.

Impairment: The loss, loss of use, or derangement of any body part, system or function. Impairment does not necessarily equate to disability since and individual could have an impairment and not be disabled from work.

Loss of wage-Earning Capacity: A computation of economic loss which takes into consideration a claimant's age, degree of disability, education, work history, training, and the availability of work in the area in which the claimant lives.

Average weekly wage: The average weekly wage for an employee is calculated at 1/52 of the employee's annual earnings.

Under the LHWCA program, the American Medical Association's (2007) *Guide to the Evaluation Permanent Impairment* is used to evaluate permanent medical impairments. It appears that the degree of impairment corresponds directly with compensation for the disability.

Venue #5: Civil Litigation, Personal Injury and Earning Capacity

This section discusses the various approaches to estimating earning capacity in the general venue of civil cases (i.e., personal injury, marriage dissolution, wrongful death, professional negligence, etc.). Over the last decade or so there has been considerable debate as to who is best qualified to offer opinion on earnings capacity. The following three positions have evolved:

The **Vocational Rehabilitation Consultant**, as generally defined by McGowan and Porter (1967), is described as a "coordinator" of services. The rehabilitation counselor relied upon and coordinated a variety of services in behalf of a person with a disability in areas of medical and vocational diagnosis, planning for services, job placement, and case closure. As the private sector of rehabilitation consulting evolved through the

1970s, the basic process was essentially the same; just the "venues" changed (SSDI, Workers' Compensation programs). When it came to the issues of economics, such as projecting future lost earnings, it was, and still is, usual and customary for the rehabilitation consultant to forward the rehabilitation report to an economist for such determinations. In the case of *Smith v. M.V. Woods Construction Co., Inc.*, (2003) the court ruled that the plaintiff's "vocational rehabilitation expert was not qualified to express opinion on past and future loss of earnings, past and future loss of household services, and future medical services; such matters are generally subject of expert testimony by an economist."

The **Vocational/Economic Consultant** was represented by a small, but growing contingent of professionals who felt they could offer testimony in both areas. With additional training and skill development, rehabilitation consultants were moving more often into the realm of making economic determinations in the specific areas of pre- and post-injury wage earning capacity, decisions regarding estimations of remaining worklife, and projections future earnings or loss.

The **Economist** is usually the professional assigned to make economic projections, including necessary adjustments in the dollar amount such as age-earnings cycles, and discounting to present value. The work of the economist is predicated on the pre and post-injury base wage calculations of the rehabilitation consultant. However, the economist must rely upon the necessary foundation data supplied by the consultant (or any other consultant providing relevant information). In *Hobbs v. Harken* (1998), an economist expert's testimony on future lost earnings was disallowed because the expert admitted that he assumed the disability was permanent when there was no medical or rehabilitation foundation. The interface between the two disciplines has been discussed at length by Dillman (1987).

However, the testimony was allowed based on the court's ruling that Dr. Isom's "methodology meets the requirements of Daubert for testing, peer review and acceptance within the professional community."

Labor Market Information

In order for a rehabilitation consultant to calculate the degree of disability for an injured worker, it is imperative that a clear understanding be made of how labor market information is developed and utilized. The U.S. Department of Labor and other agencies within the federal and State governments have developed approximately ten different occupational codes and arrangements that are used for a variety of purposes, including labor market surveys (Field & Field, 1984). The critical factor is that all of these survey codes do not employ the concept of worker trait factors in their arrangement. The first and necessary step is for a labor market survey to be assigned worker trait information so that it will be possible to identify which jobs meet or fail to meet the worker trait level of functioning of the injured worker.

The LMA approach which was developed for this purpose (Field et al., 1981, 1984) utilizes the 2000 census survey data with annual updates to adjust for labor market fluctuations. These data have been assigned appropriate levels of worker trait functioning for each of the job titles in the census data base. The census arrangement is then assigned current wage data derived from the Bureau of Labor Statistics. For example, the

Table 11.4
Summary of the Application of Selected Factors to the Different Venues

Venue	Disab	TSA	Empl	Survey	Wage Base	Act v. Exp	Work Life	Fut LE	Admis
SSA	x	x	x	x	–	–	–	–	x
VA	x	x	x	x	x	x	–	–	x
St WC	x	x	x	x	x	x	x	x	x
Fed WC	x	x	x	x	x	x	x	x	x
Civil	x	x	x	x	x	x	x	x	x

Source: Field (2008), p. 21.

counselor reviews the client's work history and refers to the *Dictionary of Occupational Titles* (DOT) (1991) to obtain the DOT codes, then turns to the *Classification of Jobs 2000* (Field & Field, 2000) to identify the appropriate Census codes. Finally, the specialist reviews the median weekly wage data and number of jobs associated with the Census codes from the Labor Market Surveys (Field, J., annualized data).

It is also critically important that provisions be made for the updating of these databases since the labor market is in a state of change and flux. Utilizing an inaccurate or inappropriate geographical database for this purpose would only result in inappropriate findings for the person in the determination of their lost employment. With the growing utilization of the rehabilitation specialist in cases of personal injury, wrongful death, divorce issues, and child cases, it important to be able to offer an opinion regarding the labor market access for these people. However, to identify 72 different worker traits on 12,741 job titles, cross-referenced to 501 Census codes is a time-consuming process. Fortunately, computer technology has made this a relatively simple and straightforward process.

The calculation of a percentage loss of access to employment market based on the analysis of the worker's residual functional capacity not only makes more sense, but insures an eminently more fair and objective approach to the determination of disability. An example printout of the Labor Market Access analysis can be found in at the end of this chapter.

Wage Loss and Earnings Capacity Analysis

Wage loss analysis refers to that procedure which addresses the amount of wages lost by a worker as a result of injury. For instance, if a worker was being paid $12,000 a year at a rate of $1,000 a month or approximately $250 per week, what would be the total amount of wages lost taking into account number of days, weeks, or months the worker was unable to return to his or her job as a result of the injury? If the injury was of such a nature that it prevented the worker from returning to work for a period of one year or more, a simple tabulation of all of the months and/or years of lost time would be added to determine the amount of lost wages as a result of the injury. The calculation of lost wages is a rather simple and straightforward process and really does not take into account many of the other factors related to the issue in question of lost earnings capacity.

Earnings capacity is related to the notion of lost future earnings related to the client's reasonable potential. In some cases, the loss of earnings capacity is straight forward. For example, a man who was 55 years old and who had been driving a truck for a living since he was 19 was injured in a motor vehicle accident leaving him tetraplegic. His loss of earnings was based on the amount of money he was making at the time of injury and projected over the remaining work life expectancy. In this case the individual probably also had achieved his realistic earnings capacity.

In other cases, this may be less clear. For example, the man in the above case also had his 18 year old nephew in the car with him. The boy suffered extensive head injuries which rendered him incapable of gainful employment for the rest of his life. Since he had very little work history (paper boy) the task for estimating loss of earnings or earnings capacity is more complicated.

One method is to opine about what specific jobs or job categories the individual might have been able to engage in (Deutsch & Sawyer, 1999). A second is based on the LPE method, mentioned earlier in this chapter, which is an estimation of the life expectancy, work force participation and probability of being employed as supported by government statistics (Brookshire & Smith, 1990; Lees-Haley, 1987). Another is to estimate the education level the person was capable of and turn to Census research about the median income a person with the those traits could be expected to earn over his or her lifetime. For clarification, the loss of earnings would generally be based on past history whereas earnings capacity would be based in prognostication or estimation based on certain "worker traits."

The first method seems somewhat flawed in that the expert's opinion may be to criticized as pure speculation depending on how the opinion was reached (*Ryals v. Home Insurance Company*, 1982).

The second and third methods are not specific to the injured party and relies on global data for a just award. This has it's own problems for both the plaintiff and defense attorneys (Field, Weed, & Grimes, 1986; Lees-Haley, 1987; Weed, 1987; Weed & Field, 1994). For example, say the 18 year old was a high school graduate but his I.Q. was 85 (average is 100) and he graduated 988 in a class of 988. Clearly the defense attorney would argue that the government statistics would over estimate the earnings as it applies to the individual. On the other hand, say the 18 year old was class president, considered well above average in intelligence and graduated in the upper third of his class. In this case, even if the parties agreed that the plaintiff had not planned to continue with his education, the plaintiff's attorney would likely argue that the government data are too conservative.

In any event, most cases do not fit neatly into various categories. It is not unusual for a plaintiff to be in their late 20's with a lower level job history but active plans to complete college "starting the next term after the injury", or a 35 year old who had just started her own business last year but is injured enough that she can not continue in the business venture but can work at some other job, or a housewife who has a college degree and was planning to return to work after the kids were old enough to take care of themselves. In yet other cases, a person may have been severely injured but able to return to a modified job with his old employer where he earned the same income, but has clearly lost the opportunity to work in the occupation of his choice and has lost access to a wide variety of occupations or prevented from advancement within his chosen profession.

Everyone's earnings capacity is not achieved at the same life stage. One author offers an age-earning cycle concept which indicates that the average individual may not hit their peak earnings until about the age of 40 (Dillman, 1987). For children, adolescents and young adults, the accuracy of loss is dependent a number of individual factors and the ability of the rehabilitation expert to take these factors and translate them into defensible figures. Earnings capacity analysis, rather than reliance on earnings history therefore generally seems more defensible for persons under the age of forty, although independent professional judgment makes the final determination.

Depending on the individual, one would expect the reliance of actual wage history for determining earnings capacity will increase as the age increases. After the peak earning years, previously suggested at about the age of 40, actual earnings would likely be the base from which the economist would project losses if the person was totally disabled (Dillman, 1987). If the individual is unable to return to work at their usual occupation, then the expert would compare actual pre-injury earnings with expected post-injury earnings. It is recommended that a similar approach, i.e., identify classes of jobs based on post-injury worker trait information rather than specific jobs, be used as the basis for the opinion. For adult clients, this can be supplemented by a labor market survey conducted in the local labor market about the availability of these suggested job titles and their wages. In many cases, the survey will fail to identify a job. On the other hand, this can be misleading since the vocational rehabilitation counselor can cultivate an occupation for most "motivated" clients with a physical disability.

At the other end of the spectrum, opinions about younger persons who have not yet settled into a career need to be approached somewhat differently; i.e., loss of earnings capacity. Figure 11.1 graphically displays the suggested approach, earnings history or earnings capacity. For children the study is based on worker traits which can be identified from school records, standardized testing, work history to date, family background including aunts, uncles, grandparents, and other factors (Isom, 2002; Weed, 2000). Worker traits include the physical demands and working conditions of the job, general educational level, vocational preparation time generally required to learn the occupation, aptitudes, interests and temperaments needed to perform the occupation.

In instances of marriage dissolution, the issue is oftentimes related to alimony rather than a disabling condition. In the case of *Gavron v. Gavron* (1988) in the State of California, the primary issue is often typical of marriage dissolution cases, namely, a stay at home wife and a wage earning husband. In this case, the wife assisted the husband in obtaining a professional degree in dentistry (working during the early years and contributing to his earning capacity), but then became a homemaker when the husband began his professional practice. Under the civil code in California, "a court is to consider as a factor [in spousal support] the supported spouse's marketable skills and ability to engage in gainful employment." Following 25 years of marriage, the wife did not return to school for further education and training, and lived primarily off the funds received through alimony. When the husband attempted to reduce the alimony amount after several years, the court ruled that the full alimony amount should continue because the supported spouse "had no prior awareness that she would be required to become self-sufficient." The code also stipulates that a professional trained in the areas of assessing marketable skills and career options be engaged in the assessment of a spousal's skills and abilities, if appropriate.

In summary, the question of lost future earnings takes on a whole new dimension and involves a much more demanding and complicated analysis to determine a fair and equitable settlement for the client than it would seem at first blush.

Figure 11.1
Earnings Capacity vs. Actual Earnings History

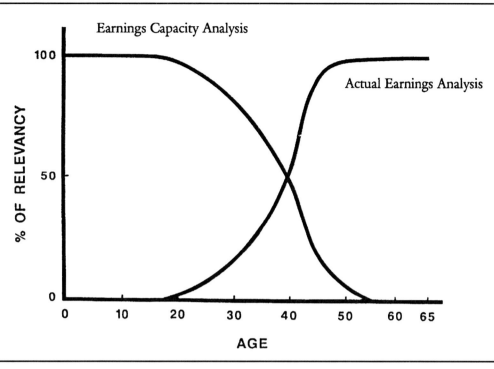

Note. Actual earnings history is based on personal history.

Factors in Determining Future Wage Loss

For purposes of illustration, let's assume that a young man by the name of John Doe was permanently and totally disabled from an injury at age 25. There was no expectation of returning to work for the remainder of his life. At the time of injury, John was employed as a construction worker making $15,000 per year. John's injury, without question, has seriously and permanently restricted his ability to earn money in the future. In a nutshell, John's lost earning capacity is measured as the difference between earning capacity if there had been no injury and earning capacity after injury (Brown & Johnson, 1983). Curtis and Wilson (1976) quote from the decision in an Alabama court case that:

> *No general rule can be formulated that would control the admission of evidence to prove a man's future earning capacity. It must be arrived at largely from probabilities; and any evidence that would fairly indicate his present earning capacity, and the probability of his increase or decrease in the future, ought to be admitted.* (p. 226)

This quote clearly highlights the difficulties in determining the future earning capacity and alludes to many of the complexities involved in such an analysis. In the final analysis, there is no precise method or approach that is consistently used in all courts for the determination of the question of future worth. While the following list is not meant to be exhaustive, the variables that are cited are issues most frequently taken into account in presenting information on future lost capacities:

For the forensic rehabilitation consultant, the task of estimating earning capacity is sometimes both confusing and difficult. The short history of this aspect of the work of the rehabilitation consultant may be clouded, controversial and muddied, to say the least, especially when trying to understand the world of estimating capacity and providing a dollar value to individual cases involving injury and disability. In addition to the concept of earning capacity, collateral issues also come into play (e.g., current and future earnings, estimating lost earnings, and estimating future lost earning). What appears to be most confusing relates to the issue of methodology; namely, how does a professional go about making determinations on any of the issues related to earning. In particular, what method or methods would meet the requirements as set forth by the Daubert (1993) and Kumho (1999) rulings of the U.S. Supreme court, and also the expectations as identified by the Federal Rules of Evidence (2002, i.e., FRE 403 and 702).

Legal and Program Definitions

This section reviews the legal definitions of many of the more critical constructs related to earning capacity. A review of the significant program areas, including civil settings, addresses the various program approaches for understanding the similarities and differences that exist relative to earning capacity.

A reasonable starting point in this discussion is to provide adequate definitions of the major constructs related to earning capacity. All of the following definitions are taken from Black's Law Dictionary (2000) and the U.S. Department of Labor, Occupational Employment Statistics); for purposes of this discussion, these definitions of terms will be used throughout this paper. This section lists the more general constructs related to earnings capacity; as each venue (SSA, OWCP, state and federal court, etc.) is discussed, additional legal terms will be introduced for each respective venue.

Capacity: The role in which one performs an act (Black's, p. 163).

Damages: Money claimed by, or ordered to be paid to, a person as compensation for loss or injury (Black's, 320).

Diminution: The act or process of decreasing, lessening, or taking away (Black's, p. 369). Earnings: Revenue gained from labor or services....(Black's, p.414).

Earnings: Remuneration (pay, wages) of a worker or group of workers for services performed during a specific period of time. The term usually carries a defining word or phrase, such as straight-time average hourly earnings. Because a statistical concept is usually involved in the term and its variations, the producers and users of earnings data should define them clearly. In the absence of such definitions, the following may serve as rough guidelines:

Hourly, daily, weekly, annual: period of time to which earnings figures, as stated or computed, relate. The context in which annual earnings (sometimes weekly earnings) are used may indicate whether the reference includes earnings from one employer only or from all employment plus other sources of income.

Average: usually refers to the arithmetic mean; that is, total earnings (as defined) of a group of workers (as identified) divided by the number of workers in the group.

Gross: usually refers to total earnings, before any deductions (such as tax withholding) including, where applicable, overtime payments, shift differentials, production bonuses, cost-of-living allowances, commissions, etc.

Straight-time: usually refers to gross earnings excluding overtime payments and (with variations at this point) shift differentials and other monetary payments. (OES).

Future Damages: Money awarded to an injured party for an injury's residual or projected effects that reduce the person's ability to function (Black's, p.321).

Lost earnings: Wages, salary, or other income that a person could have earned if he or she had not lost a job, suffered a disabling injury, or died. There can be past lost earnings and future lost earnings (Black's, p.414).

Future Lost Earnings: See lost earnings (Black's, p. 414).

Income: The money or other form of payment that one receives, usually periodically, from employment, business, investments, royalties, gifts, and the like (Black's, p.611).

Income: The receipt by an individual of any property or service which he can apply to meeting basic needs. (CFR 416.120).

Wage: Payment for labor or services, usually based on time worked or quantity produced (Black's, p.1275).

Mean wage: An average wage; an occupational mean wage estimate is calculated by summing the wages of all the employees in a given occupation and then dividing the total wages by the number of employees. (OES).

Median days away from work (Safety and Health Statistics): The measure used to summarize the varying lengths of absences from work among the cases with days away from work. The median is the point at which half of the cases involved more days away from work and half involved less days away from work. (OES)

Median wage: An occupational median wage estimate is the boundary between the highest paid 50 percent and the lowest paid 50 percent of workers in that occupation. Half of the workers in a given occupation earn more than the median wage, and half the workers earn less than the median wage. (OES)

Wages and salaries: Hourly straight-time wage rate or, for workers not paid on an hourly basis, straight-time earnings divided by the corresponding hours. Straight-time wage and salary rates are total earnings before payroll deductions, excluding premium pay for overtime and for work on weekends and holidays, shift differentials, and nonproduction bonuses such as lump-sum payments provided in lieu of wage increases. (OES)

Worklife estimates: Estimates of the number of years individuals would spend in the labor force based on mortality conditions, labor force entry and exit rates, and demographic characteristics. BLS has not produced worklife estimates since February 1986. Last publication: Worklife Estimates: Effects of Race and Education PDF 1.32 MB

Methods for Evaluating Lost Earning Capacity

There are several different approaches or methods of estimating the loss of earning capacity in cases of partial but permanent disability. The following methods are often referenced by practitioners, but are not all inclusive regarding methods that might be used. These methods have all had an impact on the development and progression of methods used today by most professionals. While each of the methods discussed emphasize the use of data and information, each method requires a significant degree of clinical judgment and decision-making on the part of the professional (see Choppa et al., 2004 for a discussion of the efficacy on professional clinical judgment in opinion development).

The Deutsch/Sawyer Model

Deutsch and Sawyer (1986) have suggested that pre-injury earnings and post-injury earnings really do not reflect an accurate picture of the person's ability to earn money. More importantly, "the client's post-accident earning capacity, or the potential to earn" (p. 8-2) is really the target of an assessment of diminished earnings. An assessment of earnings capacity would include:

1. Whether the client has a relatively well-established work identity or vocational goal;

2. The degree to which the client is established in this vocational goal;

3. To what degree the individual has developed the necessary skills and abilities required to show proficiency in the chosen vocational goal.

4. The number of years of experience the individual has in the vocational goal; and

5. The degree to which a difference exists between the individual's earned wages and the average earnings for most workers in the chosen vocational goal. (p. 8-3).

In addition to the obvious emphasis on a career goal, the model suggests that "pre-accident earnings do not accurately and consistently reflect the actual capacity to earn or develop earnings in cases involving individuals under the age of 30" (p. 8-3). This emphasis on vocational goals and age is somewhat of a departure from the LMA model which emphasizes the pre- and post-injury functional capacity evaluations. The latter model suggest a correspondence between vocational functioning and selected jobs and wages. The Deutsch and Sawyer model does include other factors for earning capacity assessment including education, intellectual development, academic development, work history and transferable skills. In establishing a wage earning capacity it is also necessary to choose a representative sample of jobs that reflect an individual's maximum capacity for developing vocational and earning potential. (p. 8-5)

The model then proceeds to suggest that a referral to an economist is appropriate to calculate an estimate the diminution of lifetime earnings. This model, while suggesting a number of variables to consider, does not provide any guidelines on procedurally what to do; a great deal of judgment and experience is required in the decision-making process for capacity assessment.

Labor Market Access/Wage Loss

The LMA approach, developed by Field & Field during the 1980's, (see also Field, Choppa & Shafer, 1984; Weed, 1987; Field, T., 1988, & Field, J. 1999) emphasizes the necessity to analyze lost wages with respect to labor market conditions. The LMA approach is based on large-scale labor market information that is cross-referenced to median weekly wages supplied by the Bureau of Labor Statistics. The labor market surveys were provided by the annual Bureau of Census surveys and adjusted by annual labor market survey information from both the federal government and state departments of labor. This methodology can be completed by hand, though tedious and time consuming, or through a computer program like Skill*TRAN*[tm] (see www.SkillTRAN.com).

The advantage of the labor market approach is that it establishes a "reasonable approximation" of a beginning wage base at the time of the injury which then can be compared with estimated earning based upon a reduced level of functioning post-injury. The alternative to this approach is to use the actual wages that were earned by the worker at the time of injury, and then to estimate what the worker might be able to do in particular jobs post-injury. The LMA approach has the added advantage of taking into account the issue and question of lost opportunity to be employed post-injury by comparing an individual's pre and post-injury level of functioning to a particular labor market. In this sense, the LMA approach takes into account specifically the questions of geography and labor market conditions within geographical areas. The other aspect of the LMA approach is that it provides approximations of potential wages for an injured worker, pre and post-injury, which can be provided to the economist who then can make projections of lost earnings or lost future earnings. However, as with any computerized approach the professional must understand the data that is generated as well as how the computer processes the data with an explanation to the satisfaction of the court (*Perez v. IBP, Inc.*, 1991; *Hughes v. Inland Container Corp.*, 1990).

The Labor Market Access approach is a two-step process. First, the pre-injury level of vocational functioning of the worker is compared to jobs in a geographical area, and secondly, the post-injury level of functioning (or the RFC) is compared to jobs that exist in the same geographical area. By comparing the worker's levels of pre- and post-injury functioning to the Pittsburgh economy, for example, it is possible to calculate a percentage of access to jobs in Pittsburgh prior to injury as well as a percentage of access to jobs after injury. This is accomplished by subtracting the number of jobs (civilian labor force) available to the worker after the injury from the number of jobs available prior to the injury and dividing the result by the number of jobs available to the person prior to injury. For example, if the number of jobs as represented by the number of people in the civilian labor force available after an injury (based on the RFC) is 2,546,811, and the number of jobs available prior to injury was 2,723,222, then 2,546,811 subtracted from 2,723,222 equals 176,411. 176,411 divided by 2,723,222 equals 6.48% which represents the personal loss of access to the employment market for jobs of which the worker has the capacity to perform. This analysis compares the client's pre- and post-injury levels of functioning against people actually employed in a geographical area. These people, constituting the civilian labor force, are in jobs each of which can be analyzed according to the worker trait arrangement.

This process is distinctly different from the AMA's *Guide to Evaluation of Permanent Impairments* approach which assigns a percentage of impairment to the person as a consequence of a loss of bodily part. The Labor Market Access approach identifies a percentage of loss to employment to a given economy based upon that person's level of vocational functioning as a result of injury. The determination of disability, then, is clearly a function of calculating a percentage loss of access to jobs (employability) within a given economy, as represented by the civilian labor force, as a result of the injured worker's level of vocational functioning (pre- to post-injury).

The approach of assigning a percentage to a loss has been a long-standing method to the determination of a disability. In some cases, it has been utilized as a guide in determining lost earning or wages and future lost earning as a direct relationship to the percentage losses identified by the appropriate category. For instance, a loss of an arm will result in X% loss of functioning for the person. This has oftentimes been translated to a similar per cent loss of employment opportunity for that worker for the remaining years of his or her work life. This is an erroneous assumption since it cannot be assumed that the loss of a bodily function by percentage is directly related to the loss of employment opportunities and/or functioning in the worker's future. Assume for a moment that a business executive, due to some accident, had to have several of his toes amputated from his left foot. According to the AMA Guide, this would result in a 15% loss of bodily functioning for this particular injury. On the other hand, the loss of three toes on the left foot has no direct bearing on the types and kinds of work that the business executive was performing either before this injury or following the injury. Although it can be argued that there is a percentage loss of bodily functioning due to the loss of the toes, it also true there is no direct relationship to the loss of functioning on the job.

On the other hand, a person who is employed as a dancer, whose job requires a great deal of balance and agility, might purport that there is a direct relationship between the loss of functioning in the left foot and potential loss of functioning on the job. The injury will probably result in a loss of job opportunities for the dancer. In other words, a determination has to be made of the level of functioning both pre- and post-injury as it relates to jobs and future jobs of the worker. It is not adequate, nor satisfactory, to argue that a percentage loss of bodily function is a direct correlation to the loss of vocational functioning. The LMA approach emphasizes the necessity of both pre and post injury functional assessment.

L-P-E and The New Worklife Tables

Brookshire and Cobb (1983), Brookshire, Cobb, and Gamboa (1987), and Brookshire and Smith (1990) proposed an innovative approach in assessing damages following an injury. By relying upon federal government data (Bureau of Labor Statistics), the L-P-E method (Life-Participation-Employment). This approach essentially is designed to provide an estimate of a person's work life and earnings by age. Earnings are adjusted by calculating the joint probabilities of Living (L) through the various ages, Participating (P) in the labor force, and being Employed (E).

Gamboa (1987) introduced the notion of assessing earnings capacity, disability, and future earnings by utilizing US government statistics to estimate the impact of sex and level of education for persons who were identified (globally) as either disabled or not disabled. In subsequent research and writings, Gamboa and his colleagues have continued to develop the approach of using government data to evaluate the capacity to work and earn money by persons who have been disabled (Gamboa, 2006; Gamboa & Gibson, 2006; Gamboa, Holland, Tierny, & Gibson, 2006; Gamboa et al., 2009; Gibson, 2010).

While these approaches justifiably take into account such factors as age, education, gender, living and employment participation, including the level of disability (if any), there are two distinct disadvantages of utilizing government statistics. First, the Gamboa approach is often cited for using global estimates of the presence and level of a disability. "Global" estimates of the presence of a disability with a worker can be somewhat inaccurate and certainly are not worker specific in terms of the worker's specific functional capacities (i.e., the *LMA* method) and potential for working and earning money. Secondly, the reliance on government data is generally not current information as government employment data and demographic statistics are often dated by one to three years

Compensation Programs

Workers' compensation, both federal and state programs, include objectives for returning injured workers to their same job, a similar job, or a new job (following training and work adjustment) and are generally referred to as "return-to-work" programs. Given the wide ranging efforts at both the state and federal levels, there are many times considerable differences in both the objectives of the programs and how these programs manage financials issues such as loss of wages, disability ratings, earnings capacity, and future earnings. Over the last three decades, state programs have often reduced or eliminated funding for rehabilitation programs as a means to improve the probability that injured workers would return to work while reducing overall costs of the compensation program. Oftentimes, state legislatures have viewed these programs as too costly for the state budget or for employers who fund workers' compensation benefits and services. Prior to the 1980's, most state workers' compensation programs included a section of their law "mandating" rehabilitation services for injured workers. The mandatory rehabilitation law was a major area of support for private sector rehabilitation programs as insurance companies would hire rehabilitation consultants to address this requirement for rehabilitation services. In the late 1980s, state governments began to cut or eliminate the mandatory requirement as a cost saving measure. While rehabilitation programming has taken on several forms, such as a lump sum payment for the injury, or severe restrictions on services offered, states continue to search for ways to address issues of compensation costs for injured workers while maintaining the central focus of returning injured workers to the employment force.

In terms of assessing disability and evaluating work capacity, government programs have relied on basic approaches to address the issue. Several state programs have relied upon a "schedule of impairments" that assigns a disability rating by body part; for example, a loss of a thumb and four fingers might be rated as a nine percent loss of total body functioning. The percentage loss would become the basis for a percentage loss of earnings for future work and income. Related to this approach is the use of the *AMA Guides to the Evaluation of Permanent Impairment* (2000) for evaluating injury. California, as a result of the *Ogilvie* (2009a; 2009b) rulings, attempted to draft a workable "formula" approach to address the issue of earnings capacity. However, the numeric formula required by the California Workers' Compensation Appeals Board in Ogilvie I and II was rejected by the California Court of Appeal in Ogilvie III (2011). (see the following articles in this special issue for a review of Ogilvie rulings and the response to Ogilvie). As a result of the flux with the California Workers' Compensation Board on how to best determine "diminished earning capacity," Van de Bittner (2003, 2006) proposes a methodology and approach involving pre and post functional capacity assessment and evaluating related socioeconomic factors before calculating future earnings. Van de Bittner also discussed in detail over 50 factors that might have some bearing in determining diminished earning capacity for the injured worker.

Computer Programs

Following the early development of the Labor Market Access program (Field & Field, 1985-1999), other vocational estimating programs were developed and have contributed significantly to the assessment of work capacity, earnings capacity, and employment opportunities. The programs all suffer from the obsolete occupational data base of the *Dictionary of Occupation Titles* (1991) and related data sets, although developers of each of the programs have attempted to adjust the data to accommodate for this deficiency as much as possible. The programs that are currently available to the forensic rehabilitation community are the *Skilltran* program (Jeff Truthan), *OASYS* (now of Skilltran, formerly by Gale Gibson), *SEER* (Software for Employment, Education and Rehabilitation by Robert Hall), and the *MVQS* (the McCroskey Vocational Quotient System by Billy McCroskey). Additional information can be obtained by reviewing each program's respective website.

Skilltran	www.skilltran.com
OASYS	www.skilltran.com
SEER	www.seersoftware.net
MVQS	www.vocationalogy.com

While these programs can be very useful in obtaining employment and earnings information that matches to a specific client, consultants should always consider computer generated output as tentative conclusions for any client analysis, and should be further tempered by clinical judgment (Choppa et al., 2004) in reaching final estimates of employment and earnings (The same holds true of the L-P-E and *The New Worklife Tables*).

The RAPEL Method

The RAPEL method (Weed, 1998; Weed, 2000) is a comprehensive approach which includes all elements needed to determine loss of access (incorporating the LMA information), loss of earning capacity, future medical care, worklife expectancy, rehabilitation plan, placeability and employability factors. The word RAPEL is a mnemonic designed to assist the rehabilitation expert with collecting the data for a jury, lawyer, judge, economist and others in order to identify client/evaluee needs and losses, and arrive at the economic impact of an injury. It may not be evident, but many of the articles on loss of earning are written by economists. Generally the economist will rely on the numbers provided to him or her by the rehabilitation expert. It is very important for the economist to receive the "right" information so a "bottom line" can be established. (See complete description of RAPEL later in this chapter.)

The Court or Jury Decides (Summary Judgment)

> *Summary judgment: This procedural device allows the speedy disposition of a controversy without the need for a trial.* (Black's, 2000).

> *Jury Instruction: A direction or guideline that a judge gives a jury concerning the law of the case.* (Black's, 2000).

It is not uncommon for state and federal courts to present all relative information through presentations (attorneys and experts) and then to charge the jury to decide the outcome on damages, including future lost earnings. This approach requires that the jury receive adequate information to presumably make an informed decision regarding damages. In cases involving a summary judgment, the same necessary information is needed by the court. Under the Virginia Model Jury Instructions (9.000), this instruction outlines the categories for damages which the jury can consider:

If you find for the plaintiff, then in determining the damages to which he is entitled, you may consider any of the following which you believe by the greater weight of the evidence was caused by the negligence of the defendant:

(1) any bodily injuries he sustained and their effect on his health according to their degree and probable duration;

(2) any physical pain and mental anguish he suffered in the past and any that he may be reasonably expected to suffer in the future;

(3) any disfigurement or deformity and any associated humiliation or embarrassment;

(4) any inconvenience caused in the past and any that probably will be caused in the future;

(5) any medical expenses incurred in the past and any that may be reasonably expected to occur in the future;

(6) any earnings he lost because he was unable to work at his calling;

(7) any loss of earnings and lessening of earning capacity, or either, that he may reasonably be expected to sustain in the future;

(8) any property damage he sustained.

Your verdict should be for such sum as will fully and fairly compensate the plaintiff for the damages sustained as a result of the defendant's negligence.

In *Aivaliotis v. S.S. Atlantic Glory* (1963), Aivaliotis, the plaintiff, was ordered to remove water from below deck of an ocean-going transport vessel. Initially, the plaintiff was hauling buckets of water from below and then dumping the water overboard while two workers below filled the buckets. After a period of time, the plaintiff switched jobs with one of the workers below, and while moving to a forward position, fell through an open hatch and fractured his left leg, and suffered a compound fracture of his right ankle, with multiple contusions over his body. Nearly a year later, after multiple surgeries (7) and infections, and extensive pain, the left leg was amputated. A physician's report (over two years later) indicated the he had reached maximum improvement medically and could be discharged. The physician stated that "I do not feel that he is fit for work as a seaman aboard a ship, but I do feel that he is fit for sedentary or light work, or work that does not involve climbing ladders, lifting or stooping." Plaintiff received a rating of "permanent-partial disability."

The court concluded that plaintiff would not "sustain any actual loss of future earnings by reason of his impairment when his previous station in life is considered." The court learned that during the long period of hospitalization, the plaintiff married an American citizen, gradually learned to speak English, improved upon his educational level, and the potential to earn more in the United States than he could if he had continued on the vessel. The court observed that "there can be little doubt as to the impairment of his earning capacity." The court reached the final conclusion:

Taking into consideration the many elements of damage which must be weighed in an effort to reasonably compensate [plaintiff] for his pain, suffering, mental anguish, embarrassment, actual loss of wages to the point of attaining maximum improvement, impairment of future earning capacity, the expense of maintenance and replacement of the prosthesis in futuro, and considering life expectancy, discounted to the present value of one dollar where appropriate, the court is of the opinion that [plaintiff] is entitled to a decree against the vessel....in the sum of $115,000.00.

In terms of how the court decided amount the settlement amount is not clear since all elements were considered together and under the single category of damages.

In the case of *Exxon Corp. v. Fulgham* (1982), the plaintiff was involved in an automobile accident which caused injury to his left hand and wrist, knee, neck and back. Following surgery and treatment (arm was in cast for six months), the physician opined that plaintiff "has approximately a 50 percent loss of use of his wrist and hand as a result of the accident...and would be restricted in his working ability because of restriction of motion in his wrist." The court, in instructing the jury, is required to be supported by the evidence. In this case, the jury was instructed to consider a loss of earning capacity which was supported by the opinion of the physician who indicated that there was a loss of 50 percent of functioning in the wrist. Exxon objected to the jury charge of a lessened earning capacity based on the fact that the plaintiff was earning $1000 per month after the injury versus only $700 per month prior to the injury. Relying of the previous case of *Aivaliotis v. Steamship Atlantic Glory*, the court ruled in that case that "one of the measures of his damage is based upon his earning capacity and not merely the amount actually earning." Consequently, the appeals court ruled that the evidence presented by the physician (50% loss of functioning, pain, loss of motion) "was sufficient for the jury to have found that by reason of the injury to the wrist, the plaintiff has sustained a lessening of earning capacity in the future." The finding was summarized:

> *The plaintiff is a man of limited education and earns his livelihood by physical effort and manual labor, specifically with the use of his arms and hands. At the time of the trial, he was an office-machine repairman. Although not a certified cabinetmaker, plaintiff is adept and skilled in the area of woodworking. There is credible evidence from which the jury could have concluded that because of his background, education, skills, and the work he performs, the type and character of the injury sustained by the plaintiff to his left wrist is such as will lessen his earning capacity and could diminish his opportunity to secure employment in the future. We find no error in the action of the trial court in permitting the jury to consider any lessening of plaintiff's future earnings capacity or his expectation of life in determining damages.*

Note that the court relied upon the client factors of the injury and its restrictions, background, education, skills, and the work performed as evidence presented to the jury. In *Scott v. Mid-Atlantic Cable* (2006), the determination of damages was addressed by consideration for a summary judgment consistent with Rule 56 of the Federal Rules of Civil Procedure as summarized in this court case:

> *Summary judgment is appropriate when the moving party can show affidavits, depositions, admissions, answers to interrogatories, pleadings, or other evidence, that has no genuine issue as to any material fact and that the moving party is entitled to a judgment as a matter of law.*

Scott, following an accident resulting in injuries, filed a claim seeking damages for "medical care expenses, pain and suffering, mental anguish, lost earning capacity, and the lost future retirement benefits." The defendants filed a motion for partial summary judgment (lost earning capacity and lost future retirement benefits). As noted in the Exxon case, "Virginia law permits a claim for lost earning capacity where the plaintiff established that the type and character of the injury" which will reduce one's earning capacity and the opportunity to be employed. Further, a consideration of earning capacity includes such factors as background, education, skills, and experience. The court denied the motion for a partial summary judgment based on the fact that there was a material fact (estimating lost earning capacity of the plaintiff) did not rely on speculation or conjecture, and the issue could be adjudicated.

In all three cases noted above, a court (via summary judgment) or a jury could determine a proper conclusion (damages) on the issue of estimating lost earning capacity and/or future employment when the relevant facts of the case are presented in a sufficient manner. The relevant elements of such a determination would include background, the nature of the injury, education, skills and experience.

A "Practical" Approach

The estimation of earnings capacity would seem to be a very complicated task given all the information that is available. Much of the confusion for forensic rehabilitation professionals results from the various approaches that have been discussed, including the pros and cons of computer programs, various occupational databases, and identifying the most critical and salient variables necessary in the analysis. In fact, Shahnasarian (2001, 2004) has emphasized the necessity of organizing and synthesizing all relevant information in the development of a case, including the use of a worksheet that has been developed for such purposes.

This proposed basic and practical approach is perhaps a synthesis of the more useful (and least controversial) concepts that have evolved over the years. Personal preference for alternative resources and/or approaches is certainly within the realm of possibility. However, what is suggested below can serve as a "benchmark" for professionals to consider and then incorporate personal preferences and experiences into an individual and preferred model.

The following steps are suggested:

1. Following a review of the case records, develop at pre-injury assessment of earning capacity. Identify a pre-injury base wage (not necessarily wage at time of injury) by identifying jobs and wages that best represent the claimant's functional capacity.

2. Identify a post-injury base wage by identifying jobs and wages that best represent the claimant's residual functional capacity.

3. Estimate the difference between the pre-injury earnings capacity and the post-injury earnings capacity.

4. Estimate the remaining work life of the claimant.

5. Calculate a range of economic loss by multiplying the difference from pre to post earnings capacity by the work life remaining.

6. If not qualified, refer to an economist for adjustment to present value. The economist's general method can serve as a guide and blueprint for the rehabilitation professional. Resources to be used might include the following:

A computerized job matching program to expedite the job identification process.

-   Either the DOT or the O*NET for describing occupations.
-   The on-line CareerInfo.NET database for wages and numbers of jobs in a local economy, or the CPS data generated by BLS.
-   The BLS Worklife Tables

Summary of Methods

The methods cited above serve as guidelines for the professional to follow in the development of a case. Of course, there will be variations for each of the methods and much of the variation will depends upon the facts of a case. Reference to Table 11.5 displays some of these differences in how a case can be developed. The RAPEL method appears to be the most comprehensive of all the methods, although this method draws upon resources and strategies from a variety of sources. The LMA method, of course, is a computerized approach developed during 1980s and 1990s and the results may be used for a portion of the RAPEL report. The original program is no longer available, although the rationale is one to consider (see website listing at the end of the chapter for three computer programs which are currently available and may be used in earnings capacity assessment). As noted earlier, the Deutsch/Sawyer model is rather global and non-specific, while the Court/Jury model is interesting and may be employed in some states. The practical method is just that: a rather straight-forward and common-sense method quite similar to the RAPEL. In terms of which method to use is really the prerogative of the practicing professional. All have been published in peer reviewed literature and all are generally accepted by the professional community.

Factors Relevant in Estimating Earning Capacity and Loss

For purposes of illustration, let's assume that a young man by the name of John Doe was permanently and totally injured at age 25. This resulted in no expectation of returning to work for the remainder of his life. At the time of injury, John was employed as a construction worker making $15,000 per year. John's injury, without question, has seriously and permanently restricted his ability to earn money in the future. In a nutshell, John's lost earning capacity is measured as the difference between earning capacity if there had been no injury and earning capacity after injury (Brown & Johnson, 1983). Curtis and Wilson (1976) quote from the decision in an Alabama court case that:

> *No general rule can be formulated that would control the admission of evidence to prove a man's future earning capacity. It must be arrived at largely from probabilities; and any evidence that would fairly indicate his present earning capacity, and the probability of his increase or decrease in the future, ought to be admitted. (p. 226)*

This quote clearly highlights the difficulties in determining the future earning capacity and alludes to many of the complexities involved in such an analysis. In the final analysis, there is no precise method or approach that is consistently used in all courts for the determination of the question of future worth. While the following list is not meant to be exhaustive and may not be relevant to all venues (see next section), the variables that are cited are issues most frequently taken into account in presenting information on future lost capacities.

1. **Age:** The age of the worker is vitally important (Eden, 1976). The younger the person is, the longer the person would be able to remain in the work force. Additionally, the younger a person is the more likely that the person will have greater opportunities for promotion within a career tract.

    Other factors that have a direct relationship to age are job mobility, further education, and career changes, to mention a few. (See also CFR 404.1563).

2. **Education and Training:** The educational or training level of a person in terms of their knowledge, skills and abilities is a major consideration in the assessment of a person's capacity to work and earn money. A reasonable source of for definitions these factors can be derived from one or more of the following two sources:

    *   CFR 404.1564 and CFR 404.1568 "Your education as a vocational factor" and "skill requirements."

    *   *Revised Handbook for Analyzing Jobs* (1992). (See Chapters 7, 8 & 9).

3. **Work Experience:** One of the best predictors of future employment is a review of relevant past work and is an excellent indicator of potential, or transferable job skills. (See CFR 404.1565)

4. **Disability and Functional Capacity:** There are several definitions of disability, again largely depending on the venue. SSA defines disability "as the inability to do any substantial gainful activity by reason of any medically determinable physical or mental impairment which can be expected to last for not less than 12 months." (CFR 404.1505). Under the Americans with Disabilities Act, a disability is defined as "a physical or mental impairment that substantially limits one or more of the major life activities (Federal Register, July 26, 1991, 1630.2.g.1). A major referent for many compensation programs is the *AMA's Guide to the Evaluation of Permanent Impairment* (5th ed., 2000) which provides quantifiable formats for assessing functioning. The functional capacity to be able to perform work is relevant both pre and post-injury and is an important consideration in most venues (i.e., CFR 404.1561; Field, 2007).

5. **Worklife Expectancy**: This factor is very similar to the age factor in that one can estimate how many years remaining the worker has within the work force (Borland & Pulsinelli, 1983). What needs to be estimated is the expected retirement date of the worker as a variable on determining remaining years of work life. In 1982 the Bureau of Labor Statistics in the Department of Labor developed work life expectancy tables as a means of assisting a determination of this question (Bulletin No. 2157, New Worklife Estimates). Another publication is Bulletin 2254, Worklife estimates: Effects of race and education (USDOL, 1986). It may be interesting to note that higher educated persons are statistically more likely to be in the workforce longer than those with less education, even though they enter the work force at a later age (e.g., 18 for high school and 22 for college). More recent worklife tables (Gamboa, 2002; and Skoog, 2002) will be discussed in another section.

Table 11.5
Methods of Earning Capacity Assessment Compared on Selected Factors

Factors	(1)	(2)	(3)	(4)	(5)	(6)	(7)	(8)	(9)
Func Assessment	Y	Y	N	M	Y	Y	Y	M	Y
Career Goal	N	Y	N	N	M	Y	Y	M	Y
Job Matching	Y	N	N	Y	Y	Y	Y	M	Y
Survey Data	Y	Y	Y	M	Y	Y	M	M	Y
Worklife Tables	N	N	Y	N	N	Y	N	M	Y
Future Earnings	N	N	Y	Y	Y	Y	Y	M	Y

Note. Y = Yes; N = No; M = Maybe; (1) Labor Market Access; (2) Deutsch-Sawyer Model; (3) LPE/The New Worklife Tables; (4) State/Federal Compensation Programs; (5) Commercial Software Programs; (6) RAPEL; (7) ECAF-2; (8) Summary Judgment by Jury; (9) A Practical Approach

6. **Wage and Gender:** The issues of wage and gender of workers in the U.S. economy are critical issues with respect to future employment opportunities. It is a well-known and documented fact that both minorities and women tend to be underemployed and under paid when compared with white male workers in the labor force. The 1990 Bureau of Labor Statistics wage data indicates that women are paid approximately 22% less than men across all occupations. The 1990 census clearly substantiated that minorities tend to be more underemployed and paid less than non-minority persons. Additionally, unemployment rates are always higher among minority group and people who are more attractive earn more than less attractive people. Clearly then, employment opportunities are not equal for people in our society, and this assumption needs to be taken into account in any future lost wage analysis. On the other hand, studies by the Brookings Institute indicate the wage differences between men and women are narrowing and women are entering more professional jobs.

7. **Geography:** Different states and sections of the country will vary in their respective opportunities for employment. For instance, the states of Florida, Arizona, Nevada, Georgia and other states bordering these big four are the fastest growing sectional economies in the country. Productivity will tend to increase which, in turn, provides a much greater opportunity for employment in all occupational categories. Conversely, the states of Alaska, Michigan, the Dakotas and Pennsylvania are in a relatively non-growth period which in turn tends to depress these economies. Geography, therefore, may be a restrictive factor in establishing future employment opportunities and may have a direct bearing on potential wage.

8. **Occupational Groups:** In geographical areas where the economy is rapidly growing and expanding, there is a much greater probability of employment in all occupational groups. While this observation may be generally true, there are clusters of occupational opportunities which may either contribute to or limit employment opportunities. For instance, in the state of Alaska in 1998 opportunities for employment in the oil business were tremendously decreased and in the 1970's and 1980's, textile occupations through Georgia, North and South Carolina were greatly diminished. Occupations in the auto industry continue to be slow through Ohio, Illinois, and Michigan, but there was great promise for future employment in these occupations in Tennessee, South Carolina and Alabama with the building of new auto plants in that state. The computer manufacturing industry slowed significantly in the silicon valley of California while occupations in web design, business management and engineering soared in nearly all sections of the country.

With respect to the individual worker, the occupational group in which one is employed will have a significant bearing on their future earnings. For instance, a man who is 30 years old and still working in entry-level occupations will most probably continue in similar entry-level occupations throughout the remainder of his life. On the other hand, a recent female MBA graduate from one of the Ivy League schools will have enormous potential for career promotions and added responsibilities throughout the remainder of her work life. In other words, some people in some jobs are very immobile in terms of occupational potential. On the other hand, other persons with higher levels of education or skill and access to opportunity will have much greater latitude of occupational mobility and earning potential.

9. **Labor Market Surveys:** An understanding of the labor market can be especially critical with respect to estimating future earnings of an adult worker. In particular, the labor market that is most germane to the worker is of utmost importance. Current employment opportunities as well as future trends are necessary in making a reliable estimate of future employment and earning. Utilizing large-scale labor surveys is possible, although most rehabilitation experts will rely on brief telephone and/or card file surveys. Sometimes it may be appropriate to obtain local or national information from the following:

   a. American Community Survey (see summary of the ACS in Field and Jayne, 2008.

   b. CPS (Current Population Survey) and SIPP (Survey of Income and Program Participation) which are both surveys generated by the U.S. Bureau of Census.

   c. Employment Development Division for the state.

   d. State career information systems often located at universities or employment offices.

   e. Manufacturing guides from the state department of labor or division of industry and trade.

   f. Wage rates for selected occupations (not available in all states) from the State Department of Labor.

   g. Personal contacts with vocational rehabilitation counselors and job service counselors.

10. **Employability:** The percentage of lost employment relates to the issue of "employability". This should not be confused with "placeability" which involves the job placement of the worker back into the work force. Employability addresses the question: "To what degree (percentage) is the worker able to be employed within any given labor market (i.e., jobs that exist vs. jobs that are available in a particular labor market)." By putting aside the issues of placement and vocational interest and taking into account the worker's functional limitations and/or capacities (both pre- and post-levels of functioning), a determination can be made regarding employability of the worker. The Labor Market Access approach calculates a "lost employment" percentage by accounting for the worker's functioning levels and comparing this functioning to an actual labor market.

11. **Life Expectancy:** Life expectancy differs from "work years remaining" for obvious reasons. Most people retire from work at or about age 65 but do keep on living. Some awards will be made on the basis of years of life remaining and not simply years of work life remaining (Hanke, 1981). This is usually considered the realm of the economist if the client is "normal" as determined by a qualified professional or the physician if the client is different from "normal." The life expectancy is particularly important in calculating damages described in life care plans.

12. **Average Weekly Wage:** Two types of wage data can be used in estimating future lost earning:

    (a) the individual worker's particular wage at the time of injury, or

    (b) the Average Weekly Wage generated by the U.S. Department of Labor. Most analyses are calculated with the worker's current wage as the beginning point of the analysis, although an analysis utilizing the average weekly wage (AWW) is possible. The functional capacity of an individual at the time of injury, a third approach, may more accurately reflect earning capacity rather than wage at the time of injury or the AWW.

13. **Median Wage:** Median wage data are available from the Bureau of Labor Statistics. These data provide "reasonable approximations" of earning for various census occupations within the labor market. The most reliable wage information is directly related to specific wages of specific jobs, although the trade-off is relating the worker's future earning potential to a few jobs and not an expanded labor market.

14. **Age-Earnings Cycle:** Earnings are not always governed by the usual factors associated with work and pay, such as training, education, the labor market, work capacities of the workers, etc. The age-earning cycle takes into account that a worker's earnings are directly related to one's age. During the worker's lifetime of earning, there is a greater growth rate of wages in the early years, a leveling off during the mid-life years, and a decline as one nears the end of the worklife (Dillman, 2000; Horner & Slesnick, 1999).

15. **Actual v. Expected Earnings:** According to Horner and Slesnick (1999) "*actual earnings* are what a person actually earns, *expected earnings* are what a person is expected to earn, while *earning capacity* is what that person is able [has the potential] to earn" (p. 13). Rather cleverly stated then is that "earning capacity is the expected earnings of a work who chooses to maximize the expectations of actual earnings" (p. 15).

16. **Future Lost Earning:** The whole point of earning capacity analysis is to determine, in an equitable and reasonable manner, future lost earnings of an injured worker. The next section discusses some of the approaches that have been employed in liability cases in the determining of future lost earnings and earning capacity. As the old philosopher once said, "You can't make your dog walk on all fours all the time." The most relevant factor in the determination of future lost earnings is the venue (program) in which the claim is being made.

17. **Estimating a Wage Base:** A wage base developed by the vocational consultant serves as a starting point for the economist in estimating loss and/or future earnings. A wage base can be established for jobs by one of eight methods: utilizing a minimum wage, the wage at time of injury, the average weekly wage, five representatives jobs from a survey based on the worker's functional capacity, job history, an average of jobs from the worker's job history, an average of the top 20 jobs from a job matching list, or the average wage of a few jobs within an immediate labor market (Field, 1993; Horner & Slesnick, 1999) (See Table 11.6)

18. **Admissibility:** With the advent of three specific U.S. Supreme Court rulings (*Daubert v. Merrill Dow Pharmaceuticals*, 1993; *Kumho Tire v. Carmichael,* 1999; *General Electric v. Joiner*, 1997) and with the growing emphasis of the Federal Rules (Stein, 2006), especially FRE 702, it is incumbent upon reha-

Table 11.6
Applying Wage Data to Each of the Venues to Establish a Wage Base (Pre-Injury)

Wage Data	SSA	VA	St-WC	Fed-WC	Civil
Min. Wage	x	x	x	x	x
Wage at Injury[1]	–	x	x	x	x
Avg Weekly Wage[2]	–	x	x	x	–
Five Jobs/Func Cap[3]	–	–	x	x	x
Job History (actual)[4]	–	x	x	x	x
Averaging Wage History[5]	–	x	x	x	x
20 Jobs/Computer[6]	–	x	x	x	x
Survey Labor Market[7]	x	x	x	x	x

[1] May over or under estimate one's capacity to work and earn money; [2] Based on global estimates; see website; [3] Matching to jobs based on assessment and capacity to work; [4] Similar to wage at time of injury; [5] Averaging of wage history would require retro-active present value; [6] Job matching computer programs; various wage databases; [7] Large scale state, regional and national surveys; aggravated data.
Source: Field (2008), p. 12.

bilitation professions to prepare recommendations and opinions that will stand the test of admissibility by state and federal courts, including the use of reliable resources (Field & Choppa, 2005; Choppa, Field & Johnson, 2006). Estimating earnings capacity and future earnings requires a reliable methodology (Field, Johnson, Schmidt, & Van de Bittner, 2006).

Approaches to Earnings Capacity Analysis

The legal and economic literature reveal several different approaches to the analysis of wage loss and earnings capacity analysis in cases of injury. All of these approaches take into account one or more of the factors discussed in the previous section, although only one, RAPEL, considers most of the factors (also see Table 11.7).

Present Value Approach

All approaches need to account for the issue of "present value" in the determination of future lost earnings (Formuzi & Pickersgill, 1985; Lebrenz & Kreidle, 1976; Schilling, 1985). Grant (1982) defines the present value rule "when future payments are to be anticipated and capitalized in a verdict, the plaintiff is entitled only to present worth. The present worth represents the amount of money at the verdict date that, when added to the amount earned on the investment of such money over the period covering the future payments, would equal the plaintiff's total estimated future yearly earnings calculated at the verdict date" (p. 4). The issue of present worth is really trying to take into account the affect of inflation on the award for damages established at the trial date. Assume that a worker was making $15,000 per year and had 20 years of work life left. When multiplied out, this figure comes to $300,000. However, $300,000 awarded today will not have the same value as each year progresses through the 20-year period. The present value question attempts to adjust the $300,000 award to take into account the loss of value in the dollar over the 20-year period.

In the case of Wendell vs. Davis (Grant, 1982), the court allowed a 6% interest rate to be used in establishing present worth. In a case at about the same time as Wendell (Grant, 1982), "the court scrapped the 6% rule in favor of allowing a jury to consider the current rate of return on a sound investment." The attempt here was to allow the jury to take into account a fair and reasonable estimate of interest on an investment as an approach to establishing present value. An alternate approach is to consider "prevailing rate of interest" as a guide in establishing present value, but in either case, there can be great debate over what is the prevailing rate of interest or the current rate of return on a sound investment.

Another approach is to use the Present Value Tables such as established by insurance companies or brokerage firms. These tables are sometimes referred to as "annuity tables." See also Lessne (1988) for present value tables.

To complicate things even further, Coyne (1982) argues that calculations of present values should take into account such factors as race, age, sex, geographical location, and other demographic considerations which can be deemed important (see previous section for definitions and issues related to some of these factors).

Inflation Discount/Real Interest Method

The inflation discount method (Maxwell, 1984; Shoot, 1983) "seeks to avoid under compensation of the victim by increasing his expected future earnings to account for inflation and then discounting to best present value by the market interest rate." (Maxwell, p. 387) The inflation discount method is really a similar approach to the one cited above with the exception that it is a simple, direct approach to determining the effects of inflation on the expected future earnings of the claimant.

The real interest rate approach, which is very similar to the discount method, (Maxwell, 1984) is an attempt to take into account two components: "(a) the market's own estimate of anticipated rates of inflation over the life of the investment; and (b) the real rate of return a lender would demand if no inflation were anticipated. (p. 390)". In order to calculate the "real" interest rate, one would subtract the average yearly inflation rate set out by the consumer price index of the Department of Labor from the annual interest rate to be derived from a prudent and non-sophisticated investment program. While the consumer price index is fixed and somewhat more predictable, the "prudent and non-sophisticated investment program" can be quite variable. As a general rule, the interest rate on the latter figure is approximately 4 to 5% which is in line with a simple passbook savings account at any FDIC savings and loan association.

Total Offset Method

The total offset method or approach, also known as the Alaska Rule (Brody, 1982; Jensen, 1983) was first established by the Supreme Court of Alaska in the case of Beaulieu vs. Elliott (Maxwell, 1984) in which the court "held that the market interest rate totally offset by price inflation and real wage inflation, therefore making it unnecessary to discount the victim's future earnings to present value" (p. 392). The total offset method takes into account two factors that are pervasive in the U.S. economy: inflation and productivity. According to Grant (1982) it is assumed that "future inflation shall be equal to future interest rates (meaning future productivity rates) with these factors offsetting." Given this assumption, it is not necessary to take into account any factors other than the expected future earnings of a worker and multiplying that figure out by remaining years of work life left. The case of Kaczkowski (Maxwell, 1984) established "The total offset method avoids the danger of speculating as to the future rate of inflation by making what we consider a very sensible accommodation: it assumes that in the long run the effects of future inflation and the discount rate will co-vary significantly with each other" (p. 395). While this appears to be a very over-simplified approach to establishing future lost earnings, and taking into account the issue of inflation, the U.S. Supreme Court, in the case of Jones and Laughlin Steel Corporation, concluded that it would not select one method over the other in the establishment of awards for future lost earnings. However, the court appeared "to find the total offset method the most attractive means of incorporating inflation into a damage award for lost future earnings" (Maxwell, 1984, p. 397). One problem with this rule is that medical expenses have a much higher inflation rate than other products and services. This rule, strictly followed, will likely assure that clients with a long life expectancy (e.g., injured at age 20) will not have enough funds for their expenses.

A Formula Approach

Coyne (1982) has established an approach which seems to be "a sensible alternative" to the other methodologies referenced above. Coyne makes an attempt to provide a comprehensive statistical model that will address issues of inflation, productivity, as well as many of the demographic factors which he considers important. Some of these factors would include age, race, sex, geographical location, medical costs, and personal maintenance costs for the remaining years of a person's life. Coyne's approach addresses specifically the following issues (pp. 30-31):

1. Projecting the annual earnings of the worker through retirement age while using a compound growth rate of some specified percentage.

2. Convert these lifetime earnings to an equal average annual income.

3. Determine the present value of the worker's average annual income by adjusting by some specified annual rate of interest.

4. Determine the worker's maintenance expenses for the remainder of the worker's life (through the utilization of a Bureau of Census document titled "Present Value of Estimated Lifetime Earnings.")

5. Convert the gross maintenance figure to an average annual figure.

6. Determine the present value of lifetime average annual maintenance at a specified figure for the remaining years of the worker's life.

7. Subtract the present value of the average annual maintenance from the present value of the average annual income.

The final dollar figure of this procedure will result in the amount of the award which should be endorsed by the court. This approach seems to take into account more of the wage loss factors which are deemed important. However, problems still exist in establishing adequate, satisfactory and/or fair rates of interest in determining present value.

The Deutsch/Raffa Model

The Deutsch/Raffa model (Deutsch & Sawyer, 1999) establishes an approach referred to as Life Care Plans which takes into account the assessment of expenses involved in a variety of factors related to future life care. The reader is referred to the chapter in this text for an explanation of the Life Care Plan and the example report. Expenses are calculated for the following areas as part of this total life plan assessment: medical care (including miscellaneous equipment), physician's services, and pharmaceutical needs, attendant care, various forms of therapy, evaluations of diagnostics, vocational rehabilitation, equipment (such as a wheel chair or prosthesis), housing and shelter costs (including renovations), transportation, and strength and health maintenance needs.

The model then proceeds to calculate a loss of earning-capacity based upon projected annual earnings and discounted to present value of future income over the remaining work years of the client's life. The projected earnings are based upon the wage level or earnings capacity of the worker at the year of injury.

Labor Market Access/Wage Loss

The LMA approach, developed by Field & Field during the 1980's, was discussed in an earlier section of this chapter (see also Field, Choppa, & Shafer, 1984; Weed, 1987; Field, 1988) and emphasizes the necessity to analyze lost wages with respect to labor market conditions. The LMA approach is based on large-scale labor market information that is cross-referenced to median weekly wages supplied by the Bureau of Labor Statistics. The labor market surveys are provided by the Bureau of Census surveys and adjusted by annual labor market survey information from both the federal government and state departments of labor.

Residual Functional Capacity

A critically important step in determining disability is to understand the concept of Residual Functional Capacity (RFC) and how this can be derived. Determining RFC is a three-point process for the rehabilitation specialist (Field, 1985). First, identification of all prior jobs of the worker needs to be made. The significant occupational characteristics and the required levels of functioning for each needs to be identified in order to determine a pre-injury level of vocational functioning. The utilization of the *Dictionary of Occupational Titles* (1991) and the *Classification of Jobs 2000* (Field & Field, 2000) are essential resources.

Second, a determination needs to be made regarding the nature and the extent of the disabling condition. The rehabilitation specialist utilizes all medical and other appropriate referral information in order to fully understand the disability and the functional limitations imposed by the disability. If further information is needed, the rehabilitation specialist must be able to identify those areas of functioning for which more information is needed and refer to the appropriate specialists for this additional data.

Third, the transferability process (see chapter 6) is used to adjust pre-injury level of functioning to a post-injury level of functioning on all relevant worker trait factors. This adjusted post-injury level of functioning is the residual functional capacity (RFC) of the worker.

Determining Labor Market Access

This RFC analysis serves as the basis for the determination of disability. Field et al. (1981, 1999) have devised an approach to the determination of the access of employment of a worker to a particular geographic area. This process is referred to as Labor Market Access (LMA). In its simplest form, the rehabilitation specialist utilizes the residual functional capacity information and applies that level of worker functioning for a particular person to a given geographical area. In other words, given the person's level of vocational functioning (levels of worker trait functioning), what percentage of the jobs, (not job titles) would this person have access to in a particular geographical setting (e.g., Pittsburgh)? The basis for the Labor Market Access approach is predicated on the assumption that all of the jobs currently held by the people in the City of Pittsburgh can be analyzed according to their levels of functioning of the worker trait factor profile. It now becomes a simple process to identify those jobs that exist in the Pittsburgh economy that match with the injured worker's level of vocational functioning (worker traits). (Refer back to pp. 202–203 for a summary of this approach.)

The RAPEL Method

The RAPEL method (Weed, 1994; Weed, 1995; Weed, 1998; Weed, 1999; Weed, 2000) is a comprehensive approach which includes all elements needed to determine loss of access (incorporating the LMA information), loss of earnings capacity, future medical care, worklife expectancy, rehabilitation plan, as well as placeability and employability factors. The word RAPEL is a mnemonic designed to assist the rehabilitation expert with collecting the data for a jury, lawyer, judge, economist and others in order to arrive at damages. It may not be evident, but many of the articles on loss of earnings are written by economists. Generally the economist will rely on the numbers provided to him or her by the rehabilitation expert. It is very important for the economist to receive the "right" information so a "bottom line" figure can be determined. Figure 11.2 and the example below outline the RAPEL ingredients.

In litigation, the rehabilitation expert retained by the defense may not have access to the evaluee. Although a personal interview is preferred, the expert may utilize other information/data to offer a reliable opinion with regard to each of the below categories. Examples include, but are not limited to:

1. When not permitted access to the evaluee, the expert may help the attorney develop deposition or interrogatory questions that mimic the interview process.

2. Request all related depositions (regarding the evaluee, family members and healthcare providers.

3. Obtain all available related work history/employment records.

4. Obtain tax records.

5. Comprehensively review records (including medical) that might address any of the topics below.

6. With regard to the rehabilitation plan, the rehabilitation consultant may work with other defense retained experts (such as physicians and neuropsychologists) to develop opinions about future care.

7. Review Day-in-the-Life video if available.

The authors suggest that an organized report summarizing the opinions be attached as a separate document to the narrative. This facilitates the economist's role, offers a well organized easy to read document, and is ready to be made into a trial exhibit.

R = Rehabilitation Plan. The client's vocational and functional limitations, strengths, emotional functioning, and cognitive capabilities are assessed utilizing information gathered from the professionals listed earlier in this chapter. This may include additional future testing, counseling, training fees, rehabilitation technology, job analysis, job coaching, placement, and other needs for improving the client's potential for employment. If there is a Life Care Plan (usually for catastrophic injuries and complex healthcare needs), it should be noted in this section and refer the reader to that document for future medical and related care.

A = Access to Labor Market (Employability). In many of these cases, an individual may very well be able to return to a job that is custom-designed around their disability or with an employer who is interested in helping an employee with mild to moderate cognitive deficits. However, the client/evaluee may not have access to the same level of vocational choices as he or she did prior to the injury. In essence, it may be that the person would appear to have no particular loss of earnings capacity but at the same time be at high risk for losing a job and then having a significant problem locating suitable employment. The access to labor market can be determined through a variety of means. One option is to utilize a computer program like SkillTRAN^{tm} to assess the effects of the disability on the person's access to the labor market (LMA) (Field & Field, 1999), based on worker traits, and the client's ability to choose in the labor market. For example, one client/evaluee may have a 50% personal loss of access to the labor market and another individual may have a personal loss of access to 95% of the labor market. Obviously, an individual who has access to 5% of the labor market should be employable or placeable, however, the difficulty factor for obtaining suitable employment has increased significantly. By placing a loss of access percentage to labor market, one can sensitize the reader to the potential difficulty for placement. Generally, this is described in a particular percentage loss of access to the client's personal labor market rather than to the national labor market. Few unimpaired people have access to 100% of the total labor market.

P = Placeability. This represents the likelihood that the client will be successfully placed in a job with or without rehabilitation or rehabilitation consultant assistance. One may need to conduct labor market surveys, job analyses, or, in pediatric cases, rely upon statistical data to opine about ultimate placeability (Weed, 2000). In some situations, the economic condition of the community may also be a factor. It is impor-

---

Figure 11.2
The RAPEL Method: A Common Sense Approach To
LIFE CARE PLANNING AND EARNINGS CAPACITY ANALYSIS
by

*R*EHABILITATION PLAN   Determine the rehabilitation plan based on the client's vocational and functional limitations, vocational strengths, emotional functioning, and cognitive capabilities. This may include testing, counseling, training fees, rehab technology, job analysis, job coaching, placement, and other needs for increasing employment potential. Also consider reasonable accommodation. A life care plan may be needed for catastrophic injuries.

*A*CCESS TO THE LABOR MARKET   Determine the client's access to the labor market. Methods include the computer programs for labor market access analysis, transferability of skills (or worker trait) analysis, disability statistics, pre- vs. post-educational levels, and experience. This may also represent the client's loss of choice and is particularly relevant if earnings potential is based on very few positions.

*P*LACEABILITY   Placeability represents the likelihood that the client could be successfully placed in a job. This is where the "rubber meets the road." Consider the employment statistics for people with disabilities, employment data for the specific medical condition (if available), economic situation of the community (may include a labor market survey), availability (not just existence) of jobs in chosen occupations. Note that the client's attitude, personality, and other factors will influence the ultimate outcome.

*E*ARNINGS CAPACITY   Based on the above, what is the pre-incident capacity to earn compared to the post-incident capacity to earn. Methods include analysis of the specific job titles or class of jobs that a person could have engaged in pre- vs. post-incident, the ability to be educated (sometimes useful for people with acquired brain injury), family history for pediatric injuries, and computer analysis based on the individual's worker traits/skills.

Special consideration applies to children, women with limited or no work history, people who choose to work below their capacity (e.g., highly educated who are farmers), and military trained.

*L*ABOR FORCE PARTICIPATION   This represents the client's work life expectancy. Determine the amount of time that is lost, if any, from the labor force as a result of the disability. Issues include longer time to find employment, part-time vs. full-time employment, medical treatment or follow up, earlier retirement, etc. Display data using specific dates or percentages. For example, an average of four hours a day may represent a 50% loss.

© Roger O. Weed, Reprinted with permission.

tant that the rehabilitation consultant recognize that the client's personality, cognitive limitations, and other factors certainly influence the ultimate outcome. For adults, it is generally useful to include an opinion about jobs that are available (actual openings) in addition to jobs that exist but are not currently available to the client.

It is likely that the client will have worker traits which match to various job titles. Matching to a job title does not suggest that the person can indeed be placed in a particular occupation. Other factors, such as location, experience, education, personality, etc. can adversely impact placement. Also, many jobs which may be appropriate for the client/evaluee are difficult to obtain. The vocational opportunity may be highly competitive or there may be very few positions available.

For example, one administrative law judge (ALJ) for a Social Security hearing was frustrated with the consistent opinion by the vocational expert that an injured employee, particularly in the poultry industry, could return to work as a "chick sexer." The ALJ was heard to tell a vocational expert that "if you ever provide me with another opinion that a person can return to work as a chick sexer, you will no longer work as a vocational expert"!

E = Earnings Capacity. Based on the rehabilitation plan, access to the labor market, and placeability factors, the client may or may not be employable in the labor market. If employment is likely, an estimate of the earnings potential is important. It is assumed that the reader is familiar with the difference between wage loss and earnings capacity analysis; however, if not, refer to topic earlier in this chapter. In general, the earnings capacity for an individual is that which they can reasonably attain and hold. For example, consider a 17-year-old who delivers papers for an income when he is catastrophically impaired and is never able to work again. Certainly, the earnings history from the paper delivery does not represent the individual's capacity. On the other hand, a 55-year-old union truck driver may exhibit earnings history that is consistent with his capacity. The considerations include whether the individual is a child or an adult and, if an adult, the industry for which they are best suited. For an example, a drywall hanger of marginal intelligence may have very well reached their earnings potential by the time they reach their 20's or early 30's. On the other hand, an attorney may not reach their potential until very late in their career.

The information with regard to the income earnings capacity can be displayed in a variety of ways depending on the client/evaluee. A summary of the general characteristics is as follows:

1. Job categories similar to parents and siblings. For pediatric cases, particularly for those with no educational history, it may be important to consider job categories that are closely related to family trends. It can be as specific as a job title if the family trends are very clear. More likely, however, the general job categories as listed in census codes or broad classes of blue-collar jobs may be appropriate. For an example, an individual may be a tractor-trailer truck driver and the earnings potential can be determined based on a broad classification of jobs which require driving as the primary essential function.

2. Ability to be educated or trained. Another useful tool for pediatric cases is the educational potential that the client could have expected to achieve prior to injury compared to that with post-injury. For example, an individual who could reasonably achieve a college education prior to injury and now can reasonably achieve a technical education can have earnings capacity based on the economist's projections on data that is available through the government. It would be a fairly simple matter to determine the earnings capacity for each level of education and that would become the loss of earnings capacity.

3. Computer generated information. Another tool that can be utilized is assessment of the client's worker traits (physical demands, environmental condition capabilities, educational levels, aptitudes, interests, temperaments, etc.) and searching the government database of 12,741 job titles to determine the likely occupations that a person with those worker traits could achieve. One can compare the pre-injury versus post-injury capabilities to determine, based on Bureau of Labor statistics and Census data, the median weekly wages for those categories. This approach generally is useful when there is collaborating information to justify the computer approach. One computer program referenced above (SkillTRAN^tm) allows the rehabilitation professional to identify the top paying 20 categories pre-injury versus post-injury. This could reasonably represent "the earnings capacity." One caution, however, when one compares the median weekly wages, the client's injury could potentially appear to increase the individual's earnings capacity because the post-injury median weekly wage average could be higher than the pre-injury wage average. This is easily explained because most likely jobs which the client will be precluded from performing post-injury

are those which require more physical capability. The more physical capability jobs generally pay less. Hence, when one removes the lower paying, but higher physically demanding positions, the earnings capacity might appear to rise. The earnings capacity, however, indicates the client should have the capability of achieving and holding onto classes of occupations which are within their worker traits and therefore, a more accurate analysis will exclude the lower paying, but more physically demanding, positions.

4. Assessment of the client's vocational potential based on their worker traits. This most closely resembles the transferability of skills approach. Although transferability of skills extends beyond the transferability of worker traits, many rehabilitation professionals are confused on this issue and often "miss the point." Generally, an individual's worker skills are based on what they learn by doing. For example, an individual may have the potential to type at 45 words per minute but not have developed the skill. A secretary who has trained and practiced to the extent that he or she can type at 45 words per minute has demonstrated a skill. Certain federal government categories are more likely to address skills than others. As published in the book *Transferable Work Skills* (Field & Weed, 1988; Field et al., 2001), the preferred method is to utilize work fields arrangements as published in the Revised Handbook for Analyzing Jobs (1991). Work fields refer to the work method verbs and tools that one uses in order to accomplish various work tasks. The government has assigned the job titles listed in the *Dictionary of Occupational Titles* (U.S. Department of Labor, 1991) to each of these categories, and one can review these categories in the *Classification of Jobs 2000* (Field & Field, 2000). Another method is to utilize the materials, products, subject matter, and services (MPSMS), also a government arrangement. This, too, can be reviewed in the *Revised Handbook for Analyzing Jobs* (1991). In this situation, the jobs can be based upon similar materials, products, subject matter, or services. Other options are discussed in the chapter on transferable work skills.

Another means to assess vocational potential is to utilize the three middle *Dictionary of Occupational Titles* (1991) numbers which refer to data, people, things. Essentially, all job titles are assessed on different levels for each of these three categories and cross-referenced to other job titles that relate to the same data, people, things arrangement.

Census codes are also arranged in 501 different categories and the 12,741 job titles are summarized into these categories. In general, census data are easily cross-referenced to wage data from the Bureau of Labor Statistics. This provides median weekly wages for a variety of jobs within the same census code.

Last, but not least, is the prerogative of the rehabilitation consultant, based on education, experience and other factors, to determine reasonable vocational opportunities for their clients.

5. Experimenting with the new O*NET database. With the advent of O*NET, SSA is exploring ways in which the database can be used in transferable skills analysis. For a discussion of the possibility, review Transferable Skills Analysis: The process of integrating the O*NET database (Field, Grimes, Havranek & Isom, 2001). There is also a committee (see previous chapter on this topic) whose charge is to develop an alternative. However, as of the date of this revision (2012) no alternative is available.

L = Labor Force Participation. This category represents an opinion about the client's expected length of time expected to be in the labor force (also known as work life expectancy). Usually an individual who has a reduced life expectancy will also be expected to have a reduced work life expectancy. At the other end of the spectrum, the client's participation in the labor force may be unchanged. An individual may also be expected to work six hours per day rather than eight hours per day, which represents a 25% loss of normal work life expectancy. Some clients have demonstrated consistent extra income by working overtime hours and this situation can be considered in this arena as well. Generally speaking the counselor will express the opinion of loss by percentage or perhaps a number of years. Generally the economist will make the actual projections. This particular area is quite complicated and most vocational counselors are not prepared to address the subtleties and the complexities of economic projections. However, the counselor can review work life estimates in the aging Worklife Estimates: Effects of Race and Education (Bulletin # 2254, USDOL, 1986). Author's note: Although some more currently privately produced worklife data are available, the data may or may not be valid. Until more peer review is available on these data, government publications are recommended.

Diminution of Capacity

Diminution of capacity represents the professional's opinion as to the economic impact of the incident. In personal injury cases this represents part-time or full-time employment compared to the expected earnings capacity prior to injury. Generally, it is recommended that the professional display various occupations and their average or median wages for several occupations. If an opinion about specific occupations or class of occupations is not reasonable, expected educational levels can be assessed, or worker trait profiles can be summarized and calculated using one of the computer program services available for this task. As noted previously what is more probable than not is an individual will change jobs and even careers and this acknowledges that likelihood.

In most instances benefits and retirement will not be included in the rehabilitation expert's opinion. This calculation will be deferred to the economist since occupations vary dramatically in the amount of expected benefits, as well as the yearly income. Some jobs are clearly seasonal and others are full-time guaranteed year round employment. All of these issues must be considered when providing the opinion.

One additional note. The rehabilitation expert is expected to provide an opinion in personal injury cases about what is more probable than not within rehabilitation certainty as represented by the standards of the profession. A client that *might* be able to return to work if given excellent rehabilitation with close follow-up and optimum case management services, does represent "what is more probable than not." For example, one case involved a 26 year old female who was a manager for a dry cleaners. She was involved in an automobile accident where a concrete truck hit her resulting in a significant head injury. She was comatose for approximately two months and suffered significant cognitive dysfunction as well as catastrophic psychological distress. The rehabilitation professional in charge of this case indicated that she believed that she would be able to put the claimant back into the work force if she were given enough time and support. Although the rehabilitation plan could certainly be described in a narrative as well as listed in the rehabilitation plan portion of the life care plan, it clearly represented an optimistic point of view. When closely questioned about the most likely scenario for this young lady, it appears that she would be unable to work in a competitive job. Perhaps sheltered workshop, or volunteer services would be more likely.

Comparison of Approaches

This review of the approaches to wage loss analysis highlights the complexities and difficulties involved in providing an adequate analysis of future lost earnings. Reference to Table 11.7 will confirm that there is no one method that provides a complete analysis of all of the factors involved in making such an analysis. The approaches of present value, discount method, the offset method, and the Coyne formula approaches are tools used primarily by the economists involved in future lost wage analysis. The approaches identified by the RAPEL, Deutsch/Raffa and LMA models are more within the purview of the rehabilitation specialist. Obviously, the rehabilitation specialist needs to have access to such tools as are provided by these three models which in turn provide vitally important information to the economist to further complete the work of future lost wage and medical cost analysis. It should be noted that many states differ in their rules with regard to this topic and the consultant should rely upon the attorney and/or the economist for guidance. Ultimately, the court will provide the final criterion on which approaches and methods are most suitable, just and fair in the evaluation and analysis of future lost earnings of injured workers.

Labor Market Information

In order for a rehabilitation consultant to calculate the degree of disability for an injured worker, it is imperative that a clear understanding be made of how labor market information can be developed and utilized. For the sake of argument, assume that there are three basic levels of labor market information, some of which are more suitable than others depending on the venue in which the case is being reviewed or adjudicated. Basically, data are generated from:

1. Federal and/or national surveys administered by the federal government. These data surveys include BLS data, Census Data, including the SIPP and CPS database, and the American Community Survey data. For purposes of code identification, the federal government, across several agencies, utilizes the Standard Occupational Code (SOC) for purposes of coordination and cross-referencing.

2. The next level of data is usually generated by Departments of Labor within the respective 50 states. These data surveys are generally coordinated and formatted with the national surveys, but reflect

Table 11.7
Comparison of Wage Loss and Future Care Approaches

Factors	Present Value	Discount/ Real Int.	Total Offset	LPE/ Worklife	LMA	Deutsch	RAPEL
Age	*	*	N	Y	N	*	Y
Worklife	Y	Y	Y	Y	N	Y	Y
Sex	*	*	N	Y	Y	*	Y
Geography	N	N	N	Y	Y	Y	Y
Occupational Group	N	N	N	N	Y	*	Y
Loss Of Enjoyment	*	*	*	N	N	N	N
Inflation	Y	Y	Y	N	N	Y	Y
Productivity	N	Y	Y	N	N	*	*
Labor Market Surveys	N	N	N	N	Y	N	Y
% Loss Employment	N	N	N	N	Y	N	Y
Life Expectancy	*	*	*	Y	N	*	*
Maintenance	N	N	N	N	N	Y	Y
Wage History	Y	Y	Y	N	N	Y	Y
Median Wage	N	N	N	N	Y	*	Y
Future Wage Loss	Y	Y	Y	Y	N	Y	Y
Future Medicals	Y	Y	Y	N	N	Y	Y

* denotes that accommodation can be made with this approach to include this factor.

more detail about specific occupations within a state. Many times there are targeted labor market surveys which investigate the numbers, types and wages of jobs within a particular occupational cluster (i.e., jobs within the allied health field).

3. The next level may be the most refined of all in that it includes a very targeted labor survey with a particular client in mind. Following an effort to establish an RFC, the consultant attempts to match the client to those jobs which clearly fit the client's level of functioning and occupational interests. This approach easily allows for finding alternate jobs based upon different scenarios regarding the client's level of functioning, such as might exist with a period of additional training for the client.

For additional information of these occupational resources, consult the list of websites in the Reference section of this paper.

Life and Worklife Tables

The following data sets are critical in the development of a case involving an estimate of earnings capacity. In a future issue of this journal, a more in-depth treatment of these resources will be examined.

DOL Work Life Tables (Bulletin 2254): The most widely used but aging source (BLS) for estimating work life in states of active and inactive, these tables are generally accepted by the courts as credible evidence. Consult the *BLS Handbook of Methods* for an explanation of how data are gathered and evaluated.

The New Work Life Tables: Known as the "Gamboa Tables," this resource which utilizes CPS data is privately developed and appears to be more controversial with regard to their reliability and validity. Admissibility in court is mixed (*Scupp, Peterson v. Grabel*, 2001; *Jackson v. Roadway Express, Inc.*, 1999; and *Hough-Scoma v. Wal-Mart Stores, Inc.*, 1999). The Gamboa Tables have been criticized (Rodgers, 2001; Skoog & Toppino, 1999), although Gamboa argues that the tables are not a problem when used properly by the expert. (See website for an excellent review of court cases and commentary).

Millimet Work Life Tables: Privately developed tables utilizing CPS data and emphasizing the states of employed, unemployed, and inactive (differs from BLS format).

Markov Process Model of Worklife Expectancies: A set of tables developed by Ciecka et al. (1995) based on age, sex, education and the activity of workers in the labor force.

Life and Worklife Expectancies: A comprehensive discussion of issues related to estimating worklife. Ciecka is one of the contributors and discusses his tables. (See Richards & Abele, 2000).

A real problem with any of the worklife tables is that they fail to distinguish adequately between types and levels of disabilities. While the Gamboa Tables purport to use the three DOL categories related to disability, these are considered by many too non-specific and global in most cases. In determining a more reasonable and accurate estimate of worklife expectancy, it is incumbent up on the forensic rehabilitation consultant to take into consideration as many of the factors (previously discussed) that are relevant to the individual case.

Summary of Approaches

Establishing a reasonable and defensible estimate of earning capacity in cases of partial, but permanent, disability may be a rather foreboding task for the rehabilitation professional. The process has been written about extensively for a period of 30 years or more. Knowing what to do and how to do it can be confusing especially when there is so much information and, in some areas, controversy. This chapter provides an overview of the landscape on determining a reduction of capacity due to an injury and disability. This reduced earning capacity, if any, is the foundation for estimating future lost earnings – part of the damages that will be settled by the court process unless agreed to by the parties beforehand. Estimating earning capacity may seem to be a formidable task. The first consideration is to remember that different venues will require a different approach or methodology. Utilization of different resources may be an issue, (i.e., which worklife table is used, and which social or demographic variables are addressed). Once a reliable methodology is developed by the practitioner, such as was illustrated in the Isom case, potential problems will be minimized. Under the recent U.S. Supreme Court rulings, and consideration of the federal rules, developing a workable methodology, while critically important, should not be insurmountable.

Working With the Economist

For rehabilitation professionals inexperienced in working with an economist, it is important to think in terms of specific dollars and percentages. The economist will take the information provided by the rehabilitation professional and display a "bottom line" figure representing damages. In order for the economist to accomplish this calculation the rehabilitation professional must be very precise and specific in the way they display data. For an example, worklife expectancy cannot be "decreased" it must be expressed in percentage terms or loss of years. Earnings capacity cannot be expressed as "this person has lost some of her earnings capacity" but must be expressed in specific dollar amounts. For a very good overview of this concept the reader is referred to the excellent article titled The necessary economic and vocational interface in personal injury cases (Dillman, 1987).

Other Forensic Support

On occasion the rehabilitation expert may participate in developing evidence or settlement aids. Included are the following:

1. "Day in the life of . . ." video. When a jury observes a tetraplegic client in the court room, they may not fully understand the challenges the person faces. For example, hygiene, toileting, feeding, activities of daily living, etc. One way to convey the information is to follow the client through a typical day. Many rehabilitation consultants assist plaintiff's attorneys with this effort by consulting on the topics to be covered and facilitating the filming. Generally, the film should less than 15-20 minutes in length to keep people interested

(Hunt, 2010). Day-in-the-Life videos are also helpful to defense experts who may not be able to interview the client.

2. Settlement Brochure. Oftentimes the plaintiff's attorney believes that when liability is clear and damages are identified, a "brochure" can be provided to the responsible party which outlines the case, evidence and damages and will help settle the case with a minimum of conflict and cost. This task can be accomplished through binders of information and pictures or through video. Many rehabilitation consultants will be asked to provide a summary of their opinions to underscore that the attorney has done their homework. For example, a 30 to 60 second segment may show the vocational consultant discussing the effects of the accident on the client's ability to work and another may show the rehabilitation nurse discussing future care requirements.

3. Summarizing Records. This task is more commonly completed by rehabilitation nurses. Compiling medicals, sorting and arranging, summarizing them with notes as to possible breach of duty, explaining in lay terms, and revealing questions to be researched. This often includes summarizing medical depositions.

4. Locating Experts. Consultants may be involved in locating both liability and damages experts through their personal network, or by researching the topic in a medical library.

5. Research. Related to the above, many attorneys need to locate definitive information about a topic and often rely upon rehabilitation consultants or paralegals to research the topic and provide literature backup to support a theory.

Defending the Case

Most rehabilitation professionals who work in the private sector will likely be faced with a deposition, testifying through an interrogatory or perhaps at a trial. Many do not understand the significance of these events. Extensive and detailed suggestions can be found in Appendix C in How to Give Your Deposition. The reader is also referred to the Do's and Don'ts section located in chapter two. Another excellent resource is the book *Depositions: The comprehensive guide for expert witnesses* (Babitsky & Mangraviti, 2007). The following represents an overview of some of the major issues.

Interrogatory: An interrogatory is a list of questions which is submitted through an attorney usually to the client and rarely to an expert. You will be asked a series of questions which is expected to elucidate the reason you were called as an expert. This is usually a prelude to a deposition. Generally the "other side" is attempting to discover what will be entered as evidence at a trial. This is a formal procedure which should not be taken lightly.

Deposition: The rehabilitation consultant's role at the deposition is similar to the role at the workers' compensation hearing. The primary difference is the location and the lack of the presence of a judge. The deposition is conducted most frequently at the office of the expert, attorney's office, or at a site convenient to the expert witness. A judge is not present to preside or to rule on objections by the counsels for plaintiff or defense. While the client/evaluee may be invited, their presence is uncommon.

There are two types of depositions which the expert is likely to face. One is an "evidence" deposition. The evidence deposition generally is called by the side that retained the expert. In this situation the attorney believes there is good reason to attempt to settle the case or the expert will not appear "live" at trial. Both attorneys will present their case similar to how it would be presented at trial. In some situations the expert will be video taped. Many physicians provide "evidence" depositions.

Another type of deposition is the "discovery" deposition. In this case the other side is attempting to uncover or discover what evidence is expected to be offered at trial (if there is one). Usually the attorney that retains the expert being deposed does not ask questions of the specialist since the attorney does not want to give away any more information than necessary.

The attorney who requested the deposition initiates direct examination. Cross and redirect examination follows. A certified court recorder records (and later transcribes) the entire testimony. Since a judge is not present to control the hearing, objections by either side are stated. The rationale for such objections are given and discussed. A ruling on each objection will be made by the judge prior to the submission of the testimony into evidence at a trial. The rehabilitation expert should be aware that although the deposition appears to be a much more informal process, its content is equally important to that of the formal courtroom testimony. The entire deposition, or selected portions of its contents, may be read at the formal hearing or trial.

The expert is offered the opportunity to "read and sign" the deposition. Although many waive their rights, it is strongly recommended that the expert read and sign. First, sometime text is absent that can entirely change what was intended. For example, the word "not" left out of a sentence. Second, reading and signing is a way to assure that the expert receives a copy of the deposition. Litigation can drag on for a few years and it is desirable to have the opportunity to refresh one's memory before deposition or trial.

Note that some professionals find themselves in awkward positions. There may be occasions where the expert in bordering on saying something that documents malpractice such as incorrectly providing records which have been subpoenaed. Remember the attorney that retains you to provide expert testimony is NOT your attorney. Do not expect the attorney to advise you, as she would for her client, if you are treading on dangerous legal territory. You are advised to consult your attorney if you have legal questions.

Subpoena: A subpoena is a formal "legal" request for records or appearance at a deposition or trial. It may or may not be a proper request. For example, you receive a subpoena for confidential records on one of your clients/evaluees. It happens to be a difficult client who you know is involved in litigation. Should you send the records? You may decide that you must comply with the threatening document. Before you do, make sure you are clear on confidentiality. Remember that a subpoena for records is not typically reviewed by a judge for appropriateness. If you do not have a records release by the client it is best to contact your personal attorney before releasing them. For example, this author had a personal injury defense attorney subpoena him for a deposition. The expert was to appear at a specific date and time, but if he submitted records, the deposition would be canceled. The author contacted the attorney to tell him records would be released when a release of information was received. The deposition and the requested for records were canceled. Another example involves a rehabilitation counselor who received a subpoena for her records on a client from a defense attorney. She felt compelled to send the records only to learn that the client's attorney was furious since she had also provided the "other side" with attorney work product which was privileged communications. Generally it is best for the rehabilitation professional to agree to provide information once the appropriateness is determined. This is accomplished by writing to the attorney who requested or subpoenaed the information and explain that as soon as proper releases or a judge's order is received the information will be provided promptly. A "Notice to Produce" carries similar responsibility. Indeed, any release of confidential information must be carefully handled.

On the other hand, a subpoena for appearing in court as a witness carries a different expectation. If the individual is to appear as a witness to the event or accident then it is expected that he or she appear or suffer possible warrant for arrest. On the other hand, if the individual is to appear as an expert witness, it is generally accepted that one can not be forced to provide an "expert" opinion.

Trial by Jury: The primary difference in other settings and jury trial is the order in which witnesses are called, and the courtroom setting. In Social Security and workers' compensation hearings, the vocational expert is usually present to hear other witnesses and is most frequently the last witness to testify. It is assumed that all other testimony may be critical to the formation of a vocational opinion. Since depositions are conducted for single witnesses, there may be no order of selection.

At the jury trial the rehabilitation expert is called to testify at the time the attorney deems to be the most critical time for such testimony. The expert most frequently testifies without the benefit of other hearing live testimony. Therefore, the preparation to answer questions based on several assumptions is critical. ("Sequestered" is a term one might hear, which means the expert will sit outside of the courtroom until called.)

Last, but not least, the presence of a jury and the necessity to sit in the witness chair adds an air of sophistication and formality which matches no other legal setting. It becomes very easy to do those things which one should not and forget to do those things one should do.

Perhaps a few recommendations should be emphasized. The consultant should realize that most of the detailed information presented to a jury will not be remembered by the panel of peers. What is remembered is their impression of the expert (see Table 11.8 for the effects of dress on juries). Therefore it is very important to avoid confrontation with the cross examining attorney and becoming an advocate for one side over another. Remaining as objective as possible is vital but very difficult in the heat of the "battle." Remember that attorneys attend a school of law and the rehabilitation consultant (effectively) attends a school of justice. One more suggestion is to speak to the jury. This is harder than it sounds. However, many juries have been sitting for days in a boring (usually) court room and may "doze off" at times. Speaking directly to the jury by getting up (with the judge's permission) and "teaching" the jury (see below) will help keep them on task and perhaps leave them with a better impression.

Table 11.8
The More Knowledgeable Scientific Expert

	Description of Pairs	Responses (n = 102)
Pair 1	Male with dark brown sports jacket	19
	Male with dark blue suit	81
Pair 2	Male with conservative tie	92
	Male with loud tie	8
Pair 3	Male with two piece suit	41
	Male with three piece suit	59
Pair 4	Female with skirt and sweater	23
	Female with skirted suit	77
Pair 5	Female with hair up	70
	Female with hair down	30
Pair 6	Male standing and illustrating	84
	Male sitting and talking	16
Pair 7	Male with dark brown sports jacket	30
	Female with gray skirted suit	70
Pair 8	Female with gray skirted suit	31
	Male with dark blue suit	69

Source: Tanton, R. L. (1979). Jury preconceptions and their effect on expert scientific testimony. *Journal of Forensic Sciences, 24,* 681-691.

Trial Exhibits: There are several ways to display evidence to a jury. One is to offer an opinion by expressing it verbally. In general, the expert will remain seated in the witness box. Other more active approaches are to write figures on a flip chart, blow up the Life Care Plan or vocational opinions on a large chart that can be seen by the jury and others, use transparencies, make slides of the evidence and, more recently, utilize computer based displays. In general, it is important to assume an educational approach. This will be more interesting to the jury and allow the expert to stand up. Research demonstrates that dress also has an effect on the jury's opinion. (See Table 11.8)

Daubert and Kumho Tire Rulings

In many contemporary forensic settings, expert witnesses are challenged to provide "reliable and valid" opinions. The genesis for the movement is associated with two court rulings: Daubert (1993) and Kumho Tire (1999). Historically, experts were allowed to testify if the person offering an opinion had knowledge, and/or experiences, that would assist the jury in determining liability and damages. Initially, the general acceptance theory was offered which indicated that scientific evidence should be based on evidence generally accepted in the specific field of knowledge (*Fry v. United States*, 1923). In 1993, the Daubert decision was heard throughout the rehabilitation world with regard to additional characteristics that were required for an individual, particularly in federal cases, to testify as an expert. Under Daubert (*Daubert v. Merrell Dow*, 1993), the expert's opinion needed to be based on scientific or valid evidence which had been subjected to peer review and publication. Daubert, on the other hand, also recognized that some propositions are too particular, too new, or of limited interest to be published. However, the ruling underscored the need for "valid" scientific evidence. In 1999, Kumaho Tire extended this to non-scientific experts (*Kumaho Tire v. Patrick Carmichael*, 1999). Under Kumaho Tire, an individual was offered as an expert on defective tires. This individual's testimony was disallowed by the trial judge because he was unable to cite literature that would demonstrate that he used a generally acceptable method. Neither could he provide evidence that anyone agreed with his method, even if it was not published, or subjected to peer review.

The primary lesson to be learned from the aforementioned court cases is to utilize data and published methods when supporting one's opinion. Please refer to Table 11.9 for general issues that the expert witness should consider. For more detailed information on this topic, read Field et al. (2000), *A Resource for the Rehabilitation Consultant on the Daubert and Kumho Rulings* (also see Chapter 12).

Summary

This chapter provides an overview of the necessary elements for rehabilitation consultants who choose to enter the employment option of expert witness or litigation consultant. If the rehabilitationist observes the protocol for conducting professional and objective damages related evaluations, a valuable service will be offered which will set a foundation for resolving litigation. However, since this area of expertise has specific rules (see selected Federal Rules of Evidence in the Appendices), it is important to obtain more information than can be presented in this chapter. Various training opportunities are also offered by professional associations, books are available and deposition hints as well as example Federal Rules for Evidence are included in this text's appendices. In addition, belonging to professional organizations, obtaining certification in the areas of expected expertise, and adhering to ethics standards will provide a foundation of excellence in practice.

Table 11.9
General Issues for the Expert Witness

- ✓ Did you use published procedures?
- ✓ Will another competent professional who reviews your report agree that you have supported your opinion or that you are using accepted procedures?
- ✓ Do you use checklists, forms, etc. to assure reliable approach to evaluation and opinion?
- ✓ Have you had adequate specialized training for the work you are undertaking?
- ✓ Are you aware of articles/books/chapters relating to the topic?
- ✓ Did you use data, where possible, to support your opinion?
- ✓ Do you know some recognized authorities in the area of expertise?
- ✓ If you are an expert witness (distinguished from consultant) did you prepare written opinion and recommendations?

Example Case

The following example addresses many of the pertinent points noted in the various models discussed earlier in this chapter. In addition to the definitions provided previously, the subsequent represents minimum information to be included on a vocational work sheet and an example work sheet can be located at the end of the chapter (see Life Care Plan chapter for sample future medical care plan).

Name:	Losta Few
Age:	44
Date of Birth:	5/4/47
Date of Incident:	6/27/89
Date of Report:	10/9/92

Summary of Case

The client states that she was driving home from work at approximately 4 p.m. when a van in front of her lost control. She reportedly slowed down to avoid hitting the van and a tractor trailer truck hit her from behind. She reports being told that her car "turned like a corkscrew for approximately 350 yards." The client states that she remembers working the day of the incident, including having her work card signed at the end of the day by a shift supervisor. She states that she does not remember the accident, but has occasional bits and pieces of memory following the accident. She states that she remembers being in the ambulance and asking someone what the lights and siren were about. She states that she remembers severe pain in her head. Apparently she was released to go home and did not stay overnight in the hospital.

Reportedly, the client has residuals of mild to moderate head injury, headaches, hip pain, and significant visual disturbance with loss of field.

Educationally she reports completing high school and six months of an approximate two year business school program involving secretarial and bookkeeping training. She did not complete the program because she states she was making more money in her jobs than the potential income from completing the business school.

Reportedly, the client's job at the time of the injury was a union position for aircraft setting up and loading flights with meals. She was a "driver" where she was one of two people on a truck who would service various flights by loading food and beverages. The client states that she started as a kitchen helper, became the lead helper, then the cook and finally into the higher paying aircraft servicing job. Reportedly, the position currently pays $9.71 per hour plus comprehensive health benefits and vacation.

She states that she did not work for approximately seven months following the accident. She returned to work for approximately five months as a driver and airplane servicer. She reports that she had a number of problems with the job, including forgetting things. She states "I thought I was losing my mind," and apparently had difficulty reading the video monitors which identified flight times and gates. She reports, for example, she would often turn right instead of left and become lost and confused. Apparently, she became fatigued and, as she worked longer, she began having headaches. She reports that she had difficulty reading airplane identifiers and transposed the numbers. For an example, the plane number might be 723 and she would remember it as 732.

She apparently had difficulty in accurately driving the catering truck and states "I was lucky I didn't hit any aircraft." She states that she experienced pain so bad she could not stand it any longer so she discontinued work. After additional time off, she returned to work in approximately February, 1991 and began working in the cafeteria. Shortly thereafter, she moved to the sandwich room and then to the dish room. All of these work stations were reported to be unsuccessful due to the residuals of the injury and she discontinued working in August, 1991.

Reportedly, the client had difficulty tolerating loud noises which made it difficult for her to understand people around her. For an example, if an employee gave her an order for food in the cafeteria she would have difficulty understanding what the person was saying. Additionally, when attempting to make salads, she had difficulty in arranging plates. For an example, arranging orange and grapefruit slices resulted in approximately five hours to arrange some 44 plates. In the dish room, she states that the heat was intense and she was unable to cope with the steam and the heat. She apparently had occasions where her vision was significantly disturbed.

The client states that she generally did "okay" in the sandwich room, but "it did me in" for after-work activity. She reports that she was highly irritable and became very fatigued and when she went home she would simply spend time in bed. Apparently, she would stay in bed both days off and reports being totally exhausted and sleeping up to 27 hours.

REHABILITATION PLAN

Recommendation	Dates	Frequency	Expected Cost
Neurological follow-up	1993-2003	Every 3 to 6 mos. for 2 to 5 yrs. then 1X/yr. for 5 yrs.	$50-75/visit excluding lab, if needed.
Medication (This client may require anti-depressants)			Unknown
Neuropsychological\ psychological support	1993-life expectancy	15 hrs. per year ave.	$100/hour
Vocational counseling, job analysis, and job placement	1992-1994	30 hours	$65-75/hour
Job coaching	1992-1994	50 to 100 hours	$15 to $25/hour

Potential complications

    a.   Accidental re-injury due to poor visual discrimination/field cuts or judgment.

    b.   Psychological adjustment to disability is more difficult, or rehabilitation plan is less successful, than expected.

    c.   Adverse reactions to medication.

(Note: frequency and duration of potential complications cannot be identified at this time and no cost is included in this plan. However, the above represent common problems.)

ACCESS TO THE LABOR MARKET

The client has experienced approximately a 96% loss of access to the competitive labor market based on the results from the Labor Market Access 92 computer based analysis. The client is unable to return to her pre-injury occupation.

PLACEABILITY

Vocational Considerations

The client cognitively and emotionally appears to have the following characteristics which impact the rehabilitation plan and her return to work:

    Average IQ
    Reduced visual and verbal memory
    Reduced memory, attention, and concentration
    Failure to maintain set
    Impaired visual selective attention
    Loss of peripheral vision with field cuts
    Impaired information processing

Avoid complex verbal instructions
Significantly reduced stamina
Increased fatigue with maximum of 3 to 4 hours per day of work activity
Problems following directions
Reduced ability to block unnecessary visual and noise distractions
Increased irritability
Need for low stress environment
Reduced ability for driving (low traffic, short distances, good light)
Avoid hazardous work areas
Avoid extensive walking
Avoid climbing and balancing if frequently part of the job
Limit to light work category

The client has suffered a moderate impact on her ability to be placed in the competitive labor market given her current level of cognitive skills and functioning. Placement is likely to be custom developed with a willing employer. Career counseling, on-the-job-training, selective placement, and job coaching will be required for this client to successfully re-enter the work force. Competitiveness, lateral and upward mobility have been significantly reduced.

EARNINGS CAPACITY

Pre-incident

The client's work history appears to represent her earning capacity. Her career track may have included potential supervisory and management positions within the airline catering service. In addition, the client reportedly frequently worked over-time.

Option 1: Earnings capacity based on earnings history

Option 2: Union aircraft food service work ($9.71/hr. Note: does not include benefits)

Post-incident

Selective entry level employment with food service industry. $4.50 - $5.25 per hour

Note 1: Worklife expectancy (see below)

Note 2: Job will require job analysis, selective placement, and job coaching.

Note 3: Expect entry into labor market 1994.

Note 4: Does not include benefits.

LABOR FORCE PARTICIPATION

According to testing and work hardening training the client has potential to work 3-4 hours per day. Therefore, the client will have a 50% reduction in worklife expectancy. This does not include the client's apparent pre-injury ability to work frequent overtime hours.

Diminution of yearly earnings to be computed by the economist based on the above opinions.

Case Illustration: Labor Market Access

The following computer prints are illustrations of the analysis of lost employment through the use of the Labor Market Access Plus 1999 computer program. The same case was run two times showing the differences in results through the manipulation of a few of the variables. This analysis is based on the transferability analysis presented in Chapter 6.

The first illustration is of Joe Example with a back strain injury. On page 266 are data relative to the wage loss analysis for this claimant. This worker was employed in Industry 6 which is Machine Trades, and in the Work Field groups of 10 and 15. These Work Field groups contain the specific Work Fields of 057 and 102.

051	Abrading	055	Milling-Turning-Planing
052	Chipping	056	Sawing
053	Boring	057	Machining
054	Shearing-Shaving		
101	Upholstering	111	Electrical-Electronic
102	Structura	121	Mechanical

Using the very same rationale as was discussed earlier in transferability, an attempt is made to keep this worker within the same Industrial area (machine trades) in which he was previously employed, and in the same Work Field groups (10 and 15) which would represent his work skills. The preceding pages to this table are a summary of the worker trait factors and their levels of capacity both pre- and post-injury. Since the labor market access analysis is an evaluation of one's loss of employability from pre- to post-injury, two worker trait profiles are entered into the program. Again referring to the table on pg. 266, the results show that this claimant had a loss of 74% of his labor market, although that labor market was very, very narrow to begin with. The analysis is based on the 1,079,093 men who comprised the civilian labor force of the Atlanta, Georgia SMSA. Prior to injury, this claimant was able to perform jobs equal to or less than those jobs held by 4893 men in that labor market pre-injury and to jobs that were held by only 1650 men with post-injury worker trait skills in the same labor market. The percentages of .59 and .15 reflect the portion of the labor market that was representative of the whole (1,079,093) resulting in a 74% loss of jobs held by men in this labor force. Seventy-four percent represents the vocational disability of this claimant given his restrictions, including transferable skills, for the Atlanta, Georgia SMSA.

The table also shows the average median wages for those jobs both pre-access and post-access, as well as the top twenty paying and the low twenty paying jobs, both pre- and post-injury.

On page 264 is a census summary of the jobs that this claimant can do both pre- and some post-injury. Use this table is to identify the jobs in the outside post column that have a sufficient frequency of men in those particular job titles that would probably best represent the more feasible job titles to pursue in order to secure a return-to-work. In particular, the following census codes are the jobs with these sufficient frequencies: 505, 518, 637, 657and 769. Pages 268-269 are a summary of the twenty top paying jobs both pre- and post-injury, and twenty of the lowest paying jobs both pre- and post-injury that would be consistent with the claimant's work skills.

On page 270 is a partial listing of the Dictionary of Occupational Titles jobs that match post-injury for the claimant. These jobs are listed in the DOT, and are not part of any labor market survey. In order to use these job titles, one must now refer to one of the survey codes and further research the possibility that some of these jobs may exist with openings, if any, within the Atlanta, Georgia MSA. These survey codes include the census, the SOC, and the SIC codes.

The second run represents the identical input information on behalf of the claimant except in this case no information entered in the environmental conditions, GOE or Temperament areas (pgs. 271). In other words, these areas of input data did not have any bearing on excluding any of the jobs that this person could have performed. A review of the chart on page 272 shows that the vocational disability in this case is 72% as represented by the numbers of workers in jobs in the same Atlanta, Georgia MSA.

One final note: The percentage loss of access to jobs pre- to post-injury is best described as a loss of employment access to that particular labor market. This may also be referred to as a claimant's vocational disability rating. Many state compensation programs as well as some cases within the field of personal injury are relying on the concept of loss of access to a labor market expressed in percentage terms. This type of analysis is one approach to answering the question of percentage loss of access to a particular geographical labor market for a person who is injured.

Summary

The ethical rehabilitation professional who practices in forensic settings provides a valuable contribution by establishing a reasonable treatment plan, helping to settle personal injury litigation, or providing the jury with information on which to base an award. Offering testimony is fraught with obstacles including introducing "hearsay" evidence (see Appendix for federal rules of evidence #703) or knowing how to develop appropriate exhibits for the courtroom. However, the domain is growing as more attorneys become aware of the value of the forensic rehabilitation expert to their cases. This growth in turn offers the experienced consultant the opportunity for expansion into a wider field.

Chapter 12
Admissible Testimony and Clinical Judgment

The Daubert Trilogy (Daubert, Kumho & Joiner)

Since the onset of the Daubert ruling by the U.S. Supreme Court in 1993 *(Daubert v. Merrill Dow Pharmaceutical* [Daubert]), one of the most talked about, written about, and frequent conference topics is the general issue of admissibility of expert opinion. Early on, several authors warned of the coming demise of any rehabilitation testimony that did not adhere sharply to the four Daubert standards (Caragonne, 1999; Feldbaum, 1997; Mayer, 1998; & Stein, 2002). Emerging as well was the less stringent view that, in light of Kumho *(Kumho Tire Company v. Carmichael* [Kumho], 1999) and Joiner *(Joiner v. General Electric* [Joiner], 1997), the Daubert factors were not meant to strictly govern all testimony, but that other factors might apply – especially in the social sciences. Several authors (Bernstein, 1998; Field, 2002; Field, 2006; Field & Choppa, 2005; Neulicht &, Barros-Bailey, 2005; Staller, 2002; and Weed & Johnson, 2006) presented a view of the Daubert issue which was much less threatening and, in fact, has resulted in being a rather relatively minor problem for rehabilitation consultants in terms of meeting the "scientific" standards. Clearly, the strict Daubert view has been on the losing side of the admissibility battle for several good reasons – a battle lost that some professionals still fail to comprehend.

Parallel to the Daubert debate has been a growing discussion of the efficacy of a reliance on the use of clinical judgment for non-science situations. In addition to Choppa et al. (2004), Downie and Macnaughton (2001) challenge the wide-spread view that all of medicine is scientific and evidenced-based.

> *The Daubert gatekeeping obligation applies not only to scientific testimony, but to all expert testimony." The key word in Rule 702 is the word "knowledge", not scientific, or technical, or specialized. Some knowledge is scientific, and in those cases the Daubert rule would more appropriately apply. In Kumho, the decision noted that "a trial judge determining the admissibility of.... testimony may (italicized in the written opinion for emphasis) consider one or more of the specific Daubert factors. The emphasis on the word "may" reflects Daubert's description of the Rule 702 as a flexible one.... the Daubert factors do not constitute a definite checklist or test. Some of those factors may be helpful in evaluating the reliability even of experienced-based expert testimony. It is only partially true that the Daubert factors must be applied in all cases (science or non-science).*

> *The US Supreme Court recognized the difficulty in applying specific criteria outlined in Daubert to all types of testimony. It held the four-part test outlined in Daubert was non-exclusive and a "flexible" approach to the assessment of reliability should be applied using factors appropriate to the particular case. In certain cases, virtually none of the specific criteria outlined in the Daubert case would be applicable. In those cases, the trial judge would be given broad discretion in considering other factors which might establish relaibility for the specific type of expert testimony at issue.*

Finally it has been well established that there exists both latitude and flexibility in the application of FRE 702 within the intent and meaning of the Daubert, Kumho, and Joiner rulings. Burnette (2000) reaches the following conclusion on the admissibility of courtroom testimony:

As noted in the Kumho ruling, *Daubert v. Merrell Dow Pharmaceuticals* (1993) launched a protracted discussion and debate on what constitutes admissible testimony in federal and state courts for the forensic rehabilitation professional. The Daubert case involved a ruling on the admissibility of a science issue – did the drug Bendectin cause the deformity in Jason Daubert (and other plaintiffs) following the ingestion of the drug during his mother's pregnancy. The Supreme Court ruling decided that the plaintiff's case was not valid since the presentation of scientific data was flawed, and generally did not meet the minimal standards of the scientific method. The early impression by Feldbaum (1997), and others (see discussion in Field, 2006) seemed to suggest that the admissibility of all testimony would also fall under the umbrella of the new Daubert standards, including rehabilitation testimony (Stein, 2002). The test of time has shown that the all-inclusion premise that Daubert is the final determinate of admissibility (with the four basic criteria for admissibility) has not been sustainable or supported for a variety of reasons.

In addition to the discussion in Field (2006), several factors are relevant in understanding the current parameters of admissible testimony for the forensic rehabilitation consultant. Daubert has been clarified and moderated by the Paoli (1994), Joiner (1997) and Kumho (1999) rulings , all of which emphasis, as the Daubert ruling did, that the four factors (scientific method, standard error rate, generally accepted, and peer reviewed) were not meant to be all-inclusive, and that other factor may apply. The Supreme Court never intended for the rules (factors) to be all inclusion and, in fact, relied heavily upon the Federal Rule 702 for the foundation of the Daubert rulings.

A Definition of Clinical Judgment

It is clear from actual court rulings, that all testimony does not require the scrutiny or strict application of the four Daubert factors. It is incumbent upon the expert to show that their testimony is both relevant and reliable as required by both the Daubert and Kumho rulings of the U.S. Supreme Court. In particular, the twin tests, as suggested by Staller, are the tests of peer review and general acceptance (the old Frye standard). The definition of clinical judgment, first drafted and published by Choppa et al. (2004), reflects the important components of FRE 702, and is consistent with the intent and meaning of the US Supreme Court cases of Daubert (1993), Joiner (1997), and Kumho (1998), all within the knowledge and skill parameters of the expert. The definition also acknowledges that rehabilitation and life care planning on behalf of a rehabilitation client must address the individual factors and issues that are germane to that particular client. In a very real sense, data and information are applied to the individual – a methodological approach of an "N of 1."

> *Clinical judgment requires that the final opinion be predicated on valid, reliable and relevant foundation information and data that are scientifically established through theory and technique building which has been tested, peer reviewed, and published, with known error rates, and is generally accepted within the professional community. In cases where any of the above factors do not apply, but other factors have greater relevance, the expert will rely on these other factors within a methodological approach, based on the expert's knowledge, skill, experience, training, or education in order to assist the trier of fact to reach a conclusion. Therefore, clinical judgment, which is the extension of the credentialing factors of the expert, encompasses all relevant factors germane to the weight of the case while discarding those factors which are not relevant, and which are allowed by the court (Choppa et al., 2004) (See endnote of this chapter).*

In support of the above concept, Richard Countiss, an attorney, co-authored an article (Countiss & Deutsch, 2002) which was the basis for a "friend of the court" brief. Drawing upon the standards for physicians, he asserts:

> *Standards exist for the evaluation and diagnosing of the patient, choosing the procedure, applying the procedure and following-up with the patient. Yet within those standards, the physician has the ability to exercise a range of professional judgments that take into consideration individual patient differences, variations in the specific nature of the disorder, and variations in how best to apply specific procedures to individual patient differences. This same need for Rehabilitation Experts/Case Managers to exercise professional judgment is a component of the Life Care Planning process. However, this must be done within the context of the standards noted and a careful balance between published, accepted standards and professional judgment must be maintained. Published standards are never an excuse for failing to exercise appropriate professional judgment yet, at the same time, one can not say that they chose to exercise professional judgment as a means to simply, and lightly, dismiss accepted standards (p. 40).*

As an alternative, the authors make a case for clinical judgment, sufficiently based on technical evidence which may be neither quantifiable or even scientific, but would certainly contain judgments based on the best information available, including scientific and/or technical information. In leading up to an appropriate understanding of the meaning of clinical judgment for the rehabilitation profession, the following considerations are presented.

The Rulings

A careful reading of the rulings (Daubert, 1993; Kumho, 1999; Joiner, 1997; and Paoli Railroad Yard PCB Litigation [Paoli], 1994) clearly suggest that the criteria for deciding on the admissibility of testimony comes with latitude (discretion) on the part of the gatekeeper with *leeway** to include other criteria which *may** be more appropriate to the facts of the case (as cited in Field, 2006). To assert that the four Daubert criteria should be the standard for all testimony is over-reaching and not supported by the Daubert and Kumho courts, or rulings from the lower courts.

The Federal Rules of Evidence: The Federal Rules of Evidence (FRE), and especially FRE 702 (see below), are the prevailing procedural and judicial guidelines for admissible testimony. In fact, the Daubert ruling was predicated largely on the FRE 702 underpinning (Daubert, 1993; also see Countiss & Deutsch, 2002).

> *If scientific, technical, or other specialized knowledge will assist the trier of fact to understand the evidence or to determine a fact in issue, a witness qualified as an expert by knowledge, skill, experience, training, or education, may testify thereto in the form of an opinion or otherwise, if (1) the testimony is based upon sufficient facts or data, (2) the testimony is the product of reliable principles and methods, and (3) the witness has applied the principles and methods reliably to the facts of the case.*

FRE 702 (as cited in Weed & Johnson, 2006) identifies both "scientific" and "specialized and technological" knowledge as if to suggest that these two entities are different. Daubert (1993), and the four-point criteria, relates directly to "science" testimony and the scientific method. "Specialized and technical" as discussed in Kumho (1999) knowledge relates more to the social sciences which are not always subject to scientific inquiry. (For a more expansive discussion of FRE 702 and how it applies to the work of the rehabilitation consultant, see Field, 2011).

Some issues can be decided by good judgment and simple common sense (Ireland, 2009, p. 120). For example, to apply the Daubert criterion of the estimation of error rate to a life care plan makes no sense at all. An estimate of standard error is a "measure of the variability of a sampling distribution" of a previous statistic, i.e. the distribution of mean scores" (Downie & Heath, 1970, p. 160). As such, there is not much in the world of the social sciences, and rehabilitation planning, in particular, that lends itself to strict scientific statistical measures. That is, through simply good judgment and common sense some issues can be addressed by way of the specialized knowledge that professionals in the rehabilitation arena possess from education, training, certifications and other professional means (Countiss & Deutsch, 2002). This specialized knowledge it utilized in opinions and recommendations based on clinical judgment as defined and generally accepted in the field (Choppa et al., 2004).

A review of subsequent rulings in the lower courts involving expert testimony from vocational rehabilitation consultants and life care planners (Field & Choppa, 2005; Weed & Johnson, 2006) clearly indicate that the four Daubert factors do not always strictly apply to the facts of the case. In fact, there is only one case (*Kinnaman v. Ford Motor Company*, 2000) the authors found in which a judge dismissed a case outright based on the Daubert factors. One issue for the Kinnaman case was that the vocational expert utilized an Internet based computer program as a foundation for her vocational opinion. The court determined that her testimony did not include "corroborating evidence that the methodology…is acceptable, had been tested and is generally accurate…and that it is used by other persons in her discipline…" (as cited in Field & Choppa, 2005, p. 13). Since similar cases have been allowed by courts in various jurisdictions (Field & Choppa), it appears that the expert may have erred by not explaining, or being able to explain, the methodology on which the computer program was based.

Staller (2002) and Countiss and Deutsch (2002) have suggested that the two Daubert criteria that reasonably relate to the social sciences are peer review and general acceptance. Furthermore, Bernstein (1998) acknowledged that the application of the four Daubert factors to non-scientific testimony would mean excluding all non-scientific testimony.

Finally, working with people, and especially people with disabilities, results in an individual work product (Choppa & Johnson, 2008). For example, it is clear and obvious that not all people with a traumatic brain injury should be treated the same. Due to the individual's unique characteristics rehabilitation plans will reflect opinions and recommendations that are relevant only to that individual (Ripley & Weed, 2010). However, the methodology for the process of determining needs could be the same for clients with substantially varying disability related differences (Countiss & Deutsch, 2002; Weed, 2010). There are several publications recounted in the Countiss and Deutsch article that provide the foundation for the value of credentials, specialized knowledge, expertise and utilization of an established methodology in developing life care plans. For example, one of the first studies of the reliability of life care planning methodology by Sutton, Deutsch, Weed, and Berens (2002) demonstrated that no significant difference was found between original life care plans and updated life care plans in two professionals' caseloads representing a wide varieties of disabilities, ages and gender. The consistent factor was that both caseloads utilized the published life care planning methodology.

There are so many individual factors (Field, 2008) such as age, gender, educational background, work experience, wage earning capacity (Dorney, 2008), and the severity of the person's disability, to name just a few. At the same time, the professional associations in the field of rehabilitation and life care planning have delineated the various competencies, procedures, methodology, standards and ethical components of a responsible rehabilitation practice with an emphasis on individual planning (Field et al., 2009). Over-reliance on large sets of survey data, or placing people into categories of disability groups, such as "severe disability" or "not severe disability", fails to reasonably account for individual differences of a person's capacity to work and earn money. That is, (example of flawed rationale) the client is considered severely disabled, therefore there is no need to evaluate the client because one only needs to know the data associated with people who are also severely disabled and those data supply the answer.

Daubert, Frye, or State Guidelines for Admissibility: The FRE 702 is the prevailing rule whether a case in being adjudicated in a "Daubert" court, and a "Frye" court, or a court governed by State rules. An excellent source of information (Table 12.1) on this issue is the court cases identifying the rule on a state-by-state survey – a chart displaying which states are governed by the Daubert or Frye standards (Sutherland, 2009). For example, for admissibility, Connecticut relies on Daubert (not Frye), Colorado relies on FRE 702, Indiana has noted that "Daubert is proper, but the judge is not bound by them," Mississippi and Ohio applies Daubert, while some states abide largely by their own rules (Kansas, Nevada, & Wisconsin). For a quick summary on a state-by-state basis, see Table 12.2. It should be apparent that Daubert applies to federal cases as modified by Kumho Tire (more latitude in admissibility). Also, in state courts, the admissibility is roughly divided between Daubert and Frye on issues of admissibility.

Table 12.1
A Fifty State Survey Concerning the Admissibility of Expert Testimony

With its opinion in *Daubert v. Merrell Dow Pharmaceuticals, Inc.*, 509 U.S. 579 (1993), the United States Supreme Court sought to provide guidance to trial judges with respect to whether and under what circumstances scientific evidence should be deemed admissible. In the fifteen years since *Daubert*, state court judges have issued numerous opinions concerning *Daubert* and its progeny, but one thing remains clear: There is no uniformity among the states or even within states. As one North Dakota judge noted in a concurring opinion, local lawyers are "adrift" among the many different amalgamations of admissibility standards. Some states, such as Tennessee, have held that the standard for admissibility is more strict than that set out in *Daubert*, while others, like Wisconsin, have adhered to a much less restrictive standard. Some apply one standard to criminal cases and another to civil cases, as in New Jersey, while still other states (Illinois and Kansas, for example) do not apply any standard at all when the "expert" testifying is the treating physician — even if the witness is testifying as to causation. At least one state, Oregon, holds that any *Daubert* type challenge is waived if not preserved during the expert's deposition. The following survey provides an overview of the standards adopted by each of the states concerning the admissibility of expert testimony.

Alabama: *Slay v. Keller Indus.*, Inc., 823 So. 2d 623 (Ala. 2001). Applying *Frye*; refusing to adopt *Daubert*.

Alaska: *Alaska v. Coon*, 974 P.2d 386 (Alaska 1999). *Adopting Daubert but see Macron v. Stromata*, 123 P.3d 992 (Alaska 2005). Rejecting the application of *Daubert* to non-scientific expert testimony; explicit rejection of *Kumho Tire*.

Arizona: *Logerquist v. McVey*, 1 P.3d 113 (Ariz. 2000). Rejecting *Daubert* and *Kumho Tire* as placing the judge in a position of ruling on weight or credibility as opposed to admissibility; retaining *Frye* and Rule 702 alone.

Arkansas: *Farm Bureau Mut. Ins. Co. of Ark., Inc., v. Foote*, 14 S.W. 3d 512 (Ark. 2000). Adopting Daubert.

California: *People v. Leahy*, 882 P.2d 321 (Cal. 1994). Refusing *Daubert* and retaining the *Kelly-Frye* test — *People v. Kelly*, 549 P.2d 1240 (Cal. 1976).

Colorado: *People v. Shreck*, 22 P.3d 68 (Colo. 2001). Noting the judge may consider Daubert, but must issue specific findings on the record as to the helpfulness and reliability factors. CRE 702/evidence rule is the appropriate admissibility standard, not *Frye*.

Connecticut: *State v. Porter*, 241 Conn. 57 (Conn. 1997). Adopting *Daubert* in lieu of *Frye*.

Delaware: *M.G. Bancorporation, Inc.,* v. Le Beau, 737 A.2d 513 (Del. 1999). Adopting the analysis of *Daubert* and *Kumho Tire.*

Florida: *Marsh v. Valyou,* 977 So. 2d 543 (Fla. 2007). Adhering to the *Frye* test, but only where the expert opinion is based on new or novel scientific techniques; noting most expert opinion testimony is not subject to Frye, such as an opinion based only on the expert's experience and training.

Georgia: *Spacht v. Troyer,* 655 S.E. 2d 656 (Ga. App. 2007). Holding that the relevant statute, OCGA § 24-9-67.1, governs expert testimony; subsection (f) allows consideration of *Daubert.*

Hawaii: *State v. Vliet,* 19 P.3d 42 (Hi. 2001). Noting that the touchstones of admissibility for expert testimony are the relevance and reliability factors under Rule 702.

Idaho: *State v. Merwin,* 962 P.2d 1026 (Id. 1998). Noting that Idaho has not expressly adopted *Daubert,* but applying its factors. See also Weeks v. Eastern Idaho Health Servs., 153 P.3d 1180 (Id. 2007). Holding that *Daubert* has not been adopted, but the judge may consider certain factors such as whether the expert's theory has been or may be tested and whether the theory has been subjected to a peer reviewed publication; declining to consider whether the theory is commonly agreed upon or has been generally accepted in the relevant scientific community.

Illinois: *Warstalski v. JSB Const. & Consulting Co.,* 892 N.E. 2d 122 (Ill. App. 2008). Holding that *Frye* applies generally, but it does not apply to medical testimony; noting a treating physician's testimony as to causation is not subject to *Frye.*

Indiana: *Kempf Contracting & Design, Inc., v. Holland-Tucker,* 892 N.E. 2d 672 (Ind. App. 2008). Noting that consideration of the *Daubert* factors is proper, but the judge is not bound by them.

Iowa: *State v. Garcia-Miranda,* 735 N.W. 2d 203 (Iowa App. 2007). Noting that Iowa courts are not required to follow *Daubert* when applying the Iowa Rules of Evidence; judges are encouraged to use *Daubert* only when the expert evidence is novel or complex.

Kansas: *State v. McHenry,* 136 P.3d 964 (Kan. App. 2006). Noting that *Frye* is to be used only when the judge considers the admissibility of opinions based on new or experimental scientific techniques. See also *Kuhn v. Sandoz Pharmaceuticals Corp.,* 14 P.3d 1170 (Kan. 2000). Holding that the *Frye* test is not applicable to an expert's "pure opinion" based on that expert's own experience, research, observation.

Kentucky: *Burton v. CSX Transp., Inc.,* 2008 WL 4691059 (Ky. 2008). Holding that *Daubert* applies under the relevant Kentucky Rule of Evidence that is similar to FRE 702.

Louisiana: *Cheairs v. State Dept. of Trans. & Development,* 861 So. 2d 536, 542 (La. 2003). Noting that the standards set forth in *Daubert* are controlling.

Maine: *Hall v. Kurz Enterprises,* 2006 WL 1669656 (Me. Super. 2006). Noting that the controlling law is embodied in *State v. Williams,* 388 A.2d 500 (Me. 1978), and is relatively indistinguishable from *Daubert.* See *Searles v. Fleetwood Homes of Penn., Inc.,* 878 A.2d 509 (Me. 2005). Noting the same, but specifically declining to adopt *Daubert.*

Maryland: *State v. Baby,* 946 A.2d 463 (Md. 2008). Holding that the admissibility of expert testimony is subject to the application of the *Frye-Reed* test for general acceptance in scientific community. *See Reed v. State,* 391 A.2d 364 (1978).

Massachusetts: *Com v. Powell,* 877 N.E. 2d 589 (Mass. 2007). Noting *Daubert* is adopted, but that a showing of general acceptance in relevant community is sufficient for admissibility regardless of any other *Daubert* factors.

Michigan: *People v. Unger,* 749 N.W. 2d 272 (Mich. App. 2008). Noting that Michigan evidentiary law incorporates *Daubert.*

Minnesota: *State v. Bartylla,* 755 N.W.2d 8 (Minn. 2008). Using the *Frye-Mack* standard of general acceptance for admissibility of novel or emerging scientific evidence, but specifying that the expert's technique must be based on a foundation that is scientifically reliable. *State v. Mack,* 292 N.W. 2d 764 (Minn. 1980).

Mississippi: *Watts v. Radiator Specialty Co.,* 990 So. 2d 143 (Miss. 2005). Applying *Daubert.*

Missouri: *State v. Daniels*, 179 S.W. 3d 273 (Mo. App. 2005). Noting that the criminal courts still follow *Frye*. See *Hawthorne v. Lester E. Cox Medical Centers*, 165 S.W. 3d 587 (Mo. App. 2005). Noting that admissibility of expert opinions in civil cases is governed by statute, § 490.065.

Montana: State v. Price, 171 P. 3d 293 (Mont. 2007). Applying Daubert, but noting that its application is proper only where introduction of novel scientific evidence is sought.

Nebraska: *State v. Schereiner*, 754 N.W. 2d 742 (Neb. 2008). Applying *Daubert* and noting that the trial court acts as a gatekeeper. *See Schafersman v. Agland Coop.*, 631 N.W. 2d 862 (Neb. **2001).**

Nevada: *Hallman v. Eldridge*, 189 P.3d 646 (Nev. 2008). Noting that the statute that governs admissibility is NRS 50.275, which tracks FRE 702; holding Nevada has not adopted *Daubert* yet and wide discretion is vested in the trial court.

New Hampshire: *Baxter v. Temple*, 949 A.2d 167 (N.H. 2008). Holding that *Daubert* applies and that its factors have been incorporated into statute, RSA 516:29-a.

New Jersey: *State v. Groen*, 2008 WL 3067920 (N.J. Super. 2008). Limiting the application of *Frye* to criminal matters. *See Thornton v. Camden County Prosecutor's Office*, 2006 WL 2361816 (N.J. Super 2006). Applying *Daubert* in civil cases.

New Mexico: *State v. Downey*, 2008 WL 4925022 (N.M. 2008). Noting that *Daubert* applies. *See State v. Albesico*, 861 P.2d 192 (N.M. 1993).

New York: *O'Brien v. Citizens, Ins. Co.*, 2008 WL 4754103 (N.Y. Sup. 2008). Holding that *Frye* applies to novel scientific theories or techniques.

North Carolina: *Howerton v. Arai Helmet, Ltd.*, 597 S.E. 2d 674 (N.C. 2004). Holding that North Carolina does not adhere to the *Daubert* standard, but trial judge must instead ask three questions: 1) Is the expert's method of proof sufficiently reliable; 2) Is the witness qualified; and 3) Is the testimony relevant?

North Dakota: *State v. Hernandez*, 707 N.W. 2d 449 (N.D. 2005). Noting that North Dakota never has explicitly adopted *Daubert* or *Kumho Tire*; expert admissibility instead is governed by North Dakota Rule of Evidence 702. The concurrence notes that the state's Rule 702 is identical to FRE 702 and that the Bar is "adrift" between *Frye*, *Daubert*, and 702.

Ohio: *Miller v. Bike Athletic Co.*, 687 N.E. 2d 735 (Oh. 1998). Adopting *Daubert*.

Oklahoma: *Christian v. Gray*, 65 P.3d 591 (Okla. 2003). Holding that *Daubert* applies to civil matters and to all expert testimony, — not just scientific or technical evidence. *See Taylor v. State*, 889 P.2d 319 (Okla. Crim. App. 1995). Adopting *Daubert*.

Oregon: *Evers v. Roder*, 103 P.3d 680 (Or. App. 2004). Noting that *Daubert* applies, but that any *Daubert* challenge to the expert opinion will be waived if it is not raised during the expert's deposition.

Pennsylvania: *Betz v. Eriee, Ins. Exchange*, 957 A.2d 1244 (Pa. Super 2008). Holding that *Frye* applies only when a party seeks to introduce novel scientific evidence; it is not implicated every time science comes into courtroom. *Com v. Puksar*, 951 A.2d 267 (Pa. 2008).

Rhode Island: DePetrillo v. Dow Chemical Co., 729 A.2d 677, 686 (R.I. 1999). Noting courts may draw guidance from Daubert with respect to the admissibility of all expert testimony even though Daubert has not been expressly adopted.

South Carolina: *State v. Council*, 515 S.E.2d 508 (S.C. 1999). Noting that South Carolina has not adopted *Daubert*, but that the state's evidentiary rule is identical to FRE 702 and sets a "very similar" standard.

South Dakota: *Kostel v. Schwartz*, 756 N.W.2d 363 (S.D. 2008). Adopting the *Daubert* standard.

Tennessee: *McDaniel v. CSX Transp., Inc.*, 955 S.W.2d 257 (Tenn. 1997). Adopting factors similar to *Daubert*, but noting that the primary inquiry is whether an expert's opinion testimony will substantially assist the trier of fact and that this inquiry is somewhat stricter than the federal rule. The *Daubert* factors are useful, but Tennessee rules require that courts take a more active role when evaluating expert evidence.

Texas: *Bechtel Corp. v. Citgo Products Pipeline Co.*, 2008 WL 4482688 (Tex. App. 2008). Applying *Daubert* factors. *See E. I. du Pont de Nemours and Co. v. Robinson*, 923 S.W.2d 549 (Tex. 1995). Finding *Daubert* persuasive.

Utah: *Haupt v. Heaps*, 131 P.3d 252 (Utah App. 2005). Noting that the state's Rule 702 applies to the admissibility question unless the expert testimony is novel and scientific. When the testimony concerns novel scientific methods or techniques, then *State v. Rinmasch*, 775 P.2d 388 (Utah 1989), requires a finding of inherent reliability prior to admissibility.

Vermont: *In re Appeal of Jam Golf*, LLC, 2008 WL 3877119 (Vt. 2008). Holding that *Daubert* applies.

Virginia: *Hasson v. Commonwealth*, 2006 WL 1387974 (Va. App. 2006). Noting that Virginia has not adopted *Frye* or *Daubert*, but that the *Daubert* factors are instructive.

Washington: *Lewis v. Simpson Timber Co.*, 2008 WL 1952125 (Wash. App. 2008). Holding that the Frye test is utilized for novel scientific evidence. *See State v. Gregory*, 147 P.3d 1201 (Wash. 2006).

West Virginia: *San Francisco v. Wendy's International, Inc.*, 656 S.E. 2d 485 (W.Va. 2007). Noting that *Daubert* applies, but that when a judge excludes an expert as unreliable under *Daubert*, that decision is reviewed de novo. *See also Witt v. Burackes*, 443 S.E. 2d 196 (W.V. 1993).

Wisconsin: *State v. Swope*, 2008 WL 4923663 (Wis. App. 2008). Noting that Wisconsin employs a much less restrictive "relevancy test" for the admissibility of expert testimony — not *Frye* or *Daubert*.

Wyoming: *Dean v. State*, 194 P.3d 299 (Wyo. 2008). Noting that *Daubert* and its progeny had been adopted in *Bunting v. Jamison*, 984 P.2d 467 (Wyo. 1999).

Table 12.2
A State-by-State Summary on Applying Daubert, Frye, or State Rules

State	Governing Rule	Comment
Alabama	Frye	Refusing to Adopt Daubert
Alaska	Daubert	Rejecting Daubert in non-science cases
Arizona	Frye/702	Rejecting Daubert
Arkansas	Daubert	
California	Kelly/Frye	Refusing Daubert
Colorado	CRE 702	May consider Daubert
Connecticut	Daubert	
Delaware	Daubert	
Florida	Frye	Based of scientific; most opinion based on expert's experience and training.
Georgia	State rules	Allows consideration of Daubert
Hawaii	702	
Idaho	State rules	Daubert factors of testing and peer review; not including general acceptance
Illinois	Frye	But not to medical testimony
Indiana	Daubert	But not bound by factors.
Iowa	State rules	Not required to follow Daubert
Kansas opinion	Frye	Applies to science; not does apply to expert's pure
Kentucky	Daubert	Similar to 792
Louisiana	Daubert	Controlling

Maine	State rules	Daubert/Not Daubert
Maryland	Frye	
Massachusetts	Daubert	Emphasis on general acceptance
Michigan	Daubert	
Minnesota	Frye	Foundation must be reliable
Missouri	Frye	Governed by State statute
Montana	Daubert	Applies to novel scientific evidence
Nebraska	Daubert	Trial court is gatekeeper
New Hampshire	Daubert	Incorporated into State statute
New Jersey	Frye/Daubert	Frye in criminal; Daubert in civil
New Mexico	Daubert	
New York	Frye	
North Carolina	Neither	Three questions: reliable, qualified, relevant
North Dakota	ND 702	Bar is adrift between Frye, Daubert and 702
Ohio	Daubert	
Oklahoma	Daubert	Applies to all testimony - scientific and technical
Oregon	Daubert	But will be waived if not raised during deposition
Pennsylvania	Frye	For novel scientific evidence
Rhode Island	Daubert	Not expressly adopted but applies to all testimony
South Carolina	State	Identical to FRE 702
Tennessee	State	Similar to Daubert rules, but court take a more active role in considering factors for admissibility
Texas	Daubert	
Utah	State 702	Emphasis on reliability
Vermont	Daubert	
Virginia	Neither	But Daubert factors are instructive
Washington	Frye	
West Virginia	Daubert	
Wisconsin	Neither	A much less restrictive "relevancy test"
Wyoming	Daubert	

Appreciation is acknowledged for permission to include the information in Table 1 (exact content) and Table 2 (summary of content) by Ms. Kari Sutherland. Reprinted with permission from *ProTe: Solutio, 2*(10), 2009, pp. 14-15. Summarized from Sutherland (2009).

A Review of Relevant Cases

Since Daubert, thousands of cases have been adjudicated that have included issues related to admissibility of expert testimony, many cases have been challenged from all areas of subjects and content, including the social sciences. A documented case in the field of rehabilitation consulting describes a typical process of an *in limine* Daubert challenge (Choppa, Field, & Johnson, 2005). A review of some earlier cases has be completed and presented in earlier publications (Field & Choppa, 2005; Field 2006; Field et al., 2006).

The following is a review and summary of selected cases that have been published by either a federal or state court. Not all cases reviewed involve the work of a rehabilitation consultant, but issues are identified that are potentially germane to the rehabilitation profession. Keep in mind while reviewing these few cases that the Daubert, or Frye, or State rules will differ; take a look (Tables 11.1 or 11.2) as to which rules may apply in each case. Cases are discussed by a topical area.

"Judgment Call"

Sometimes one hears of an expert relying on their experience and training (as suggested by the Florida Rules) as the basis for their opinion. In *Garland v. Rossknecht* (2001), an economist (not a rehabilitation consultant) presented testimony on reduced earning capacity. Garland, the plaintiff, was injured in an automobile accident resulting in a neck injury with persistent headaches. Garland's chiropractor concluded that Garland suffered a seven percent loss of whole body functioning. The economist concluded that Garland had a "ten percent disability or earning capacity reduction." The opinion was based "solely on information conveyed from Garland" (there was no VE involved in the case); When pressed on how he arrived at his opinion, the economists stated, "it was a judgment call." While the economist admitted that he had no expertise in "converting impairment ratings into physical vocational limitations," the Circuit Court "nevertheless allowed [economist] to testify without limitation." It was interesting to note that the economist did concede that "a vocational expert has competence that I do not have to take physical limitations and translate them into vocational limitations."

The South Dakota Supreme Court reversed in part and remanded for a new trial based on the conclusion that the Circuit Court abused its discretion in allowing the economist's opinion on Garland's percentage of disability. The Circuit Court noted that the objections by the defense regarding the economist's opinion which went to the credibility of the testimony, not admissibility, a decision that the court ruled that the jury could decide the credibility issue. The Supreme Court's rationale included this assessment: "when dealing with expert opinion, the court must fulfill a gate keeping function, ensuring that the opinion meets the prerequisites of relevance and reliability before admission." With respect to the "judgment call" issue, the court addressed this directly by dealing with the gatekeeper function of admissibility, and did not necessarily rule that the expert's judgment and opinion was wrong. Rather, the expert was testifying outside his area of expertise and with no foundation (a VE's analysis on vocational functioning).

The issues in this case are: proper expertise and foundation information; abuse of discretion (*General Electric v. Joiner*); and "judgment call."

Expert Bias

Expert bias has everything to do with the impartial and objective opinion of the expert. The *Federal Rules of Civil Procedure* (Rule 26.a.2.B) states:

> *(B) Except as otherwise stipulated or directed by the court, this disclosure shall, with respect to a witness who is retained or specially employed to provide expert testimony in the case or whose duties as an employee of the party regularly involve giving expert testimony, be accompanied by a written report prepared and signed by the witness. The report shall contain a complete statement of all opinions to be expressed and the basis and reasons therefore; the data or other information considered by the witness in forming the opinions; any exhibits to be used as a summary of or support for the opinions; the qualifications of the witness, including a list of all publications authored by the witness within the preceding ten years; the compensation to be paid for the study and testimony; and a listing of any other cases in which the witness has testified as an expert at trial or by deposition within the preceding four years.*

Several citations (noted above) address the issue of expert bias. In *Lichtor v. Clark*, discovery was directed at the issue of an expert deriving a large portion of his income from a particular party or referral source. The court had the discretion to allow testimony as to the annual amount the expert derived from testimony activities and the amount received, and can be viewed as going to the credibility of the expert.

In *Buck v. Chin* (a Florida District Court of Appeal case), under Florida Rules the discovery of an expert witness at trial may include:

1. *The scope of employment in the pending case and the compensation for such service.*

2. *The expert's general litigation experience, including the percentage of work performed for plaintiffs and defendants.*

3.   *The identity of other cases within a reasonable period of time in which the expert has testified by deposition or trial.*

4.   *An approximation of the portion of the expert's involvement as an expert witness, which may be based on the number of hours, percentage of hours, or percentage of earned income derived from serving as an expert witness.*

In this case, the expert, a physician, derived about two-thirds of his practice from one liability insurer, and over one million dollars from a single defense source. The court observed that "this fact alone should be sufficient to allow the plaintiff to argue that [expert] might be more likely to testify favorably on behalf of one side rather than the other." A similar case (*Elkins v. Syken,* 1996) discusses in more detail the elements of the examination of expert who appear to testify with bias. In *B.F. Specialty v. Charles M. Shedd,* the WV Appeals Court noted that "a trial judge has broad discretion in the control and management of discovery . . . And that an abuse of discretion [occurs] when its ruling on discovery motions are clearly against the logic of the circumstances then before the court, and are so arbitrary and unreasonable as to shock our sense of justice and to indicate a lack of careful consideration." Finally, in *Trower v. Jones,* The Supreme Court of Illinois held that

(1) it was proper to inquire how much plaintiff's medical expert witness was earning annually from services related to rendering expert testimony, and it was proper to inquire into such income for the two years immediately preceding trials, and (2) inquiry into the frequency with which Plaintiff's medical expert witness testified for plaintiffs was permissible.

In *Noffke v. Perez,* the plaintiff's expert was requested to turn over personal income tax records in order to explore the possibility of a bias on the part of the expert. The Supreme Court of Alaska ruled that the lower court did not abuse its discretion in ordering the records, especially since the disclosure would not be public, but within the confidentially of the court. The plaintiff was fined $900.00 by the lower court for failing to turn over the tax records in a timely manner; the higher court did not reverse this ruling as the ruling was also within the discretion of the court.

For the vocational expert, these rulings should bring some awareness of the need to balance one's practice between plaintiff and defense work which should alleviate any concern regarding the amount of income and primary source of consulting referrals.

Scope of VE Practice

In *Smith & Smith v. M.V. Woods Construction,* the vocational expert was not qualified to offer opinions in areas in which he testified. The court set aside "the verdict with respect to damages for past and future loss of earnings, past and future loss of household services, and future medical expenses" for the plaintiff who sustained a back injury while tossing concrete blocks at a construction site. The court ruled that the lower court "abused its discretion in allowing plaintiff's expert to testify concerning those elements of damages. "Nothing in the record suggest that [VE's] area of expertise includes assessing the damages", and resulted "in a lack of proper foundation for the expert's opinion." The Court quoted from *Daum v. Auburn Memorial. Hospital* that "an expert witness must possess the requisite skill, training, knowledge and experience to ensure that an opinion rendered is reliable."

The vocational expert needs to understand the parameters of his or her areas of expertise and be careful to offer testimony only in those areas. Even if an attorney requests an opinion outside of one's perceived area of expertise, one should proceed with due caution.

Admissibility of Testimony Under Daubert

Reference again to Table 12.2 will clearly indicate that this world of presenting expert testimony is not governed exclusively by the Daubert ruling; approximately one half of the states are governed by Frye, their respective state rules, and some combination of all three. This is made very clear in *Epp v. Lauby* (a Nebraska state leaning toward Daubert) where the court observed: "So long as the expert's opinion is based on reliable methodology, his or her opinion is admissible, whether or not the court agrees with the expert's opinion." The court added that "the Daubert test does not stand for the proposition that scientific knowledge must be absolute or irrefutable. It would be reasonable to conclude that the subject of scientific testimony must be known to a certainty; arguably, there are no certainties in science."

Loss of Labor Market Access *equals* Loss of Earning Capacity?

In *Eastman v. The Stanley Works et al.* The vocational expert testified that the "appellee's injury renders him incapable of performing 80 to 85 percent of jobs for which he was qualified prior to his injury." The issue has to do with the expert failing to indicate whether or not the lost access to jobs would pay the say or more of the job currently held. The court observed that "only if the loss of those job opportunities quantifiably reduced the amount which (appellee) was capable of earning before his injury will he have proven with reasonable certainty that he has suffered future economic loss." Testimony was disallowed.

Earnings Capacity v. Actual Earnings

In *Boland-Maloney Lumber Company v. Burnett & Burnett*, an economic expert's testimony was challenged by the plaintiff because the expert failed to use the plaintiff's actual career at the time of injury to calculate a loss of earning capacity, but instead used a "proxy,' such as the titles of construction supervisor and construction manager. The expert, who had worked in the field of vocational counseling and rehabilitation since 1965, "based his testimony on the interview with the plaintiff, information on the [plaintiff's] employment and work history, and upon the nature of the [plaintiff's] injuries." The expert argued that the worker's actual earnings were not indicative of the worker's earning power. The court ruled:

> *Although [expert's] testimony was not based on [plaintiff's] actual earnings at the time of injury, nothing precludes testimony by a vocational expert on the impairment of a plaintiff's power to earn money, or the use of a 'proxy' to do so where current earnings are not indicative of the plaintiff's earning power. The trial court did not abuse its discretion.*

This case is important because it allows for the correct and creative approach to assessing vocational capacity and not just mere performance, i.e., a person not performing to their level of capacity.

A Restitution Case

In *United States of America v. Pearson*, the defendant was found guilty of crimes against two persons, and further agreed to pay restitution of $100,000.00 to the government to be divided equally between the two victims. A vocational expert, for the plaintiff, evaluated the two victims and determined that each victim should receive $912,976.00 for the estimated future costs of medical care, treatment and services. The appeals court disallowed the expert's recommendation of $912,976 and remanded the case for a more precise explanation of the estimation of future medical costs for the victims. The court also observed that the victims had "some problems before and that it was difficult to quantify or pinpoint the etiology of the victims' mental health issues that required on-going treatment." In other words, pre-existing conditions may have been present with the victims of the crime.

An Attorney in the Room

Selve Muse-Freeman v. Imran Bhatti involved the issue of a life care planner for the defense who objected to the presence of the plaintiff's attorney being present during her interview and evaluation. The court ruled that, pursuant to Federal Rule of Civil Procedure 26(c)(1)(E), that the life care planner could complete the evaluation without the presence of the plaintiff's attorney. The Rule reads:

> *A court may, for good cause, issue an order to protect a party or person from annoyance, embarrassment, oppression or undue burden or expense, including one or more of the following . . . . (E) designating the persons who may be present while the discovery is conducted.*

This case was published in the *Journal of Life Care Planning* (2009), along with a comment by the expert (Koslow, 2009).

Last Minute Research

In *Stevens v. Bangor and Aroostook Railroad Company*, a vocational expert was allowed to testify after being challenged for a lack of factual basis of her testimony. The court ruled that a trial court "has wide discretion in determining the admissibility of expert testimony." The VE's "vocational report was based on her review of the plaintiff's medical records and prior work experience, a meeting with the plaintiff during which they discussed his skills and relied upon [methods] typically used by persons in her field." Regarding the last minute research and a lack of notice to the railroad, the court ruled that this was "a management issue at the discretion of the trial court." The trial court offered to instruct the jury to ignore any information the expert acquired after discovery, but the defense didn't take the court up on the offer. There was no abuse of discretion.

As a note of caution, experts need to be cautious when asked to include "after discovery" information; generally this is not allowable unless agreed to by all parties (plaintiff, defense, and the court).

ADA on a Case-by-Case Basis

PGA Tour, Inc. v. Casey Martin (2001), while not directly a vocational issue or involving a vocational expert, the case is instructive about the proper application of disability legislation - the *American with Disability Act* (ADA). Casey was born with a degenerative circulatory disorder (Klippel-Trenauney-Weber syndrome) which obstructs the blood flow to his legs. From being a teammate of Woods at Stanford University to moving to the PGA Tour, Casey's right leg became progressively worse with severe pain and fatigue. There was also the potential of hemorrhaging, blood clots and eventual amputation. Casey petitioned the PGA for a use of a cart so that he could continue playing; the issue, according to the PGA, was that a cart would appreciably change the nature of the competition. "The Court ruled that the PGA Tour was a place of public accommodation under the ADA, and that providing a cart would not fundamentally alter the nature of the event because the fundamental nature of golf is shot-making" (Goren, 2002). This case illustrates a different, but important, case that could have drawn upon the knowledge and skills of a rehabilitation consultant.

A Life Care Plan (Damages for the Non-Injured)

Osorio, St of NY Workers'Comp Bd is case involving a vocational expert in a very unusual manner. Jane Doe, who worked in the World Trade Center (Tower 1) on the 83rd floor; Jane Doe died on 9/11/2001. The interesting aspect of this case involved a child (John), age 10 who was a member of the family that was largely supported by the income generated by his half-sister, Jane Doe. John had significantly donated to the personal care and emotional support of Jane who possessed issues related to autism. The VE crafted a life care plan for John which became part of the case development that was eventually presented to the NY WC Board. Long term support was provided for John.

Expert Cannot Cite a Source

Ollis v. Knecht involved the testimony of an expert on the issue of loss of income of a person who had died in an automobile accident. The primary issue was the abuse of discretion by the trial court for denying the opportunity of the expert to testify. The expert was unable to provide a citation of a resource that was mentioned as the basis of his rationale – a "mirror image approach." The [expert] "did not provide any citation to authority to support his assertion that the mirror image approach is generally accepted . . . the trial court judge did not have to believe [expert's] bald assertion." The trial court did not abuse its discretion.

Learned Treatises

In *Crane v. Newt Wakeman, M.D.*, Inc. the court ruled that for a learned treatise "to be authoritative, there must be some evidence of general acceptance and accreditation of the text or treatise within the profession. This can be established by the expert himself, the testimony of other experts in the field, or judicial notice." However, "mere familiarity of a witness with a publication or periodical does not render it authoritative (*Grippe v. Momtazee*, 1986). Using or relying on "learned treatises" by an expert can open a can of worms during cross-examination. First, for a resource or text to be considered "authoritative" by other experts in the field, or to be generally accepted, is no simple task. Nothing in the rehabilitation literature to date has addressed this issue. Secondly, it may be more reasonable for an expert to talk about resources that are "highly regarded" or "generally accepted" rather than be referred to as "authoritative.

No Specific Facts

In *Doren v. Battle Creek Health System*, the vocational expert stated that the plaintiff's "physical impairments preclude her from engaging in most of the jobs in the local and national economy as a registered nurse" indicating that she had a physical impairment that substantially limited one of her major life activities, including her usual occupation. The court ruled that the VE failed to provide enough specific facts and the testimony was disallowed. *Federal Rule of Civil Procedure* 56(e) states that "a party must offer specific facts showing that there is a genuine issue at trial.

Relevant Case Studies

The following four cases represent examples of actual court decisions which are relevant to the above topic. The first three court decisions allow testimony and the fourth represents a situation where the expert was well qualified based on credentials, but the expected testimony was deemed unreliable and the person was excluded from testifying. The fifth case represents an attempt by an expert to offer his opinion based on a "hybrid" of two well known methodologies, but resulted in an appeal and remand for new trial on damages. Perhaps of special interest is case #3, Hanford Nuclear Reservation, where extensive transcripts and information has been published (see below for more information). The expert overcame objections because he was able to substantiate his opinions based on, experience, education, special skills and reliance on standards and methodologies generally accepted by other practicing professionals in the field of rehabilitation consulting.

Case #1: Testimony allowed although expert's credibility and plan foundation was successfully questioned and case remanded for new trial.

Francis Adeola and grace Adeola, individually and for the use and benefit of their minor child, Fadeka Joyce Adeola v. Dr. Shawn M. Kemmerly, Dr. Michael A. Frierson, Dr. Niels J. Linschoten and Ochsner Clinic State of Louisiana Court of Appeals, First Circuit 2001 CA 1231 (Judgment Rendered: June 21, 2002)

The first case (*Adeola et al., v. Dr. Shawn M. Kemmerly*) involves a plaintiff who was a young child who had routine blood work as a part of a well baby check-up. The stick site became infected, but initially was diagnosed as a sprained wrist. By the time that the correct diagnosis was made, the infection had become quite serious with bone infection, compounded by other complications, "resulting in a weaker, shorter, severely scarred arm, in addition to permanent limitations on her activities and movements" (p. 3).

The appealing party, Louisiana Patient's Compensation Fund (LPCF), argued that an exorbitant award for damages was reached by the jury after a judge purportedly improperly allowed testimony without proper cross-examination of the expert's credentials in front of the jury "...thereby preventing the jury from having a basis for evaluating credibility . . . ." (p. 2).

At trial, the defendant requested, and the trial court granted, a Daubert/Foret hearing of the life care planning expert outside of the jury's presence. After the hearing, but before the jury returned to the courtroom, the judge commented that he thought the proffered professional was "eminently qualified as a life care planner and rehabilitation expert" p. 4). Citing Rule 702, the judge decided that the jury would benefit from hearing his testimony. However, when court resumed with the jury present, when the defendant counsel attempted to conduct voir dire, he was told by the judge that qualifications were already covered in the hearing. As an apparent way to shorten the process, the judge instructed the jury as follows, "As previously indicated, the court has instructed you as to testimony of expert witnesses because even though the court finds one to be an expert, the weight to be given is decided by you" (p. 5) and instructed the attorney not to question the expert about his background or credentials.

The defendant's attorney argued that he should have been allowed to conduct voir dire in front of the jury since it could affect the jury's view of the expert's credibility. In agreement, the appeals court commented, "Without a full cross examination of [the expert's] background, qualifications and credentials, the jury could not properly weigh [the expert's] testimony and evidence, nor properly determine the value of the evidence and testimony. The lack of a full cross examination impermissibly denied LPCF the right to fully present its case and therefore, it was denied the right to a fair trial" (p. 8). Further, "We conclude that [the expert's] testimony, the weight of his testimony, and the credibility determination regarding his credentials and qualifications as an expert witness, were of critical importance to the jury's decision. We cannot conduct a meaningful *de novo* review because it would involve eliminating all of [the expert's] testimony, thereby depriving plaintiff of a jury trial on the quantum issue" (p. 9). The bottom line; the judgment was vacated and remanded for a new trial.

One important aspect of the above case is that the role of the judge as a gatekeeper does not necessarily mean that the judge will prevent an expert from testifying when their credibility may be under scrutiny. Instead, the jury will be charged with assessing not only the value of the testimony but the credibility of the witness as well.

Case #2: Expert's testimony was neither speculative nor unreliable and appeal was denied.

Ruby Kay Ballance et al. v. Wal-Mart, No. 98-1702, U.S. Court of Appeals for the 4th Circuit, 1999, U.S., App. Lexis 7663

In *Ballance et al. v. Wal-Mart*, 1999, while shopping at Wal-Mart, the plaintiff fell when she apparently slipped on plastic hangers left on the floor. The main focus of the appeal was whether Wal-Mart was liable for the injuries which were complicated by pre-existing conditions (asymptomatic congenital spine defects). However, part of the appeal (the only part to be addressed in this summary) was the argument by Wal-Mart that the damages related experts should have had their testimony limited under the standards as set forth by *Daubert v. Merrell-Dow Pharmaceuticals* decision relating to scientific expert evidence. Identified were the well known four factors: (1) The extent to which the theory has been or can be tested; (2) Whether the theory has been subjected to peer review and/or publication; (3) The technique's potential rate of error; and (4) Whether the underlying theory or technique has been generally accepted as valid by the relevant scientific community.

Further, under *Kumho Tire v. Carmichael*, the Supreme Court extended the gate keeping function to all expert testimony, not just "scientific" testimony. ". . . the Court explained that this discretion is not confined to application discussed in Daubert. Id. At *9-10. Rather the district court has 'considerable leeway' to examine any number of factors in determining whether expert testimony is reliable; these factors may included, but are not limited to, the Daubert factors" (p. 4). In the case of Kumho Tire, the district court was correct in the decision to exclude the testimony of the tire expert as unreliable.

In the Ballance case, the expert offered two alternative life care plans: One where treatment successfully stabilized the patient's medical condition and the other in the event the patient's condition declined. Wal-Mart did have their own expert witness to counterclaim come of the plaintiff's expert's opinions.

Wal-Mart argued that one of the medical experts, on which much of the life care plan was based, offered opinions which were speculative and unreliable. Some future care and conditions might be "possible" and Wal-Mart argued the testimony would have been limited. However, Wal-Mart's expert testified that (for an example) an anticipated surgery was 80% likely to be successful, but agreed it could also worsen the condition (including loss of bowel and bladder function and the ability to walk).

Turning to the life care plan, Wal-Mart argued that future care plans are contingent upon future events and choices and therefore are unreliable and speculative. Additionally, they argued that under Federal Rules of Evidence 403,*** the life care plan expert's testimony should have been limited. However, the district court was found to have exercised proper discretion and the appeal was rejected. First, this case underscores the value of separating probable vs. possible future care. In the original format of the life care plan literature (Deutsch & Raffa, 1981, *Damages in Tort Action*) the authors included a page for listing "Potential Complications" for which no prediction of duration or frequency could be determined. Secondly, opinions based on clinical judgment relating to two possible scenarios were accepted as reasonable and reliable.

Case #3: Expert did possess specialized skills and knowledge and relied upon accepted methodologies and was allowed to testify.

In RE Hanford Nuclear Reservation, No. CY-91-3015-WFM, United States District Court for the Eastern District of Washington at Spokane (January 21, 2005). [Also see Choppa, T., Field, T., & Johnson, C. (2005). The Daubert challenge: From case referral to trial. Elliott & Fitzpatrick: Athens, GA for extensive transcripts and notes regarding this case.]

In this case, the Daubert related hearings took prior to trial. A rather extensive challenge was launched with examples as follows (1) the expert is not qualified to offer opinions regarding radiation, (2) the expert relied exclusively on plaintiffs' experts, (3) expert "worked here as an information coordinator and scrivener, not medical or rehabilitation expert" (Choppa, Field & Johnson, p. 42), (4) portions of the life care plan were not based on "more probably than not" concept, (5) past cost analysis was simply a compilation as determined by plaintiffs' experts, and (6) the expert's opinion included personal observation of the plaintiffs under the guise of an expert opinion. In addition to the rebuttal by a plaintiff's attorney, the expert offered his own report with extensive support for how a life care planner conducts an evaluation and publishes an opinion. Topic headings included experience, ethics, associations, existing standards, and specific responses to the defendant's motion.

The court's ruling was that the expert would be able to testify regarding the data in the life care plan, although unless medical testimony supported surgery, this item should be removed. Additionally, the expert could testify about his interactions with the plaintiff but may not offer an expert opinion as to the plaintiff's credibility.

Case #4: Expert for the plaintiff was deemed well qualified, but opinions were not consistent with foundation testimony and opinions and she was excluded.

Cindy Taylor, Individually and as Guardian Ad Litem for Brody Patrick Wright and Arthur M. Taylor vs. Speedway Motorsports Inc. and Charlotte Motor Speedway, LLC, doing business as Lowe's Motor Speedway; Tindal Corporation, formerly Tindall concrete Products, Inc and Anti-Hydro International , N.C., Mecklenburg County Super. Ct.: 01-CVS-12107

This case relates to a successful motion to exclude a life care planning expert who was expected to testify on behalf of the plaintiff. The judge embellished on his ruling on March 7, 2003 with following commentary.

" . . . the Court notes that the witness [for the plaintiff] wishes to express an opinion or numerous opinions without the proper foundation, in the opinion of the Court, having been laid for the expression of said opinions. The Court finds that these opinions are entirely speculative, for example, including, but not limited to, the following examples: Expressing her opinions as to how the plaintiffs would be seen and treated by various health care providers in years to come and the cost of that, without evidence to substantiate that or lay a proper foundation for that. Secondly, expressing opinions as to the medical equipment of the plaintiffs 15 or more years in the future, when the treating physicians have not indicated in their testimony any substantiation for this opinion. The record is devoid of any such evidence, in the opinion of the Court. Third, that she expresses opinions as to what surgery would be needed and the frequency of surgery for as far out as ten years from now when there is no medical evidence to support that. The Court finds, in its discretion, that the proffered testimony is unreliable and is not relevant therefore. I am basing this ruling in part on Kumho Tire vs. Carmichael – I do not have the U.S. citation, it's 119 Supreme Court 1167;Daubert vs. Merrell Dow Pharmaceuticals, 509 U.S. 579; State vs. Bullard, 312 NC 129; State vs. Spencer, 119 NC Appellate 662. Further, the Court finds that the proffered testimony would not be helpful and will not assist the jury in understanding the evidence or determining the facts in issue. Further, the Court finds that for all of the above reasons the probative value of such testimony is substantially outweighed by the danger of unfair prejudice, misleading the jury, and waste of time. The Court further notes and finds as a fact that there has been no peer review of the testimony or of the anticipated testimony of this witness. There is no publication to which reference has been made in any testimony that would substantiate this. There has been no offer of visual aids to assist the jury. And for all of these reasons the testimony of [the expert witness] is excluded" (pp. 33-34).

The wording by the judge encompasses several areas of interest. First, the qualifications of the expert were not in dispute, just the expected testimony. Second, Daubert and Kumho Tire cases were referenced as justification for the judge's "gate keeping" discretion which disallowed testimony rather than giving the jury the responsibility to determine the credibility of witness. Third, another topic which the judge asserted in his commentary was related to Federal Rules of Evidence 403 which indicated that the testimony was, in essence, a waste of the court's time.

A discussion ensued with regard to some deposition testimony which was read where conflicting opinions seemingly were expressed. One example was when the judge referenced the testimony of the treating psychologist stating, "… and it's [the opinions of the life care planner] contrary to what I thought was an outstanding witness, Dr. Owens" (p. 23) and whose recommendations the life care planner apparently ignored or did not accept.

Case #5: Expert testified at trial that the client was 50 to 60% disabled by combing two well known methodologies into a hybrid approach, resulting in an appeal and remand for new trial on damages (for this issues and others).

Elcock vs. K-Mart Corp. (1998, US Ct of Appeals, 3rd Cir, No. 98-7472)

There were several issues discussed in this appeal, but a central theme was related to the expert's "thin" vocational rehabilitation education and knowledge and his unique application of two existing disability determination methodologies. The court allowed the expert to testify without allowing a Daubert type hearing. K-Mart asserted that the expert provided unreliable testimony on which, in part, the jury relied when determining the damage award. The court of appeals agreed.

The expert opined that Elcock was between 50 and 60 percent vocationally disabled and that this disability was permanent. When pressed for an explanation of the methodology used, he testified:

> "I use a combination of the procedure recommended by Fields [sic] which is to look at level of pre-injury access to the labor market and post injury access and the percentage and the difference between those percentages Fields says is the loss of jobs or the lost percentage. I also looked at which is what I normally do at the procedure recommended by Anthony Gamboa and he suggests that you look at all the factors involved in the client's analysis, injury, test results, psychological results, the client's statements, and so on, and then you as the clinician must make a, you as a vocational expert must make an estimate. And so what I do is I use Fields analysis as a starting point and then I revert to Gamboa to depart from Fields [sic] to come up with an estimate" (p. 20).

The appeals court countered with: "However, we are inclined to view [the expert's] admittedly novel synthesis of the two methodologies as nothing more than a hodgepodge of the Fields and Gamboa approaches, permitting [the expert] to offer a subjective judgment about the extent of Elcock's vocational disability in the guise of a reliable expert opinion" (p. 21). It is valuable to note that: "K-Mart does not dispute that the Fields[sic] and Gamboa approaches are accepted methodologies in the vocational rehabilitation field; what it does challenge is [expert's] combination method" (p. 20).

The court needed to determine if the expert was qualified to testify regarding vocational rehabilitation by education, experience, knowledge, training and skill and the testimony would assist the jury in reaching a decision. There is an extensive review of these factors in the appeals court decision. Further, the expert was allowed to express opinions based in part on clinical judgment, which was termed in the appeal as the expert's "ipse dixit statement" (p. 18) or because he said it, therefore it is so. However, the appeals court rejected the expert's opinions based in part on the lack of evidence that the hybrid concept was generally accepted and the case was remand for a new trial on damages.

Hedonics

According to *Black's Law Dictionary* (7th ed., 2004), hedonic damages refers to "damages that attempt to compensate the loss of the pleasure of being alive." Franz (1996) discusses the relevance of hedonics damages in civil litigation. This journal issue includes content of hedonics from two prominent writers and thinkers on the topic. Dr. Tom Ireland, often a critic on testimony involving hedonics (Ireland, 1993, 1996, 2000), discusses the views of three writers in the field – Drs. Stan Smith, Robert Johnson, and Brian McDonald. Dr. Stan Smith, along with two colleagues, presented a paper on estimating the value of household management services. Both papers are commented on by Kent Jayne, a vocational economist, who knows both of these gentlemen on a personal/professional basis. The following paragraphs are included to highlight some of the discussion points to the value-of-life notion and readers are urged to consult the various studies that are cited.

As Ireland points out in his paper, hedonics received its first big splash with the case of *Sherrod v. Berry* (1985) in which Dr. Smith testified as an expert on the issue of loss of pleasure, and is credited with first using the phrase "hedonic damages." Brookshire and Smith (1990) are frequently cited as two of the pioneers in the hedonics movement and both have contributed significantly to the literature over the last two decades. Smith (1990) argued that "the most appropriate measure for the value of life is to base it on a wide body of literature measuring the cost-benefit of life saving programs using the willingness-to-pay methodology" (p. 43). Even with this simple notion that loss should be compensated, the basis for making such determinations is not without its critics (Viscusi, 1990a; Viscusi, 1990b; Havrilesky, 1990). Viscusi, in particular identifies several concerns related to the valuing of life; namely, the ambiguity of how damages should be established, assuming that all wrongful death cases would result in similar awards – again, with no guidelines for determining such awards, and the problem of misuse by experts who would have more interest in the award than through the undisciplined use of value-of-life concepts. In a more recent paper, Viscusi (2007) again cautions the misuse of the value of a statistical life (VSL) when economic experts tend to use the VSL as a basis for adding on other elements for a damage settlement. Havrilesky (1993) makes a distinction between the value of the avoidance of injury and the value of an individual's whole like. The value of an anonymous (statistical) person's life may be decidedly different from that value that an individual person may place on their own life. Evaluating the value of damage, or the value of one's life, perhaps should be addressed by taking into account a variety of factors about a person (Field et al., 2009). Further, Albrecht (1994) presents an excellent critique of Havrilesky's anonymous/statistical notion of valuing a life. Staller et al. (1994) join in the criticism of the "willingness to pay" rationale as the basis for estimating the statistical value of a life.

The emergence of the theory and practice of hedonics in litigation has spawned a variety of issues that have been discussed and examined by several authors. Miller (1990) has reviewed the value of life from the perspective employment economics by evaluating sixty-seven different studies on the topic. Referring to his study as the "statistical value of a life," Miller concludes that the value of the enjoyment of life is probably in the range of $1.35 million (calculated in 1988 dollars), after taking into consideration by subtracting the value of after-tax earnings, the value of household production, and the value of financial security. Frankel and Linke (1992) investigate three important issues related to hedonics: the value-of-life concept, the wide divergence in value-of-life estimates by experts, and the value-of-life concept and the value-of-life estimates in wrongful death and personal injury litigation. The authors note that loss has historically been associated with the loss of earnings and earnings capacity.

Describing and measuring the loss of pleasure was addressed by Berla et al., (1990) with the development of the Lost Pleasure of Life Scale (LPL) which evaluated the areas of practical functioning, emotional/psychological functioning, social functioning, and occupational functioning. Each area of functioning was rated/evaluated on a subjective scale of functioning: minimal (loss), mild, moderate, severe, extreme and catastrophic. The authors suggested that the LPL scale could be used in assessing the loss of pleasure of life for litigation purposes. Following a rather poignant critique by Carragonne (1993), of the LPL scale, Berla, et al., (1995) answered Carragonne in a spirited rebuttal by writing that "no scale dealing with human behavior [is] 100% precise," and that "expert testimony is to provide a jury with information that meets the standard's within one's profession and with a reasonable degree of professional certainty" (once again, this sounds like "clinical judgment; see Field et al., 2009).

One final note: It does not seem that the "specialty" of hedonics is going away anytime soon – if at all. As long as courts allow such testimony to be admitted, the issues surrounding hedonics will certainly continued to be debated. As Ireland (2000) indicated in his analysis of recent court decisions, "judge have generally not looked with favor on the hedonic damage concept" (p. 202). It might be more accurate to say the some courts (judges) in some jurisdictions (e.g., Nevada) do continue to allow hedonics testimony, especially since the decision of hedonics seems to be alive and well (see Climo, 2102).

Conclusion

A review of the legal literature would suggest that admissibility issues are smoothing out after a decade of uncertainty following the Daubert decision. Rehabilitation experts need not be threatened by the potential threat of a "Daubert challenge" or of the various state-by-state rules for state courts. However, an expert in areas of the vocational rehabilitation and life care planning need to be credentialed properly, to offer services and testimony within their area of expertise, rely upon reliable foundation information and data, and be clear on selected methodologies that have been generally accepted and peer reviewed. The cases that are reviewed in this booklet should be both instructive and helpful for experts as these and similar cases do offer useful guidelines on the admissibility of testimony.

In conclusion, the issues surrounding admissibility of testimony, in view of the more scientific criteria of Daubert and the broader standard established by Kumho and Joiner, have been largely settled. An emphasis on the appropriate methodology or methodologies is in order. Clearly, given the fact that individual persons require individual attention through evaluation and assessment, planning, resource development, and the reliance on foundation data and information, a reasonable course is to apply clinical judgment skills to problem-solving consistent with all the facts of the case. Objective data (i.e., test scores, computer analyses, consultants' reports) are required "to provide a concrete basis for the making of some decisions, and to make somewhat less intuitive some of the clinical judgments which have to be made when objective data are lacking" (Super & Crites, 1949, p. 596). Furthermore, court rulings underscore that testimony must be reliable and based on generally accepted methodology. The days of opinions founded simply on one's experience or offering some unique obscure, esoteric theory are probably over. In the final analysis, however, in instances of opinion development with most rehabilitation cases, the rehabilitation and life care planning consultant must rely on a methodology that includes clinical judgment.

Endnote

Revised Definition of Clinical Judgment

Clinical judgment requires that the final opinion be predicated on valid, reliable and relevant foundation information and data which is scientifically established through theory and technique building which has been tested, peer reviewed and published, with a known error rate, and is generally accepted within the professional community of the subject disciple. In cases where any of the above factors do not apply, but others factors have greater relevance, the expert will rely on these other factors within a methodological approach which has been peer reviewed and generally accepted, coupled with the expert's specialized knowledge, skill, experience, training and education in order to assist the trier of fact to reach a conclusion. Therefore, professional clinical judgment, which is the extension of the credentialing factors of the expert, and the reliance on relevant and reliable methodology, encompasses all relevant factors germane to the weight of the case, and which is allowed by the court.

This definition of clinical judgment has been revised by Field, Choppa, and Johnson (Unpublished, 2012) from the original (Choppa et al., 2004) and has been reviewed and approved by the authors of the initial publication (A. Choppa, personal communications, April 12, 2012).

Chapter 13
ADA and Reasonable Accommodation

The Americans with Disabilities Act

The Americans with Disabilities Act (ADA) of 1990 (PL 101-336) with the 2008 ADA Amendments Act (ADAAA) (P.L. 110-325) are laws which prohibit discrimination against persons with disabilities in employment, government programs and services, public accommodations and services, and telecommunications. The enactment of such a law evolved through many years of earlier laws and policy attempts at reducing discrimination and elevating opportunities for persons with disabilities. (Note: The ADA was originally enacted in the "public law" format but was later published in the United States Code [USC]. Titles I, II, III, and V of the original law are located in Title 42, chapter 126, of the United States Code beginning at section 12101.) To provide a foundation for the ADA and ADAA, some historical perspective is useful.

The first major legislation was the Smith-Fess Act (P.L. 66-236) passed in 1920. Smith-Fess provided funding for counseling, training, prosthetic appliances, and job placement for the physically disabled with industrial injuries. In 1935, a similar vocational rehabilitation program became a permanent part of the Social Security Act. Borden-LaFollette (P.L. 78-113) broadened the definition of disability to include the mentally ill and retarded, and expanded services for the physically disabled as well as a provision for the blind. Under Eisenhower's administration, rehabilitation took a giant leap forward with the establishment of graduate training and research programs, improving rehabilitation centers such as workshops and facilities, and authorizing services for the severely disabled.

The Vocational Rehabilitation Act of 1965 (P.L. 89-333) authorized the construction of rehabilitation facilities, and generally expanded services, including the extended evaluation and assessment of persons with disabilities. Next Congress extended the Act (P.L. 90-391) to include programs in vocational evaluation and work adjustment for the "disadvantaged," follow-up to employment services, and services to families. In 1973, the Act was amended again to emphasize more services to the severely disabled and more involvement of the disabled person in their own rehabilitation process. Annual evaluations of eligibility within programs and affirmative action programs were established. The final building block was the 1978 law (P.L. 95-602) that continued the emphasis on providing services for the severely disabled, the creation of the National Institute of Handicapped Research and the National Council on the Handicapped, new construction of rehabilitation centers, and provisions for independent living centers.

Affirmative Action

While laws with the best of intentions are passed, compliance with those laws is not always quick nor voluntary. Congress passed P.L. 93-112, which required those affected entities not only to comply but to develop a plan to show how they would comply. Title V of this law established what has become known as "affirmative action." Section 502 (1973 Rehabilitation Act) addresses the issues of architectural and transportational barriers. These two issues were directly connected to the discrimination of any person with a disability where that program or activity was receiving any Federal financial assistance.

Section 503

The most critical part of the law, however, was Section 503, which squarely addressed the issue of employment.

(a) Any contract in excess of $2,500 entered into by any Federal department or agency for the procurement of personal property and nonpersonal services (including construction) for the United States shall contain a provision requiring that, in employing persons to carry out such contract the part contracting with the United States shall take affirmative action to employ and advance in employment qualifications handicapped individuals as defined in Section 7(6). The provisions of this section shall apply to any subcontract in excess of $2,500 entered into by a prime contractor in carrying out any contract for the procurement of personal property and nonpersonal services (including construction) for the United States. The president shall implement the provisions of this section by promulgating regulations within ninety days after the date of enactment of this section.

(b) If any handicapped individual believes any contractor has failed or refuses to comply with the provisions of his contract with the United States, relating to employment of handicapped individuals, such individual may file a complaint with the Department of Labor. The Department shall promptly investigate such complaint and shall take such action thereon as the facts and circumstances warrant, consistent with the terms of such contract and the laws and regulations applicable thereto.

(c) The requirements of this section may be waived, in whole or in part, by the President with respect to a particular contract or sub-contract, in accordance with guidelines set forth in regulations which he shall prescribe, when he determines that special circumstances in the national interest so require and states in writing his reasons for such determination. (P.L. 93-112)

Intent of Section 503

Any employer receiving federal funds in excess of $2,500 shall be required to take positive action in the hiring of handicapped persons and to assure that a plan is developed and maintained to promote the employment, retention, and advancement of such individuals. Furthermore, the employer must show that qualified handicapped individuals are given equal consideration for available job opportunities along with any and all other applicants. In some cases, the employer must develop an Affirmative Action Plan.

Handicapped Individual Defined

The law (P.L. 93-112, Sec. 7[6]) defines a handicapped individual as anyone "who (a) has a physical or mental disability which for such individual constitutes or results in a substantial handicap to employment, and (b) can reasonably be expected to benefit in terms of employability from vocational rehabilitation services."

Furthermore, HEW issued regulations to ensure that federally assisted programs and activities are governed without discrimination on the basis of an individual's handicap. These regulations offer the following definitions:

(j) "Handicapped person." (1) "Handicapped persons" means any person who (i) has a physical or mental impairment which substantially limits one or more major life activities, (ii) has a record of such an impairment, or (iii) is regarded as having such an impairment. (2) As used in paragraph (j) (1) of this section, the phrase: (i) "physical or mental impairment" means (A) any physiological disorder or condition, cosmetic disfigurement, or anatomical loss affecting one or more of the following body systems: neurological; musculo-skeletal; special sense organs; respiratory, including speech organs; cardiovascular; reproductive; digestive; genito-urinary; hemic and lymphatic; skin; and endocrine; or (B) any mental or psychological disorder, such as mental retardation, organic brain syndrome, emotional or mental illness, and specific learning disabilities.

(ii) "Major life activities" means functions such as caring for one's self, performing manual tasks, walking, seeing, hearing, speaking, breathing, learning, and working.

(iii) "Has a record of such an impairment" means has a history of, or has been misclassified as having a mental or physical impairment that substantially limits one or more major life activities.

(iv) "Is regarded as having an impairment" means (A) has a physical or mental impairment that does not substantially limit major life activities only as a result of the attitudes of others toward such impairment; or (C) has none of the impairments defined in paragraph (j) (2) (i) of this section but is treated by a recipient as having such an impairment.

Qualified Handicapped Individual

With respect to employment, a "qualified handicapped individual" under ADA is one who is capable of performing a particular job with a reasonable accommodation to the individuals handicapping condition. *The possession of a handicap by itself does not qualify an individual for employment through affirmative action* (also see additional definitions relating directly to ADAAA).

Reasonable Accommodation

In many cases, a person with a handicapping condition is not prevented from performing work for which he/she may be qualified. Such a case has no particular relevance to hiring practices to persons with disabilities. On the other hand, a person with a handicap may be able to perform a particular job only if there is some accommodation to the job itself, the job site, physical barriers to the job site, or restroom accessibility. As stated in the law, persons with disabilities must have access to all facilities used by the non-disabled. This adds a new dimension to "Essential Function."

(1) Will it increase the likelihood of employment for the handicapped individual?

(2) With accommodation, will the individual be able to demonstrate an adequate job performance?

(3) Will the accommodation impose undue hardship on the employer?

In many ways, the fine line between reasonable accommodation and undue hardship remains unclear and disputed. However, perhaps more important is the intent of the employer to comply with intent of the law. Some accommodations can be very costly (such as a whole new restroom), especially for the small employer; however, many accommodations can be made with no or minimal cost to the employer. Some examples are (a) creating ramps to buildings, (b) reserving parking areas, (c) altering a work bench, (d) removing obstructions in walkways, (e) replacing foot controls with hand controls, and (f) altering job tasks. As a general rule, a person with a disability must have access to all the facilities that a person without a disability would have access to, with respect to not only the job itself, but also all aspects of the work environment.

Related Employment Laws

While the pieces of vocational rehabilitation legislation were the primary building blocks for ADA and the ADAA, many other federal laws and programs contributed as well. Summarized in Table 13.1 are several of these related federal laws and a brief description of the various contributions to assistance to persons with disabilities.

The most important features of all these laws reflect the growing concern of the American people toward people with disabilities. These concerns are reflected in the passage of several laws that increase opportunities for "the handicapped" and establish the rights of people with disabilities in terms of their accessibility to employment. Basically, these programs:

1. Provide equal opportunity for employment without discrimination because of a disability.

2. Assure that there is a procedure for due process in cases of discrimination.

3. Provide subsistence and/or benefits for the aged, blind, or disabled who may not be able to work.

4. Provide benefits for injured workers.

5. Provide opportunities for employment in state and local programs, including job training.

6. Provide assistance to industries who are inclined to offer special assistance and programming to the disabled worker.

7. Provide unemployment benefits.

8. Provide rehabilitation services to persons with disabilities, which hopefully will result in a return to employment.

The essence and intent of these laws are not only right and proper in terms of providing assistance to the disabled, but they also serve to assist the employer in the placement of the disabled worker in business and industry. More importantly, however, is the maintenance and/or restoration of personal worth and dignity of the injured worker, especially when a person with a disability is able to be employed as a result of any utilization of the benefits as provided by these laws.

Summary of ADA

The Americans with Disabilities Act is clearly an extension of P.L. 93-112 (The Vocational Rehabilitation Act of 1973) and seeks to vastly broaden the intent of the previous law to all aspects of the American society.

Table 13.1
Summary of Employment Laws

Vocational Rehabilitation	Adult vocationally handicapped person.	To provide services for rehabilitation and/or restoration to world or work.
Title VII	All working people.	Administers equal opportunity to employment without regard to race, color, religion, sex, or national origin.
Sec. 503	Adult handicapped workers.	Requires employers to provide affirmative employment action to qualified disabled workers.
Fair Labor Standards Act	All working people.	Allows for less than minimum wage for handicapped workers in noncompetitive work center.
Projects with Industry	Qualified handicapped workers.	Encourages employers to provide modified employment to qualified workers.
CETA	Economically disadvantaged, unemployed, and underemployed.	Provides training and employment opportunities at state and local levels.
Workers' Compensation Injured workers.	Injured workers.	Provides disability compensation and death benefits to injured workers.
Social Security Disability Insurance	Disabled workers.	Provides monthly cost benefits to persons who are disabled due to injury or disease.
Unemployment Insurance	Unemployed workers.	Benefits for workers who became Insurance unemployed — up to 39 weeks.
Federal Employees Compensation	Injured workers.	Provides disability compensation and death benefits to injured federal employees.
Vietnam Veterans Act	All veterans.	Assures affirmative action in employment for all veterans.

The 2008 amendments were necessary because the Supreme Court had interpreted the law in ways not intended by Congress. From the 2008 amendments (ADA.gov):

Congress finds that

(1) in enacting the Americans with Disabilities Act of 1990 (ADA), Congress intended that the Act "provide a clear and comprehensive national mandate for the elimination of discrimination against individuals with disabilities" and provide broad coverage;

(2) in enacting the ADA, Congress recognized that physical and mental disabilities in no way diminish a person's right to fully participate in all aspects of society, but that people with physical or mental disabilities are frequently precluded from doing so because of prejudice, antiquated attitudes, or the failure to remove societal and institutional barriers;

(3) although Congress expected that the definition of disability under the ADA would be interpreted consistently with how courts had applied the definition of an individual with a disability under the Rehabilitation Act of 1973, that expectation has not been fulfilled (p. 4).

And, a major point to keep in mind:

(4) Congress has the expectation that the Equal Employment Opportunity Commission will revise that portion of its current regulations that defines the term "substantially limits" as "significantly restricted" to be consistent with this Act, including the amendments made by this Act (p. 6). (Note: That is, "significantly restricted" as interpreted by the EEOC was not consistent with the meaning as discussed in the "substantially limits" section that was intended by Congress.)

For a layperson's explanation, from a Podcast on this topic (Brennan, 2008), prior to the Amendments the courts ruled:

> *. . . before you decide whether a person is substantially limited, you don't just look at their disability, you have to look at what their disability is like with the mitigating measure. So, if a person is substantially limited without medication, but when they're on medication, they're not substantially limited, then they won't have a disability. And this really did narrow the definition of who was covered. Because, even things like hearing aids, which in most cases do not return a person's hearing to the same hearing that other people have, still that wasn't considered a disability, because with the hearing aid, they weren't substantially limited in a major life activity* (para. 4).

And then a few years later in 2002, in a case called *Toyota v. Williams*, the Supreme Court focused on the word "substantially" from the definition of the "disability" and gave us a definition of "substantially" that meant "considerably" or "to a large degree." At the same time, the court also narrowed the scope of "major life activity" saying that if you're going to say that a major life activity is limited, what that major life activity must be is something that is of central importance to most people's daily lives (para. 5).

The ADA has new rules for the definition of "disability," and they include the definition of disability must be construed in favor of broad coverage to the maximum extent permitted. And the term "substantially limits" is to be interpreted consistently with the ADA Amendment Act. And an impairment that substantially limits one major life activity need not limit other major life activities to be considered a disability. And an impairment that is episodic or in remission is a disability if it would substantially limit a major life activity when active. And mitigating measures shall not be a factor when determining whether an impairment substantially limits a major life activity. The only mitigating measures that can be considered are ordinary eye glasses and contact lenses that fully correct visual acuity or eliminate refractive error. And people who are only "regarded as" being disabled are NOT entitled to reasonable accommodations or modifications (para. 8). (Also see U.S. Department of Labor, 2008)

The ADA and the amendments are presented under five major sections known as "Titles" (abstracted from the law, ADA.gov, 2008):

Title 1: Employment

The intent of this section of the law is to require the employer to make reasonable accommodations so that any qualified individual with a disability can demonstrate adequate performance of the essential functions of a job without undue hardship to the employer.

Title 2: Public Services

No qualified individual with a disability shall be denied the benefits or excluded from participation in services, programs, or activities within the public sector.

Title 3: Public Accommodations and Services

No individual shall be discriminated against on the basis of disability from the full and equal enjoyment of goods, services, facilities, privileges, advantages or accommodations of any public place.

Title 4: Telecommunications

Making interstate and intrastate telecommunications available to hearing- and speech-impaired individuals. Relay based communication is an example.

Title 5: Miscellaneous Provisions

Various elements for the application of the first four titles including: construction, prohibition against retaliation, architectural and transportation barriers, technical assistance, illegal drug use, and amendments to the rehabilitation act.

Civil Rights Act of 1991

The Civil Rights Act of 1991 establishes appropriate remedies for the intentional discrimination and unlawful harassment in the workplace.

With respect to the issues of disability and accommodation (Sec. 102a2), the Act specifically cites the Americans with Disabilities Act of 1990 (Sec. 505a1 & Sec. 102b5), and the Rehabilitation Act of 1973 (Sec. 501). Compliance will be encouraged through the enforcement of punitive and compensatory damages to be levied for violation of any sections of the Acts cited above. The amount of the damages will be according to the following schedule for companies with numbers of employees in each of 20 or more calendar weeks in the current or preceding calendar year:

14 - less than 101 employees	$50,000
100 - less than 201 employees	$100,000
200 - less than 501 employees	$200,000
more than 500 employees	$300,000

While this schedule of damages is to penalize specific violations, employers should be helped to understand the enormous benefits in establishing work practices (hiring, accommodating for disabilities, and non-discrimination rules) that would reduce any potential threat of legal action for reasons of employment discrimination or unfair employment practices. The advantages and benefits of following the guidelines set forth in the Rehabilitation (1973), ADA (1990), and Civil Rights (1991) Acts (see Appendix A) will be realized through the development of a healthier, productive, and profitable workplace for all parties concerned.

Employment Issues

Title 1 of the American with Disabilities Act identifies and defines many important issues related to employment. Each of these issues is discussed separately within the context of the Federal Register. A working understanding of these issues is necessary for the rehabilitation consultant to demonstrate if he/she will be an effective consultant with the employer.

Discrimination Prohibited

This brief section that follows (Table 13.2) is a very important section and one that best summarizes the essence and intent of the new ADA law. Much on the discussion that follows relates directly to this summary.

Who is the Employer (ADA.gov, 2008)

(A) In general. The term "employer" means a person engaged in an industry affecting commerce who has 15 or more employees for each working day in each of 20 or more calendar weeks in the current or preceding calendar year and any agent of such person, except that, for two years following the effective date of this subchapter, an employer means a person engaged in an industry affecting commerce who has 25 or more employees for each working day in each of 20 or more calendar weeks in the current or preceding year and any agent of such person.

(B) Exceptions. The term "employer" does not include:

(i) the United States, a corporation wholly owned by the government of the United States, or an Indian tribe; or

(ii) a bona fide private membership club (other than a labor organization) that is exempt from taxation under section 501(c) of title 26 (p. 9).

Relevant Definitions

With regard to the other relevant definitions (ADA.gov, 2008):

(1) Disability. The term "disability" means, with respect to an individual

Table 13.2
Discrimination

It is unlawful for a covered entity to discriminate on the basis of disability against a qualified individual with a disability in regard to:

(a) Recruitment, advertising, and job application procedures;

(b) Hiring, upgrading, promotion, award of tenure, demotion, transfer, layoff, termination, right of return from layoff, and rehiring;

(c) Rates of pay or any other form of compensation and changes in compensation;

(d) Job assignments, job classifications, organizational structures, position descriptions, lines of progression, and seniority lists;

(e) Leaves of absence, sick leave, or any other leave;

(f) Fringe benefits available by virtue of employment, whether or not administered by the covered entity;

(g) Selection and financial support for training, including: apprenticeships, professional meetings, conferences and other related activities, and selection for leaves of absence to pursue training;

(h) Activities sponsored by a covered entity including social and recreational programs; and

(i) Any other term, condition, or privilege of employment.

(A) a physical or mental impairment that substantially limits one or more major life activities of such individual;

(B) a record of such an impairment; or

(C) being regarded as having such an impairment (as described in paragraph [3]) (p. 7).

(2) Major Life Activities

(A) In general. For purposes of paragraph (1), major life activities include, but are not limited to, caring for oneself, performing manual tasks, seeing, hearing, eating, sleeping, walking, standing, lifting, bending, speaking, breathing, learning, reading, concentrating, thinking, communicating, and working.

(B) Major bodily functions. For purposes of paragraph (1), a major life activity also includes the operation of a major bodily function, including but not limited to, functions of the immune system, normal cell growth, digestive, bowel, bladder, neurological, brain, respiratory, circulatory, endocrine, and reproductive functions.

(3) Regarded as having such an impairment. For purposes of paragraph (1)(C):

(A) An individual meets the requirement of "being regarded as having such an impairment" if the individual establishes that he or she has been subjected to an action prohibited under this chapter because of an actual or perceived physical or mental impairment whether or not the impairment limits or is perceived to limit a major life activity.

(B) Paragraph (1)(C) shall not apply to impairments that are transitory and minor. A transitory impairment is an impairment with an actual or expected duration of 6 months or less (p. 7).

Special notes have been added to the law to further define the intent of Congress (abstracted here):

The definition of "disability" in paragraph (1) shall be construed in accordance with the following:

(A) The definition of disability in this chapter shall be construed in favor of broad coverage of individuals under this chapter, to the maximum extent permitted by the terms of this chapter (emphasis added).

(B) The term "substantially limits" shall be interpreted consistently with the findings and purposes of the ADA Amendments Act of 2008.

(C) An impairment that substantially limits one major life activity need not limit other major life activities in order to be considered a disability.

(D) An impairment that is episodic or in remission is a disability if it would substantially limit a major life activity when active.

(E) (i) The determination of whether an impairment substantially limits a major life activity shall be made without regard to the ameliorative effects of mitigating measures such as

(I) medication, medical supplies, equipment, appliances, low-vision devices (which do not include ordinary eyeglasses or contact lenses), prosthetics including limbs and devices, hearing aids and cochlear implants or other implantable hearing devices, mobility devices, or oxygen therapy equipment and supplies.

(II) use of assistive technology;

(III) reasonable accommodations or auxiliary aids or services; or

(IV) learned behavioral or adaptive neurological modifications.

(ii) The ameliorative effects of the mitigating measures of ordinary eyeglasses or contact lenses shall be considered in determining whether an impairment substantially limits a major life activity (pp. 8-9). (Note: Eye glasses or contacts are the only devices one can use that, if eyesight is corrected, one can not claim a disability- that is, the disability has been mitigated by the assistive technology).

Once this determination has been made with regard to disability and the limits of a major life activity, a "case by case" determination of substantial limits of the impairment must be made with regard to work. A three-point test of specific factors (Table 13.3) has been suggested in making this determination.

In applying the above captioned criteria, it is not necessary that a person be totally prevented from performing work in order to be considered substantially limited with the major life activity of working. A person may be considered "substantially limited in working if the individual is significantly restricted in the ability to perform a class of jobs or a broad range of jobs in various classes, when compared with the ability of the average person with comparable qualifications to perform those same jobs." Furthermore a person may not necessarily actually have an impairment if they are "regarded" as having an impairment. See below.

Regarded as having such an impairment. For purposes of paragraph (1)(C) (ADA.gov, 2008):

(A) An individual meets the requirement of "being regarded as having such an impairment" if the individual establishes that he or she has been subjected to an action prohibited under this chapter because of an actual or perceived physical or mental impairment whether or not the impairment limits or is perceived to limit a major life activity (p. 7).

However:

(B) Paragraph (1)(C) shall not apply to impairments that are transitory and minor. A transitory impairment is an impairment with an actual or expected duration of 6 months or less. A three point test (Table 13.4) is provided to evaluate this situation (p. 7).

Typical examples of each of these points would include (1) high blood pressure, (2) attitudes of co-workers due to facial scar, (3) rumors of HIV virus, respectively. If an employer failed to hire a person on the basis of any one of the three points, the employer would be discriminating in terms of employment. Accordingly, if a

---

Table 13.3
Factors in Determining Substantial Limitations to Work

(1) The geographical area to which the individual has reasonable access;

(2) The job from which the individual has been disqualified because of an impairment, and the number and types of jobs utilizing similar training, knowledge, skills, or abilities, within that geographical area, from which the individual is also disqualified because of the impairment (class of jobs); and/or

(3) The job from which the individual has been disqualified because of an impairment, and the number and types of jobs utilizing similar training, knowledge, skills or abilities, within that geographical area, from which the individual is also disqualified because of the impairment (broad range of jobs in various classes).

Table 13.4
Being "Regarded" as Having a Disability

(1) The individual may have an impairment which is not substantially limiting but is perceives by the employer or other covered entity as constituting a substantially limiting impairment;

(2) The individual may have an impairment which is only substantially limiting because of the attitudes of others toward the impairment; or

(3) The individual may have no impairment at all but is regarded by the employer or other covered entity as having a substantially limiting impairment.

---

person can show that an employer made a hiring decision based on "perceptions" of this nature, the employer would be basing the decision on a discriminatory course.

Qualified Individual

For someone to seek protection under the ADAAA, they must be qualified. According to ADA.gov (2008), a qualified individual means someone who:

without reasonable accommodation, can perform the essential functions of the employment position that such individual holds or desires. For the purposes of this subchapter, consideration shall be given to the employer's judgment as to what functions of a job are essential, and if an employer has prepared a written description before advertising or interviewing applicants for the job, this description shall be considered evidence of the essential functions of the job (p. 9).

A determination of whether an individual who is disabled is "qualified" for a job can be addressed in two steps:

1. Does the individual meet the necessary prerequisites for the job, such as training, educational, certifications, experience, etc?

2. Does the individual possess the capacity to perform the "essential functions" of the job, with or without reasonable accommodation?

The employment decision should be made at the time of the job possibility, taking into account the individual's capabilities for meeting the essential functions, and not being concerned with past or future factors due to mitigating circumstances.

Direct Threat (ADA.gov, 2008)

Employers do not need to hire the individual if they can show that the employment of the person with a disability poses a direct threat, which is defined as: "a significant risk to the health or safety of others that cannot be eliminated by a modification of policies, practices, or procedures or by the provision of auxiliary aids or services" (p. 34).

This standard must apply to all employees within the workplace and not just to people with disabilities. If a direct threat does exist, the employer needs to consider an available form of accommodation as a means to reduce the threat to an acceptable level. A critical point on this issue is the determination of the extent of the threat (or risk to self or others). Table 13.5 outlines the specific elements of such an assessment.

Furthermore, the determination of threat must be made on the basis of medical evidence and other objective information, excluding perceptions of "irrational fears, patronizing attitudes, or stereotypes." The evidence may be obtained from previous work experience, medical opinions, and the input from rehabilitation counselors, physical therapists, and other professionals.

Selection Criteria, Tests and Standards

One may not use employment selection criteria that will discriminate, which includes (ADA.gov, 2008):

Table 13.5
Factors in Determining Risk & Threat

(1)   The duration of the risk.

(2)   The likelihood that the potential harm will occur.

(3)   The nature and severity of the potential harm.

(4)   The imminence of the potential harm.

(1) using qualification standards, employment tests or other selection criteria that screen out or tend to screen out an individual with a disability or a class of individuals with disabilities unless the standard, test, or other selection criteria, as used by the covered entity, is shown to be job-related for the position in question and is consistent with business necessity; and

(2) failing to select and administer tests concerning employment in the most effective manner to ensure that, when such test is administered to a job applicant or employee who has a disability that impairs sensory, manual, or speaking skills, such test results accurately reflect the skills, aptitude, or whatever other factor of such applicant or employee that such test purports to measure, rather than reflecting the impaired sensory, manual, or speaking skills of such employee or applicant (except where such skills are the factors that the test purports to measure) (p. 10).

The purpose of this provision in the Act is to ensure that persons with disabilities are not excluded from a job unless they are actually unable to perform the job. Whatever job criteria are applied to an individual, disabled or not, cannot be used to screen out (intentionally or not) the applicant when the criteria has no relationship to the job or is not consistent with the "business necessity" of the company. The job criteria must be directly related to the "essential functions" of the job, which is, in turn, related to the business necessity of the company. In some cases, any difference between the applicant's actual ability(s) and the job criteria can be resolved through some form of accommodation.

The utilization of selection criteria, including the administration of tests, must be related directly to the essential functions of a job. A person, disabled or otherwise, cannot be excluded from access or opportunity to a job if the person meets those minimum standards for that job. Likewise, a person may not be excluded from a employment even when they do not meet the criteria for the job if the person could satisfy the criteria with the provision of reasonable accommodation for the job.

In the practice of evaluating applicants for a job, individuals with disabilities cannot not be excluded from a job that they could perform because their disability prevents them from taking a test for that job or subsequent employer-provided training. There must be reasonable accommodation applied in cases where the applicant, who might have a disability, takes a test for a job. In cases of impairments related to sensory, manual, or speaking skills, the employer, especially upon advanced notice, must provide alternative and accessible tests. The employer is also permitted to interview applicants, including persons with disabilities, with respect to the applicant's capacity to perform the essential functions of a job. The inquiry must be related to the essential functions and may include an evaluation of how the person with a disability might be able to perform the job with accommodations. The intent of this part of the law is to ensure fair hiring practices, based on fair and accommodating (if necessary) testing procedures for all applicants, including persons with disabilities.

Related to the selection process are permissible/non-permissible questions regarding the person's disability. According to the ADAA (2008), "A covered entity shall not require a medical examination and shall not make inquiries of an employee as to whether such employee is an individual with a disability or as to the nature or severity of the disability, unless such examination or inquiry is shown to be job-related and consistent with business necessity" (p. 12).

However: "A covered entity may conduct voluntary medical examinations, including voluntary medical histories, which are part of an employee health program available to employees at that work site. A covered entity may make inquiries into the ability of an employee to perform job-related functions" (p. 10).

Role of Job Analysis

Rehabilitation professionals have been conducting job analyses for years (Alexander, Davis, & Weisman, 1985; Lytel & Botterbusch, 1981; USDOL, 1991; Weed, Taylor, & Blackwell, 1991). This process provides to employers an understanding of all of the traits associated with performing job duties, and such information can assist injured employees to return to work. Weed, Blackwell, and Taylor (1991) note that rehabilitationists in both the private and public sectors have utilized a specific format to observe and document job tasks, duties, etc. This information can assure injured employees that they will not be required to engage in duties which may result in injury, or in the instance of a work history, re-injury. A job analysis also provides specifics to physicians with regard to the physical demands, environmental conditions, etc. that are required in a particular job. This information allows the physician to formulate a professional opinion as to the appropriateness of the job with respect to physical requirements.

Since the initiation of the ADA, coupled with the expanded worker traits available in the Classification of Jobs 2000 (Field & Field, 1999), the character of job analysis for the private sector has dramatically changed. Publications are available to assist private sector rehabilitation professionals with conducting job analyses that are consistent with the ADA guidelines and the new worker trait listings. (Blackwell, Conrad, & Weed, 1992; Field & Norton, 1992; Knowles & Williams, 1992; Weed & McMahon, 1992).

Completing a job analysis is a very important step in establishing important information about duties, requirements, traits, and other information within the workplace. While not required by law, job descriptions do contribute to the identification of essential functions. Systematically completed job analyses, using a similar format, also contribute substantially to a standardized approach for writing job descriptions. See separate chapter on Job Analysis for suggested steps, procedures and formats.

Identification of Essential Functions

When conducting a job analysis in light of the ADA, it becomes clear that some of the tasks associated with the job description may be essential to the performance of the job and others may be marginal or can be modified, eliminated, transferred, or reassigned. Accordingly, part of the role of conducting job analyses then is to assist the employer in listing of essential functions of each job. Although the ADA does not require job descriptions, it appears that a functional approach to job analysis and job descriptions will assist employers in appropriate placement and compliance with ADA. Certainly, having a detailed functional listing of the essential requirements of the job attached to the job announcement will provide prospective employees with much more detail regarding precisely what the employment opportunity entails. The ADA Technical Assistance programs through the United States offers ways to avoid discrimination by having these data available to applicants, including those with disabilities, prior to being interviewed for a job. (See various technical assistance manuals available at http://www.ada.gov/publicat.htm or visit the regional resource by selecting from the locations at the National Network website, http://adata.org/Static/ Home.aspx)

The employer is then able to ask the employee if he or she would have any problems performing any of the functions associated with the job requirements. An example listed in the Technical Assistance Manual (USEEOC, 1992) indicates that an individual with one arm should not be asked how the disability would affect driving but whether the person "has a valid driver's license and whether he or she can perform any special aspect of the driving that is required with or without accommodation" (p. V-11).

Furthermore, the employer may ask prospective employees how they might be able to perform certain tasks if they have functional limitation(s) that could interfere with those tasks. Such an inquiry provides the foundation for reasonable accommodation.

The law makes clear that the employer's judgment is paramount regarding what functions are essential, "and if an employer has prepared a written description *before* advertising or interviewing applicants for the job, this description shall be considered evidence of the essential functions of the job (p. 10)." (Emphasis added.)

Historically, from the Technical Assistance Manual (USEEOC, 1992), consideration for essential functions of the job include whether:

1. the position exists to perform the function;

2. there are limited number of other employees available to perform the function or among whom the function can be distributed; and

3. the function is highly specialized and the person in the position is hired for special expertise or ability to perform it.

Clearly, the amount of time that one performs various tasks within the job could be considered good evidence for essential functions of the job. However, there are also occasions where an employee might perform a task only once per month (such as monthly payroll) which cannot be transferred to another individual. This could be considered an essential function of the job even though it is rarely performed.

Reasonable Accommodation

A significant part of the law relates to what is reasonable with regard to accommodating the individual in their pale of employment. According to the ADAAA (ADA.gov, 2008), the term "reasonable accommodation" may include:

(A) making existing facilities used by employees readily accessible to and usable by individuals with disabilities; and

(B) job restructuring, part-time or modified work schedules, reassignment to a vacant position, acquisition or modification of equipment or devices, appropriate adjustment or modifications of examinations, training materials or policies, the provision of qualified readers or interpreters, and other similar accommodations for individuals with disabilities (p. 10).

Certainly, many individuals with disabilities can perform essential functions of the job without modification or accommodation. The purpose of this section, however, is to focus on issues associated with identifying reasonable accommodation. The examples, therefore, will assume that people without a need for any kind of accommodation will not require further attention.

Reasonable accommodation is intended to include equal opportunity when applying for a job and to assist qualified individuals with a disability to perform essential functions of the job. In addition, the employee with a disability should also enjoy equal benefits and privileges of employment when compared to people without disabilities. Clearly, reasonable accommodation extends to assisting people in the application process. A simple example is that an individual using a wheelchair should have access to the employment opportunity via an accessible personnel office.

Accommodations are considered "reasonable" in part when they are effective. The guidelines do not require the employer to provide the "best" or most expensive option but only one which will effectively work (USEEOC, 1992). In addition, the employer is only obligated to provide reasonable accommodation when there are known limitations. Therefore, it becomes the responsibility of the applicant to make these issues known to the employer. If, as on some occasions, it is unknown as to what accommodation can be made or, if it is otherwise necessary, specific documentation can be required from rehabilitation professionals, physicians, and so forth to verify the necessity for the accommodations. What is "reasonable" for each is specifically assessed on a case by case basis and determined initially by the employer. For an example, large employers may more easily be able to provide a barrier-free work site, and smaller employers might redistribute work tasks in order to overcome the same physical impairment (Mueller, 1990). See Table 13.6 for a summary of reasonable accommodation points.

Accessibility vs. Accommodation

Accessibility refers primarily to the effort of making programs, services, buildings, transportation and communications "accessible" (or the opportunity for all persons to participate). Regarding the workplace, persons with disabilities must have access to fair and equal opportunities to apply for a job, enter parking lots and buildings, and generally enjoy the rights, privileges and benefits of all the other workers.

Accommodation refers to the effort of making the necessary changes in a variety of ways that will "accommodate" (or make whatever changes, adjustments, or modifications necessary) a person to the work-related activity given that person's disability. This may mean that assistance be provided in taking a pre-employment test (e.g., a reader for a person with visual impairments); a change at the work station (e.g., lower a bench for a person in a wheelchair); or structural changes in the general environment (e.g., rebuilding a restroom, or building a ramp). With regard to financial assistance, it is useful for the rehabilitation consultant to know about three resources available to businesses (McMahon, 2010):

• The architectural barriers removal deduction

Table 13.6
Reasonable Accommodation

1. Accommodations that are required to ensure equal opportunity in application process.

2. Accommodations that enable the employer's employees with disabilities to perform the essential functions of the position held or desired.

3. Accommodations that enable the employer's employees with disabilities to enjoy equal benefits and privileges of employment as are enjoyed by employees without disabilities.

- Disabled tax credit (emphasis on credit vs deduction)
- Work opportunity tax credit.
- Accommodation and Essential Functions

To be qualified for a job, a person (with a disability or not) must be able to perform the essentials functions of that job, with or without reasonable accommodation. On the other hand, one way for a job to be accommodated is to reduce or reassign one or more of the marginal functions. This is not the case with the essential functions that are viewed as the fundamental tasks of a job. If a qualified person with a disability could perform a job with some accommodation, then the employer is obligated to explore ways in which the job can be modified. Reference to Table 13.7 will provide the employer a suggested guideline in responding to a request for job accommodation.

Making the Accommodations

There are several different types of accommodations that can be made in the work setting. Many times an accommodation can be achieved at little or no expense, although other accommodations will take considerable innovation and expense. An instrumental point is that the ADA requires the employer to engage in an interactive process, which means to talk with the employee (McMahon, 2010). If the employer fails to do so and a complaint is successful, additional financial penalties can be levied.

According to McMahon (2010), the good news is that data regarding the cost of accommodations reveals that the cost is zero for more than two-thirds of the people because two-thirds do not need accommodations. Eighteen percent need accommodations that cost less than $600, and only 7% need accommodations that cost $600 or more. The following are some suggestions:

Job restructuring: The order or manner in which the essential functions are completed can be altered or changed, without reducing or eliminating the essential functions of the job.

Task simplification: Taking a complex task and reducing it to its most basic elements so that the worker can more easily complete the job.

Table 13.7
Process of Determining the Appropriate Reasonable Accommodation

1. Analyze the particular job involved and determine its purpose and essential functions.

2. Consult with the individual with a disability to ascertain the precise job-related limitations imposed by the individual's disability and how those limitations could be overcome with a reasonable accommodation.

3. In consultation with the individual to be accommodated, identify potential accommodations and assess the effectiveness each would have in enabling the individual to perform the essential functions of the position.

4. Consider the preference of the individual to be accommodated and select and implement the accommodation that is most appropriate for both the employee and the employer.

Modifying the work station: Activities of a job task can be modified in a variety of ways that might include larger handles on machinery, lower benches, different equipment, and more.

Assistive work aides: Similar to modification strategies, there may be simple, but useful work aides that would make the job easier (e.g. better lighting, better switches, reading devices, lifts or rolling tables rather than carrying materials, and more).

Assistant or attendant: Sometimes having a "job coach" is helpful, especially for persons with developmental disabilities, although assistants may be required for persons with visual impairments, or attendants with physical disabilities.

Undue Hardship

Employers may assert that the required accommodations will cause an undue hardship on the company. Typically, this is interpreted to be the unreasonable cost associated with the modification. The ADA provides the following guidelines (ADA.gov, 2008):

(A) In general. The term "undue hardship" means an action requiring significant difficulty or expense, when considered in light of the factors set forth in subparagraph (B).

(B) Factors to be considered. In determining whether an accommodation would impose an undue hardship on a covered entity, factors to be considered include

(i) the nature and cost of the accommodation needed under this chapter;

(ii) the overall financial resources of the facility or facilities involved in the provision of the reasonable accommodation; the number of persons employed at such facility; the effect on expenses and resources, or the impact otherwise of such accommodation upon the operation of the facility;

(iii) the overall financial resources of the covered entity; the overall size of the business of a covered entity with respect to the number of its employees; the number, type, and location of its facilities; and

(iv) the type of operation or operations of the covered entity, including the composition, structure, and functions of the workforce of such entity; the geographic separateness, administrative, or fiscal relationship of the facility or facilities in question to the covered entity (p. 10).

Considerations for undue hardship include the cost of the accommodation, the financial resources of the facility, the overall size and number of employees, the type of operation, the geographical separateness, and the functions of the work force.

Reasonable Accommodations Examples

Relying, in part, upon experiences at the Center for Assistive Technology and Environmental Access at the Georgia Institute of Technology as well as literature regarding effective accommodations, this section will outline various no-cost to high-cost accommodations that can be considered for people with various functional limitations (Corthell & Thayer, 1986; Job Accommodation Network, 2011; McCray, 1987; Mueller, 1990; USEEOC, 1992; Weed & Field, 1990).

Reduced Function From Back Injuries

- Lifting tasks redistributed to others;
- Use of pulleys or hydraulic/electric lifts;
- Alternating sitting and standing at work station;
- Carts to transport materials rather than lift and carry;
- Rearranging work area to limit stooping, bending, carrying, and lifting;
- Electric, hydraulic, or ergonomically designed chairs;
- Lifts or hoists for picking up materials;
- Use of two persons to carry objects that are normally assigned to one person.

Reduced Physical Functions

- Job task reassignments;
- Rearranged work area for physical efficiency;
- Book elevators, file carousels, or lazy Susan;
- Clamps, jigs, clips, or other stabilizing devices;
- Arm supports for wrists and hands;
- Enlarged keyboards, keyguards, alternate keyboards;
- Powered hand tools;
- Voice activated systems or voice recognition systems, including environmental controls
- Hands free telephone adaptions;
- Automated office equipment such as electric staplers, pencil sharpeners, envelope openers, manual or electronic Rolodex;
- Able Office or other customized work stations.

Hearing Impairments

- Hearing aids or amplification;
- Telephonic devices for the deaf (TDD) capabilities;
- Use of telecommunications relay centers;
- Written rather than verbal communication;
- Visual cues: signage, interpreters, lines on floor, pictures;
- Workers faced toward each other;
- Captioned training films/videos;
- Flashing or visual alarms.

Visual Impairments

- Well lighted work areas, use of lamps;
- Magnifying devices;
- Synthesized voice word processors (e.g., JAWS);
- Talking calculators, clocks, and watches;
- Braille instructions or tactile signage;
- Reading machines (e.g. Kurzweil; the Reading Edge);
- Voice recognition systems (e.g. Dragon Dictate);
- Large character software (e.g., Zoomtext; Zygo).

Cognitive Impairments From Acquired Brain Injuries

- Job coaching;
- Behavior therapy techniques for training such as reinforcement schedules, rewards, or tokens;
- Avoidance of distracting environments;
- Memory notebooks, timers, visual cues;
- Photographs of work sequence;
- Jigs or adaptive devices for correct arrangement of products to be packaged or repaired;
- "User friendly" software adapted to workers' needs.

Psychiatric Functioning Impairments

- Phone use during the work day to provide support through communication with family, counselors, etc.;
- Supervisor, job coach, or support personnel nearby;

- Work from home;

- Flexible hours (to allow for attendance at support groups, therapy sessions, or doctor visits);

- Minimized distractions or interaction with coworkers by arranging for off-hours work;

- Job-sharing, part-time, or hourly opportunities (including work that will not jeopardize entitlement programs, such as SSI or Medicaid eligibility);

- Lateral job movement with the same employer to find a match with supportive supervisors and co-workers;

- Individualized training or job coaching;

- Reserved time for communication between the employee, supervisor, and mental health professional;

- Beepers, by both employees and support personnel (job coaches, counselors, supervisors), to provide a reliable means of communication;

- Personal stereos (MP3 player) to play recorded work instructions, therapeutic suggestions, calming music, or a familiar voice;

- Video teleconference phones in order for a single job coach or support personnel to visually interact with several employees from a central location;

- Psychologist or trained behavior specialist to specify the appropriate working conditions and reinforcers.

High Tech Options

Technology has increasingly been used to save lives. Over the past two decades technology has been improved dramatically, and it is currently not unusual for people who are ventilator-dependent tetraplegics to return home to live rather than reside in hospitals or skilled nursing care facilities. This presents medical-legal ethics problems for many since some clients do not want to live when they are catastrophically impaired. On the one hand, this seems to be a benefit, but on the other, since people are now returning home when just a few years ago they were unable to sustain life, it has created a complex problem for many. In July of 1989, for instance, a tetraplegic who was originally injured in 1971 successfully went to court to have life-sustaining technology disconnected.

A referral to one of the authors involves a lady who suffered a brain stem stroke and has been reduced to eye blinking as her method of communication. The catastrophic effects of the brain stem dysfunction render the client incapable of any facial movement, head control, breath control or muscle control other than eye blinks. Just a few years ago, one blink for yes and two blinks for no would be the maximum communication available to her. However, there are now several programs such as Eye Tracker or Eyegaze, which permit people to select letters of the alphabet with their eyes. This allows them to communicate, call for help, write letters, and control their environment. For the client whose capability is limited to eye blinking, this is a major advancement. In some ways it is astounding that she continues to live. On the other hand, it is certainly a blessing to know that a technology exists that will assist this young women in interacting with her environment. This section is intended to provide a very basic overview into rehabilitation technology. Several books and resources are available for those people who are interested in more information.

What is rehabilitation technology? The publication *Rehabilitation Technologies* (1986) by the Research and Training Center at the University of Wisconsin-Stout, defines it as "compensatory strategies and adaptive equipment used to increase, maintain, or improve functional capabilities of persons with disabilities" (p.1). The authors note that rehabilitation technology extends far beyond products. Educational methods, tools, techniques, as well as methods and styles of application are included as "technology".

Historically, it is interesting to note that some occupational therapy adaptive aids, which technically fall under the umbrella of rehabilitation technology, have been included in the Rehabilitation Amendments of 1973. A major boost was evident, however, when in 1986 the Rehabilitation Amendments included rehabilitation technology as an area of emphasis for public funded programs. In 1988 this law was extended to include Independent Living Centers and activities of daily living. In 1994, with amendments in 1998 and 2004, the Assistive Technology Act has radically improved access to technology. Thus, rehabilitation technology, which is a new specialty field for rehabilitation, has seen significant growth in recent times.

In response to the interest in technology as it related to people with disabilities, the Rehabilitation Engineering and Assistive Technology Society of North America (but commonly known as RESNA because the initial name was "Rehabilitation Engineering Society of North America") was formed around 1980 (see http://resna.org). RESNA brought together a number of different disciplines, all of which have an interest in assisting persons with a disability by using technology. Rehabilitation engineers, occupational therapists, physical therapists, rehabilitation counselors, and others have joined this organization. A yearly conference that reveals the progress over the previous year has shown to be popular. Many people show their "wares", and proceedings of the symposium are published, incorporating poster presentations, workshops, and other data presented during the annual conference. RESNA also offers a certification as an assistive technologist in three categories.

Many professionals and clients think of rehabilitation technology as high tech and complicated devices. Rehabilitation technology extends the gamut of services and products. Rehabilitation technology can be as simple as putting bricks under the feet of a table to allow access by a person in a wheelchair or it can include a robotic assisted computerized workstation for high-level tetraplegics.

Often the question is asked, "is the cost worth the benefit?" For an example, a prototype of a workstation including customized computers, robot arm assisted technology, and motorized book shelves with motorized carousel costs in excess of $100,000. On the other hand, as these custom constructed workstations are accepted and used by persons with disabilities, reliability increases and costs decrease. For an example, a tetraplegic workstation is now available through the Georgia Institute of Technology for less than $20,000, which includes computer and software. McMahon (2010) in his ADA related video *Facts are Stubborn Things* argues that the cost of replacing an employee is also very expensive and accommodations are typically less than the alternative.

Sometimes the benefit has to do with quality of life rather than productivity. As one becomes helpless, they also become more lethargic and more depressed. Figure 13.1 demonstrates the impact of helplessness on the person's psychological capability of dealing with his or her situation. This scale applies to psychological as well as physiological helplessness. Clearly individuals who suffer catastrophic injuries and may be tetraplegic may find that their lack of control over their environment, work place, or, indeed, their own survival, leads them to believe that they are incapable of being a productive citizen. In the previously cited example of the young women with a brain stem stroke, place yourself in her position. Without a doubt most people would want anything they could obtain that would allow them to at least communicate.

Another example. Rick, a client, was injured in an accident in 1986. He was attending church with his family and was not feeling well. He went home to obtain some medication, and, while returning to church, he was involved in a head-on collision with an 87-year-old individual who was driving on the wrong side of the road. The client was considered dead by the emergency medical personnel. It turned out, however, that he was still clinging to life. Although he was wearing a seat belt, the impact of the accident was substantial enough to break the seat belt which also broke a number of bones in his body. When he awoke in the hospital he was unable to move anything other than his eyes. Fortunately, after several weeks, he regained some use of his head and one arm.

Rick still has no functional voice although he can whisper with a rasp so that in a quiet environment, conversation is reasonable. He is unable to perform most physical functions and is basically a tetraplegic. To add to his complications, he is unable to use his neck to the extent that he would be able to effectively utilize a mouth stick. When this author was initially introduced to the client, he stated that he could not see any reason for the author's involvement since Rick was unable to work. For the first few weeks, regular counseling and problem solving with regard to moving home took up most of the time; however, after several weeks, he said to the author, "There are three things that bother me. The first is I can't pick up my kids, the second is I can't hug my wife, and the third is I am not productive." This signaled the beginning of careful scrutiny of skills, education, cognitive ability, and other factors. After talking with his past employer, it was revealed that he had an exceptional work history. A referral was made to the Division of Rehabilitation Services in order to pay for the cost of learning something about computers and programming. The client's work history primarily involved construction and site supervising of commercial office buildings.

Shortly after he was discharged from the hospital, an augmentative communication specialist was able to convince the insurance company to purchase a computer and a head wand interactive device (LROPE) that allowed the client to aim a beam of light at a computer screen to select letters on a picture of a key board as if he were typing. This proved to be reliable and opened up doors for simple communication and word processing. A referral to a computer training program for persons with disabilities revealed fairly substantial intel-

Figure 13.1
The Effects of Helplessness

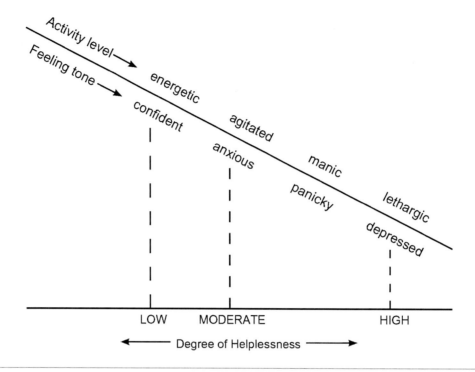

Source: *Matheny & Riordan (1979).*

lectual capabilities that could be developed. Referral to the Georgia Institute of Technology resulted in a custom designed workstation that allowed the client to have maximum access and maximum independence in educational pursuits. In addition, after his church raised money for a van, he was enrolled in a building construction program at the Georgia Institute of Technology where, on December 11, 1993, he graduated with highest honors. Although it took another two years to secure suitable employment, he did return to work full-time and has since retired after a number of years of employment where he contributed to society in many ways, including paying income taxes.

Rick has been invited to talk about his experience with the rehabilitation counseling program students at Georgia State University. After approximately two years of recovery from a catastrophic injury, he has discovered that technology has raised him from total helplessness to an optimistic and productive individual. Photograph 1 shows Rick with his workstation. Since he is unable to obtain books from the bookshelf, a book elevator is employed. The book elevator will bring a book from one of the levels to a reading position. In addition, he is unable to obtain files from a file cabinet. A file carousel, which is automated by switches, will bring a file to a reading position, similar to the book elevator. The workstation includes a mechanism that will open letters and staple papers so that he is independent in many mail and report tasks. The computer and printer are placed in such a way so to maximize his capabilities of reading and operating the devices.

Photograph 2 is a rehabilitation technology robotic assisted workstation for a high-level tetraplegic. This workstation has similar features to the one described above, with the exception that a robot arm assists in retrieving files and operating the book shelf.

Summary

In summary, the Americans with Disabilities Act as amended brought widespread visibility to a number of issues associated with successfully placing people with disabilities on the job. A job analysis geared to identify essential functions of the job is a first step toward accommodation. What is "reasonable" for reasonable accommodation is dependent on the size and capabilities of an employer as well as the experience and interests of the person assessing the options.

Many employers will have little or no experience in identifying reasonable accommodations. Similarly, a number of rehabilitation professionals will discover that consulting with employers regarding reasonable accommodations is foreign to their experience. This chapter outlines several issues associated with the ADA as well as examples and resources for the private rehabilitation consultant. Perhaps, by beginning with this basic level of awareness, professionals in the private sector can assume the leading role in facilitating the implementation of the ADA and fulfilling its promise.

High Tech Work Station for Brain Stem Tetraplegia

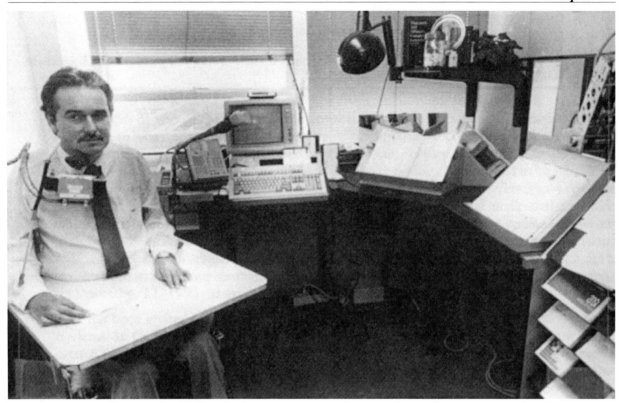

Robotic Arm Assisted Workstation for High Level Tetraplegia

Appendix A
References

Albrecht, G. (1994). The application of the hedonic damages concept to wrongful death and personal injury litigation. *Journal of Forensic Economics, 7*(2), 143–150.

Alexander, D., Davis, D., & Weisman, G. (Eds.). (1985). *Designing jobs for handicapped workers.* Washington, DC: RESNA.

Allen, F. (1965). *The big change.* New York, NY: Bantam.

American Academy of Orthopaedic Surgeons. (n.d.). *Manual for orthopaedic surgeons in evaluating permanent physical impairment.* Chicago, IL: Author.

American Medical Association (1970, 1984, 1990, 2009). *AMA guide to evaluation of permanent impairment.* Chicago, IL: Author.

Americans with Disabilities Act. (1995). Cost of accommodation. *ADA Pipeline, 4*(3), 9.

Amsterdam, P. (2004). Medical Equipment Choices and the Role of the Rehab Equipment Specialist in Life Care Planning. In R. Weed (Ed.), *Life care planning and case management handbook* (2nd ed., pp. 741–760). Winter Park, FL: CRC Press.

Anastasi, A. (1982). *Psychological testing* (5th ed.). New York, NY: Macmillan.

Anderssen, G., & Cocchiarella, L. (Eds.). (2000). *Guides to the evaluation of permanent impairment.* Chicago, IL: American Medical Association.

Arden, L. (1996). *The work-at-home source book.* Boulder, CO: Live Oaks.

Arokiasamy, C., Rubin, S., & Rossler, R. (1995). Sociological aspects of disability. In S. Rubin & R. Rossler (Eds.), *Foundations of the vocational rehabilitation process* (4th ed.). Austin, TX: Pro-Ed.

Azrin, N., & Besalel, V. (1980). *Job club counselor's manual.* Baltimore, MD: University Park Press.

Babitsky, S., & Mangraviti, J. (2007) *Depositions: The comprehensive guide for expert witnesses.* Falmouth, MA: SEAK.

Backer, T., & Reading, B. (1989). *Rehabilitation technology resource guide: A manual for rehabilitation professionals and consumers.* Los Angeles, CA: Human Interaction Research Institute.

Baker, W., & Seek, M. (1993). *Determining economic loss in injury and death cases* (2nd ed.). New York, NY: McGraw-Hill.

Banja, J. (1995). Professional or hired gun? The ethics of advocacy in life care planning. *Journal of Private Sector Rehabilitation, 9*(2 & 3), 85–90.

Barros-Bailey, M. (2012). The 12-step labor market survey methodology in practice: A case example. *The Rehabilitation Professional, 20*(1), 1–12.

Barros-Bailey, M., Carlisle, J., Graham, M., Neulicht, A., & Taylor, B. (2008). Who is the client? *Journal of Life Care Planning, 7*(3), 125–132.

Barros-Bailey, M., & Neulicht, A. (2005). Opinion validity: An integration of quantitative and qualitative data. *The Rehabilitation Professional, 13*(2), 33–41.

Bellante, D. M. (1972). A multivariate analysis of a vocational rehabilitation program. *Journal of Human Resources, 7,* Spring, 226–241.

Berens, D., & Weed, R. (2010). The role of the vocational counselor in life care planning. In R. Weed & D. Berens (Eds.), *Life care planning and case management handbook* (3rd ed., pp. 41–61). Winter Park, FL: CRC Press.

Berkowitz, M. (1980). *Work disincentives and rehabilitation.* Falls Church, VA: Institute for Information Studies.

Berkowitz, M. (1988). Forestalling disincentives to return to work. *Journal of Private Sector Rehabilitation, 3*(2), 51–55.

Berla, E., Brookshire, M., & Smith, S. (1990), Hedonic damages and personal injury: A conceptual approach. *Journal of Forensic Economics, 3*(1), 1–8.

Bernhard, K. (1984). *A comparison of motivation and interpersonal values in private and public sector rehabilitation counseling professionals* (Unpublished doctoral dissertation). Gonzaga University, Spokane, WA.

Bernstein, D. E. (1998). Non-scientific experts: What degree of judicial scrutiny should they face? *Working Paper #89, Critical Legal Issues,* Washington Legal Foundation.

Bitner, J. (1979). *Introduction to rehabilitation.* St. Louis, MO: C. V. Mosby.

Black, H. (1990). *Black's law dictionary* (6th ed.). St. Paul, MN: West.

Blackwell, T. (1991) *The vocational expert primer.* Athens, GA: Elliott & Fitzpatrick.

Blackwell, T. (1995). An ethical decision making model for life care planners. *The rehabilitation professional, 3*(6), 18–28.

Blackwell, T., Choppa, T., Davis, W., Farnsworth, K., Field, T., . . . Weed, R. (2000). *A resource for rehabilitation consultants on the Daubert and Kumho rulings.* Athens, GA: Elliott & Fitzpatrick.

Blackwell, T., & Conrad, A. (1990). *Job analysis for the private sector.* Athens, GA: Elliott & Fitzpatrick.

Blackwell, T. Conrad, A., & Weed, R. (1992). *Job analysis and the ADA: A step by step guide.* Athens, GA: Elliott & Fitzpatrick.

Blackwell, T, Field, T., & Field, J. (1993). *Vocational expert under Social Security.* Athens, GA: Elliott & Fitzpatrick.

Blackwell, T., Field, T., Kelsay, M., Johnson, C., & Neulicht, A. (2005). *The vocational expert: Revised and updated.* Athens, GA: Elliott & Fitzpatrick,

Blackwell, T., Martin, W., & Scalia, V. (1994). *Ethics in rehabilitation: A practical guide for rehabilitation professionals.* Athens, GA: Elliott & Fitzpatrick.

Blackwell, T., Weed, R., & Powers, A. (1994a). *Life care planning for spinal cord injured: A resource manual for the case manager.* Athens, GA: Elliott & Fitzpatrick.

Blackwell, T., Weed, R., & Powers, A. (1994b). *Life care planning for the brain injured: A resource manual for the case manager.* Athens, GA: Elliott & Fitzpatrick.

Blum, J. (1992, September). *Current case law review and trends.* Presented at the Medical Case Management Conference IV.

Bolles, R. (1989, 2000, 2012). *What color is your parachute?* Berkeley, CA: Ten Speed Press.

Bolles, R., & Brown, D. (2000). *Job-hunting for the so-called handicapped.* Berkeley, CA: Ten Speed Press:

Bolton, B., & Cook, D. (1980). *Rehabilitation client assessment.* Baltimore, MD: University Park Press.

Bonfiglio, R. (2010). The role of the physiatrist in life care planning. In R. Weed & D. Berens (Eds.), *Life care planning and case management handbook* (3rd ed., pp. 17–26). Winter Park, FL: CRC Press.

Borland, M., & Pulsinelli, R. (1983, Summer). Equalizing wage differences, work life expectancy tables and wrongful death litigation. *Trial Lawyers Guide,* 213–219.

Boschen, K. (1989). Early intervention in vocational rehabilitation. *Rehabilitation Counseling Bulletin, 32*(3), 254–265.

Botched diagnosis results in amputation. (1984, February). *Trial News,* p. 14–15.

Brenes, L., & McFarlane, F. (1981). Accountability: The case review process in rehabilitation. *Journal of Applied Rehabilitation Counseling, 12*(1), 4–8.

Brodwin, M. (2008). Rehabilitation in the private-for-profit sector: Opportunities and challenges. In S. Rubin & R. Roessler (Eds.), *Foundations of the vocational rehabilitation process* (6th ed., pp. 501–523). Austin TX: Pro-Ed.

Brodwin, M., Tellez, F., & Brodwin, S. (1992). *Medical, psychosocial, and vocational aspects of disability.* Athens, GA: Elliott & Fitzpatrick.

Brodwin, M., Tellez, F., & Brodwin, S. (2002). *Medical, psychological and vocational aspects of disability* (2nd ed.). Athens, GA: Elliott & Fitzpatrick.

Brodwin, M., Siu, F.W., Howard, J., & Brodwin, E. R. (2009). Medical, psychological and vocational aspect of disability (3rd ed.). Athens, GA: Elliott & Fitzpatrick.

Brody, M. (1982). Inflation, productivity, and the total offset method of calculating damages for lost future earnings. *University of Chicago Review*, Fall, 1003–1025.

Brookshire, M., & Cobb, W. E. (1983). The life-participation-employment approach to worklife expectancies in personal injury and wrongful death cases. *For the Defense*, July, 20–25.

Brookshire, M., Cobb, W. E., & Gamboa, A. M. (1987). Work-life of the partially disabled. *Trial, 23*(3), 44–47.

Brookshire, M., & Smith S. (1990). *Economic/hedonic damages: The practice book for plaintiff and defense attorneys.* Cincinnati, OH: Anderson.

Brown, C., & McDaniel, R. (1987). Perceived desirability of applicants having back injuries. *Journal of Private Sector Rehabilitation, 2*(2), 89–94.

Brown, M., & Johnson, D. (1983).Wrongful death and personal injury: Economics and the law. *South Dakota Law Review*, 1–23.

Bryan, W. V. (1999). Multicultural aspects of disabilities: A guide to understanding and assisting minorities in the rehabilitation process. Springfield, IL: Charles C. Thomas.

Bureau of Labor Statistics. (1982). *The female-male earnings gap: A review of employment and earnings issues.* Bureau of Labor Statistics, Report 673.

Bureau of Labor Statistics. (1986). *Worklife estimates: Effects of race and education.* U.S. Department of Labor, Bureau of Labor Statistics, Bulletin 2254.

Bureau of the Census. (1998). Statistical Abstract of the United States. Washington, DC: Government Printing Office

Burnette, G. (2000). *Fire scene investigation: The Daubert challenge.* Retrieved from gburnette@bbplaw.com

Bush, T. E. (1996). *Social security disability practice* (Rev.). Costa Mesa, CA: James.

California Workers' Compensation Institute. (1991). *Vocational rehabilitation: The California experience, 1975-1989.* San Francisco: Author.

Caragonne, P. (1999). The concept of peer review: Purpose, use and standards. In T. Field & D. Stein (Eds.), *Scientific v. non-scientific and related issues of admissibility by rehabilitation consultants* (pp. 73–85). Athens, GA: Elliott & Fitzpatrick.

Carlson, R. (1999). Experts, judges and commentators: The underlying debate about an expert's underlying data. *Mercer Law Review* (47, 481).

CARP. (1992). *Vocational rehabilitation: Debunking the myths.* Chico, CA: California Association of Rehabilitation Professionals.

CARP. (1993). *Q & A: Questions and answers about vocational rehabilitation.* Chico, CA: California Association of Rehabilitation Professionals.

Chase, P. (Ed.). (1983). *Management control project final report.* Athens, GA: University of Georgia.

Cho, D. W., & Schuermann, A. C. (1980). Economic costs and benefits of private gainful employment of the severely handicapped. *Journal of Rehabilitation,* July, August, September, 28–32.

Choppa, A., Cutler, F., Gann, C., Olson, T., Owings, S., . . . Siefer, J. (1992). *Vocational evaluation in private sector rehabilitation.* University of Wisconsin- Stout: Materials Development Center.

Choppa, A., Field, T., & Johnson, C. (2006). *The Daubert challenge: From case referral to trial.* Athens, GA: Elliott & Fitzpatrick.

Choppa, A., & Johnson, C. (2008). Response to Field: Earning capacity assessment. *Estimating Earning Capacity: A Journal of Debate and Discussion, 1*(1), 41–42.

Choppa, A., Johnson, C., Fountaine, J., Shafer, K., Jayne, K., Grimes, J., & Field, T. (2004). The efficacy of professional clinical judgment: Developing expert testimony in cases involving vocational rehabilitation and care planning issues. *Journal of Life Care Planning*, 3(3), 131–150.

Choppa, A., Shafer, K., & Seifkner, J. (1997). *Basics of developing a civil litigation case.* Athens, GA: Elliott & Fitzpatrick.

Chrisler, J. (1989). Impact of retirements on State Agency rehabilitation personnel. *Journal of Rehabilitation, 55*(3), 13–16.

Ciecka, J., & Donley, T. (1995). A Markov process model of worklife expectations based on labor market activity in 1992-93. *Journal of Legal Economics*, 5(3), 17–41.

Climo, T. A. (2012). Quantifying loss of value of life as a component of pain and suffering: Complying with state's admission of hedonic damages. *Forensic Rehabilitation and Economics: A Journal of Debate and Discussion, 5*(1), 35–44.

Cohen, S. (1984). *When the going gets rough.* New York, NY: Bantam Books.

Conley, R. W. (1965). *The economics of vocational rehabilitation.* Baltimore, MD: Johns Hopkins.

Conley, R. W. (1969). A benefit-cost analysis of the vocational rehabilitation program. *Journal of Human Resources, 4*, 226–252.

Corthell, D., & Thayer, T. (1986). *Rehabilitation technologies.* Menomonie, WI: University of Wisconsin-Stout, Research and Training Center Wisconsin.

Cottone, R. (1982). Ethical issues in private-for-profit rehabilitation. *Journal of Rehabilitation Counseling, 13*(3), 14–17.

Counsel on Rehabilitation Education. (1983). *CORE accreditation standards of 1983.* Chicago, IL: Author.

Countiss, J., & Deutsch, P. (2002). The life care planner, the judge and Mr. Daubert. *Journal of Life Care Planning, 1*(1), 35–44.

Coyne, W. (1982, January). Present value of future earnings: A sensible alternative to simplistic methodologies. *Insurance Council Journal*, 25–31.

Crawford, B. (1982). The rehabilitation counseling profession and private enterprise. *Journal of Applied Rehabilitation Counseling, 13*(3), 31, 36.

Creswell, J. (1994). *Research design: Qualitative and quantitative approaches.* Thousand Oaks, CA: Sage.

Cross, D. (1979). A defense attorney looks at private rehabilitation. *Journal of Rehabilitation, 45*(3), 37–38.

Curtis, W., & Wilson, L. (1976). Determining loss of earnings resulting from impairment and death. *Alabama Lawyer, 45*(3), 221–229.

Cutler, F., & Ramm, A. C. (1987). Labor market access: An evolving concept in the evaluation of vocational disability. *Journal of Private Sector Rehabilitation, 2*(3), 143–148.

Deneen L., & Hessellund, T. (1981). *Vocational rehabilitation of the injured worker.* San Francisco, CA: Rehab Publications.

Deneen, L., & Hessellund, T. (1986). *Counseling the able disabled.* San Francisco, CA: Rehab Publications.

Dennis, M., & Dennis, K. (1998). Job search software under Daubert: Will it withstand scruity as part of expert opinion? *Journal of Forensic Vocational Analysis, 1*(3), 19–28.

Deutsch, P., & Fralish, K. (1988). *Innovations in head injury.* New York, NY: Mathew Bender.

Deutsch, P., & Raffa, F. (1981). *Damages in tort action* (Vols. 8 and 9). New York, NY: Mathew Bender.

Deutsch, P., & Sawyer, H. (1986, 1993, 1999). *Guide to rehabilitation*. New York, NY: Mathew Bender.

Deutsch, P. (1997). Rehabilitation into the twenty-first century: Can we meet the standards? *Journal of Forensic Vocational Analysis, 1*(1), 41–49.

Deutsch, P., Allison, L., & Reid, C. (2003). An introduction to life care planning: History, tenets, methodologies and principles. In P. Deutsch & H. Sawyer (Eds.), *Guide to Rehabilitation* (pp. 5.1–5.61). White Plains, NY: Ahab.

Deutsch, P., Sawyer, H., Jenkins, W., & Kitchen, J. (1986). Life care planning in catastrophic case management. *Journal of Private Sector Rehabilitation, 1*(1), 13–27.

Deutsch, P., Weed, R., Kitchen, J., & Sluis, A. (1989). *Life care plans for the head injured: A step by step guide*. Orlando, FL: Paul M. Deutsch Press.

Deutsch, P., Weed, R., Kitchen, J., & Sluis, A. (1989). *Life care plans for the spinal cord injured: A step by step guide*. Orlando, FL: Paul M. Deutsch.

Diagnostic and statistical manual of metal disorders (2005). Washington, DC: APA.

Dictionary of occupational titles (1991, 4th ed.). Washington, DC: U.S. Department of Labor.

Dillman, E. (1987). The necessary economic and vocational interface in personal injury cases. *Journal of Private Sector Rehabilitation, 2*(3), 121–142.

Dillman, E. (1988). Interfacting the economic and vocational in personal injury cases. *Journal of Forensic Economics, 1*(2), 56–76.

Dillman, E. (1989a). *Labor market access: Implications for forensic economists*. Monograph Series, June issue. El Paso, TX: International Business Planners.

Dillman, E. (1989b). *Vocational foundation for the economist in personal injury cases*. Monograph Series, April issue. El Paso, TX: International Business Planners.

Dillman, E. (1989c). The age-earnings cycle: Earnings by education. *Journal of Forensic Economics, 2*(1).

Dillman, E. (1992). *An evaluation of economic damages*. El Paso, TX: International Business Planners.

Dillman, E. (1993). *Economic Tables*. El Paso, TX: International Business Planners.

Dillman, E. (1994). Life care plans: An economic perspective. *Trial Diplomacy Journal, 17*(3).

Dillman, E. (1998). *An evaluation of economic damages of I. M. Example*. El Paso, TX: International Business Planners.

Dillman, E. (2000). Vocational and economic roles in appraising earning capacity. In T. Field (Ed.), *Issues in forensic rehabilitation: A national seminar proceedings* (pp. 277–321). Athens, GA: Elliott & Fitzpatrick.

Dillman, E. (2010). The role of the economist in life care planning. In R. Weed & D. Berens (Eds.), *Life care planning and case management handbook* (3rd ed., pp. 303–317). Winter Park, FL: CRC Press.

Dillman, E., Field, T., Horner, S., Slesnick, F., & Weed, R. (2002). *Approaches to estimating lost earnings: Strategies for the rehabilitation consultant*. Athens, GA: Elliott & Fitzpatrick,

Division of Labor. (1984). *Colorado workers' compensation act*. Denver, CO: Author.

Donham, D. (1990). *On-site job analysis training manual*. Seattle, WA: WKRS.

Dorland's illustrated medical dictionary (latest printing). Philadelphia, PA: W.B. Saunders.

Dorney, D. (2008). What does it mean? An N of 1. *Estimating Earning Capacity: A Journal of Debate and Discussion, 1*(2), 131–132.

Downie, N. M., & Heath, R. W. (1970). *Basic statistical methods* (3rd ed.). New York, NY: Harper & Row Publishers.

Downie, R., & MacNaughton, J. (2001). *Clinical judgment: Evidence in practice*. New York, NY: Oxford University Press.

Dupont (1981). *Equal to the task.* Wilmington, DE: Author.

Dymond, (1969). The role of cost benefit analysis in formulating manpower policy. In G. G. Somers & W. D. Wood (Eds.), *Cost-benefit analysis of manpower policies.* Kingston, Ontario: Hanson & Edgar.

Dysart, W., & Zuckett, T. (2000). The permissible scope of cross-examination of expert medical witnesses. *Journal of the Missouri Bar, 56*(5). Retrieved from http://www.mobar.org/journal/2000/speoct/dysart.htm

Eden, P. (1976). Estimating human life values. *Practical Lawyer*, September, 77–88.

Edwards, P., & Edwards, S. (1994). *Working from home.* New York, NY: Putnam.

Experimental-resources.com. (2011). *Definition of research.* Retrieved from http://www.experiment-resources.com/definition-of-research.html#ixzz1h00Ds7K1

Fadely, D. (1987). Job coaching in supported employment work programs. Menomonie, WI: Materials Development Center, University of Wisconsin-Stout.

Farley, R. (1996). *The American family: Who we are, how we got here, where are we going.* New York, NY: Russell Sage.

Farrell, G. P., Knowlton, S. K., & Taylor, M. C. (1989). Second chance: Rehabilitating the American worker: A case management approach to long-term disability can result in savings. *Journal of Private Sector Rehabilitation, 4*(3-4), 111–119.

Feldbaum, C. (1997). The Daubert decision and its interaction with the federal rules. *Journal of Forensic Vocational Analysis, 1*(1), 49–75.

Field, J. (Annually, 1985-2000). *Labor market surveys.* Athens, GA: Elliott & Fitzpatrick.

Field, J., & Field, T. (1980, 1985, 1988, 1992). *Classification of jobs according to worker trait factors.* Athens, GA: Elliott & Fitzpatrick.

Field, J., & Field, T. (1985, 1988, 1992, 1999). *Labor market access* [Computer program]. Athens, GA: Elliott & Fitzpatrick.

Field, J., & Field, T. (1993). *Work fields: Codes and definitions.* Athens, GA: Elliott & Fitzpatrick.

Field, J., & Field, T. (1999). *The COJ 2000 with an O*NET crosswalk* (5th ed.). Athens, GA: Elliott & Fitzpatrick.

Field, J., & Field, T. (2001). *Labor market access 2000 (software program).* Athens, GA: Elliott & Fitzpatrick.

Field, J., & Field, T. (2004). *The transitional classification of jobs* (6th ed.). Athens, GA: Elliott & Fitzpatrick.

Field, T. (1979). The psychological assessment of vocational functioning. *Journal of Applied Rehabilitation Counseling, 10*(3), 124–129.

Field, T. (1985). *Transferable work skills.* Athens, GA: Elliott & Fitzpatrick.

Field, T. (1987). *Labor market access rationale and research.* Athens, GA: Elliott & Fitzpatrick.

Field, T. (1993, 1999). *Strategies for the rehabilitation consultant: Transferability, loss of employment, lost earnings and damages.* Athens, GA: Elliott & Fitzpatrick.

Field, T. (1994). *Cross-examining the vocational expert: A guide for attorneys.* Athens, GA: Elliott & Fitzpatrick.

Field, T. (Ed.). (1998). *Forensic casebook: Illustrations of how to report findings.* Athens, GA: Elliott & Fitzpatrick.

Field, T. (Ed.). (2000). *Issues in forensic rehabilitation: A national seminar.* Athens, GA: Elliott & Fitzpatrick.

Field, T., Bussey, P, Connor, B., Chopp, T., Davis, E., Davis, W., . . . Towne, J. (1994). *A study guide for the certified case managers exam.* Athens, GA: Elliott & Fitzpatrick.

Field, T. (2002a). Transferable skills analysis: A common sense approach. *Journal of Forensic Vocational Analysis, 5*(1), 29–40.

Field, T. (2002b). The admissibility of 'soft science testimony' under Daubert and Kumho. In T. Field & & D. Stein (Eds.), *Science v. non-science and related issues of admissibility testimony by rehabilitation consultants* (pp. 23–35). Athens, GA: Elliott & Fitzpatrick.

Field, T. (2006). Vocational expert testimony: What we have learned during the post-Daubert era. *Journal of Vocational Forensic Analysis, 9*(1), 7–18.

Field, T. (2007). *Transferable skills analysis: A basic guide to finding related jobs.* Athens, GA: Elliott & Fitzpatrick.

Field, T. (2008). Estimating earning capacity: Venues, factors and methods. *Estimating Earning Capacity: A Journal of Debate and Discussion, 1*(1), 5–40.

Field, T. (2011). Federal rule 702: What is the meaning and implications of this rule for the forensic rehabilitation counselor. *The Rehabilitation Professional, 19*(4), 113–119.

Field, T. (2012, in press). Earning capacity assssment: A historical review. *Rehabilitation Professional.*

Field, T., Barros-Bailey, M., Riddick-Grisham, S., & Weed, R. (2009). *Standard of care: Making sense of practice, ethical, legal, and credentialing guidelines in forensic rehabilitation.* Athens, GA: Elliott & Fitzpatrick.

Field, T., & Choppa, A. (2005). *Admissible testimony: A content analysis of selected cases involving vocational experts with a revised clinical model for developing opinion.* Athens, GA: Elliott & Fitzpatrick.

Field, T., Choppa, T., & Shafer, L. (1984). *Labor market access* (Rev. ed.). Athens, GA: Elliott & Fitzpatrick.

Field, T., Choppa, A., & Weed, R. (2009). Clinical judgment: A working definition for the rehabilitation professional. *Rehabilitation Professional, 17*(4), 185–193.

Field, T., & Emener, W. (1982). Rehabilitation counseling in the 80's: The coming of Camelot. *Journal of Applied Rehabilitation Counseling, 13*(1), 40–45.

Field, T., & Field, J. (1983). An analysis of the data-people-things arrangement of the Dictionary of Occupational Titles. *Vocational Evaluation and Work Adjustment Bulletin, 16*(1), 13–19.

Field, T., & Field, J. (1987). *Casebook: Rehabilitation in the private sector.* Athens, GA: Elliott & Fitzpatrick.

Field, T., & Field, J. (1993). *Work fields: Codes and definitions.* Athens, GA: Elliott & Fitzpatrick.

Field, T., Grimes, J., Havranek, J., & Isom, R. (2001). *Transferable skills analysis: An overview of the process of integrating the O*NET database.* Athens, GA: Elliott & Fitzpatrick.

Field, T., & Hamilton, T. (1987). Estimating disability and lost employment. *Trial, 23*(3), 39–43.

Field, T., & Huberty, B. (1997). *The rehabilitation consultant as a social security claimant's representative.* Athens, GA: Elliott & Fitzpatrick.

Field, T., Johnson, C., Schmidt, R., & Van de Bittner, E. (2006). *Methods and protocols: Meeting the criteria of general acceptance and peer review under Daubert and Kumho.* Athens, GA: Elliott & Fitzpatrick.

Field, T., & Jayne, K. (2008). Estimating worklife: BLS, Markov, and disability adjustments. *Estimating Earning Capacity: A Journal of Debate and Discussion, 1*(2), 75–86.

Field, T., & Norton, L. (1992). *ADA resource manual for rehabilitation consultants.* Athens, GA: Elliott & Fitzpatrick.

Field, T., & Orgar, W. (1984). *Measuring worker traits.* Athens, GA: Elliott & Fitzpatrick.

Field, T., & Pettit, L. (1985). *Measuring physical capacities.* Athens, GA: Elliott & Fitzpatrick.

Field, T., & Sink, J. (1979). *VDARE training manual.* Athens, GA: Elliott & Fitzpatrick.

Field, T., & Sink, J. (1981). *The employers' manual.* Athens, GA: Elliott & Fitzpatrick.

Field, T., & Sink, J. (1981). *The vocational expert*. Athens, GA: Elliott & Fitzpatrick.

Field, T., & Stein, D. (2002). *Science vs. non-science and related issues of admissibility of testimony by rehabilitation consultants*. Athens, GA: Elliott & Fitzpatrick.

Field, T., & Weed, R. (1987). Determining disability: A labor market approach. *Journal of Applied Rehabilitation Counseling, 18*(1), 3–5.

Field, T., Weed, R., & Grimes, J. (1986). *The vocational expert handbook*. Athens, GA: Elliott & Fitzpatrick.

Ford, M., & Jensen, S. (2003). Labor market survey: An effective tool for vocational case management. *Lippincott's Case Management, 9*(10), 50–52.

Formuzi, P., & Pickersgill, J., (1985, February). Present value of economic loss. *Trial*, 22–27.

Foster, E., & Skoog, G. (2004). The Markov assumption for worklife expectancy. *Journal of Forensic Economics, 17*(2), 167–183.

Frankel, M., & Kinke, C., (1992). The value of life and hedonic damages: Some unresolved issues. *Journal of Forensic Economics, 5*(3), 233–247.

Gamboa, A. M. (1987). *Worklife expectancy of disabled versus non-disabled persons by sex and level of educational attainment*. Louisville, KY: Vocational Economics Press.

Gamboa, A. M. (2006). Key issues in assessing economic damages in cases of acquired brain injury. *Brain Injury Professional, 3*(3), 36–37.

Gamboa, A. M., & Gibson, D. S. (2006). *The new worklife expectancy tables: Revised 2006 by gender, level of educational attainment, and level of disability*. Louisville, KY: Vocational Econometrics.

Gamboa, A. M., Holland, G. H., Tierney, J. P., & Gibson, D. S. (2006). American community survey: Earnings and employment for persons with traumatic brain injury. *NeuroRehabilitation, 21*(4), 327–333.

Gamboa, A. M., Tierney, J. P., Gibson, D. S., Clauretie, T. M., Missum, R. E., Berla, E. P., & Newton, J. (2009). A vocational economic rationale. *Estimating Earning Capacity: A Journal of Debate and Discussion, 2*(2), 97–124.

Gamboa, A. (2006). *The new worklife expectancy tables*. Lexington, KY: Vocational Econometrics.

Gamboa, A. (2006). Understanding worklife expectancy. *Journal of Forensic Vocational Analysis, 9*(1), 33–41.

Gamboa, A., Tierney, J., & Holland, G. (2006). Worklife and disability: Confronting the myths. *The Rehabilitation Professional, 14*(3), 46–53.

Gardener, J. A. (1988). *Improving vocational rehabilitation outcomes: Opportunities for earlier intervention*. Cambridge, MA: Workers Compensation Research Institute.

Gardener, J. A. (1991). Early referral and other factors affecting vocational rehabilitation outcome for the workers' compensation client. *Rehabilitation Counseling Bulletin, 34*(3), 197–209.

Garner, B. A. (Ed.). (2000). *Black's law dictionary* (7th ed.). St. Paul, MN: West Group.

Gibson, D. S. (2001). *Daubert, disability and worklife expectancies*. Unpublished paper, Vocational Econometrics, Louisville, KY.

Gibson, D. S. (2010). Disability and worklife expectancy tables: A response. *Journal of Vocational Economics, 13*(3), 309–318.

Gilbride, D., & Burr, F. (1993). Self-directed labor market survey: An empowering approach. *Journal of Job Placement, 9*(2), 13–17.

Giles, F. L. (1992). *The vocational rehabilitation of minorities*. (ERIC Document Reproduction Service No. ED358592)

Glass, G., & Hopkins, K. (1984). *Statistical methods in education and psychology* (2nd ed.). Englewood Cliffs, NJ: Prentice-Hall.

Graham, M. H. (1978). Impeaching the professional expert witness by showing a financial interest. *Trial Lawyers Guide, 22*, 188–213.

Grant, L. (1982). Damages for loss of future earnings in personal injury awards: Pennsylvania locks its revolving door approach. *Dickinson Law Review*, Fall, 1–19.

*Guides to the evaluation of permanent impairment (*4th ed.). (2000). Chicago, IL: American Medical Association.

Gustafson, S., & Rose, A. (2003). Investigating O*NET's suitability for the Social Security Administration's Disability Determination Process. *Journal of Forensic Vocational Analysis*, 6(1), 3–15.

Hammermesh, D., & Biddle, J. (1993). *Beauty and the labour market* (working paper no. 4518). Cambridge, MA: National Bureau of Economic Research.

Handler, B., & Sample, P. (1994). *Beyond brain injury: A manual for supported employment providers*. Athens, GA: Elliott & Fitzpatrick.

Hanke, S. (1981). How to determine lost earnings capacity. *Practical Lawyer*, July, 27–34.

Hankins, B., & Dunn, P. (2008). Integrating the opinions of different experts in determining lost earning capacity in personal injury cases. *Journal of Forensic Vocational Analysis*, 11(1), 25–32.

Hannings, R., Ash, P., & Sinick, D. (1972). *Forensic psychology and disability adjudication: A decade of experience.* Vocational experts in the Bureau of Hearings and Appeals. SSA No. 72-10284, 141.

Hardin, E. (1969). Benefit-cost analysis of occupational training programs: A comparison of recent studies. In G. G. Somers & W. D. Wood (Eds.), *Cost-benefit analysis of manpower policies*. Kingston, Ontario: Hanson & Edgar.

Hardin, E., & Borus, M. (1971). *The economic benefits and costs of retraining*. Lexington, MA: Heath and Company.

Havranek J. (Ed.). (1988). *Physical capacity and work hardening therapy: Procedures and applications*. Athens, GA: Elliott and Fitzpatrick.

Havranek, J. (1991). The social and individual costs of negative attitudes toward persons with physical disabilities. *Journal of Applied Rehabilitation Counseling, 22*(1), 15–20.

Havranek, J. (1993). Historical perspectives on the rehabilitation counseling profession and the disability management movement: The emergence of a new paradigm. *NARPPS Journal, 8*(4), 157–167.

Havranek, J. (2007). *Advanced issues in forensic rehabilitation*. Athens, GA: Elliott & Fitzpatrick.

Havranek, J., Dillman, E., Field, T., Grimes, J., & Weed, R. (1997). *Forensic rehabilitation: A resource for vocational experts.* Athens, GA: Elliott & Fitzpatrick.

Havranek, J., Field, T., & Grimes, J. (2001). *Vocational assessment: Evaluating employment potential*. Athens, GA: Elliott & Fitzpatrick.

Havranek, J., Field, T., & Grimes, J. (2005). *Vocational assessment: Evaluating employment potential* (Rev. ed.). Athens, GA: Elliott & Fitzpatrick.

Havranek, J., Grimes, J., Field, T., & Sink, J. (1994). *Vocational assessment: Evaluating employment potential*. Athens, GA: Elliott & Fitzpatrick.

Havrilesky, T. (1990). Valuing life in the courts: An overview. *Journal of Forensic Economics*, 3(3), 71–74.

Hedden, J. (1989). Desired characteristics of vocational experts as perceived by legal professionals of the Wisconsin State Bar Association. *Journal of Private Sector Rehabilitation, 4*(2), 67–85.

Hester, E. J., & Decelles, P. G. (1991). A comprehensive analysis of private sector rehabilitation services and outcomes for workers' compensation claimants. *Journal of Job Placement, 7*(2), 5–10.

Hill, N. (1960). *Think and grow rich*. New York, NY: Ballantine.

Hilligoss, N. (2004). Life care planning for depressive disorders, obsessive compulsive disorders and schizophrenia. In R. Weed (Ed.), *Life Care Planning and Case Management Handbook* (2nd ed., pp. 425–454). Winter Park, FL: CRC Press.

Horner, S., & Slesnick, F. (1999). The valuation of earning capacity: Definition, measurement and evidence. *Journal of Forensic Economics*, *12*(1), 13–32.

Hughes, A. J. (1988). Labor market access analysis and profile. *Journal of Private Sector Rehabilitation, 3*(3-4), 129–138.

Huneke, B. (1982). Working with chronic low back clients in rehabilitation: The need for early intervention. *Journal of Applied Rehabilitation Counseling, 13*(1), 15–17.

Hunt, M. (2010). Day-in-the-life video production in life care planning. In R. Weed & D. Berens, *Life care planning and case management handbook* (3rd ed., pp. 811–819). Boca Raton, FL: CRC Press.

IDEA Notebook. (2005). New IDEA becomes law. *Exceptional Parent*, *35*(2), 5–7.

International Association of Industrial Accident Boards and Commissions. (1984). *An overview of vocational rehabilitation in workers' compensation*. Washington, DC: Author.

Ireland, T. (1993). The misapplication of the hedonic damages concept to wrongful death and personal injury litigation: A comment. *Journal of Forensic Economics*, *6*(3), 273–275.

Ireland, T. (1996). The value of an individual's life to whom? A comment. *Journal of Forensic Economics*, *9*(4), 343–346.

Ireland, T. (2000). Recent legal decisions regarding hedonic damages: An update. *Journal of Forensic Economics*, *13*(2), 189–204.

Ireland, T. (2009). Markov process work-life expectancy tables, the LPE method for measuring worklife, and why the Gamboa-Gibson Worklife Expectancy Tables are without merit. *The Rehabilitation Professional, 17*(3), 111–126.

Isom, R. (2002a). Proving partial loss of earning capacity: A common sense aid. In In E. Dillman, T. Field, S. Horner, F. Slesnick, & R. Weed (Eds.), *Approaches to estimating lost earnings: Strategies for the rehabilitation consultant*. Athens, GA: Elliott & Fitzpatrick.

Isom, R. (2002b). Pediatric earning capacity: Developing a defensible estimate of potential earnings. In E. Dillman, T. Field, S. Horner, F. Slesnick, & R. Weed (Eds.), *Approaches to estimating lost earnings: Strategies for the rehabilitation consultant*. Athens, GA: Elliott & Fitzpatrick.

Isom, R. (2003). *Preliminary rehabilitation assessment of Ryan Minton*, in case of Minton & Minton v. Savage. Unpublished report.

Jackson, J. (Producer) (April 12, 1992). *Workers' comp: $3 billion dollar scam* [Videotape]. New York, NY: 60 Minutes/CBS News.

Jacques, M. (1970). *Rehabilitation counseling: Scope and services*. Boston, MA Houghton Mifflin, Co.

Janikowski, T., & Riggar, T. (1999). Training and competency of vocational experts. *Journal of Forensic Vocational Assessment, 2*(1).

Jensen, E. (1983). The offset method for determining economic loss. *Trial*, 84.

Johnson, L., Ley, R., & Benshoof, P. (1993). Estimating economic loss for a facially disfigured minor: A case study. *Journal of Legal Economics*, 1–9.

Jones, K (1986). *The effect of attorney involvement in the workers' compensation system on time, benefits cost and return to work*. The Issues Papers, Second National Forum on Issues and Vocational Assessment, 39–45. Menomonie, WI: University of Wisconsin at Stout.

Kapes, J., & Mastie, M. (eds.) (1988). *A counselor's guide to career assessment instruments* (2nd ed.). Alexandria, VA: Nation Career Development Association.

Karl, J., & Weed, R. (2007). Home assessment in life care planning. *Journal of Life Care Planning, 5*(4) 159–171.

Kilcher, D. G., Kilcher, J., & Taylor, D. (1998). *CDMS study guide for the certified disability management specialist exam*. Athens, GA: Elliott & Fitzpatrick.

Kitchen, J., & Brown, E. (2004). Life care planning resources. In R. Weed (Ed.). Life care planning and case management handbook (2nd ed., pp. 721–740). Winter Park, FL: CRC Press.

Kitchen, J., Cody, L., & Deutsch, P. (1989). *Life care plans for the brain damaged baby: A step by step guide*. Orlando, FL: Paul M. Deutsch Press.

Kitchen, J., Cody, L., & Morgan, N. (1990). *Life care plans for the ventilator dependent quad: A step by step guide*. Orlando, FL: Paul M. Deutsch.

Knoblach, C., & McNabb, J. (1993). *Workers' compensation fee schedules as of 1/26/93 for services provided by rehabilitation professionals*, Boston, MA: National Association of Rehabilitation Professionals in the Private Sector.

Kontosh, L., & Wheaton, J. (2003). Transferable skills analysis and standards of practice: Wherever the two shall meet? *Journal of Forensic Vocational Analysis, 6*(1), 41–48.

Koslow, T. (2009). Case: Selvie Muse-Freeman v. Bhatti, M.D. *Journal of Life Care Planning, 8*(2), 81–82.

Lamb, R., & Rogawski, A. (1978). Supplemental security income and the sick role. *American Journal of Psychiatry, 13*(5), 1221–1224.

Lebrenz, G., & Kreidle, J. (1976, March). Present value of lost wages: Explanation and application. *Illinois Bar Journal*, 424–428.

Lee, B. (2003). A decade of the Americans with Disabilities Act: Judicial outcomes and unresolved problems. *Industrial Relations, 42*(1), 11–30.

Lees-Haley, P. (1987). Proof of economic loss with LPE: Disability, validity, and baloney. *Journal of Private Sector Rehabilitation, 2*(4), 191–199.

Lees-Haley, P. (1991). *Pseudoscientific mumbo jumbo: An introduction to psychological claims*. Encino, CA: Grandmother Hunter's Own.

Lees-Haley, P. (1993). *The last minute guide to psychological and neuropsychological testing*. Athens, GA: Elliott & Fitzpatrick.

Lessne, R. (1988). *Present value tables*. Athens, GA: Elliott & Fitzpatrick.

Lewin, S., Ramseur, J., & Sink, J. (1979). The role of private rehabilitation: Founder, catalyst, competitor. *Journal of Rehabilitation, 45*(3),16–19.

Lewis. J. C., & Matkin, R. E. (1990). Cost savings from timely referral for rehabilitation intervention of California workers' compensation recipients. *Journal of Private Sector Rehabilitation, 5*(1), 3–9.

Lynch, R., & McSweeney, K. (1981). The professional status of rehabilitation counselors in State/Federal vocational rehabilitation agencies. *Journal of Applied Rehabilitation Counseling, 12*(4), 186–190.

Lynch, R. (1979). Vocational rehabilitation of workers' compensation clients. *Journal of Applied Rehabilitation Counseling, 9*(4), 164–167.

Lytel, R. B., & Botterbusch, K. F. (1981). *Physical demands job analysis: A new approach*. Menomonie, WI: U.S. Department of Labor.

Mackleprang, R., & Salsgiver, R. (2009). *Disability: A diversity model approach in human service practice*. Chicago, IL: Lyceum Books.

Maki, D., & Tarvydas, V. (2012). *The professional practice of rehabilitation counseling*. New York, NY: Springer.

Mariani, M. (1999). Replace with a database: O*Net replaces the Dictionary of Occupational Titles. *Occupational Outlook Quarterly, 43*(1), 3–9.

Marshall, C. (2001). *Rehabilitation and American Indians with disabilities: A handbook for administration, practitioners and researchers*. Athens, GA: Elliott & Fitzpatrick.

Marth, P. (1975, October). Loss of enjoyment of life: Should it be a compensable element of person injury damages? *Wake Forest Law Review*, 459–472.

Martin, G., & Vavoulis, T. (1998). *Determining economic factors* (10th ed.). Costa Mesa, CA: James.

Mason, J. (1982). Railroad rehabilitation counseling. *Journal of Applied Rehabilitation Counseling, 13*(4), 20–22.

Matheny, K., & Riordan, R. (1979). *Therapy American style.* Chicago, IL: Nelson Hall.

Matkin, R. (1982). Rehabilitation services offered in the private sector: A pilot investigation. *Journal of Rehabilitation, 48*(4), 31–33.

Matkin, R. (1983a). Legal and ethical challenges in the private rehabilitation sector. *Rehabilitation Literature, 44*(8), 206–209.

Matkin, R. (1983b). The roles and functions of rehabilitation specialists in the private sector. *Journal of Applied Rehabilitation Counseling, 14*(1), 14–27.

Matkin, R. (1985). *Insurance rehabilitation: Service applications in disability compensation systems.* Austin, TX: Pro-Ed.

Matkin, R., & Riggar, T. (1985). *The rise of private sector rehabilitation and its effect on training programs.* Unpublished manuscript.

Maxwell, P. (1984). Computing lost future earnings in light of Jones & Laughlin v. Pfeifer. *Florida State University Law Review, Summer,* 375–400.

May, V. (1983). The vocational expert witness: Expanding the marketplace. *Vocational Evaluation and Work Adjustment Bulletin, 16*(3), 100–102.

Mayer, L. (1998). Admissibility of vocational expert testimony post-Daubert: A statistical validation of the vocational quotient as a predictor of labor market entry wage. *Journal of Forensic Vocational Analysis, 1*(3), 3–18.

McCollom, P. (2004). Application of life care planning principles in elder care management. In R. Weed (Ed.), *Life Care Planning and Case Management Handbook* (2nd ed., pp. 591–611). Winter Park, FL: CRC Press.

McCray, P. (1987). *Job accommodation handbook.* Burndale, MN: RPM Press.

McCray, P. (1994). *The job accommodation handbook* (2nd ed.). Tucson, AZ: RPM Press.

McCroskey, B (2003). *Billy Joe McCroskey's most significant papers on rehabilitation research.* Athens, GA: Elliott & Fitzpatrick.

McCroskey, B. (1979). *The effects of source of evaluative data, severity of client disability, and client age group on the degree to which clients' residual employability profiles match their actual employment outcome profile* (Unpublished doctoral dissertation). University of Georgia, Athens, GA.

McCroskey, B., Wattenbarger, W., Field, T., & Sink, J. (1977). *Vocational diagnosis and assessment of residual employability.* Athens, GA: Authors.

McGowan, J., & Porter, T. (1964). *An introduction to employment service counseling.* Columbia, MO: University of Missouri.

McGowan, J., & Porter, T. (1967). *An introduction to the vocational rehabilitation process* (Rev. ed.). Washington, DC: U.S. Government Printing Office.

McMahon, B. (2010). *Facts are stubborn things* [video]. University of Wisconsin-Madison.

McMahon, B., Matkin, R., Growick, B., Mahaffey, D., & Gianforte, G. (1983). Recent trends in private sector rehabilitation. *Rehabilitation Counseling Bulletin, 27*(1), 32–47.

McMahon, B., & Shaw, L. (1991). *Work worth doing.* Orlando, FL: Paul M. Deutsch Press.

MDC (1982). *A guide to job analysis.* Stout, WI: Author.

Messmer, M. (1999). *Job hunting for dummies* (2nd ed.). Indianapolis, IN: Wiley.

Miller, A., Treiman, D., Cain, P., & Roos, P. (Eds.). (1980). *Work, jobs and occupations: A critical review of the dictionary of occupational titles.* Washington, DC: National Academy Press.

Miller, T. (1990). The plausible range for the value of life: Red herrings among the mackerel. *Journal of Forensic Economics, 3*(3), 17–39.

Millimet, D., Nieswiadomy, M., & Slottje, D. (2003). *Marriage, children, and worklife expectancy.* Unpublished paper, Southern Methodist University.

Moore, C., Ferrin, J., Haysbert, N., Brown, S., Cooper, P., Deibel, J., ... Cantrell, C. (2009). Employment outcome rates of African American versus white consumers of vocational rehabilitation services: A meta-analysis. *Journal of Applied Rehabilitation Counseling, 40*(3), 3–10.

Mueller, J. (1990). *The workplace workbook: An illustrated guide to job accommodation and assistive technology.* Washington, DC: Dole Foundation.

Mullholland, K., Sniderman, R., & Yankowski, T. (1994). Early intervention and vocational rehabilitation: An assessment of workers' compensation reforms in California. *NARPPS Journal, 9*(1), 10–20.

Murphy, P., & Williams, J. (1998). *Assessment of rehabilitation and quality of life issues in litigation.* Boca Raton, FL: CRC Press.

Nadolsky, J. (1971). Vocational evaluation theory in perspective. *Rehabilitation Literature, 32*(8), 226–231.

National Institute of Handicapped Research. (1985). Vocational rehabilitation in the private-for-profit sector. *Rehab Brief, 8*(3), 1–4.

National Occupational Information Coordinating Committee (1984). *Improved career decision-making through the use of labor market information.* Training materials. Denton, TX: National Labor Market Information Training Institute.

Neff, W. (1966). Problems of work evaluation. *Personnel and Guidance Journal, 44*(7), 682–688.

Neulicht, A., Gann, C., Berg, J., & Taylor, R. (2007). Labor market search: Utilization of labor market research and employer sampling by vocational experts. *The Rehabilitation Professional, 15*(4), 29–44.

Noble, J. H., & Conley, R. W. (1987). Accumulating evidence on the benefits and costs of supported and transitional employment for persons with severe disabilities. *Journal of the Association for Persons with Severe Handicaps, 12*(3), 163–174.

*O*NET development of prototype content model* (1995). Salt Lake City, UT: Utah Department of Employment Security.

*O*NET 98* (CD ROM, 1998). Washington, DC: U.S. Department of Labor, Employment and Training Administration.

*O*NET dictionary of occupational titles* (1998). Indianapolis, IN: JIST.

Obermann, C. (1967). *A history of vocational rehabilitation in America.* Minneapolis, MN: T.S. Denison.

O'Brien, D. K. (1987). Membership notes: Placement attitudes. *Journal of Private Sector Rehabilitation, 2*(2), 115–118.

Occupational outlook handbook (Annual). Washington, DC: Bureau of Labor Statistics.

Office of Hearings and Appeals. (1990). *Vocational expert handbook.* Baltimore, MD: Office of Hearings and Appeals.

Oklahoma State University Research Foundation. (1970). *Readings in computer based guidance.* Washington, DC: Office of Education.

Olsheski, J., & Growick, B. (1987). Factors associated with the acceptance of rehabilitation services by injured workers. *Journal of Applied Rehabilitation Counseling, 18*(3), 16–19.

Parker, R., & Hansen, C. (1981). *Rehabilitation counseling.* Boston, MA: Allyn & Bacon.

Parker, Y. (2002). *The damn good resume guide: A crash course in resume writing.* New York, NY: Ten Speed Press.

Peters, T., & Waterman, R. (1982). In search of excellence. New York, NY: Harper & Row.

Physician's desk reference (latest printing). Oradell, NJ: Medical Economics Company.

PL 101-336 (1990). *Americans with Disability Act.* Washington DC: U.S. Government Printing Office

Pope, A., & Tarlov, A. (1991). *Disability in America: Toward a national agenda for prevention.* Washington, DC: National Academy Press.

Porot, D. (1995). *The PIE method for career success*. St. Paul, MN: Jist.

Power, P. (2006). *A Guide to vocational assessment* (4th ed.). Austin, TX: ProEd.

Rasch, J. (1985). *Rehabilitation of workers' compensation and other insurance claimants*. Springfield, IL: Charles C. Thomas.

Reagles, K., & Rynd, D. (2003). *The valuation of household production in cases of personal injury and wrongful death*. Athens, GA: Elliott & Fitzpatrick.

Rehab Brief. (1985). *A marketing approach to job placement* (Vol. VIII, No. 4). Washington, DC: National Institute of Handicapped Research.

Rehabilitation Internationa.l (1981). *The economics of rehabilitation: International perspectives*. Washington, DC: Author.

Revised handbook for analyzing jobs (1991). Washington, DC: U.S. Department of Labor.

Rice, E. (1993). Member comment. *Rehab Prose, 8*(4), 4–6.

Richards, H., & Abele, J. (1999). *Life and worklife expectancies* (2nd ed.). Tucson, AZ: Lawyers & Judges.

Richardson, J. H. (1979). Expert witness fees: Proposals for change in Pennsylvania. *Dickerson Law Review, 83*, 315–337.

Ripley, D., & Weed, R. (2010). Life care planning for acquired brain injury. In R. Weed & D. Berens (Eds.), *Life Care Planning and Case Management Handbook* (3rd ed., pp. 348–381). Boca Raton, FL: CRC Press.

Rodgers, J. (2001). Exploring the possibility of worklife expectancies for specific disabilities. *The Earnings Analyst, 4*(1), 1–36.

Rogers, H.W. (1941). *The law of expert testimony*. Albany, NY: Mathew Bender.

Rossler, R., & Farley, R. (1993). *Return to work*. Fayetteville, AR: Arkansas Research & Training Center.

Roughan, J. (1990). Case management: Definition, process and perspective. *The Case Manager*, April, May, June, 40–46.

Rubin, S., & Rossler, R. (1987). *Foundations of the vocational rehabilitation process*. Baltimore, MD: University Park Press.

Rubin, S., & Rossler, R. (1995). *Foundations of the vocational rehabilitation process* (4th ed.). Austin, TX: Pro-Ed.

Rubin, S., & Roessler, R. (2008). *Foundations of the vocational rehabilitation process* (6th ed.). Austin TX: Pro-Ed.

Russell, L. (1982). *An investigation of the use of the Vocational Diagnostic and Assessment of Residual Employability profile as a counseling intervention to improve the self-concept, adjustment to disability, and perceived vocational potential of physically disabled rehabilitation clients* (Unpublished doctoral dissertation). University of Georgia, Athens, GA.

Sawyer, F. (1989, April 20). *Burning questions. Working in America: Hazardous duty*. New York, NY: ABC News.

Saxon, J., Alston, P., & Holbert, D. (1994). *Principles for research in rehabilitation*. Athens, GA: Elliott & Fitzpatrick.

Schaper, R. E. (1977).The contingent compensation of expert witnesses in civil litigation. *Indiana Law Review, 52*, 671–687.

Schilling, D. (1985, March). Estimating the present value of future income losses: An historical simulation 1900-1982. *Journal of Risk and Insurance*, 100–116.

Schultze, Q. (2012). *Resumes 101*. Berkeley, CA: Ten Speed Press.

Seyler, C. D., & Chauvina, J. C. (1989). Placement technique variables and subject variables associated with successful rehabilitation outcome. *Journal of Private Sector Rehabilitation, 4*(1), 3–8.

Shahnasarian, M. (2001). *Assessment of earning capacity*. Tucson, AZ: Lawyers and Judges.

Shahnasarian, M. (2004a). The earning capacity assessment form: An introduction and study of its efficacy. *The Rehabilitation Professional, 12*(1), 41–53.

Shahnasarian, M. (2004b). *Assessment of earning capacity* (2nd ed.). Tucson, AZ: Lawyers and Judges.

Shahnasarian, M. (2004c). *Earning capacity assessment form*. Athens, GA: Elliott & Fitzpatrick.

Shahnasarian, M. (2010). Earning capacity assessment: Operationalizing a theory. *Forensic Rehabilitation and Economics: A Journal of Debate and Discussion, 3*(2), 111–124.

Shahnasarian, M., & Leitten, C. L., (2008). The earnings capacity assessment form: A study of its reliability. *The Rehabilitation Professional, 16*(2), 71–82.

Sharf, M., Donham, D., Williams, C., & Ryan, L. (1987). Private sector rehabilitation: The Washington experience. *Journal of Private Sector Rehabilitation, 2*(2), 105–110.

Shoot, B. (1983). Lost earnings: The discount/inflation problem. *Trial Lawyers Quarterly*, 27–34.

Shrey, D. (1979). The rehabilitation counselor in industry: A new frontier. *Journal of Applied Rehabilitation Counseling, 9*(4), 168–172.

Sink, J. (1977). Trends in rehabilitation. *Journal of Rehabilitation, 43*(1), 36–40.

Sink, J., & Field, T. (1981). *Vocational assessment planning and jobs*. Athens, GA: Elliott & Fitzpatrick.

Skoog, G., & Toppino, D. (1999). Disability and the new worklife expectancy tables from Vocational Econometrics, 1998: A critical analysis. *Journal of Forensic Economics, 12*(3), 239–254.

Smith, S. (1986). *Worklife estimates: Effects of race and education*. Bulletin 2254. Washington, DC: U.S. Department of Labor, Bureau of Labor Statistics.

Smith, S. V. (1990). Hedonic damages in the courtroom setting: A bridge over troubled waters. *Journal of Forensic Economics, 3*(3), 1990, 41–48.

Smits, J., & Ledbetter, J. (1979). The practice of rehabilitation counseling within the administrative structure of the State-Federal programs. *Journal of Applied Rehabilitation Counseling, 10*(2), 78–84.

Social Security Administration. (1993). *The vocational expert handbook*. Baltimore, MD: Bureau of Hearings and Appeals, Social Security Administration.

Social Security Administration. (1995). Code of federal regulations, 20: Parts 400-499. Washington, DC: U.S. Government Printing Office.

Social Security Administration. (2000). Titles II and XVI: Use of vocational expert and vocational specialist evidence, and other reliable occupational information in disability decisions. SSR 00-4p Policy Interpretation Ruling.

Staff. (1993, April 26). Claims rise. *USA Today*, p. B-1.

Staller, J. (2002). '*Soft science' conundrum: Daubert, Kumho and economics*. Washington, DC: Center for Forensic Economic Studies.

Staller, J., Sullivan, B. And Friedman, E., (1994). Value of life estimates – Too imprecise for courtroom use: A note. *Journal of Forensic Economics, 7*(3), 215–219.

Standard occupational classification (1998). Washington, DC: U.S. Department of Commerce.

Stein, D. (2002). The scientific method is the standard for vocational evaluation and vocational expert testimony. In T. Field & D. Stein (Eds.), *Scientific v. non-scientific and related issues of admissibility by rehabilitation consultants* (pp. 23–35). Athens, GA: Elliott & Fitzpatrick.

Stein, D. (2006). *Rules, civil procedure and evidence: A guide for the forensic rehabilitation consultant*. Athens, GA: Elliott & Fitzpatrick.

Stoddard, S., Jans, L., & Kraus, L. (1998). *Chartbook on work and disability in the United States, 1998*. An InfoUse Report. Washington, DC: U.S. National Institute on Disability and Rehabilitation Research

Sue, D. W., & Sue, D. (1999). *Counseling the culturally different: Theory and practice* (3rd ed.). New York, NY: John Wiley.

Super, D. (1957). *The psychology of careers*. New York, NY: Harper.

Super, D., & Crites, J. (1962). *Appraising vocational fitness*. New York, NY: Harper and Row.

Sutherland, K. (2009). A fifty-state survey concerning the admissibility of expert testimony. *Pro Te: Solutio, 2*(1), 14–15.

Sutton, A., Deutsch, P., Weed, R., & Berens, D. (2002). Reliability of life care plans: A comparison of original and updated plans. *Journal of Life Care Planning, 1*(3), 187–194.

Swanson, D. (1991). *The resume solution: How to write and use a resume that gets results.* Indianapolis, IN: JIST.

Tanton, R. L. (1979). Jury preconceptions and their effect on expert scientific testimony. *Journal of Forensic Sciences, 24*, 681–691.

Task Force #1. (1975). Vocational evaluation services in the human delivery system. *Vocational Evaluation and Work Adjustment Bulletin, 8* (special edition), 7–48.

Taylor, J. Harp, J., & Elliott, T. (1991). Neuropsychologists and neurolawyers. *Neuropsychology, 5*(4), 293–305.

Taylor, L., Golter, M., Golter, G., & Backer, T. (1985). *Handbook of private sector rehabilitation*. New York, NY: Springer.

The O*NET dictionary. (1998). Indianapolis, IN: JIST.

Thomas, R., Lewis, J., & Jensen, N. (1988). Job seekers' guide to employment. San Diego, CA: Regain.

Thompson, R. (1992, July). Workers' comp costs: Out of control. *Nation's Business*, 22–30.

Thornburgh, D., & Fine, D. (2000). Pausing to reflect on the ADA after 10 years. *Exceptional Parent, 58*, 60–62.

Thornton, C. (1985). Benefit/cost analysis of social programs: Deinstitutionalization and educational programs. In R. H. Bruininks & K. C. Lakin (Eds.), *Living and learning in the least restrictive environment.* Baltimore, MD: Paul H. Brooks.

Thrush, R. (1993). *ADA: Essential function identification*. El Cajon, CA: Accessibility Press.

Toppino, D., Reed, & Agrusa, J. (1998). *The ABCs of rehabilitation economics*. Athens, GA: Elliott & Fitzpatrick.

Townsend, M. (1966). S*heltered workshops – A handbook*. Washington, DC: National Association of Sheltered Workshops and Homebound Programs.

Treon, R. (1979). Private rehabilitation of injured persons: A plaintiff-lawyer's perspective. *Journal of Rehabilitation, 45*(3), 34–36.

Trimble, M. (1977). The defendant's vocational rehabilitation expert witness. *The Chronicle, 23*, 886–891.

Truthan, J., & Karman, S. (2003). Transferable skills analysis and vocational information in a time of transition. *Journal of Forensic Vocational Analysis, 6*(1), 17–25.

U.S. Bureau of the Census. (1990). *Demographics data.* Author: Washington, D.C: Author.

U.S. Chamber of Commerce. (Annual). *Analysis of workers' compensation laws*. Washington, DC: Author.

U.S. Department of Commerce. (1989). *Labor force status and other characteristics of persons with a work disability, 1981 to 1988, #160*. Washington, DC: Author.

U.S. Department of Education. (1987). *Private sector rehabilitation: Lessons and options for public policy.* Washington DC: Author.

U.S. Department of Health and Human Services. (1981). *Social Security regulations: Rules for determining disability and blindness*. Washington DC: Author.

U.S. Department of Health, Education, and Welfare. (1966). *The Vocational Rehabilitation Act as amended through 1965*. Washington, DC: Author.

U.S. Department of Health, Education, and Welfare. (1974). Vocational rehabilitation program: Implementation provisions, rules and regulations. *Federal Register, 39*(235), 42470–42507. Washington, DC: Author.

U.S. Department of Justice. *Federal rules of evidence* (as amended 2002). Washington, DC: Author.

U.S. Department of Justice. *Federal rules of civil procedure* (2006). Washington, DC: Author.

U.S. Department of Labor. (1983). *Job tenure and occupational change*, 1981. Washington, DC: Bureau of Labor Statistics.

U.S. Department of Labor. (1992). *Revised handbook for analyzing jobs*. Washington, DC: U.S. Government Printing Office.

U.S. Department of Labor. (1998). *Standard occupational classification*. Washington, DC: U.S. Government Printing Office.

U.S. Department of Labor. (2000). *Occupational outlook handbook*. Washington, DC: U.S. Government Printing Office.

U.S. Department of Labor. (Annual). *Occupational outlook handbook*. Washington, DC: Author.

U.S. Department of Labor. (1977, 1986, 1991). *Dictionary of occupational titles*. Washington, DC: Author.

U.S. Department of Labor. (1982). *A guide to job analysis*. Stout, WI: Materials Development Center.

U.S. Department of Labor. (1988). *Area wage survey* (BLS # 3045-18). Washington, DC: Author.

U.S. Department of Labor. (1998). *O*NET 98 database.* Washington, DC: Authors.

U.S. Department of Labor. (1981). *Characteristics of occupations defined in the dictionary of occupational titles*. Washington, DC: Author.

U.S. Department of Labor. (1986). *Work life estimates: Effects of race and education*. (Bulletin #2254). Washington, DC: U.S. Government Printing Office.

U.S. Department of Labor. (1991). *Revised handbook for analyzing jobs*. Washington, DC: Author.

U.S. Government Printing Office (1995). *Code of federal regulations, 20*: parts 400-499. Washington, DC: Author.

Underwood, C. (1981). *Prediction of vocational outcomes for rehabilitation clients using the VDARE process* (Unpublished doctoral dissertation). University of Georgia, Athens, GA.

USEEOC (1992). *ADA technical assistance manual*. Pittsburgh, PA: U.S. Government Printing Office.

Van de Bittner, E. E. (2003). Evaluating workers' compensation claims for permanent and total disability in California: A vocational rehabilitation methodology. *Journal of Forensic Vocational Analysis, 6*(2), 77–88.

Van de Bittner, E. E. (2006). Determining diminished future earning capacity in state workers' compensation: The California model. *Journal of Forensic Vocational Analysis, 9*(1), 19–32.

Van de Bittner, E. E. (2012, in press). Evaluating employability and earning capacity to obtain the most accurate permanent disability rating in California's workers' compensation cases after Ogilvie III. *The Rehabilitation Professional*.

Vander Kolk, C. (1992). *Litigated disability cases: A guide for utilizing the vocational expert*. Athens, GA: Elliott & Fitzpatrick.

Vander Vegt, D. E., Summit, W. J., & Field, T. (1981). Labor market access. Athens, GA: Elliott & Fitzpatrick.

Vierling, L. (2002). *Court decisions involving the Americans with Disabilities Act: A resource guide for rehabilitation professionals*. Athens, GA: Elliott & Fitzpatrick.

Viscusi, W. (1990). The economic bass for estimates of the value of life. *Journal of Forensic Economics, 3*(3), 61–70.

Viscusi, W. (1990). The value of life: Has voodoo economics come to the courts? *Journal of Forensic Economics, 3*(3), 1–15.

Vocational expert handbook (1990). Washington, DC: Office of Hearings and Appeals, Social Security Administration: Author.

Wainscott, E. (1978). Computation of lost future earnings in personal injury and wrongful death actions. *Indiana Law Review*, 647–691.

Walls, R. T. (1982). Disincentives in vocational rehabilitation: Cash and in-kind benefits from other programs. *Rehabilitation Counseling Bulletin, 26*(1), 37–45.

Walls, R. T., Dowler, D. L., & Misra, S. (1985). A conservative economic evaluation of VR case service costs using the minimum wage criterion. *Journal of Rehabilitation Administration, 9*(3), 92–97.

Walls, R. T., Masson, C., Werner, T. (1977). Negative incentives to vocational rehabilitation. *Rehabilitation Literature, 38*(1), 143–150.

Washburn, W. (1992). *Worker compensation, disability, and rehabilitation: The fraud of compulsory medical and vocational "rehabilitation" to end disability claims*. Arlington, VA: CEDI.

Watkins, C. (2004). The role of the speech-language pathologist and assistive technology in life care planning. In R. Weed (Ed.), *Life care planning and case management handbook* (2nd ed., pp. 145–216). Winter Park, FL: CRC Press.

Wattenbarger, W. (1981). The assessment of transferable work skills in the adjudication of Social Security disability insurance claims (Unpublished doctoral dissertation). University of Georgia, Athens, GA.

Wattenbarger, W., Field, T., McCroskey, B., & Grimes, J. (1982). A comparison of the vocational recommendations of three groups of VR professionals. *Rehabilitation Counseling Bulletin, 25*(4), 235–238.

Weed, R. (1986a). Labor market access and wage loss analysis. *Journal of Private Sector rehabilitation, 1*(1), 28–40.

Weed, R. (1986b). *Writing rehabilitation plans for workers' compensation claimants*. Atlanta, GA: Georgia Workers' Compensation Board.

Weed, R. (1986c). The efficacy of the labor market access rationale in estimating loss of employability and average weekly wage (Unpublished doctoral dissertation). University of Georgia, Athens, GA.

Weed, R. (1987a). A study of the efficacy of the labor market access analysis. *Journal of Private Sector Rehabilitation, 2*(3), 157–170.

Weed, R. (1987b). Social security example evaluation. In T. Field (Ed.), *Casebook: Rehabilitation in the private sector* (pp. 115–118). Athens, GA: Elliott & Fitzpatrick.

Weed, R. (1987c). Pain basics. *Journal of Private Sector Rehabilitation, 2*(2), 65–71.

Weed, R. (1987d). Computer applications in rehabilitation. In P. Deutsch & H. Sawyer (Eds.), *Guide to Rehabilitation, 5,* 1–5. New York, NY: Mathew Bender.

Weed, R. (1988a). Earnings v. earnings capacity: The labor market access method. *Journal of Private Sector Rehabilitation, 3*(2), 57–64.

Weed, R. (1988b). Review of physical capacity assessment and work hardening therapy: Procedures and applications. *Journal of Private Sector Rehabilitation, 3*(2), 89.

Weed, R. (1988c). A review of the labor market access plus computer program. *Journal of Applied Rehabilitation Counseling, 19*(3).

Weed, R. (1991). Support for recreation and leisure time activities in life care plans. *The Rehab Consultant, 3*(1), 1–3. Orlando, FL: Paul M. Deutsch.

Weed, R. (1992, August 15). Economist's role and ethical issues in life care planning. *Orthotist & Prosthetist Business News*, 1, 4.

Weed, R. (1994). Evaluating the earnings capacity of clients with mild to moderate acquired brain injury. In C. Simkins (Ed.), *Guide to understanding, evaluating and presenting cases involving traumatic brain injury for plaintiff lawyers, defense lawyers and insurance representatives*. Washington, DC: National Head Injury Foundation.

Weed, R. (1995). Forensic rehabilitation. In A. E. Dell Orto & R. P. Marinelle (Eds.), *Encyclopedia of disability and rehabilitation* (pp. 326–330). New York, NY: Macmillan.

Weed, R. (1995). Objectivity in life care planning. *Inside Life Care Planning, 1*(1), 1–5.

Weed, R. (1998). Aging with a brain injury: The effects on life care plans and vocational opinions. *The Rehabilitation Professional, 6*(5), 30–34.

Weed, R. (1998). Life care planning: An overview. *Directions in Rehabilitation, 9*(11), 135–147.

Weed, R. (Ed.) (1998). *Life care planning and case management handbook*. Boca Raton, FL: CRC Press.

Weed, R. (2000). The worth of a child: Earnings capacity and rehabilitation planning for pediatric personal injury litigation cases. *The Rehabilitation Professional, 8*(1), 29–43.

Weed, R. (2002). The life care planner: Secretary, know-it-all, or general contractor? One person's perspective. *Journal of Life Care Planning, 1*(2), 173–177.

Weed, R. (2002). Assessing the worth of a child in personal injury litigation cases. *The Rehabilitation Professional, 8*(1), 29–42.

Weed, R. (Guest Editor). (2002). Special issue on the assessment of transferable skills in forensic settings. *Journal of Forensic Vocational Analysis, 5*(1), 1–60.

Weed, R. (2004a). Life care planning: Past, present and future. In R. Weed (Ed.), *Life care planning and case management handbook* (2nd ed., pp. 1–16). Winter Park FL: CRC Press.

Weed, R. (2004b). Forensic issues for life care planners. In R. Weed (Ed.), *Life care planning and case management handbook* (2nd ed., pp. 351–357). Winter Park, FL: CRC Press.

Weed, R., & Berens, D. (Eds.). (2010). *Life care planning and case management handbook* (3rd ed.). Boca Raton, FL: St. Lucie/CRC Press

Weed, R., & Berens, D. (Eds.). (2001). *Life care planning summit 2000 proceedings*. Athens, GA: Elliott & Fitzpatrick.

Weed, R., & Engelhart, L. (2005). Vehicle modifications: Useful considerations for life care planners. *Journal of Life Care Planning, 4*(2&3), 115–125.

Weed, R., & Field, T. (1986). The differences and similarities between public and private sector vocational rehabilitation: A literature review. *Journal of Applied Rehabilitation Counseling, 17*(2), 11–16.

Weed, R., & Field, T. (1990, 1994, 2001). *Rehabilitation consultant's handbook*. Athens, GA: Elliott & Fitzpatrick.

Weed, R., & Field, T. (2012). *Rehabilitation consultant's handbook* (4th ed.). Athens, GA: Elliott & Fitzpatrick.

Weed, R., & Hill, J. (1999). *CRC exam guide to success* (6th ed.). Athens, GA: Elliott & Fitzpatrick.

Weed. R., & Hill, J. (2008). *CRC exam guide to success* (9th ed.). Athens, GA: Elliott & Fitzpatrick.

Weed, R., & Johnson, C. (2006). *Life care planning in light of Daubert and Kumho*. Athens, GA: Elliott & Fitzpatrick.

Weed, R., & Lewis, S. (1994). Workers' compensation rehabilitation and case management are cost effective: True or False? *Journal of Rehabilitation Administration, 18*(4), 217–224.

Weed, R., & McMahon, B. (1992). Enhancing the nature and role of professional job analysis. In N. Hablutzel & B. McMahon (Eds), *The Americans with disabilities act: Access and accommodations* (pp. 129–138). Orlando, FL: Paul M. Deutsch Press.

Weed, R., & Riddick S. (1992). Life care plans as a case management tool. *Rehab Prose, 8*(1), 3–4.

Weed, R., & Riddick, S. (1992). Life care plans as a case management tool. *The Individual Case Manager Journal, 3*(1), 26–35.

Weed, R., & Sluis, A. (1990). *Life care plans for the amputee: A step by step guide*. Orlando, FL: Paul M. Deutsch Press.

Weed, R., & Taylor, C. (1990). Labor market surveys: The backbone of the rehabilitation plan. *NARPPS Journal & News, 5*(4), 27–32.

Weed, R. O., Taylor, C. M., & Blackwell, T. L. (1991). Job analysis for the private sector. *NARPPS Journal & News, 6*(4), 153–158.

Weed, R., & Whitescarver, C. (1987). Rehabilitation technology in Georgia. *GRA Newsletter.*

Weed, R., & Whitescarver, C. (1987). Robotics and technology in rehabilitation. *Determining Disability and Worth, 2*(2), 1–3. Athens, GA: Elliott & Fitzpatrick.

Weed, R., & Whitescarver, C. (1989). The exciting potential of hi-tech workstations. *Journal of Rehabilitation, 55*(3), 10–12.

Wells, G. (1994). *Finding jobs on main street*. Athens, GA: Elliott & Fitzpatrick.

White, L. (1983). *Human debris: The injured worker in America*. New York, NY: Seaview/Putnam.

Wiegley, R. D. (1977). Legal profession – witnesses – contingent fees for expert witnesses. *Wisconsin Law Review*, 1977, 603–614.

Winkler, T., & Weed, R. (2004). Life care planning for spinal cord injury. In R. Weed (Ed.), *life care planning and case management handbook* (2nd ed., pp. 483–539). Winter Park FL: CRC Press.

Wolf, R. (1985). Earnings loss experts can document damages. *The Vocational Expert, 2*(2), 5.

Work, jobs, and occupations: A critical review of the Dictionary of Occupational Titles. (1980). Washington, DC: National Research Council, Committee of Occupational Classification.

Workers Compensation Research Institute. (1988). Improving vocational rehabilitation outcomes: Opportunities for earlier intervention, *WCRI Research Brief, 4*(7), Cambridge, MA.

Worrall, J. D. (1978). A benefit-cost analysis of the vocational rehabilitation program. *Journal of Human Resources, 22*(3), 285–297.

Wright, G. (1980). *Total rehabilitation*. Boston, MA: Little, Brown.

Wright, T., & Leung, P. (1993). *Meeting the unique needs of minorities with disabilities*. Washington, DC: National Council on Disability.

Yankowski, T. P., & Sniderman, R. L. (1991). Return to work: Rehabilitation of the injured worker in California. *National Association of Rehabilitation Professionals in the Private Sector Journal and News, 6*(6), 245–250.

Zasler, N. (1994). A physiatric perspective on life care planning. *Journal of Private Sector Rehabilitation, 9*(2 & 3), 57–62.

Legal Citations

$110,000 for fractured wrist in maritime settlement. (1983, November). *Trial News,* p. 7, 12.

$190,000 to truck driver for cervical injuries. (1984, April). *Trial News,* p. 6.

$800,000 settlement in construction fall. (1984, March). *Trial News,* p. 11.

Adams v. Apfel, (US 10th, 97-5140).

Adeola et al. v. Kemmerly, 822 So. 2d 722 (LA. Ct. App. 2002).

Aivaliotas v. S.S. Atlantic Glory, US Dist Ct, Virginia, Norfolk Div, 214F Supp 568, 1963.

B.F. Speciality Company v. Charles M. Shedd Company, Sp Ct of Appl of West Virginia, Civ No. 87-C-518-2, 1996.

Ballance et al. v. Wal-Mart Stores, Inc. U.S. App. Lexis 7663 (4th Cir. 1999).

Boland-Maloney Lumber Company, Inc. v. Burnett & Burnett, KY Ct of Appl, No. 2008-CA-000059-MR, 2009.

Buck v. Chin, 3rd Dist Ct of Appl, FL 3D08-2809, 2009.

Daubert v. Merrell Dow Pharmaceuticals, Inc. (U.S. Supreme Court, 92-102). 1993.

Daum v. Auburn Memorial Hospital, 198 AD2d 899.

Doren v. Battle Creek Health System, 187 F.3d 595 (6th Cir 1999).

Drury v. Corvel Corporation, 1:92 CV 2801 RCF. United States District Court for the Northern District of Georgia, Atlanta Division, 1993.

Eastman v. The Stanley Works et al. 180 OH Appl.3d 844, 2009-Ohio-634.

Elcock v. K-Mart Corp, 1998, U.S. Ct Appl, 3rd Cir, No. 98-7472.

Elkins v. Syken, 672 So.2d 517 FL 1996.

Elliott v. United States, 877 F. Supp. 1569 (M.D. GA. 1992).

Epp v. Lauby, 271 Neb. 640 2006.

Equal Employment Opportunity Commission v. Sara Lee Corp. (US 4th, 00-1534).

Exxon Corp. v. Fulgham. Sup Ct of VA, 294 S.E.2d 894 (1982).

Fairchild v. United States, 769 R. Supp. 964 (W.D. LA, 1991).

Fenton v. Callahan, (US 8th, 97-3000).

Frye v. United States, 293 F 1013 (D.C. Cir. 1923)

Garland v. Rossknecht, 2001 SD Sp Ct 42.

Gavron v. Gavron, 203 Cal. App. 3d 705 (1988).

General Electric Corp. v. Joiner, 522 U.S. Sp Ct, 136 (1999).

*Haddock v. Apfe*l, *(U.S. 10th, 98-7063).*

Hanford Nuclear Reservation Litig., 350 F. Supp. 2d 871 (D.WA, 2004).

Heckler v. Campbell, 103 S. Ct. 1952 (1983).

Hobbs v. Harken, Ct of App Mo W Dist 969 S.W.2d 318(1998).

Hughes v. Inland Container Corp., Sup Ct of Kansas, 247 Kan 407, 1990.

Jackson v. Chater, (US 7th, 95-3462).

Joiner v. General Electric. 96-188, US Sp Ct 1997.

Jones v. Apfel, (U.S. 11th, 98-6797).

Jones and McLaughlin Steel Corp. V. Pfeifer, 462 U.S. 523 (1983).

Kaczkowski v. Bolubasz, 491 Pa. 561, 421 A. 2d 1027 (1980).

Kemp v. Miami Quality Concrete, 410 So. 2d. 199 (1982).

Kerns v. Apfel, (US 8th, 98-160). *Kim Manufacturing, Inc. v. Superior Metal Treating, Inc.* 537 S W Reporter, 2d. 424 (1976).

Kinnaman v. Ford Motor Company, 79 F.Supp. 2d 1096 (E.D. Mo. 2000).

Klingman v. Kruschke (1983). 339 N.W. 2d 603.

Kumho Tire Company v. Carmichael. 526 US Sp Ct 137, 1999.

Kumho v. Patrick Carmichael. (US Supreme Court, 97-1709).

Lichtor v. Clark, 845 S.W.2d 55, 66 (Mo. Appl 1992).

Malczewski v. McReynolds, 630 P. 2d, 285 (1981).

Marks v. Mobile Oil, 562 F. Supp, 769 (1983).

McKay v. Toyota Manufacturing, USA, Inc. (US 6th, 95-5617).

McQueen v. Apfel, (US 5th, 99-168).

Minton & Minton v. Savage, 250th Judicial Dist, Travis County, TX (2004).

Monessen Southwestern R. Co. V. Morgan, 486 U.S. 330 (1988).

Nicholson v. The Boeing Company. (US 4th, 98-3058).

Noffke v. Perez & Perez, Alaska Sp Ct 6240, 178 P3rd 1141 2008.

Norwest Bank v. Kmart Corp., US Dist. Ct., Northern Dist. of Indiana, 3:94-CV-78RM.

Ogilvie v. City and County of San Francisco, Opinion and Decision after Reconsideration, En Banc, WCAB No. ADJ1177048 (SFO 0487779), 74 CCC 248 (2009, February 3 a 1191357382.

Ogilvie v. City and County of San Francisco, Opinion and Decision after Reconsideration, En Banc, WCAB No. ADj1177048 (SFO 0487779), 74 CCC 1127 (2009, September 3).

Ogilvie v. WCAB and *City and County of San Francisco v. WCAB,* A126344; A126427 (2011).

Ollis v. Knecht, 16D01-9909-CT-97, Ct of Appl of Indiana, 2001.

Palmer v. Jackson, NC Ind. Comm. (I.C. NO. 859146).

Paoli Railroad Yard PCB Litigation, 35 F.3rd 717 (3rd Cir. 1994).

Parson v. City of Chicago (1983).

Perez v. IBP, Inc., 16 Kan. App. 277, 826 P.2nd 520 (Kan. Ct. App. 1991)

PGA Tour, Inc. V. Martin, 532 U.S. 661, 121 Sp. Ct. 1879, 149 L. Ed.2d 904, 2001.

Ryals v. Home Insurance, 410 So. 2d 827 (1982).

Selvie Muse-Freeman v. Imran Bhatti, US Dist Ct for Dist of NJ, 07-3638 (AET), 2008. Also,

Smith v. Bowen (US 4th, 87-837).

Smith & Smith v. M.V.Woods Construction Co., Inc. 764 N.Y.S.2d 749 (2003).

Stevens v. Bangor and Aroostook Railroad Company, U.S. Ct of Appl, 1st Cir, 97 F3d 594, 1996.

Taylor v. Speedway Motorsports, Inc. 01-CVS-12107, Sup Ct, NC.

Trower v. Jones, 121, Ill Sp Ct, 2d 211 (1988).

United States of America v. Pearson, U.S. Ct Appl, 2nd Cir, No. 07-0142-cr 2008.

Virginia model jury instruction. (Rel. 4-12/03), No. 9,000.

Walker v. New Fern Restorium, 409 So. 2d., 1201 (1982).

Websites

Messmer, M. (n.d.). Five tips for better résumé writing. Retrieved, December 28, 2011 from http://www.dummies.com/how-to/content/five-tips-for-better-resume-writing.html

http://www.files.georgia.gov/SBWC/Files/McrProcedureManual2011.pdf

ADA (2011). Home Page. Retrieved from http://www.ada.gov

ADA.gov (2009) *Americans with Disabilities Act of 1990, as amended* http://www.ada.gov/ pubs/adastatute08.pdf

American Medical Association. (2007). *Guides to the Evaluation of Permanent Impairment,* (6th ed.). Available at https://catalog.ama-assn.org/Catalog/product/product_detail.jsp?productId=prod920005

American Society of Safety Engineers. (2011). *Impact of Accident Costs on Businesses*. Retrieved from http://www.asse.org/professionalaffairs-new/bosc/impact.php

Bolles, R. (2009). *What color is your parachute, part 1?* [Video]. Available at http://www.youtube.com/watch?feature=endscreen&v=Sxrhyo2MlWo&NR=1

Bolles, R. (2009). *What color is your parachute, part 1?* [Video]. Available at http://pacificcoast.tv/video/richard-bolles-what-color-is-your-parachute-part-1-of-4

Brennan, J. (2008). *Disability Law Lowdown*. Available at http://dll.ada-podcasts.com/shownotes/DLLPod18.php

Bureau of Labor Statistics. (2010a). *Labor Force Statistics from the Current Population Survey*. Available at http://www.bls.gov/cps/

Bureau of Labor Statistics. (2010b). *Employed persons by major occupation and sex, 2008 and 2009 annual averages*. Available at http://www.bls.gov/cps/wlftable10-2010.htm

Bureau of Labor Statistics. (2011). *Persons with a Disability: Labor Force Characteristics Summary*. Available at http://www.bls.gov/news.release/disabl.nr0.htm

Commission for Case Manager Certification. (n.d.). *Definition and Philosophy of Case Management*. Retrieved December 23, 2011 from http://www.ccmcertification.org/about-us/about-case-management/definition-and-philosophy-case-management.

Commission on Rehabilitation Counselor Certification (2011). *Disclosure and Release Forms*. Available at http://www.crccertification.com/pages/disclosure_and_release_forms/42.php

Council on Rehabilitation Educations. (2011). *Standards for Rehabilitation Counselor Education Programs*. Available at http://www.core-rehab.org/PDF%20Documents/rcestand.05192011.pdf

DOLETA. (1998). *PUBLIC LAW 105–220—AUG. 7, 1998, Workforce Investment Act*. Available at http://www.doleta.gov/usworkforce/wia/wialaw.pdf

DOLETA. (2004). *Technical Amendments to the Workforce Investment Act of 1998*. Retrieved from http://www.doleta.gov/usworkforce/wia/amendments.cfm

Emerson, S. (2009). *Evidentiary rules affecting expert testimony: The thirteen commandments*. Retrieved from www.mobar.org/data/esqoa/may22/emerson-part1.pdf

Elliott & Fitzpatrick, Inc. www.elliottfitzpatrick.com

Federal rules of evidence. http://www.law.cornell.edu/rules/fre

Federal rules of civil procedure. http://www.law.cornell.edu/rules/fre/rules.htm

Fisher, A. (2011). *Checking out job applicants on Facebook? Better ask a lawyer*. Retrieved from http://management.fortune.cnn.com/2011/03/02/checking-out-job-applicants-on-facebook-better-ask-a-lawyer/

Goren, W. (2002). *Much ado about something - and something you may not know: The Supreme Court in Toyota Motor Manufacturing v. Williams, and PGA Tour, Inc. v. Martin*. Retrieved from www.dcba.org/brief/mayissue/2002/art30502.htm

Halstrom, F. (2000). *Proving partial loss of earning capacity*. Halstrom Law Offices: www.halstrom.com.

Humphreys, S. (1998). U.S. Supreme Court applies Daubert standard to "non-scientific" expert testimony. Available at www.pagedepot.com/EENR/Daubert.htlm

International Association of Industrial Accident Boards and Commissions. (2011). *About the IAIABC*. Retrieved from http://www.iaiabc.org/i4a/pages/index.cfm?pageid=3277

Job Accommodation Network. (2012). *Frequently Asked Questions*. Retrieved from http://askjan.org/

Khimm, S. (2011, Sept 13). The Great Recession in five charts. *The Washington Post*. Available at http://www.washingtonpost.com/blogs/ezra-klein/post/the-great-recession-in-five-charts/2011/09/13/gIQANuPoPK_blog.html

Messmer, M. (nd). Five tips for better résumé writing. Retrieved, December 28, 2011 from http://www.dummies.com/how-to/content/five-tips-for-better-resume-writing.html

National Dissemination Center for Children with Disabilities. (2009). *Assistive Technology Act*. Retrieved from http://nichcy.org/laws/ata

Occupational Information Development Advisory Panel (2011). *FAQs*. Retrieved from http://www.ssa.gov/oidap/

Occupational Safety and Health Administration. (2011). *Making the Business Case for Safety and Health*. Retrieved from http://www.osha.gov/dcsp/products/topics/businesscase/costs.html

Rule 56 of the federal rules of civil procedure. Retrieved from http://www.law.cornell.edu/rules/frcp Scott v. Mid-Atlantic Cable. US Dist Ct for the E Dist of VA, 40144 (2006).

Self Directed Search. (2009). *Discover the careers that best match your interests and abilities*. Retrieved from http://www.self-directed-search.com/

Simwork. (2011). ErgosIItm . Retrieved from http://www.simwork.com/products/ergos/ergos.htm

Social Security Administration (2011a). *Work Site*. Retrieved from http://www.ssa.gov/work/

Social Security Administration (2011b). *Occupational Information Development Advisory Panel*. Retrieved from http://www.ssa.gov/oidap/

Social Security Administration, (2000). Titles II and XVI: Use of vocational expert and vocational specialist evidence, and other reliable occupational information in disability decisions. SSR 00-40p. *Policy Interpretation Ruling,* retrieved from www.ssa.gov.

State Board of Workers' Compensation (July 2011). Rehabilitation & managed care procedure

State Board of Workers' Compensation. (July 2011). *Rehabilitation & managed care procedure manual*. Available at http://www.files.georgia.gov/SBWC/Files/McrProcedureManual2011.pdf

Terrell, J., & Richards, D. (2011). *Looking for a job? Consider writing a personal biography*. Retrieved from http://blog.spu.edu/cib/tag/richard-nelson-bolles/

Truthan, J. (2010) *About SkillTRAN*. Retrieved from http://www.skilltran.com/about.htm

U. S. Census Bureau (2010). Quick Facts: U.S. Retrieved from http://quickfacts.census.gov/qfd/states/00000.html

U. S. Department of Education. (2001). *State vocational rehabilitation services program*. Available at http://wdcrobcolp01.ed.gov/Programs/EROD/org_list.cfm?category_ID=SVR

U. S. Department of Labor. (2000). *Guide to Occupational Exploration*. Bulletin 2520, Washington, DC: Government Printing Office (available on-line at http://stats.bls.gov/ocohome.htm

U. S. Department of Labor. (2008). *The ADA Amendments Act of 2008: Frequently Asked Questions*. Retrieved 1/3/2012 from http://www.dol.gov/ofccp/regs/compliance/faqs/ADAfaqs.htm#Q8

U.S. Chamber of Commerce. (2011). *Analysis of Workers' Compensation Laws*. Available at https://secure.uschamber.com/2011-analysis-workers-compensation-laws

U.S. Chamber of Commerce. (2005). *Analysis of Workers' Compensation Laws*. Retrieved from http://www.uschamber.com/sites/default/files/reports/05sample.pdf

U.S. Department of Health and Human Services. (2003). Summary of HIPAA privacy rule. Available at http://www.hhs.gov/ocr/privacy/hipaa/understanding/summary/privacysummary.pdf

University of Idaho (2003). *Definition of research*. Retrieved from http://www.webs.uidaho.edu/info_literacy/modules/module2/2_1.htm

University of Iowa. (2010). *University of Iowa News Services*. Retrieved from http://news-releases.uiowa.edu/2010/october/101210vocation_grant.html

Valpar. (2011). *Joule: More than a FCE*. Retrieved from http://www.valparint.com/

Vocational Research Institute. (2011). *Legacy products*. Retrieved from http://www.vri.org/products Washington State Department of Labor and Industries. (2011). *Labor market surveys*. Retrieved from http://apps.leg.wa.gov/WAC/default.aspx?cite=296-19A-010

Laws, Policy & Regulations

A Disability Claimant's Capacity to Do Past Relevant Work, In General. *SSR 82-62.*

ANSI (1961). *Specifications for making buildings and facilities accessible to, and usable by, the physically handicapped.* New York, NY: American National Standards Institute.

Authors. (1988). *A summary guide to social security and supplemental security income for the disabled and blind.* Social Security Administration, No. 64-030.

Authors. (1994). *Reference manual on scientific evidence.* Washington, DC: Federal Judicial Center. Manual available at Authors, *ADA: Accessibility guidelines for buildings and facilities.* Washington, D.C. U.S. Architectural and Transportation Barriers Compliance

Capability to Do Other Work – The Medical-Vocational Rules as a Framework for Evaluating Solely Nonexertional Impairments. *SSR 85-15.*

Capacity to Do Other Work – The Medical-Vocational Rules as a Framework for Evaluating a Combination of Exertional and Nonexertional Impairments. *SSR 83-14.*

Capacity to Do Other Work – The Medical-Vocational Rules as a Framework for Evaluating Exertional Limitations Within a Range of Work or Between Ranges of Work. *SSR 83-12.*

Current Status of the Dictionary of Occupational Titles and the Occupational Information New (O*NET). *Memorandum and Letter #500, SSA, December 3, 1999.*

Code of federal regulations (latest printing, 20: Parts 400-499). Washington, DC: U.S. Government Printing Office.

Code of federal regulations, 20, Parts 400 - 499, 1995. Washington, DC: U.S. Government Printing Office.

Definition of highly marketable skills for individuals close to retirement age – Titles II and XVI of the Social Security Act.

Determining Capacity to Do Other Work – The Medical-Vocational Rules of Appendix 2. SSR 83-10.

Equal Employment Opportunity Commission. (1992). *Americans with Disabilities Act: Technical assistance manual,* and *Resource directory.* Washington, DC: U.S. Authors.

Past Relevant Work - The Particular Job or Occupation as Generally Performed. SSR 82-61.

Social Security Administration (1970). *Disability evaluation under social security: A handbook for physicians.* Social Security Administration, No. SSI-89.

Social Security Administration (1981). *Social security regulations: Rules for determining disability and blindness.* Social Security Administration, No. 64-014.

Social Security Administration (latest printing). *The vocational expert handbook.* Baltimore: Bureau of Hearings and Appeals, Social Security Administration.

Social Security Administration. (June, 1987). *Vocational experts: Testifying at disability hearings: A self-study guide.* Social Security Administration, No. 70-009.

Social Security Handbook (latest printing). SSA.

Social Security Rulings (latest printing). SSA.

Southeast Disability and Business Technical Assistance Center (1993). Court enters judgment in first EEOC suit under Americans with Disabilites Act. *ADA Pipeline, 2*(3), 3.

The 137 Unskilled Sedentary Occupations. SSR 96-9p Social Security Ruling.

Use of vocational expert or other vocational specialist in determining whether a claimant can perform past relevant work – Titles II and XVI of the Social Security Act.

Use of Vocational Expert and Vocational Specialist Evidence, and Other Reliable Occupational Information in Disability Decisions. *SSR 00-4p Policy Interpretation Ruling.* (2000)

Use of Vocational Experts or Other Vocational Specialists in Determining Whether a Claimant Can Perform Past Relevant Work. *AR 90-3(4), 837 F.2d 635, 4th Cir. 1987.*

Using the Grid Rules as a Framework for Decision making When an Individual's Occupational Base is Eroded by a Non-exertional Limitation. *Sykes v. Apfel, 288 F.ed 259 (3d Cir. 2000).*

Work Skills and Their Transferability as Intended by the Expanded Vocational Factors Regulations. *SSR 82-41 Policy Ruling.*

Appendix B
Glossary of Terms

abrogate — to annul or cancel.

acquit — to set free or judicially discharge.

actual damages — losses that can be readily proven to have been sustained.

adjudicate — to settle judicially workers compensation program which functions to a) replace income lost by workers disabled by a job-related injury or sickness, b) restore earnings capacity and return to productive employment, and c) prevent or reduce industrial accidents.

ADL — activities for daily living: eating, dressing, shaving, grooming, etc.

administrative hearing — less formal than due process, used to settle disagreements regarding eligibility, type of service, quality of service, etc. between a client and a service provider, with a third party (administrator) present to help settle differences.

admissible evidence — evidence which can be received by the trier of fact (judge or jury).

adversary process — a contest by two opposing parties. adverse party - the person on the opposite side of litigation.

affirmative defense — one which serves as a basis for proving some new fact.

age of majority — age at which a person may contract sui juris; which is 18 in most states. Sometimes referred to as full age; legal age; majority; adulthood.

ALJ — (Administrative Law Judge) oversees adjudication process and assesses the employability or need for a vocational expert for social security disability insurance appeals. Also used in other jurisdictions

ALJ hearing — most common judicial setting for vocational expert, used to determine eligibility for federal and state service programs.

ambulation — walking with braces and/or crutches.

amicus curiae — friend of the court. One who gives information to the court on some matter of law which is in doubt. A brief summary by one who is not a party to a lawsuit.

anosmia — loss of the sense of smell.

anoxia — a lack of oxygen. Brain cells need oxygen to exist. When blood flow to the brain is reduced or when oxygen in the blood is low, brain cells are damaged.

answer — document filed by the defendant named in a case which responds to claims made in the complaint. It must be filed within a certain time (usually thirty days) or the case goes to default.

a posteriori — from the most recent point of view. That which can only be known from experience.

appellant — the party who appeals a decision.

appellate court — a court having jurisdiction to review law as a result of a prior determination of the same case.

a priori — to reason from factual and historical knowledge that certain facts are true.

arachnoid membrane — the middle of three membranes protecting the brain and spinal cord.

arbitration hearing —a voluntary arrangement under which a condensed version of the case is informally presented to a panel, usually of retired judges, who then reach a decision that is binding on all parties.

areflexia — without reflexes.

assumption of risk — document which exists where the plaintiff is not at fault in the matter but, nevertheless, is aware of and consents to the negligence of the defendant. The proximate cause is that event in a natural sense which produces an injury and without which the injury would not have occurred.

attest — to affirm as true.

atypical appearance — refers to the characteristics of an individuals physique and carriage that are inconsistent with what is considered acceptable by a culture; problem is social, not mechanical, and there is a tendency for others to assume atypical behavior in those who appear different.

autonomic dysreflexia (hyperreflexia) — a potentially dangerous reaction including high blood pressure, sweating, chills, pounding headache, which may occur in persons with spinal cord injury above the sixth thoracic level. Often caused by an over-distended bladder or other stimulation. In rare cases can lead to stroke or death.

bailiff — court employee whose duty is to keep order in the courtroom and render general assistance to the judge.

bar — the complete body of attorneys.

bench — the court; the judges composing the court.

bladder training — method by which the bladder is trained to empty without an indwelling catheter. Involves drinking measured amounts of fluid, allowing bladder to fill and empty at timed intervals.

bona — good or virtuous.

bowel program — establishment of a "habit pattern" or a specific time to empty the bowel so that regularity can be achieved. For spinal cord injured clients, this may occur every two days (a.m. or p.m.) and be initiated or aided by a suppository medication.

burden of proof — the duty of a party to substantiate allegation so that dismissal can be avoided. To convince the tryer of facts as to the truth of a claim. Civil cases - proving by a preponderance of the evidence, while in criminal cases the state's persuasion burden is met only by proof beyond reasonable doubt. In some equity matters and more recent Supreme Court decisions, clear and convincing evidence.

calculi — stones that may form in either kidney or bladder. Bladder stones are fairly easily removed; kidney stones may require lithotripsy (shock wave shattering) or major surgery.

catheter — a flexible plastic tube of varying sizes utilized for withdrawing fluids from or introducing fluids into a cavity of the body. This tubing is also used in specialized medical procedures.

cauda equina — the collection of spinal roots descending from the lower part of the spinal cord (the conus medullaris - T-11 to L-2), occupying the vertebral canal below the spinal cord; these roots have some recovery potential.

causation — being the cause of something produced or of something happening.

cerebrospinal fluid — the liquid which fills the ventricles of the brain and surrounds the brain and spinal cord.

cervical — the upper spine (neck) area of the vertebral column.

challenge for cause — effort to remove a juror because of bias, interests or other disqualification. There is no limit on the amount of challenges made for cause, but the judge must rule whether the challenge is valid or invalid.

challenge to the array — a challenge to an entire panel of jurors on the ground that the selection process was flawed.

charge of the court — the time of the trial during which the court explains the applicable law to the jurors, more often than not, in an incomprehensible manner.

Circuit court — courts whose jurisdiction extends over several counties or districts, and of which terms are held in the various counties or districts to which their jurisdiction extends.

civil suit — when a wrong has been committed (but not used to prosecute criminal activities), one of the major options of the injured party is to sue for damages from injuries.

clear and convincing — a standard of proof beyond preponderance but below reasonable doubt. Less than the degree required in criminal cases but more than that required in ordinary civil actions.

clerk — the court clerk who assists the judge in record keeping at the trial.

closed head injury — trauma to the head that does not penetrate or fracture the skull, but damages the brain. May also be referred to as acquired brain injury.

cognition — the conscious process of the mind by which we are aware of thoughts and perception, including all aspects of perceiving, thinking, and remembering.

collateral sources — funds or service from sources other than the defendant. This includes plaintiff's (the injured party) own insurance, company insurance, veteran's benefits, social security, government benefits, and public services.

collusion — the making of an agreement with another for the purposes of fraud.

coma — a state of unconsciousness from which the patient cannot be aroused, even by powerful stimulation.

communication limitation — breakdown in the process by which information is exchanged between individuals through common symbols, signs, or behavior.

complaint — the document filed by the plaintiff to begin a lawsuit. It must name the parties, identify the jurisdiction of the case, state what happened and set forth the relief demanded.

complete injury — this term is used for spinal cord injured when there is an absence of sensory and motor function in the lowest sacral segment.

compos mentis — mentally competent.

consciousness limitation — unconsciousness and other defects in consciousness constitute a serious functional limitation. Epilepsy is an example cause, but there are many other disability conditions that contribute to problems of attention, reality orientation, and perception or awareness.

conspiracy — the combination of two or more people who propose to commit a criminal or unlawful act or to commit a lawful act by criminal and unlawful means, or by concerted action to accomplish and unlawful purpose.

contempt of court — either an act or an omission tending to obstruct or interfere with the orderly administration of justice in the court. To impair the dignity of the court or to impair respect for its authority.

contingency fees — receipt of payment for services dependent upon amount of money that is either earned or saved as a result of the adjudication; controversial method of compensation which raises ethical questions.

contracture — stiffening from shrinking or fibrosis to the tissue surrounding the joint, to the point it can no longer be moved through its normal range.

corpus juris — the body of law.

corpus delicti — the body of the crime. Objective proof that a crime has been committed. Not the body of a victim of a homicide. In a murder prosecution, prima facie evidence showing that the alleged victim met death by criminal agency. The weight of proof is beyond reasonable doubt.

court reporter — a person who is authorized to record court proceedings as they occur.

Credi's technique — a technique of pressing down and inward over the bladder to facilitate voiding. Often used with the spinal cord injured patient.

cross examination — questioning the witness after the other side has completed direct examination. Generally, the person conducting the cross-examination must limit him/herself to the topics or subject matter raised during the direct examination of this witness by the other side. At trial, hearing, or upon taking of deposition.

CT scan/computerized tomography (also known at CAT scan) — a series of computerized X rays of the brain at various levels to reveal its structure. This procedure shows the more obvious changes such as a hematoma.

culpable — deserving of moral blame. Fault rather than guilt.

cyst (post traumatic cystic myelopathy) — a common accompaniment to spinal cord injury, a collection of fluid within the spinal cord, usually localized at the site of injury; may ascend up the cord and lead to neurological deterioration, loss of sensation, pain, dysreflexia. Cysts can form in months or years after an injury. Their cause is not known. Surgery is sometimes indicated to drain the cavity using a shunt.

cystogram (CG) — X-ray taken after injecting dye into the bladder.

cystometric examination — test of bladder function; part of full urodynamic evaluation; measures pressure of bladder forces vs. volume.

damages — Money awarded to one party in a lawsuit based on injury or loss caused by the other. There are many different types or categories of damages that occasionally overlap, including compensatory, general, nominal, punitive, special, statutory, and treble.

damages (general) — Those that did in fact result from the wrong, directly and proximately, and without reference to the special character, condition, or circumstances of the plaintiff.

damages (special) — Those which are the actual, but not the necessary, result of the injury complained of, and which in fact follow it as a natural and proximate consequence in the particular case, that is, by reason of special circumstances or conditions.

debilitation or exertional limitation — debilitation is a condition in which the individual is in a weakened state for an extended time period. This weakness results in diminished capacity to engage in various physical tasks; may derive from various physical and mental impairments.

decubitus — a bed sore or discolored, open area of skin damaged by pressure. Common areas to this breakdown of skin are the buttocks, hip, shoulder areas, ankles, heels, and elbows.

de facto — by virtue of the deed. Reality.

default judgment — a judgment entered against a defendant because of the defendant's failure to respond to a plaintiff's action.

defense — can be denial, or a plea opposing the truth or validity of a plaintiff's case.

deficit — a lacking or deficiency in the amount or quality of functioning.

demand — (n.) The assertion of a legal right; a legal obligation. (v.) To claim one's due; to require, to ask relief. To call in court.

demonstrative evidencea — that evidence addressed directly to the senses without intervention of testimony. Such evidence is concerned with real objects which illustrate some verbal testimony and has no probative value in itself. (May include charts, diagrams, medical illustration, etc.)

dendrite — microscopic tree-like fibers extending from a nerve cell (neuron). Receptors of electrochemical nervous impulse transmissions.

de novo hearing — a new hearing. Usually the judgment of the trial court is suspended and the reviewing court determines the case as though it originated in the reviewing court.

deposition — a discovery device by which one party asks oral questions of the other party or of a witness for the other party; similar to appearance in court with the adversary present and opportunity for cross-examination. The person being deposed is called the deponent. The deposition is conducted under oath outside the courtroom, usually in one of the lawyer's offices. Usually a procedure for the other side to "discover" what the expert will say at trial. Deposition for preparation of testimony may be taken when the witness cannot appear live at trial.

dermatome — this term refers to the area of the skin innervated by the sensory axons within each segmental nerve (root).

deviation from standard of care — departure from established or usual degree of care which a reasonably prudent person should exercise in the same or similar circumstances.

Dictionary of Occupational Titles — defines job titles existing in the national labor market and provides detailed descriptions of each position.

diminution of earning capacity — the economic loss of the value of the support, services, and contributions which the beneficiaries would have received if the victim had lived or had not been injured.

diplopia — double vision; the perception of two images of a single object.

direct threat — (Americans with Disabilities Act term) means a significant risk of substantial harm to the health or safety of the individual or others that cannot be eliminated or reduced by reasonable accommodation. The determination that an individual poses a "direct threat" is based on an individualized assessment of the individual's present ability to safely perform the essential functions of the job. This assessment shall be based on a reasonable medical judgment that relies on the most current medical knowledge and/or on the best available objective evidence. In determining whether an individual would post a direct threat, the factors to be considered include:

(1) the duration of the risk;

(2) the nature and severity of the potential harm;

(3) the likelihood that the potential harm will occur; and

(4) the imminence of the potential harm.

directed verdict — a verdict returned by the jury at the direction of the trial judge. Usually done when the judge feels that opposing party fails to present a prima facie case. May occur when a necessary defense is not presented.

disability — 1) any physical, mental, or emotional condition that is chronic or long-lasting (not acute or temporary), which is severe enough to limit the individual's functioning and which results in, or threatens to be, a handicap to productive activity. 2) in workers' compensation can be termed temporary total, temporary partial, permanent partial and permanent total. 3) in social security a person is disabled if they are unable to do any full-time work which is considered substantial gainful activity (SGA). 4) in personal injury cases a client may have a vocational disability from some work and not others. The individual may be able to work part-time which is represented by a percentage loss. 5) (Americans with Disabilities Act term) with respect to an individual, disability means:

(1) A physical or mental impairment that substantially limits one or more of the major life activities of such individual;

(2) A record of such impairment; or

(3) being regarded as having such an impairment.

Physical or mental impairment means:

(1) Any psychological disorder, or condition, cosmetic disfigurement, or anatomical loss affecting one or of the following body systems: neurological, musculoskeletal, special sense organs, respiratory (including speech organs), cardiovascular, reproductive, digestive, genitourinary hemic and lymphatic, skin, and endocrine; or

(2) Any mental or psychological disorder, such as mental retardation, organic brain syndrome, emotional or mental illness, and specific learning disabilities.

Major life activities means functions such as caring for oneself, performing manual tasks, walking, seeing, hearing, speaking, breathing, learning, and working.

Is "regarded as having such an impairment" means:

(1) Has a physical of mental impairment that does not substantially limit major life activities but is treated by a covered entity as constituting such limitation;

(2) Has a physical or mental impairment that substantially limits major life activities only as a result of the attitudes of others toward such impairment; or

(3) Has none of the impairments defined in Paragraph (2) of this section but is treated by a covered entity as having a substantially limiting impairment.

discovery — parties may obtain discovery by one or more of the following methods: depositions upon oral examination or written questions, written interrogatories, production of documents or things or permission to enter upon land or other property for inspection and other purposes, physical and mental examinations.

Parties may obtain discovery regarding any matter, not privileged, that is relevant to the subject matter of the pending action and this may include the existence, description, nature, custody, condition, and location of any books, documents, or other tangible things and the identity and location of persons having knowledge of any discoverable matter. The pre-trial devices that can be used by one party to obtain facts and information about the case from the other party in order to assist the party's preparation for trials.

dismissal without prejudice — dismissal of the lawsuit which allows it to be refiled at a later date (usually within six months).

DOT — (see Dictionary of Occupational Titles)

due process settings — formal adversary settings which involve a plaintiff, defendant, and judge.

dura mater — outermost of three membranes protecting the brain and spinal cord.

dysfunctional behavior — emotional disorders are associated with deviance from behavior defined by the culture as appropriate; may stem from physical disabilities or cultural disadvantages, but emotional or dysfunctional behaviors impact upon the total individual.

earnings loss — the individual's expected loss of earnings, if any, which results from the injury. Loss of earnings is based on history whereas loss of earnings capacity is projected into the future.

earnings capacity — ability of individual to obtain and hold the highest paying of jobs to which he might have access. Access is determined by worker traits, work skills and amount of training.

ECG/EKG electrocardiogram — monitoring heart rate and rhythm by positioning electrode pads on the patient's chest, which are connected to a monitor.

edema — swelling; common in legs and feet. The body tissues contain an excessive amount of fluid (plasma), increasing skin sensitivity and risk of pressure sores.

EEG/electroencephalogram — recording electrical activity of the brain by positioning electrodes on the scalp or on or in the brain itself.

elements of damages — pain and suffering, loss pay, medical, and support.

employability — exists if a person possesses skills, abilities, and traits necessary to perform a job; the kinds and types of jobs which a person with a disability might be able to perform.

equitable defense — recognized by courts of equity.

essential functions — (an Americans with Disabilities Act and 1973 rehab act term) fundamental job duties of the employment position the individual with a disability holds or desires. Does not include the marginal functions of the position. A job function may be considered essential for any of several reasons, including but not limited to the following:

(1) The function may be essential because the reason the position exists is to perform the function.

(2) The function may be essential because of the limited number of employees available among whom the performance of that job function can be distributed; and/or

(3) The function may be highly specialized so that the incumbent in the position is hired for his or her expertise or ability to perform the particular function.

Evidence of whether a particular function is essential includes, but is not limited to:

(1) The employer's judgment as to which functions are essential;

(2) Written job descriptions prepared before advertising or interviewing applicants for the job;

(3) The amount of time spent on the job performing the function;

(4) The consequence of not requiring the incumbent to perform the function;

(5) The terms of a collective bargaining agreement;

(6) The work experience of past incumbents in the job; and/or

(7) The current work experience of incumbents in similar jobs.

examination (direct) of witness — testimony of witness is elicited by the propounding of questions to him or her after he or she has been sworn in and under the supervision of the judge, the question must call for relevant and material testimony and must be free from vagueness, uncertainty, and ambiguity. Subject to reasonable or necessary exceptions the questions, except on cross-examination, should not be leading or subjective.

exculpatory — evidence or statements tending to justify or excuse defendant from fault or guilt.

exertional level — physical abilities necessary for certain types of jobs; includes sedentary, light, medium, heavy, and very heavy.

expert witness — an expert is a skillful or experienced person, or possessing special or peculiar knowledge acquired from practical experience. A witness who has been qualified as an expert and who thereby will be allowed to assist the jury in understanding complicated and technical subjects not within the understanding of the average lay person.

Federal court — the courts of the United States as created either by Article III of the U.S. Constitution, or by Congress (e.g., U.S. Courts of Appeals or U. S. Claims Court).

FES — (see functional electrical stimulation)

flaccidity — muscles are soft and limp.

forensic rehabilitation — rehabilitation as related to legal principles and cases; required to enable a court of law to arrive at a proper conclusion on a contested question affecting a disabled person's life or property.

functional electrical stimulation — the application of electric current, often controlled by a computer, to paralyzed muscles to produce function (walking, bike riding exercise, hand control, etc).

functional limitations — result from physical, mental, and emotional disabilities which adversely affects the workers capacity to function at a job.

gait training — instruction in walking, with or without equipment.

grandfather clause — certain logical provisions which permit persons engaged in business or profession before the passage of an act regulating that business or profession to receive a license or prerogative without meeting the criteria of new entrants into the field.

grievance — one's charges that something imposes an illegal obligation or burden. A denial or an equitable or legal right or cause of injustice.

guardianship — a person lawfully invested with the power, and charged with the duty, of taking care of the person and managing the property and rights of another person, who, for defect of age, understanding, or self-control is considered incapable of administering his own affairs.

habeas corpus — used in the criminal and civil contexts. A procedure for obtaining a judicial determination of the legality of an individual's custody. In the criminal context, bringing the petitioner before the court to decide on the legality of confinement. Related to due process of law.

halo — a metal ring used for patients with upper spinal cord injuries which surrounds or encircles the patient's head, allowing for proper alignment of the neck and spinal column in order to prevent further injury to the spinal cord.

handicap — the effect of the disability on the ability to perform gainful work.

hearsay — statement, other than one being made by the declarant, while testifying at the trial or hearing, offered in evidence to prove the truth of the matter asserted. See appendix for Federal Rules of Evidence 703 for more detail.

hearsay rule — a statement made other than by a witness while testifying at the hearing offered to prove the truth of a matter stated. Hearsay is inadmissible evidence. Oral or written statements are nonadmissible. When a witness is asked what some other person told them, it is inadmissible if the material being described is for the purpose of determining the truth of the matter asserted. If it is elicited merely to show that the words were spoken, it is admissible. However, if the transmission of information from one professional to another is based upon facts and data normally relied upon by that profession, it is not considered hearsay. For example, the vocational consultant may rely upon the data provided by a vocational evaluator.

hedonics — enjoyment of life or the value of life itself.

heterotopic ossification (HO) — is the formation of new bone deposits in connective tissue surrounding the major joints, primarily hip and knee. Incidence as high as 53 percent reported in spinal cord injury, more commonly in higher level injuries. Peak incidence is four months post injury. The cause of HO is unknown. Often treated with the medication Didronel.

iatrogenic — resulting from the activity of physicians. Originally applied to disorders induced in the patient by autosuggestion based on the physician's examination, manner, or discussion, the term is now applied to any adverse condition in a patient occurring as the result of treatment by a physician or surgeon.

illiteracy — inability to read or write; generally little or no formal education.

impeachment — to charge a public official with wrongdoing. With reference to the testimony of a witness, to call into question the evidence offered for that purpose. Can also occur by showing the witness is unworthy of belief. Sometimes by the witness' own statements

in camera — meaning in chambers. A room adjacent to the courtroom where the judge performs the duties of his office. Also applies if the judge performs a judicial duty or act while the court is not in session.

in loco parentis — in the place of the parent.

incidental damages — losses reasonably incident to or conduct giving rise to a claim for actual damages, such as expenses.

incompetency — inability. A relative term which is employed to mean disqualification, inability, or incapacity. It may be used to show a lack of physical, intellectual, or moral fitness.

incomplete injury — in spinal cord injury, if partial preservation of sensory and/or motor functions is found below the neurological level and includes the lowest sacral segment, the injury is defined as incomplete. Sacral sensation includes sensation at the anal mucocutaneous junction as well as deep anal sensation. The test of motor function is the presence of voluntary contraction on the external anal sphincter upon digital examination.

incontinent — lack of bladder and/or bowel control.

indwelling catheter — a flexible tube retained in the bladder, used for continuous urinary drainage. Can enter bladder via urethra or through an opening in the abdomen (suprapubic ostomy).

informed consent — consent given only after a full notice is given as to what is being consented to.

intermittent catheterization program (ICP) — using a catheter for emptying the bladder on a schedule; catheter is not left in bladder.

interrogatory — a pretrial discovery method consisting of a set of written questions drawn up for the purpose of obtaining information of interest in the case from a party or witness.

invisible limitation — these conditions that are concealed or unapparent but nonetheless limit functions and create special problems. People who appear normal are expected to perform work without special considerations; thus, someone with a cardiac disability may be unable to lift, but others who have to do extra work because of this person's limitation may be resentful.

IVP (also IVU) intravenous pyelogram — an x-ray of the kidney after intravenous injection of contrast material; used to determine anatomy. Often used with the spinal cord injured to determine if there is damage to the kidney.

jejunostomy tube (J -tube) — a type of feeding tube surgically inserted into the small intestine.

job description — narrative description of activities and requirements of a job; does not necessarily accurately reflect what a worker will actually do in that job.

job analysis — formalized process for observing jobs as they are performed, collecting descriptive data about these jobs from workers, employers, and observations, then translating these data into a standardized set of traits required of workers performing these jobs. Includes physical, aptitudes, interest, temperament and other factors.

jurisdiction — court or courts which has the authority to try a particular case. It is determined either by the residence of the parties or the subject matter of the lawsuit.

jury — a group of citizens who will decide the issues or questions of fact at the trial

KUB — an x-ray of the abdomen, showing the kidneys, ureters, and bladder.

laminectomy — an operation sometimes used to relieve pressure on the spinal cord.

late anterior decompression — surgical procedure to reduce pressure on spinal cord caused by bone fragments, and to restore normal anatomy to the spine. May be helpful for patients who have had less than anticipated neurological recovery; those who have significant residual bony deformation of the spinal canal may be candidates.

leading question — A question posed by a trial lawyer which is improper on direct examination because it suggests to the witness the answer that the witness should deliver.

lesion — an injury or wound; any pathologic or traumatic injury to the spinal cord.

liability — all character of debts and obligations; condition of being responsible for a possible or actual loss, penalty, evil, expense or burden.

life care costs — (see Life Care Plans) .

Life Care Plan — estimates of the costs of life time care for the catastrophically injured. Topics include medical services, products, architectural changes, transportation and any other costs associated with caring for the client

life expectancy — the period of time in which a person of a given age and sex is expected to live according to statistical (i.e., actuarial) tables.

limited education — some ability in reasoning, arithmetic, and language skills, but not enough to perform semi-skilled or skilled job; generally the 7th to 11th grades according to definition by the Social Security Administration.

LMA — (Labor Market Access) a method for determining the employability and loss of access to the labor market of an individual with a disability. Utilizes the vocational diagnosis and assessment of residual employability process (VDARE) to determine residual functional capacity, lists nature and extent of disabling conditions, and uses transferability process to adjust preinjury level of functioning to postinjury level on all relevant factors. The rehabilitation consultant then identifies the percentage of jobs available to the individual before and after the injury. The loss of employability access represents the percentage of vocational disability for the client.

loss of access — generally related to the loss of access to the labor market. Persons with injuries may suffer a reduction in the numbers of jobs which are available to them as a result of reduced worklife expectancy (such as earlier retirement, or part-time rather than full time work) or due to functional limitations which prevent the client from choosing certain occupations. This is usually expressed in terms of a percentage reduction.

lumbar — pertaining to area just below the thoracic spine; the lower back.

marginal education — ability in reasoning, arithmetic, and language skills sufficient to perform simple, unskilled types of jobs; generally, 6th grade & below according to definition by the Social Security Administration.

mediation — process employed to facilitate settlement in which a disinterested person attempts to get all parties to make their best offer in confidence to see if compromise can be reached, Often employed where multiple parties are involved.

medical malpractice — normally a doctor does not warrant a promise a particular result or cure. If such a warranty or promise is given, then the patient has a "breach of contract" action against the doctor. Doctors use language to their patients that the court will interpret as a guarantee.

mens rea — a guilty mind. A general intent to do a prohibited act.

mental limitation — retardation and learning disabilities are grouped as a functional limitation, although the causal circumstances are quite different; both refer to a hindrance or negative effect in the learning and performance of activities and to other overt manifestations of inadequate mental function.

mental anguish — compensable injury embracing all forms of mental as opposed to physical injury. Can include distress, grief, anxiety, fright, and bereavement.

mistrial — a trial that is terminated and declared void prior to the jury's returning a verdict. Usually because of some fundamental error prejudicial to the defendant which cannot be cured by instructions to the jury. Sometimes because of a jury's inability to reach a verdict (hung jury). It does not result in a judgment for any party. It indicates a failure of trial. In criminal prosecution it may prevent re-trial under the doctrine of double jeopardy.

mobility limitations — function of getting from one place to another is limited; may be caused either by physical disability or environmental barriers.

motion — an application to the court requesting an order or a rule in favor of the applicant.

motivity limitation — the inability to properly produce, direct, and/or control bodily movements as required by specific activities and situations. Different from mobility in that motivity refers to the ability or power to move an object or to do another task normally performed by using the musculoskeletal system, rather than denoting the movement of one's body from one place to another.

MRI/magnetic resonance imaging — a diagnostic procedure that uses magnetic fields to create pictures of the brain's soft tissue. MRI can provide a more detailed picture than the CT scan.

myelogram — a diagnostic test in which an opaque liquid is injected into the spinal canal, producing an outline of it on x-rays or fluoroscope. Outdated by modern imaging diagnostics (see MRI).

myotome — this term refers to the collection of muscle fibers innervated by the motor axons within each segmental nerve (root).

negligence — the omission to do something which a reasonable man guided by ordinary considerations which ordinarily regulate human affairs, would do, or the doing of something which a reasonable man would not do. Harm due to the conduct that was unreasonable.

neurolaw — field of jurisprudence which relates to litigation involving traumatic brain injury and spinal cord injury.

neurological level, sensory level and motor level — the first of these terms refers to the most caudal segment of the spinal cord with normal sensory and motor function on both sides of the body. The segments at which normal function is found often differ by side of body and in terms of sensory vs. motor testing. Thus, up to four different segments may be identified in determining the neurological level, i.e., right sensory, left sensory, right motor, left motor. In cases such as this, it is strongly recommended that each of these segments be separately recorded and that a single "level" not be used, as this can be misleading in such cases. When the term Sensory Level is used, it refers to the most caudal segment of the spinal cord with normal sensory function on both sides of the body; the Motor Level is similarly defined with respect to motor function. These "levels" are determined by neurological examination of: (1) a key sensory point within each of 28 dermatomes on the right and 28 dermatomes on the left side of the body, and (2) a key muscle within each of 10 myotomes on the right and 10 myotomes on the left side of the body.

nominal damages — a trivial sum as recognition that a legal injury was sustained although slight. The amount is usually so small (one dollar) as not to constitute damages.

non compos mentis — not having control over the mind or intellect. Insane.

non-exertional impairment — does not limit physical exertion and does not directly affect ability to sit, stand, walk, lift, carry, push, or pull; does have impact on ability to work.

notice to produce — the document which requires the opposite party to produce certain documents or records for inspection and copying by the party making the demand.

on-site job analysis — trained job specialist observes person(s) actually performing a job in the natural setting and evaluates elements of the job with a standard format and set of criteria.

on-the-job evaluation — used to evaluate client on those job characteristics which can only be determined on an actual job.

orthosis splint — brace used to support, align, and improve function of movable parts of the body.

opening statement — remarks made by each attorney after the jury is selected containing an overview of their side of the case. Argument at this stage is not permitted.

pain limitation — pain refers to an unpleasant sensation characterized by throbbing, aching, shooting or other unpleasant feelings associated with bodily injury or disorder. When pain is continuing, unremitting, uncontrollable, and severe, it may constitute a severe functional limitation to normal living. Much depends on the individual's tolerance for pain as well as secondary rewards for the suffering of pain.

pain and suffering — pain is often experienced at the time the accident happens, during medical treatment, and during recovery (if there is a recovery). Mental suffering of distress can also occur (e.g. fright, humiliation, fear and anxiety, loss of companionship, unhappiness, depression, inconvenience, etc.).

paraplegia — this term refers to impairment or loss of motor and/or sensory function in the thoracic, lumbar or sacral (but not cervical) segments of the spinal cord, secondary to damage of neural elements within the spinal canal. With paraplegia, arm functioning is spared, but, depending on the level of injury, the trunk, legs and pelvic organs may be involved. The term is used in referring to cauda equina and conus medullaris injuries, but not to lumbosacral plexus lesions or injury to peripheral nerves outside the neural canal.

partial disability — exists if the individual cannot perform some or all of the work for which he or she was fitted prior to the injury.

peripheral nervous system — nerves outside the spinal cord and brain of the central nervous system. If damaged, peripheral nerves usually have the ability to regenerate.

persistent vegetative state — a condition in which the patient is unable to speak or follow simple commands and does not respond in any psychologically meaningful way. The transition from coma to a vegetative condition reflects changes from a period of no response to the internal or external environment, other than reflexively, to a state of wakefulness but with no indication of awareness. Normal levels of blood pressure and respiration are automatically maintained.

physiatrist — a physician whose specialty is physical medicine and rehabilitation. Usually the physician who follows chronic illness/injury patients.

placeability — economic conditions and employer attitudes are such that a person can actually be placed in a job; the difficulty in placing a person with a disability in a job.

plaintiff — the party initiating the law suit defendant - the person against whom a civil or criminal action is brought judge - decides the issues or questions of law. If there is no jury at the trial, then the judge decides both the questions of law and the questions of fact.

plateau — a temporary or more permanent leveling off in the recovery or rehabilitation process.

power of attorney — an instrument in writing whereby one person, as principal, appoints another as his agent and confers authority to perform certain specified acts or kinds of acts on behalf of principal.

pre-hearing conference — commonly used to resolve differences evolving from educational placement of handicapped students.

precedent — a previously described case which is used as an authority for the disposition of future cases.

preemptory challenge — the right to remove a juror without any particular reason. Each party in a civil case is normally allowed six preemptory challenges to a panel of jurors.

preponderance of the evidence — one of the three types of requirements to carry the burden of proof. It is generally defined as that weight of the evidence which is sufficient to incline the mind of an impartial juror to one side or the other. This is often referred to as a featherweight of evidence or merely enough to tip the scales toward one party or the other. It is distinguished from clear and convincing evidence and evidence beyond a reasonable doubt.

pressure sore — a skin ulceration leading to tissue death, caused by excessive pressure which interferes with blood flow to a localized area. Also known as decubitus ulcer. Very preventable; very expensive to treat.

pretrial order — court order entered intoby agreement with both sides which narrows the issues and charts the course of the trial. It identifies what witnesses are expected to testify, what evidence is expected to be introduced, and what the jury will be told are the principal issues in the case.

privileged communications — communications which occur in a setting of either legal or other professional confidentiality. Closely related to confidentiality but differs in that privilege is written into various licensing legislation. Allows those who are presenting to resist legal pressure to disclose contents unless waived by the client. A breach of the confidentiality can result in a suit.

pro bono publico — for the public good or welfare; where an attorney or other professional takes a case without compensation for the purpose of advancing a social cause or representing a party who cannot afford it.

products liability — does not refer to a particular tort. Rather, it describes an entire area of potential liability for injury caused by products that have been placed on the market.

proof beyond a reasonable doubt — type of proof which, while not enough to remove all doubt from the mind of the juror, is nevertheless sufficient to remove all reasonable doubts from the minds of the jurors as to the particular point. It is applied only in criminal cases.

proof by clear and convincing evidence — that standard of proof which is between a preponderance of the evidence and removal of all reasonable doubt. It is middle ground in types of proof required. It is used only in specialized circumstances.

prosecution — pursuit of a lawsuit or a criminal trial. The criminal equivalent of litigant in a civil suit.

punitive (exemplary) damages — compensation in excess of actual damages. A kind of punishment to the wrongdoer.

quadriparesis and paraparesis — use of these terms is discouraged, as they describe incomplete lesions imprecisely. Instead, the ASIA Impairment Scale provides a more precise approach.

quadriplegia (also known as tetraplegia) — paralysis affecting all four body limbs. In spinal cord injury, usually results from damage to cervical spine.

qualifications of experts — an expert must be shown to possess scientific, technical, or other specialized knowledge sufficient to convince the court that the witness has expertise in a particular area. A witness may be qualified as an expert by reason of knowledge, skill, experience, training, or education. A witness may be qualified as an expert by virtue of any one such factor, or upon a combination of any of the five factors. Specific degrees, certificates of training, or memberships in professional organizations are not required.

qualified individual with disability — (an Americans with Disabilities Act term) an individual with a disability who, with or without reasonable accommodations, can perform the essential functions of the employment position that such individual holds or desires. For the purposes of this title, consideration shall be given to the employer's judgment as to what functions of a job are essential, and if an employer has prepared a written description before advertising or interviewing applicants for the job, this description shall be considered evidence of the essential functions of the job.

range of motion — an exercise in movement to the joint, so to prevent contractures.

reasonable accommodation —

(1) Modifications or adjustments to a job application process that enable a qualified applicant with a disability to be considered for the position such qualified applicant desires; or

(2) Modifications or adjustments to the work environment, or to the manner of circumstances under which the position held or desired is customarily performed, that enable the individual with a disability to perform the essential functions of that position; or

(3) Modifications or adjustments that enable a covered individual to enjoy equal benefits and privileges of employment as are enjoyed by its other similarly situated employees without disabilities.

Reasonable accommodation may include but is not limited to:

(1) Making existing facilities used by employees readily accessible to and usable by individuals with disabilities; and

(2) Job restructuring; part-time or modified work schedules; reassignment to a vacant position; acquisition or modifications of equipment or devices; appropriate adjustment or modifications of examinations, training materials, or policies; the provision of qualified readers or interpreters; and other similar accommodations for individuals with disabilities.

To determine the appropriate reasonable accommodation, it may be necessary for the covered entity to initiate an informal, interactive process with a person with a disability in need of the accommodation. This process should identify the precise limitations resulting from the disability and potential reasonable accommodations that could overcome those limitations.

reasonable doubt — refers to the degree of certainty required of a juror for a legally valid determination of the guilt of a criminal defendant. The judge will generally use this term and instructions to the jury to indicate that innocence is to be presumed unless the guilt is so clearly proven that the jury can see no reasonable doubt. It does not require proof so clear that no possibility of error exists.

recess — an adjournment of a trial or a hearing which is temporary and which occurs after the commencement of the trial. If there is going to be substantial delay, it's called a continuance. A temporary dismissal is called a sine die.

reflux — the backflow of urine from the bladder into the ureters and kidneys, sometimes caused by excessive bladder pressure.

regeneration — in spinal cord injury, regrowth of axonal tissue via some as yet unknown biologic process.

rehabilitation — the provision of any kind of service provided individuals to correct, aid, or compensate for their handicapping problems.

rehabilitation counseling — a process in which a counselor and a client are involved which will help the client make effective utilization of personal and environmental resources for the best possible vocational, personal, and social adjustment.

rehabilitation technology — compensatory strategies and adaptive equipment to increase or improve functional capabilities of persons with disabilities; used to enhance vocational, educational, and/or independent living opportunities for persons with disabilities; technological methods of achieving practical outcomes in the rehabilitation process.

residual functional capacity — a disabled person's remaining physical and mental work potential and capacity.

res judicata — "the thing is decided" - a description given to the point when the issue before the court is finally decided and all appeals are finished.

restricted environment — barrier resulting from a disability that inhibits the choice of where a person can be comfortable and safe; includes situations in which the person would risk injury, health, or well-being because of personal inadequacy in tolerance, agility, perception, or other expression of compatibility with the environment.

retainer — compensation paid in advance to an attorney or an expert for services to be performed in a specific case.

retrograde pyelogram (RP) — insertion of contrast material directly into kidney via the ureters. Used to detect obstructions, especially stones.

ROM — range of motion, the normal range of movement of any body joint; also refers to exercises to maintain this range and prevent contractures. Active ROM refers to the ability of the client to move their own joints. Passive ROM refers to the movement of the joint by someone else, e.g., physical therapist.

rule of sequestration — when this rule is invoked, all witnesses (other than the one testifying) must be removed, or sequestered, from the courtroom so they cannot hear other testimony in the case which may alter their testimony.

sacral — refers to the fused segments of the lower vertebrae or lowest spinal cord segments below the lumbar level.

sanction — action which may be taken by the court against a party which fails to comply with the rules of procedure. This usually relates to discovery and the failure to produce information.

scanning — an active, usually visual search of the environment for information. Used in reading, driving, and other daily activities.

seizure — an uncontrolled discharge of nerve cells which may spread to other cells throughout the brain. The sudden attack is usually momentary, but may be accompanied by loss of bowel and bladder control, tremors, and/or aggressiveness.

sensory integration — interaction of two or more sensory processes in a way which enhances the adaptiveness of the brain.

sensory limitation — result of defect(s) in the transmission of information from the environment to the mind; usually occurs as a result of damage in the nervous system which includes the brain and the sense organs.

sensory scores and motor scores — numerical summary scores that reflect the degree of neurological impairment associated with the SCI.

sensory stimulation — arousing the brain through any of the senses.

sequencing — contracting muscles in an orderly and meaningful manner or reading. listening, and expressing thoughts.

settlement — an agreement by which parties having disputed matters between them reach or ascertain what is coming from one to the other.

shunt — a procedure of removing excessive fluid usually from the brain or spinal cord. A surgically placed tube connected from the ventricles deposits fluids into the abdominal cavity, heart, or large veins of the neck.

situational assessment — utilizes actual jobs in workshop setting to determine clients' physical tolerance and frustration tolerance.

skeletal level — this term refers to the level at which, by radiographic examination, the greatest vertebral damage is found.

skill level — level of knowledge of work activity and degree of judgment required to perform a certain job; includes unskilled, semi-skilled, and skilled. Usually a term used in social security cases. Skills are learned by doing.

skill — see transferability of skills.

social security — benefit you receive after the age of 65 or you may receive benefits if you have a disability that prevents you from earning a living.

social security disability insurance (SSDI) — insurance on which to live if the client has a total disability preventing him or her from performing any work. In order to receive these benefits, the individual must have paid into the insurance system for a minimum period of time.

spasticity — normal reaction in people with upper motor neuron injuries (generally above L-1), hyperactive muscles move or jerk involuntarily. In some people spasticity can be caused by bladder infections, skin ulcers, and other sensory stimulus. Spasticity is caused by excessive reflex activity below the level of lesion; since the activities are not longer coordinated by the brain, they are exaggerated. Some spasticity can be beneficial for circulation and muscle shape. If severe, though, it can interfere with normal activities, and can hasten contractures as muscles shorten. Treatment often includes physical therapy, mainly stretching of spastic muscles; hydrotherapy; massage; drugs (baclofen, dantrolene, diazepine); nerve blocks (injection of agents such as phenol); surgery (neurectomy, the interruption of peripheral nerves; rhizotomy, dividing anterior and posterior nerve roots in the spinal canal; myelotomy, cutting the reflex arc). Orthopedic treatments may include lengthening tendons in the legs to decrease spasticity.

special damages — those compensatory damages that are peculiar to the particular plaintiff. (e.g. medical expenses, loss of earnings, insanity resulting from the tort). Special damages usually must be specifically placed in the complaint.

special master — a private person, usually a lawyer, appointed by the court to perform certain fact-finding tasks in a particular case.

sphincterotomy — irreversible cutting of bladder sphincter muscle, to eliminate spasticity and related voiding problems. Usually performed on spinal cord injured patients.

sphincterotomy(non-surgical) — an experimental technique using small doses of botulinum toxin on the spastic external urethral sphincter; reportedly stops contraction in affected muscles, may be reversible.

standard of care — in law of negligence, that degree of care which a reasonably prudent person should exercise in the same or similar circumstances.

statute of limitations — the various laws which determine how long a person has in which to file a lawsuit after an injury or event has occurred which gives rise to the lawsuit.

statute of repose — law which sets the final cutoff period for any personal injury action or other action regardless of the tolling of the statute of limitations.

strict liability — liability without a showing of fault. An example would be that someone who engages in an activity that has an ultrahazardous nature is liable for all injuries caused by his enterprise even without showing negligence. A recently developed area of strict liability concerns product liability.

subpoena ducs tecum — request from anyone having documents pertinent to the issue to produce them at the trial or deposition.

subpoena — a command to appear at a certain time and place to give testimony upon a certain matter.

subrogation — the right of one who has paid an obligation which another should have paid to be indemnified by the other.

substance dependency — encompasses psychological dependency (mental or emotional need to take a drug for relief of tensions or discomfort or for pleasure) and/or physical dependence (occurrence of biochemical reaction or physical symptoms when the drug is discontinued).

substantial gainful activity — significant mental or physical activities done for pay or profit.

substantially limits — (an Americans with Disabilities Act term)

(1) Unable to perform a major life activity that the average person in the general population can perform; or

(2) Significantly restricted as to the condition, manner, or duration under which an individual can perform a particular major life activity as compared to the condition, manner, or duration under which the average person in the general population can perform that same major life activity.

(3) Significantly restricted in the ability to perform either a class of jobs or a broad range of jobs in various classes as compared to the average person having comparable training, skills, and abilities. The inability to perform a single, particular job does not constitute a substantial limitation in the major life activity of working.

summary judgment — where there is no factual dispute (and thus nothing for a jury to decide), the court decides what law should apply to the issue in question and makes a ruling. Often used to quickly end a case which has no merit.

summons — the official notice by the court that a complaint has been filed, and that an answer is required. It is usually attached to the complaint.

superior court — courts of general or extensive jurisdiction. As the official style of a tribunal, the term "superior court" bears a different meaning in different states. In some it is a court of intermediate jurisdiction between the trial courts and the chief appellate court; elsewhere it is the designation of the trial courts.

supplemental security income (SSI) — a living allowance by the government for persons who can not work and do not have access to other sources of income or disability insurance.

suprapubic cystostomy — a small opening made in the bladder and through the abdomen to remove large stones or establish a catheter urinary drain.

tetraplegia (preferred to quadriplegia) — this term refers to impairment or loss of motor and/or sensory function in the cervical segments of the spinal cord due to damage of neural elements within the spinal canal. Tetraplegia results in impairment of function in the arms as well as in the trunk, legs and pelvic organs. It does not include brachial plexus lesions or injury to peripheral nerves outside the neural canal.

thoracic — pertaining to the chest, vertebrae or spinal cord segments between the cervical and lumbar arcas.

tort — a wrong. A private or civil wrong or injury independent of a contract resulting from a breach of a legal duty.

total disability — exists if the individual is unable to return to preinjury employment and unable (due to an injury) to obtain employment with similar livelihood.

tolling the statute of limitations — a set of circumstances which prevent the running of the statute of limitations (usually the age of the plaintiff).

tracheotomy — surgical opening in windpipe to facilitate breathing.

transferability of skills — skills that were used in one job can be interchanged or substituted into another job; used to determine the employability of a person. Skills are learned by doing; e.g., typing 40 words per minute. Often confused with "worker traits".

trial — the offering of testimony before a competent tribunal according to established procedures.

uncertain prognosis — involves the stress and ambiguity of those medical conditions that have an unpredictable course or termination and leave the person with anxiety over the uncertainty of future plans.

undue hardship — (an Americans with Disabilities Act term) an action requiring significant difficulty or expense, when considered in light of the factors set forth below.

Factors to be considered include:

(1) the nature and cost of the accommodation needed under the Act;

(2) the overall financial resources of the facility or facilities involved in the provision of the reasonable accommodation; the number of persons employed at such facility; the effect of expenses and resources, or the impact otherwise of such accommodation upon the operation of the facility.

(3) the overall financial resources of the covered entity; the overall size of the business of a covered entity with respect to the number of its employees; the number, type, and location of its facilities; and

(4) the type of operation or operations of the covered entity, including the composition, structure, and functions of the work force of such entity; the geographic separateness, administrative, or fiscal relationship of the facility or facilities in question to the covered entity.

VDARE Process — (Vocational Diagnosis and Assessment of Residual Employability) uses client's work history as a basis upon which to build an assessment of client vocational functioning capacities.

venue — a neighborhood, and synonymous with "place of trial". It refers to the possible place or places for the trial of a suit. Among several places where jurisdiction could be established.

ventilator — equipment that does the breathing for the patient who is unable to breathe on their own. The machinery serves to deliver air in the appropriate percentage of oxygen and at the appropriate rate. Sometimes referred to as a respirator.

verdict — the opinion of a jury or a judge sitting as a jury on a question of fact.

vertebrae — the bones that make up the spinal column and protect the spinal cord.

vocational assessment — process by which vocational expert determines loss of vocational functioning due to a disability and helps clients to correlate their characteristics as workers with the characteristics of occupations.

vocational counseling — process of helping clients understand the relationship of evaluation data to real jobs and clarify feelings about these assets and liabilities as they relate to the potential for vocational independence.

vocational disability — a comparison (usually expressed as a percentage) of pre- and post-injury jobs which were/are within reasonable reach of the individual.

vocational rehabilitation — provision of any rehabilitation services (including medical, educational, social, etc.) to a vocationally handicapped person for the purpose of occupational (re)adjustment in work that may or may not be financially remunerative.

vocational rehabilitation counselor — specializes in working primarily with individuals who are psychologically, mentally or physically impaired in helping them to make vocational adjustments. Includes adjustment counseling, career counseling, rehabilitation planning, etc.

voir dire — to speak the truth. Examination by the court or by attorneys of prospective jurors to determine the qualification of a jury service. To determine if cause exists for a challenge to excuse them.

wage loss analysis — a procedure which addresses the amount of wages lost to a worker as a result of an injury. Often confused with earnings capacity analysis.

waiver — an intentional and voluntary giving up or surrender of a known right. For example, waiving the right to privileged communications.

weight of the evidence — the relative value of the totality of evidence presented on one side of a judicial dispute in light of the evidence presented by the other side. Refers to the persuasiveness of testimony of witnesses.

work product — work done by an attorney in the process of representing a client which is ordinarily not subject to discovery. It can generally be defined as writings, statements, or testimony which would substantially invade an attorney's legal impressions or legal theories about appending litigation. An attorney's legal impressions and theories would include his tactics, strategy, opinions, and thoughts.

work samples — extends the evaluation process by allowing clients to experience work activities and relate worker traits to actual jobs.

worker compensation — an employee will receive compensation for wages, medical and other costs for an industrial accident without having to prove the employer was negligent.

worklife expectancy — number of years an individual can be expected to work (after adjusting for layoffs, illness, disability, time between jobs, and the like).

writ — a written judicial order to perform a specified act, or giving authority to have it done.

wrongful birth — a medical malpractice claim brought by the parents of an impaired child, alleging that negligent treatment or advice deprived them of the opportunity to avoid conception or terminate the pregnancy.

wrongful death — type of lawsuit brought on behalf of a deceased person's beneficiaries that alleges that death was attributable to the willful or negligent act of another.

wrongful life — refers to type of medical malpractice claim brought on behalf of a child born with birth defects, alleging that the child would not have been born but for negligent advice to, or treatment of, the parents.

zone of partial preservation — this term refers to those dermatomes and myotomes caudal to the neurological level that remain partially innervated in spinal cord injury. When some impaired sensory and/or motor function is found below the lowest normal segment, the exact number of segments so affected should be recorded for both sides as the ZPP. The term is used only with complete injuries.

Appendix C
How to Give Your Deposition

(Note: The following was prepared by the law department for the Alyeska Pipeline company in Anchorage, Alaska. No author or date was available.)

You have been asked to give your deposition in a lawsuit. When you give a deposition, you simply give testimony, under oath, in much the same way you will eventually testify in court. The lawyer on the other side will ask you questions about the facts of the lawsuit. You will answer them as honestly and as carefully as you can, and a reporter will write down everything that is said. The reporter will them type your deposition in the form of booklets and distribute them to the lawyers on each side.

Depositions are important and we would like to give you some general information about them. Please do not feel impatient or resentful at being told many things that you may already know perfectly well; many people have never had occasion to become familiar with deposition procedures. This has been designed to help them as much as possible, so they do not worry unnecessarily. For others, this may simply be a review exercise.

It may seem to you to be a waste of time to answer questions that you will probably have to answer again when this case goes to trial, but there are good reasons for a deposition.

First, it sometimes eliminates the need for any trial at all. If the attorney on the other side feels that your testimony represents an honest account of the facts of the case, and decides that the law is "on your side", then he may conclude that continued opposition is a mistake. In that event, he will recommend settlement of the claim to his client.

But even if that does not happen, the deposition helps to save time and money by shortening the trial when it does get to court. From the deposition you give, and from the depositions of the other party and witnesses, the attorneys on both sides learn exactly what the issues are and what evidence must be presented in court. This saves time at the trial on details which have no bearing on the case.

A third reason for taking depositions is to protect the parties to a lawsuit. When a case ultimately goes to trial, important witnesses might be too ill to attend, or out of the state, or they may have died. If the witnesses actually attend the trial, as they usually do, they testify in person, of course; but is it is impossible for them to be there, their depositions can be used in court so that no important testimony is lost. Otherwise, a party could conceivably lose his case because he did not have a witness; testimony to verify his information.

Finally, a deposition is important because it represents a certain set of facts as one witness believed and swore them to be. If later, during trial, that witness tells a different story, the deposition may be used to show that he does not really know the true facts, or that he is deliberately dishonest.

You can see, therefore, why your deposition is important and why your testimony must be given with great care.

We have been given the exact time and place of your deposition and it is important that everyone be as prompt as possible. Your attorney will make arrangements to meet you in advance of the deposition, in case you have any last-minute questions.

Now, first, try not to be nervous about your deposition. There is nothing to be frightened of. A deposition is an informal proceeding, usually held in one of the attorneys' offices, and I'm sure you'll feel comfortable once you're there. There will probably be only four people present — you and your attorney, the other attorney, and the court reporter — although the other attorney may have his client with him, which would make five.

Please be quietly, but carefully, dressed — as though, for instance, you were applying for a job. Good grooming and plain, inconspicuous clothes are best. This is important, because the opposing attorney may be getting his first impression of you and that impression can sometimes make a great difference in his attitude. If you create a quiet, serious impression, you (and your case) will be treated with respect and courtesy; but if you are overdressed and "too flashy", or careless about your appearance, the other attorney may think you are deliberately trying to "show off", or that you are rude or indifferent, and he may react accordingly. For the same reason, please do not chew gum or eat anything while we are there; not only does that make a poor impression, but it also makes it difficult for the court reporter to understand you.

Of even greater importance is your general behavior. Please, at all costs, keep your dignity and do not allow yourself to become angry or impolite. The other attorney may seem to repeat the same questions over and over, or he may become belligerent and sarcastic. But do not let your resentment get the best of you. For one thing, it may lead you into making thoughtless remarks that distort the truth of what you're saying. For another thing, bear in mind that the other attorney is testing you; he wants to know exactly how you will react in court, if he discovers that you can be baited into losing your temper, he will make good use of the knowledge later, because he knows that angry witnesses are careless witnesses, and that they make a very poor impression on judges and juries.

Finally, remember that your attorney is there to protect you from being bullied or harassed. If questions are repeated too often or you are asked questions that seem "out of line" to you, let him do the objecting and let him do any arguing that has to be done. You will have to keep calm and rely on his judgment even when you think he thought to be interrupting or arguing; sometimes he can learn more about a case from the questions that are asked that the other attorney can learn from your answers. You know the old saying about giving someone enough rope to hang himself? Well, it works both ways at a deposition. We'll talk about your end of the problem in a minute, but the point now is that your attorney may want to hear every question the other lawyer can think of, and in that case, he won't be interrupting him.

The procedure is fairly informal and when you reach the other attorney's office or whatever place the deposition is taken, there will undoubtedly be a certain amount of friendly small talk before the formal questions begin. the other attorney will probably be congenial and the conversation easy and relaxed. But remember that it is his job to win this case for the other side. Do not, therefore, say anything about the case except during the deposition. If he mention sit, let your attorney make any necessary comments, because his job is to protest you. Don't be impolite, but avoid the subject of the lawsuit entirely. If you are questioned and cannot avoid answering, tell the other attorney, as pleasantly as possible, that you would rather he talked to your attorney about anything to do with the case.

The other attorney may have his client with him. If that happens, don't let it disturb you. Just be cool and polite and any awkwardness in the situation will take care of itself.

Now, the deposition. If you can remember three rules, nothing will go wrong.

Number one is LISTEN TO THE QUESTION.

Number two is GIVE ONLY THE ANSWER THAT THE QUESTION DEMANDS AND NOT ONE WORD MORE.

land the last rule is TELL THE ABSOLUTE TRUTH.

If you can follow those rules, your deposition will be fine and you won't have to worry about testifying at the trial, because you'll have passed your "initiation" test with flying colors.

Let's go back to rule number one: LISTEN TO THE QUESTION. We emphasize this because it is so easy to misunderstand a question or to misinterpret unfamiliar words in a question. It is easier to misunderstand a lawyer than anyone else because we tend to make questions more complicated than they should be. So: listen very carefully. If the question is put too fast, ask the attorney to repeat it more slowly; if you don't understand exactly what he's getting at, ask him to explain what he means. If there is an unfamiliar word in the question, be perfectly candid and say that you don't understand that particular word. Lawyers are often absentminded about legalistic words and phrases and use them without thinking, so don't feel at all embarrassed about not recognizing them.

For example, lawyers use the words "prior" and "subsequently" instead of "before" and "after", and witnesses are frequently confused by the terms. Attorneys say "inspect" when they mean just "look at". They say, "please be responsive to the question", and they don't mean they want any special type of answer, like yes or no, they simple mean, "Please answer the question". Finally, people don't always realize that when an attorney says "before", he means all the time before a certain event, not just before; and that applies to "after", too; he means any time after, not just immediately after.

Don't worry about any of those terms. The whole point is that if you hear them and cannot decide exactly what the attorney means, ask him — and don't give your answer until he has made his question perfectly clear to you.

All right, now the second rule. GIVE ONLY THE ANSWER THAT THE QUESTION DEMANDS AND NOT ONE WORD MORE. Let's put it another way. Don't volunteer a thing. For instance: if you are asked, "what did you do at 10 p.m.?" and the correct answer is, "I went to bed", then say, "I went to bed." Do not say, " I went to bed but later the telephone woke me up and I couldn't sleep so I went outside for a walk." If you are asked, "Did you talk to Mrs. Smith Monday afternoon?", and you did, then say "yes." Do not say, "Yes, and after that I also talked to Mrs. Jones and Mr. Brown." If the attorney asks, "And what did Mrs. Smith say at that time?" and Mrs. Smith said she was sick, then say, "Mrs. Smith said she was sick." Do not say, Mrs. Smith said she was sick, but I talked to her on the phone later and she said it was only hayfever and she felt better."

We cannot emphasize this too strongly: Do not say one word that is not necessary, because every unnecessary word is a potential problem: not because we have any crucial facts we are trying to hide, but because people who give long, rambling answers tend to get careless as they go along and the more they say, the more apt they are to make a mistake.

We'll show you how a small mistake, that is both innocent and unintentional, can hurt your case. Let's pretend that you were in one of those chain-reaction freeway accidents in which five cars have been hit by the car behind them during the evening rush hour. An argument has arisen about what order the five cars were in, and which driver hit which cars. You were a passenger in the last car and you distinctly remember the colors of each car so your testimony about their order is vital to the case. At your deposition the lawyer asks about the order of the cars and how you can be so sure, and you tell him the colors and that you are certain your memory is good. Then the lawyer asks: "What were you doing earlier that afternoon?" The correct answer is, "I went to a movie." But the lawyer has been so friendly and sympathetic, and seems so genuinely interested in everything about you, that you become conversational and reply, "Well, I'm sort of a movie fan so I went to see the show at the Paramount because Paul Newman was in it."

Now, you've made a small mistake: you meant to say the Rialto Theater, which is in the same block as the Paramount, but you weren't really concentrating and you don't even realize you've misspoken.

All right, let's pretend an unusual coincidence — (although you'd be surprised how often "unusual" coincidences actually occur). Let's suppose the attorney happens to realize you've made the mistake because he went to see the Paul Newman picture himself and knows it was the Rialto and not the Paramount. But, he says nothing more and does not correct you.

Later, you're testifying at the actual trial and the same attorney asks the same questions, and he is still hoping to prove you are wrong about the order of the cars. But there's one difference: This time he asks you which Theater you went to, and when you answer, you have walked into a trap that is meaningless in itself — but let's see what happens: If you say Rialto, he reminds you that you said Paramount before; if you say Paramount, he offers to prove that you are wrong.

Now, obviously, the matter of which Theater has nothing to do with the accident. But by the time you've admitted you made a mistake and straightened it out, in front of the jury, you will undoubtedly feel a little nervous and rattled. And now the attorney has become less sympathetic than you remembered, and you hear him say: "Now, the truth is, you might also have made a little mistake about the color of the cars, isn't that right? And if you made even one little mistake, the order of the cars is entirely different, isn't that true? Now, are you prepared to swear that you absolutely could not have made a mistake?"

No matter which way you answer that question, it is going to be troublesome. The attorney has raised some doubt in the jurors' minds about the accuracy of your memory — and all because of a careless remark THAT NEED NOT HAVE BEEN MADE IN THE FIRST PLACE. The question did not ask you to tell about the movie.

Well, that example is not wholly realistic, but it does illustrate our point. Our point is: Please think about your answers before you make them, and do not add any details that are unnecessary.

One more rule: TELL THE ABSOLUTE TRUTH. This is not to imply that you would deliberately lie; it is unintentional mistakes that we are most concerned about. These usually happen for one of three reasons: One, the witness is afraid to say, "I don't know" or "I don't remember", and so he either guesses at the answer or attempts to reconstruct the events as they might have happened. You can see the danger of guessing from the Theater story we just talked about — guessing can cause the same result as a careless mistake. You can avoid such predicaments. Just admit right away you don't know, or you don't remember.

Don't be argumentative or apologetic about not knowing. Don't say, "Well, nobody could remember a thing like that!" or, "You wouldn't expect me to remember such a detail if you knew what happened." Don't say, "Well, that was a long time ago and I'm afraid I can't remember the exact words", or "I'm not very good at distances."

Just be polite, give the most accurate answer you can, and if you can't give an answer say so.

A second reason for unintentional mistakes: The witness doesn't take time to think about his answer, and in his hurry to respond, some fact or incident simply slips his mind. Suppose you have been in two car accidents and have broken your left ankle both times. j You are suing for the second accident, and the attorney asks you to describe all the injuries you've had to your left ankle. Naturally, the previous car wreck leaps to your mind, but you completely forgot that when you were in high school, you were once on crutches for a week because of a bad sprain to your left ankle.

A third reason: Take the same example, only this time you suddenly do remember the old sprain but you think to yourself, "Oh, Oh! I even forgot to tell that to my own attorney"; or, "I can't see any point in mentioning something that happened 25 years ago"l or, "I forgot to write that down on the insurance questionnaire, so maybe I'll get in trouble if I bring it up now." So you just leave it out of your answer entirely.

All right, it doesn't matter which reason causes you to leave out the fact of the sprained ankle, because no matter what the reason is, you've made a serious mistake by failing to tell the whole truth, and it can be much more damaging to your case than smaller mistake about the Theater name. A jury can be persuaded that it's easy to simply misspeak the name of a Theater, but they know a week on crutches is a pretty big event in the life of a high school kid, and they will find it difficult to believe you could completely forget it. The only alternative the jury has is to believe you deliberately concealed the fact, and if a jury thinks you have lied once, they will find it hard to believe anything else you tell them.

Let me repeat: Do not guess at an answer, and do not try to fill in likely sounding details that you don't actually remember. It is perfectly all right to say, "I don't know", and it is a thousand times safer than guessing.

Do not forget a fact through sheer carelessness. Take your time and think back as far as is necessary to make sure you are not leaving out a fact.

Another reminder: Do not try to decide whether to tell a fact or not, and do not try to estimate the effect any answer may have on the case. There is no decision to be made and the effect is beside the point, because you must give the correct factual answer if it represents an honest answer to the question you're asked. Do not worry about perjury. Perjury has nothing to do with testimony given by a witness who is trying to be honest; it only concerns the testimony of a witness who deliberately lies, or hides the truth, and it is rarely difficult to tell the difference. Do not worry about "trick questions". On television, attorneys spring marvelous traps in a blaze of glory. In actual trials, trick questions are rare, because attorneys know they have a way of backfiring. In any event, just stick to the truth and it won't matter whether a question is a "trick" or not.

Let's consider, briefly, your feelings about the attorney on the other side. He will probably be courteous and seem very sympathetic. But please resist the desire to say too much simply because it's the first opportunity you've had to tell your side of the story to someone on the other side, and he is not there to help you.

On the other hand, you may tend to feel a little resentful toward him; that is natural, but it can sometimes cause you to leave something out "just for spite", so please remember two things: Your attorney needs to know every single fact, and if you've forgotten to tell him one, the sooner he knows it, the better. If you don't remember it until you are giving your deposition, then tell it, because there's not way he can find out sooner. And second, remember that the other attorney probably already knows the answers to the questions, or he will find out through investigation whether you have given him the correct answers. He will have made a very thorough inquiry into every facet of this case before he ever gets to the deposition.

It all adds up to one thing: With the absolute truth, we stand a very good chance of winning the case; with less than the truth, we have almost no chance at all.

Only two more brief remarks: If you do make a mistake, and you realize it during the deposition, say so and correct it. Just say, "Pardon me, but I made a mistake earlier in one of my answers and I'd like to correct it." The attorney will let you do so.

If you do not remember it until after the deposition is over, tell your attorney as soon as possible and he will correct it another way.

That's all. Don't try to remember everything. Just keep the three short rules in mind — listen to the question; give only the answer that the question demands and not one word more; tell the absolute truth.

Meanwhile, if you think of any question you want cleared up, please make a note of it, and your attorney will discuss it with you before you have to give your deposition.

Appendix D
Federal Rules of Evidence

With amendments to February l, 1984

ARTICLE VII. OPINIONS AND EXPERT TESTIMONY

Rule 702. Testimony by Experts

If scientific, technical, or other specialized knowledge will assist the trier of fact to understand the evidence or to determine a fact in issue, a witness qualified as an expert by knowledge, skill, experience, training, or education, may testify thereto in the form of an opinion or otherwise.

Notes of Advisory Committee on Proposed Rules

An intelligent evaluation of facts is often difficult or impossible without the application of some scientific, technical, or other specialized knowledge. The most common source of this knowledge is the expert witness, although there are other techniques for supplying it.

Most of the literature assumes that experts testify only in the form of opinions. The assumption is logically unfounded. The rule accordingly recognizes that an expert on the stand may give a dissertation or exposition of scientific or other principles relevant to the case, leaving the trier of fact to apply them to the facts. Since much of the criticism of expert testimony has centered upon the hypothetical question, it seems wise to recognize that opinions are not indispensable and to encourage the use of expert testimony in non-opinion form when counsel believes the trier can itself draw the requisite inference. The use of opinions is not abolished by the rule, however. It will continue to be permissible for the experts to take the further step of suggesting the inference which should be drawn from applying the specialized knowledge to the facts. See Rules 703 to 705.

Whether the situation is a proper one for the use of expert testimony is to be determined on the basis of assisting the trier. "There is no more certain test for determining when experts may be used than the common sense inquiry whether the untrained layman would be qualified to determine intelligently and to the best possible degree the particular issue without enlightenment from those having a specialized understanding of the subject involved in the dispute." Ladd, Expert Testimony, 5 Vand.L.Rev. 414, 418 (1952). When opinions are excluded, it is because they are unhelpful and therefore superfluous and a waste of time. 7 Wigmore #1918.

The rule is broadly phrased. The fields of knowledge which may be drawn upon are not limited merely to the "scientific" and "technical" but extend to all "specialized" knowledge. Similarly, the expert is viewed, not in a narrow sense, but as a person qualified by "knowledge, skill, experience, training or education." Thus within the scope of the rule are not only experts in the strictest sense of the word, e.g., physicians, physicists, and architects, but also the large group sometimes called "skilled" witnesses, such as bankers or landowners testifying to land values.

Rule 703. Bases of Opinion Testimony by Experts

The facts or data in the particular case upon which an expert bases an opinion or inference may be those perceived by or made known to him at, or before the hearing. If of a type reasonably relied upon by experts in the particular field in forming opinions or inferences upon the subject, the facts or data need not be admissible in evidence.

Notes of Advisory Committee on Proposed Rules

Facts or data upon which expert opinions are based may, under the rule, be derived from three possible sources. The first is the firsthand observation of the witness, with opinions based thereon traditionally allowed. A treating physician affords an example. Rheingold, The Basis of Medical Testimony, 15 Vand.L.Rev. 473,489 (1962). Whether he must first relate his observations is treated in Rule 705. The second source, presentation at the trial, also reflects existing practice. The technique may be the familiar hypothetical question or having the expert attend the trial and hear the testimony establishing the facts. Problems of determining what testimony the expert relied upon, when the latter technique is employed and the testimony is in conflict, may be resolved by resort to Rule 705. The third source contemplated by the rule consists of presentation of data to the expert outside of court and other than by his own perception. In this respect the rule is designed to broaden the basis for expert opinions beyond that current in many jurisdictions and to bring the judicial practice into line with the practice of the experts themselves when not in court. Thus a physician in his own practice bases his diagnosis on information from numerous sources and of considerable variety, including statements by patients and relatives, reports and opinions from nurses, technicians and other doctors, hospital records, and X rays. Most of them are admissible in evidence, but only with the expenditure of substantial time in producing and examining various authenticating witnesses. The physician makes life-and-death decisions in reliance upon them. His validation, expertly performed and subject to cross-examination, ought to suffice for judicial purposes. Rheingold, supra, at 531; McCormick #15. A similar provision is California Evidence Code #801(b).

The rule also offers a more satisfactory basis for ruling upon the admissibility of public opinion poll evidence. Attention is directed to the validity of the techniques employed rather than to relatively fruitless inquiries whether hearsay is involved. See Judge Feinberg's careful analysis in Zippo Mfg. Co. v. Rogers Imports, Inc., 216 F.Supp. 670 (S.D.N.Y. 1963). See also Blum et al, The Art of Opinion Research: A Lawyer's Appraisal of an Emerging Service, 24 Chi.L.Rev. 1 (1956); Bonynge, Trademark Surveys and Techniques and Their Use in Litigation, 48 A.B.A.J. 329 (1962); Zeisel, The Uniqueness of Survey Evidence, 45 Cornell L.Q. 322 (1960); Annot., 76 A.L.R.2d 919.

If it be feared that enlargement of permissible data may tend to break down the rules of exclusion unduly, notice should be taken that the rule requires that the facts or data "be of a type reasonably relied upon by experts in the particular field." The language would not warrant admitting in evidence the opinion of an "accidentologist" as to the point of impact in an automobile collision based on statements of bystanders, since this requirement is not satisfied. See Comment, Cal.Law Rev. Comm'n. Recommendation Proposing an Evidence Code 148-150 (1965).

Rule 704. Opinion on Ultimate Issue

Testimony in the form of an opinion or inference otherwise admissible is not objectionable because it embraces an ultimate issue to be decided by the trier of fact.

Notes of Advisory Committee on Proposed Rules

The basic approach to opinions, lay and expert, in these rules is to admit them when helpful to the trier of fact. In order to render this approach fully effective and to allay any doubt on the subject, the so-called "ultimate issue" rule is specifically abolished by the instant rule.

The older cases often contained strictures against allowing witnesses to express opinions upon ultimate issues, as a particular aspect of the rule against opinions. The rule was unduly restrictive, difficult of application, and generally served only to deprive the trier of fact of useful information. 7 Wigmore #1920, #1921; McCormick #12. The basis usually assigned for the rule, to prevent the witness from "usurping the province of the jury," is aptly characterized as "empty rhetoric." 7 Wigmore #1920, p. 17. Efforts to meet the felt needs of particular situations led to odd verbal circumlocutions which were said not to violate the rule. Thus a witness could express his estimate of the criminal responsibility of an accused in terms of sanity or insanity, but not in terms of ability to tell right from wrong or other more modern standard. And in cases of medical causation, witnesses were sometimes required to couch their opinions in cautious phrases of "might or could," rather than "did," though the result was to deprive many opinions of the positiveness to which they were entitled, accompanied by the hazard of a ruling of insufficiency to support a verdict. In other instances the rule was simply disregarded, and, as concessions to need, opinions were allowed upon such matters as intoxication, speed, handwriting, and value, although more precise coincidence with an ultimate issue would scarcely be possible.

The abolition of the ultimate issue rule does not lower the bars so as to admit all opinions. Under Rules 701 and 702, opinions must be helpful to the trier of fact, and Rule 403 provides for exclusion of evidence which wastes time. These provisions afford ample assurances against the admission of opinions which would merely tell the jury what result to reach, somewhat in the manner of oath-helpers of an earlier day. They also stand ready to exclude opinions phrased in terms of inadequately explored legal criteria. Thus the question, "Did T have capacity to make a will?" would be excluded, while the question; "Did T have sufficient mental capacity to know the nature and extent of his property and the natural objects of his bounty and to formulate a rational scheme of distribution?" would be allowed. McCormick #12.

For similar provisions see Uniform Rule 56(4); California Evidence Code #805; Kansas Code of Civil Procedures #60-456(d); New Jersey Evidence Rule 56(3).

Rule 705. Disclosure of Facts or Data Underlying Expert Opinion

The expert may testify in terms of opinion or inference and give his reasons therefor without prior disclosure of the underlying facts or data, unless the court requires otherwise. The expert may in any event be required to disclose the underlying facts or data on cross-examination.

Notes of Advisory Committee on Proposed Rules

The hypothetical question has been the target of a great deal of criticism as encouraging partisan bias, affording an opportunity for summing up in the middle of the case, and as complex and time consuming. Ladd Expert Testimony, 5 Vand.L.Rev. 414, 426-427 (1952). While the rule allows counsel to make disclosure of the underlying facts or data as a preliminary to the giving of an expert opinion, if he chooses, the instances in which he is required to do so are reduced. This is true whether the expert bases his opinion on data furnished him at secondhand or observed by him at firsthand.

The elimination of the requirement of preliminary disclosure at the trial of underlying facts or data has a long background of support. In 1937 the Commissioners on Uniform State Laws incorporated a provision to this effect in the Model Expert Testimony Act, which furnished the basis for Uniform Rules 57 and 58. Rule 4515, N.Y. CPLR (McKinney 1963), provides:

"Unless the court orders otherwise, questions calling for the opinion of an expert witness need not be hypothetical in form, and the witness may state his opinion and reasons without first specifying the data upon which it is based. Upon cross-examination, he may be required to specify the data . . . ." See also California Evidence Code #802; Kansas Code of Civil Procedure #670-456, #670-457; New Jersey Evidence Rules 57, 58.

If the objection is made that leaving it to the cross-examiner to bring out the supporting data is essentially unfair, the answer is that he is under no compulsion to bring out any facts or data except those unfavorable to the opinion. The answer assumes that the cross-examiner has the advance knowledge which is essential for effective cross-examination. This advance knowledge has been afforded, though imperfectly, by the traditional foundation requirement. Rule 26(b)(4) of the Rules of Civil Procedure, as revised, provides for substantial discovery in this area, obviating in large measure the obstacles which have been raised in some instances to discovery of findings, underlying data, and even the identity of the experts. Friedenthal, Discovery and Use of an Adverse Party's Expert Information. 14 Stan.I.Rev. 455 (1962).

These safeguards are reinforced by the discretionary power of the judge to require preliminary disclosure in any event.

Rule 706. Court Appointed Experts

(a) Appointment. The court may on its own motion or on the motion of any party enter an order to show cause why expert witnesses should not be appointed, and may request the parties to submit nominations. The court may appoint any expert witnesses agreed upon by the parties, and may appoint expert witnesses of its own selection. An expert witness shall not be appointed by the court unless he consents to act. A witness so appointed shall be informed of his duties by the court in writing, a copy of which shall be filed with the clerk, or at a conference in which the parties shall have opportunity to participate. A witness so appointed shall advise the parties of his findings, if any; his deposition may be taken by any party; and he may be called to testify by the court or any party. He shall be subject to cross-examination by each party, including a party calling him as a witness.

(b) Compensation. Expert witnesses so appointed are entitled to reasonable compensation in whatever sum the court may allow. The compensation thus fixed is payable from funds which may be provided by law in criminal cases and civil actions and proceedings involving just compensation under the fifth amendment. In other civil actions and proceedings the compensation shall be paid by the parties in such proportion and at such time as the court directs, and thereafter charged in like manner as other costs.

(c) Disclosure of Appointment. In the exercise of its discretion, the court may authorize disclosure to the jury of the fact that the court appointed the expert witness.

(d) Parties' experts of own selection. Nothing in this rule limits the parties in calling expert witnesses of their own selection.

Notes of Advisory Committee on Proposed Rules

The practice of shopping for experts, the venality of some experts, and the reluctance of many reputable experts to involve themselves in litigation, have been matters of deep concern. Though the contention is made that court appointed experts acquire an aura of infallibility to which they are not entitled. Levy, Impartial Medical Testimony — Revisited, 34 Temple L.Q. 416 (1961), the trend is increasingly to provide for their use. While experience indicates that actual appointment is a relatively infrequent occurrence, the assumption may be made that the availability of the procedure in itself decreases the need for resorting to it. The ever-present possibility that the judge may appoint an expert in a given case must inevitably exert a sobering effect on the expert witness of a party and upon the person utilizing his services.

ARTICLE VIII. HEARSAY

Notes of Advisory Committee on Proposed Rules

Introductory Note: The Hearsay Problem

The factors to be considered in evaluating the testimony of a witness are perception, memory, and narration. Morgan, Hearsay Dangers and the Application of the Hearsay Concept. 62 Harv.L.Rev. 177 (1948), Selected Writings on Evidence and Trial 764, 765 (Fryer ed. 1957); Shientag, Cross-Examination—A Judge's Viewpoint, 3 Record 12 1948); Strahorn, A Reconsideration of the Hearsay Rule and Admissions, 85 U.Pa.L.Rev. 484,485 (1937), Selected Writings, supra, 756,757: Weinstein, Probative Force of Hearsay, 46 Iowa L.Rev. 331 (1961). Sometimes a fourth is added, sincerity, but in fact it seems merely to be an aspect of the three already mentioned.

In order to encourage the witness to do his best with respect to each of these factors, and to expose any inaccuracies which may enter in, the Anglo-American tradition has evolved three conditions under which witnesses will ideally be required to testify: (l) under oath, (2) in the personal presence of the trier of fact, and (3) subject to cross-examination.

(1) Standard procedure calls for the swearing of witnesses. While the practice is perhaps less effective than in an earlier time, no disposition to relax the requirement is apparent, other than to allow affirmation by persons with scruples against taking oaths.

(2) The demeanor of the witness traditionally has been believed to furnish trier and opponent with valuable clues. Universal Camera Corp. v. N.L.R.B. 340 U.S. 474, 495-496, 71 S.Ct. 456, 95 L.Ed. 456 (1951); Sahm, Demeanor Evidence: Elusive and Intangible Imponderables, 47 A.B.A.J. 580 (1961), quoting numerous authorities. The witness himself will probably be impressed with the solemnity of the occasion and the possibility of public disgrace. Willingness to falsify may reasonably become more difficult in the presence of the person against whom directed. Rules 26 and 43(a) of the Federal Rules of Criminal and Civil Procedure, respectively, include the general requirement that testimony be taken orally in open court. The Sixth Amendment right of confrontation is a manifestation of these beliefs and attitudes.

(3) Emphasis on the basis of the hearsay rule today tends to center upon the condition of cross-examination. All may not agree with Wigmore that cross-examination is "beyond doubt the greatest legal engine ever invented for the discovery of truth," but all will agree with his statement that it has become a "vital feature" of the Anglo-American system. 5 Wigmore #1367. p.29. The belief, or perhaps hope, that cross-examination is effective in exposing imperfections of perception, memory, and narration is fundamental. Morgan, Foreword to Model Code of Evidence 37 (1942).

The logic of the preceding discussion might suggest that no testimony be received unless in full compliance with the three ideal conditions. No one advocates this position. Common sense tells that much evidence which is not given under the three conditions may be inherently superior to much that is. Moreover, when the choice is between evidence which is less than best and no evidence at all, only clear folly would dictate an across-the-board policy of doing without. The problem thus resolves itself into effecting a sensible accommodation between these considerations and the desirability of giving testimony under the ideal conditions.

The solution evolved by the common law has been a general rule excluding hearsay but subject to numerous exceptions under circumstances supposed to furnish guarantees of trustworthiness. Criticisms of this scheme are that it is bulky and complex, fails to screen good from bad hearsay realistically, and inhibits the growth of the law of evidence.

Since no one advocates excluding all hearsay, three possible solutions may be considered: (1) abolish the rule against hearsay and admit all hearsay; (2) admit hearsay possessing sufficient probative force, but with procedural safeguards; (3) revise the present system of class exceptions.

Rule 801. Definitions

The following definitions apply under this article:

(a)   Statement. A "statement" is (1) an oral or written assertion or (2) nonverbal conduct of a person, if it is intended by him as an assertion.

(b)   Declarant. A "declarant" is a person who makes a statement.

(c)   Hearsay. "Hearsay" is a statement, other than one made by the declarant while testifying at the trial or hearing, offered in evidence to prove the truth of the matter asserted.

(d)   Statements which are not hearsay. A statement is not hearsay if —

(1) Prior statement by witness. The declarant testifies at the trial or hearing and is subject to cross-examination concerning the statement, and the statement is (A) inconsistent with his testimony, and was given under oath subject to the penalty of perjury at a trial, hearing, or other proceeding, or in a deposition, or (B) consistent with his testimony and is offered to rebut an express or implied charge against him of recent fabrication or improper influence or motive, or (C) one of identification of a person made after perceiving him; or

(2) Admission by party-opponent. The statement is offered against a party and is (A) his own statement, in either his individual or a representative capacity or (B) a statement of which he has manifested his adoption or belief in its truth, or (C) a statement by a person authorized by him to make a statement concerning the subject, or (D) a statement by his agent or servant concerning a matter within the scope of his agency or employment, made during the existence of the relationship, or (E) a statement by a coconspirator of a party during the course and in furtherance of the conspiracy.

(As amended Pub.L. 94-113, #1,Oct. 16, 1975, 89 Stat.576.)

Notes of Advisory Committee on Proposed Rules

Subdivision (a). The definition of "statement" assumes importance because the term is used in the definition of hearsay in subdivision (c.) The effect of the definition of "statement" is to exclude from the operation of the hearsay rule all evidence of conduct, verbal or nonverbal, not intended as an assertion. The key to the definition is that nothing is an assertion unless intended to be one.

It can scarcely be doubted that an assertion made in words is intended by the declarant to be an assertion. Hence verbal assertions readily fall into the category of "statement." Whether nonverbal conduct should be regarded as a statement for purposes of defining hearsay requires further consideration. Some nonverbal conduct, such as the act of pointing to identify a suspect in a lineup, is clearly the equivalent of words, assertive in nature, and to be regarded as a statement. Other nonverbal conduct, however, may be offered as evidence that the person acted as he did because of his belief in the existence of the condition sought to be proved, from which belief the existence of the condition may be inferred. This sequence is, arguably, in effect an assertion of the existence of the condition and hence properly includable within the hearsay concept. See Morgan, Hearsay Dangers and the Application of the Hearsay Concept, 62 Harv.L.Rev. 177,214,217 (1948), and the elaboration in Finman, Implied Assertions as Hearsay: Some Criticisms of the Uniform Rules of Evidence, 14 Stan.L.Rev 682 (1962). Admittedly evidence of this character is untested with respect to the perception, memory, and narration (or their equivalents) of the actor, but the Advisory Committee is of the view that these dangers are minimal in the absence of an intent to assert and do not justify the loss of the evidence on hearsay grounds. No class of evidence is free of the possibility of fabrication, but the likelihood is less with nonverbal than with assertive verbal conduct.

Rule 802. Hearsay Rule

Hearsay is not admissible except as provided by these rules or by other rules prescribed by the Supreme Court pursuant to statutory authority or by Act of Congress.

Notes of Advisory Committee on Proposed Rules

The provision excepting from the operation of the rule hearsay which is made admissible by other rules adopted by the Supreme Court or by Act of Congress continues the admissibility thereunder of hearsay which would not qualify under these Evidence Rules. The following examples illustrate the working of the exception:

Federal Rules of Civil Procedure

Rule 4(g): proof of service by affidavit.

Rule 32: admissibility of depositions.

Rule 43(e): affidavits when motion based on facts not appearing of record.

Rule 56: affidavits in summary judgment proceedings.

Rule 65(b): showing by affidavit for temporary restraining order.

Federal Rules of Criminal Procedure

Rule 4(a): affidavits to show grounds for issuing warrants.

Rule 12(b)(4): affidavits to determine issues of fact in connection with motions.

Rule 803. Hearsay Exceptions: Availability of Declarant Immaterial

The following are not excluded by the hearsay rule, even though the declarant is available as a witness:

(1)   Present sense impression. A statement describing or explaining an event or condition made while the declarant was perceiving the event or condition, or immediately thereafter.

(2)   Excited utterance. A statement relating to a startling event or condition made while the declarant was under the stress of excitement caused by the event or condition.

(3)   Then existing mental, emotional, or physical condition. A statement of the declarant's then existing state of mind, emotion, sensation, or physical condition (such as intent, plan, motive, design, mental feeling, pain, and bodily health), but not including a statement of memory or belief to prove the fact remembered or believed unless it relates to the execution, revocation, identification, or terms of declarant's will.

(4)   Statement for purposes of medical diagnosis or treatment. Statements made for purposes of medical diagnosis or treatment and describing medical history, or past or present symptoms, pain, or sensations, or the inception or general character of the cause or external source thereof insofar as reasonably pertinent to diagnosis or treatment.

(5)   Recorded recollection. A memorandum or record concerning a matter about which a witness once had knowledge but now has insufficient recollection to enable him to testify fully and accurately, shown to have been made or adopted by the witness when the matter was fresh in his memory and to reflect that knowledge correctly. If admitted, the memorandum or record may be read into evidence but may not itself be received as an exhibit unless offered by an adverse party.

(6)   Records of regularly conducted activity. A memorandum, report, record, or data compilation, in any form, of acts, events, conditions, opinions, or diagnoses, made at or near the time by, or from information transmitted by, a person with knowledge, if kept in the course of a regularly conducted business activity, and if it was the regular practice of the business activity to make the memorandum, report, record, or data compilation, all as shown by the testimony of the custodian or other qualified witness, unless the source of information or the method or circumstances of preparation indicate lack of trustworthiness. The term "business" as used in this paragraph includes business, institution, association, profession, occupation, and calling of every kind, whether or not conducted for profit.

(7) Absence of entry in records kept in accordance with the provisions of paragraph (6). Evidence that a matter is not included in the memoranda reports, records, or data compilations, in any form, kept in accordance with the provisions of paragraph (6), to prove the nonoccurrence or nonexistence of the matter, if the matter was of a kind of which a memorandum, report, record, or data compilation was regularly made and preserved, unless the sources of information or other circumstances indicate lack of trustworthiness.

(8)   Public records and reports. Records, reports, statements or data compilations, in any form, of public offices or agencies, setting forth (A) the activities of the office or agency, or (B) matters observed pursuant to duty imposed by law as to which matters there was a duty to report, excluding, however, in criminal cases

matters observed by police officers and other law enforcement personnel, or (C) in civil actions and proceedings and against the Government in criminal cases, factual findings resulting from an investigation made pursuant to authority granted by law, unless the sources of information or other circumstances indicate lack of trustworthiness.

(9) Records of vital statistics. Records or data compilations, in any form, of births, fetal deaths, deaths, or marriages, if the report thereof was made to a public office pursuant to requirements of law.

(10) Absence of public record or entry. To prove the absence of a record, report, statement, or data compilations, in any form, or the nonoccurrence or nonexistence of a matter of which a record, report, statement, or data compilation, in any form, was regularly made and preserved by a public office or agency, evidence in the form of a certification in accordance with rule 902, or testimony, that diligent search failed to disclose the record, report, statement, or data compilations, or entry.

(11) Records of religious organizations. Statements of births, marriages, divorces, deaths, legitimacy, ancestry, relationship by blood or marriage, or other similar facts of personal or family history, contained in a regularly kept record of religious organizations.

(12) Marriage, baptismal, and similar certificates. Statements of fact contained in a certificate that the maker performed a marriage or other ceremony or administered a sacrament, made by a clergyman, public official, or other person authorized by the rules or practices of a religious organization or by law to reform the act certified, and purporting to have been issued at the time of the act or within a reasonable time thereafter.

(13) Family records. Statements of fact concerning personal or family history contained in family Bibles, genealogies, charts, engravings on rings, inscriptions on family portraits, engravings on urns, crypts, or tombstones, or the like.

(14) Records of documents affecting an interest in property. The record of a document purporting to establish or affect an interest in property, as proof of the content of the original recorded document and its execution and delivery by each person by whom it purports to have been executed, if the record is a record of a public office and an applicable statute authorizes the recording of documents of that kind in that office.

(15) Statements in documents affecting an interest in property. A statement contained in a document purporting to establish or affect an interest in property if the matter stated was relevant to the purpose of the document, unless dealings with the property since the document was made have been inconsistent with the truth of the statement or the purport of the document.

(16) Statements in ancient documents. Statements in a document in existence twenty years or more the authenticity of which is established.

(17) Market reports, commercial publications. Market quotations, tabulations, lists, directories, or other published compilations, generally used and relied upon by the public or by persons in particular occupations.

(18) Learned treatises. To the extent called to the attention of an expert witness upon cross-examination or relied upon by him in direct examination, statements contained in published treatises, periodicals, or pamphlets on a subject of history, medicine, or other science or art, established as a reliable authority by the testimony or admission of the witness or by other expert testimony or by judicial notice. If admitted, the statements may be read into evidence by may not be received as exhibits.

(19) Reputation concerning personal or family history. Reputation among members of his family by blood, adoption, or marriage, or among his associates, or in this community, concerning a person's birth, adoption, marriage, divorce, death, legitimacy, relationship by blood, adoption, or marriage, ancestry, or other similar fact of his personal or family history.

(20) Reputation concerning boundaries or general history. Reputation in a community, arising before the controversy, as to boundaries of or customs affecting lands in the community, and reputation as to events of general history important to the community or State or nation in which located.

(21) Reputation as to character. Reputation of a person's character among his associates or in the community.

(22) Judgment of previous conviction. Evidence of a final judgment, entered after a trial or upon a plea of guilty (but not upon a plea of nolo contendere), adjudging a person guilty of a crime punishable by death or imprisonment in excess of one year, to prove any fact essential to sustain the judgment, but not including,

when offered by the Government in a criminal prosecution for purposes other than impeachment, judgments against persons other than the accused. The pendency of an appeal may be shown but does not affect admissibility.

(23) Judgment as to personal, family or general history, or boundaries. Judgments as proof of matters of personal, family or general history, or boundaries, essential to the judgment, if the same would be provable by evidence of reputation.

(24) Other exceptions. A statement not specifically covered by any of the foregoing exceptions but having equivalent circumstantial guarantees of trustworthiness, if the court determines that (A) the statement is offered as evidence of a material fact; (B) the statement is more probative on the point for which it is offered than any other evidence which the proponent can procure through reasonable efforts; and (C) the general purposes of these rules and the interests of justice will best be served by admission of the statement into evidence. However, a statement may not be admitted under this exception unless the proponent of it makes known to the adverse party with a fair opportunity to prepare to meet it, his intention to offer the statement and the particulars of it, including the name and address of the declarant.

(As amended Pub.L. 94-149, #1(11), Dec 12, 1975, 89 Stat.805.)

Notes of Advisory Committee on Proposed Rules

The exceptions are phrased in terms of nonapplication of the hearsay rule, rather than in positive terms of admissibility, in order to repel any implication that other possible grounds for exclusion are eliminated from consideration.

The present rule proceeds upon the theory that under appropriate circumstances a hearsay statement may possess circumstantial guarantees of trustworthiness sufficient to justify nonproduction of the declarant in person at the trial even though he may be available. The theory finds vast support in the many exceptions to the hearsay rule developed by the common law in which unavailability of the declarant is not a relevant factor. The present rule is a synthesis of them, with revision where modern developments and conditions are believed to make that course appropriate.

In a hearsay situation, the declarant is, of course a witness, and neither this rule nor Rule 804 dispenses with the requirement of firsthand knowledge. It may appear from his statement or be inferable from circumstances.

Federal Rules of Evidence Changes
(702 & 703)

There have been changes [effective 12/1/00] to both 702 and 703. You can read the changes, the committee notes and the comments at *www.law.umich.edu/thayer/scpropamend.htm*.

Rule 702. Testimony by Experts

If scientific, technical, or other specialized knowledge will assist the trier of fact to understand the evidence or to determine a fact in issue, a witness qualified as an expert by knowledge, skill, experience, training, or education, may testify thereto in the form of an opinion or otherwise, if (1) the testimony is based upon sufficient facts or data, (2) the testimony is the product of reliable principles and methods, and (3) the witness has applied the principles and methods reliably to the facts of the case.

COMMITTEE NOTE

Rule 702 has been amended in response to Daubert v. Merrell Dow Pharmaceuticals, Inc., 509 U.S. 579 (1993), and to the many cases applying Daubert, including Kumho Tire Co. v. Carmichael, 119 S.Ct. 1167 (1999). In Daubert the Court charged trial judges with the responsibility of acting as gatekeepers to exclude unreliable expert testimony, and the Court in Kumho clarified that this gatekeeper function applies to all expert testimony, not just testimony based in science. See also Kumho, 119 S.Ct. at 1178 (citing the Committee Note to the proposed amendment to Rule 702, which had been released for public comment before the date of the Kumho decision). The amendment affirms the trial court's role as gatekeeper and provides some general standards that the trial court must use to assess the reliability and helpfulness of proffered expert testimony. Consistently with Kumho, the Rule as amended provides that all types of expert testimony present questions of admissibility for the trial court in deciding whether the evidence is reliable and helpful. Consequently, the admissibility of all expert testimony is governed by the principles of Rule 104(a). Under that Rule, the proponent has the burden of establishing that the pertinent admissibility requirements are met by a preponderance of the evidence. See Bourjaily v. United States, 483 U.S. 171 (1987).

Daubert set forth a non-exclusive checklist for trial courts to use in assessing the reliability of scientific expert testimony. The specific factors explicated by the Daubert Court are (1) whether the expert's technique or theory can be or has been tested—that is, whether the expert's theory can be challenged in some objective sense, or whether it is instead simply a subjective, conclusory approach that cannot reasonably be assessed for reliability; (2) whether the technique or theory has been subject to peer review and publication; (3) the known or potential rate of error of the technique or theory when applied; (4) the existence and maintenance of standards and controls; and (5) whether the technique or theory has been generally accepted in the scientific community. The Court in Kumho held that these factors might also be applicable in assessing the reliability of non-scientific expert testimony, depending upon "the particular circumstances of the particular case at issue." 119 S.Ct. at 1175.

No attempt has been made to "codify" these specific factors. Daubert itself emphasized that the factors were neither exclusive nor dispositive. Other cases have recognized that not all of the specific Daubert factors can apply to every type of expert testimony. In addition to Kumho, 119 S.Ct. at 1175, see Tyus v. Urban Search Management, 102 F.3d 256 (7th Cir. 1996) (noting that the factors mentioned by the Court in Daubert do not neatly apply to expert testimony from a sociologist). See also Kannankeril v. Terminix Int'l, Inc., 128 F.3d 802, 809 (3d Cir. 1997) (holding that lack of peer review or publication was not dispositive where the expert's opinion was supported by "widely accepted scientific knowledge"). The standards set forth in the amendment are broad enough to require consideration of any or all of the specific Daubert factors where appropriate.

Courts both before and after Daubert have found other factors relevant in determining whether expert testimony is sufficiently reliable to be considered by the trier of fact. These factors include:

(1) Whether experts are "proposing to testify about matters growing naturally and directly out of research they have conducted independent of the litigation, or whether they have developed their opinions expressly for purposes of testifying." Daubert v. Merrell Dow Pharmaceuticals, Inc., 43 F.3d 1311, 1317 (9th Cir. 1995).

(2) Whether the expert has unjustifiably extrapolated from an accepted premise to an unfounded conclusion. See General Elec. Co. v. Joiner, 522 U.S. 136, 146 (1997) (noting that in some cases a trial court "may conclude that there is simply too great an analytical " between the data and the opinion proffered").

(3) Whether the expert has adequately accounted for obvious alternative explanations. See Claar v. Burlington N.R.R., 29 F.3d 499 (9th Cir. 1994) (testimony excluded where the expert failed to consider other obvious causes for the plaintiff's condition). Compare Ambrosini v. Labarraque, 101 F.3d 129 (D.C.Cir. 1996) (the possibility of some uneliminated causes presents a question of weight, so long as the most obvious causes have been considered and reasonably ruled out by the expert).

(4) Whether the expert "is being as careful as he would be in his regular professional work outside his paid litigation consulting." Sheehan v. Daily Racing Form, Inc., 104 F.3d 940, 942 (7th Cir. 1997). See Kumho Tire Co. v. Carmichael, 119 S.Ct. 1167, 1176 (1999) (Daubert requires the trial court to assure itself that the expert "employs in the courtroom the same level of intellectual rigor that characterizes the practice of an expert in the relevant field").

(5) Whether the field of expertise claimed by the expert is known to reach reliable results for the type of opinion the expert would give. See Kumho Tire Co. v. Carmichael, 119 S.Ct.1167, 1175 (1999) (Daubert's general acceptance factor does not "help show that an expert's testimony is reliable where the discipline itself lacks reliability, as, for example, do theories grounded in any so-called generally accepted principles of astrology or necromancy."); Moore v. Ashland Chemical, Inc., 151 F.3d 269 (5th Cir. 1998) (en banc) (clinical doctor was properly precluded from testifying to the toxicological cause of the plaintiff's respiratory problem, where the opinion was not sufficiently grounded in scientific methodology); Sterling v. Velsicol Chem. Corp., 855 F.2d 1188 (6th Cir. 1988) (rejecting testimony based on "clinical ecology" as unfounded and unreliable).

All of these factors remain relevant to the determination of the reliability of expert testimony under the Rule as amended. Other factors may also be relevant. See Kumho, 119 S.Ct. 1167, 1176 ("[W]e conclude that the trial judge must have considerable leeway in deciding in a particular case how to go about determining whether particular expert testimony is reliable."). Yet no single factor is necessarily dispositive of the reliability of a particular expert's testimony. See, e.g., Heller v. Shaw Industries, Inc., 167 F.3d 146, 155 (3d Cir. 1999) ("not only must each stage of the expert's testimony be reliable, but each stage must be evaluated practically and flexibly without bright-line exclusionary (or inclusionary) rules."); Daubert v. Merrell Dow Pharmaceuticals, Inc., 43 F.3d 1311, 1317, n.5 (9th Cir. 1995) (noting that some expert disciplines "have the courtroom as a principal theatre of operations" and as to these disciplines "the fact that the expert has developed an expertise principally for purposes of litigation will obviously not be a substantial consideration.").

A review of the caselaw after Daubert shows that the rejection of expert testimony is the exception rather than the rule. Daubert did not work a "seachange over federal evidence law," and "the trial court's role as gatekeeper is not intended to serve as a replacement for the adversary system." United States v. 14.38 Acres of Land Situated in Leflore County, Mississippi, 80 F.3d 1074, 1078 (5th Cir. 1996). As the Court in Daubert stated: "Vigorous cross-examination, presentation of contrary evidence, and careful instruction on the burden of proof are the traditional and appropriate means of attacking shaky but admissible evidence." 509 U.S. at 595. Likewise, this amendment is not intended to provide an excuse for an automatic challenge to the testimony of every expert. See Kumho Tire Co. v. Carmichael, 119 S.Ct.1167, 1176 (1999) (noting that the trial judge has the discretion "both to avoid unnecessary 'reliability' proceedings in ordinary cases where the reliability of an expert's methods is properly taken for granted, and to require appropriate proceedings in the less usual or more complex cases where cause for questioning the expert's reliability arises.").

When a trial court, applying this amendment, rules that an expert's testimony is reliable, this does not necessarily mean that contradictory expert testimony is unreliable. The amendment is broad enough to permit testimony that is the product of competing principles or methods in the same field of expertise. See, e.g., Heller v. Shaw Industries, Inc., 167 F.3d 146, 160 (3d Cir. 1999) (expert testimony cannot be excluded simply because the expert uses one test rather than another, when both tests are accepted in the field and both reach reliable results). As the court stated in In re Paoli R.R. Yard PCB Litigation, 35 F.3d 717, 744 (3d Cir. 1994), proponents "do not have to demonstrate to the judge by a preponderance of the evidence that the assessments of their experts are correct, they only have to demonstrate by a preponderance of evidence that their opinions are reliable. . . . The evidentiary requirement of reliability is lower than the merits standard of correctness." See also Daubert v. Merrell Dow Pharmaceuticals, Inc., 43 F.3d 1311, 1318 (9th Cir. 1995) (scientific experts might be permitted to testify if they could show that the methods they used were also employed by "a recognized minority of scientists in their field."); Ruiz-Troche v. Pepsi Cola, 161 F.3d 77, 85 (1st Cir. 1998) ("Daubert neither requires nor empowers trial courts to determine which of several competing scientific theories has the best provenance.").

The Court in Daubert declared that the "focus, of course, must be solely on principles and methodology, not on the conclusions they generate." 509 U.S. at 595. Yet as the Court later recognized, "conclusions and methodology are not entirely distinct from one another." General Elec. Co. v. Joiner, 522 U.S. 136, 146 (1997). Under the amendment, as under Daubert, when an expert purports to apply principles and methods in accordance with professional standards, and yet reaches a conclusion that other experts in the field would not reach, the trial court may fairly suspect that the principles and methods have not been faithfully applied. See Lust v. Merrell Dow Pharmaceuticals, Inc., 89 F.3d 594, 598 (9th Cir. 1996). The amendment specifically provides that the trial court must scrutinize not only the principles and methods used by the expert, but also whether those principles and methods have been properly applied to the facts of the case. As the court noted in In re Paoli R.R. Yard PCB Litig., 35 F.3d 717, 745 (3d Cir. 1994), "any step that renders the analysis unreliable . . . renders the expert's testimony inadmissible. This is true whether the step completely changes a reliable methodology or merely misapplies that methodology."

If the expert purports to apply principles and methods to the facts of the case, it is important that this application be conducted reliably. Yet it might also be important in some cases for an expert to educate the factfinder about general principles, without ever attempting to apply these principles to the specific facts of the case. For example, experts might instruct the factfinder on the principles of thermodynamics, or bloodclotting, or on how financial markets respond to corporate reports, without ever knowing about or trying to tie their testimony into the facts of the case. The amendment does not alter the venerable practice of using expert testimony to educate the factfinder on general principles. For this kind of generalized testimony, Rule 702 simply requires that: (1) the expert be qualified; (2) the testimony address a subject matter on which the factfinder can be assisted by an expert; (3) the testimony be reliable; and (4) the testimony "fit" the facts of the case.

As stated earlier, the amendment does not distinguish between scientific and other forms of expert testimony. The trial court's gatekeeping function applies to testimony by any expert. See Kumho Tire Co. v. Carmichael, 119 S.Ct. 1167, 1171 (1999) ("We conclude that Daubert's general holding — setting forth the trial judge's general 'gatekeeping' obligation — applies not only to testimony based on 'scientific' knowledge, but also to testimony based on 'technical' and 'other specialized' knowledge."). While the relevant factors for determining reliability will vary from expertise to expertise, the amendment rejects the premise that an expert's testimony should be treated more permissively simply because it is outside the realm of science. An opinion from an expert who is not a scientist should receive the same degree of scrutiny for reliability as an opinion from an expert who purports to be a scientist. See Watkins v. Telsmith, Inc., 121 F.3d 984, 991 (5th Cir. 1997) ("[I]t seems exactly backwards that experts who purport to rely on general engineering principles and practical experience might escape screening by the district court simply by stating that their conclusions were not reached by any particular method or technique."). Some types of expert testimony will be more objectively verifiable, and subject to the expectations of falsifiability, peer review, and publication, than others. Some types of expert testimony will not rely on anything like a scientific method, and so will have to be evaluated by reference to other standard principles attendant to the particular area of expertise. The trial judge in all cases of proffered expert testimony must find that it is properly grounded, well-reasoned, and not speculative before it can be admitted. The expert's testimony must be grounded in an accepted body of learning or experience in the expert's field, and the expert must explain how the conclusion is so grounded. See, e.g., American College of Trial Lawyers, Standards and Procedures for Determining the Admissibility of Expert Testimony after Daubert, 157 F.R.D. 571, 579 (1994) ("[W]hether the testimony concerns economic principles, accounting standards, property valuation or other non-scientific subjects, it should be evaluated by reference to the 'knowledge and experience' of that particular field.").

The amendment requires that the testimony must be the product of reliable principles and methods that are reliably applied to the facts of the case. While the terms "principles" and "methods" may convey a certain impression when applied to scientific knowledge, they remain relevant when applied to testimony based on technical or other specialized knowledge. For example, when a law enforcement agent testifies regarding the use of code words in a drug transaction, the principle used by the agent is that participants in such transactions regularly use code words to conceal the nature of their activities. The method used by the agent is the application of extensive experience to analyze the meaning of the conversations. So long as the principles and methods are reliable and applied reliably to the facts of the case, this type of testimony should be admitted.

Nothing in this amendment is intended to suggest that experience alone—or experience in conjunction with other knowledge, skill, training or education — may not provide a sufficient foundation for expert testimony. To the contrary, the text of Rule 702 expressly contemplates that an expert may be qualified on the basis of experience. In certain fields, experience is the predominant, if not sole, basis for a great deal of reliable expert testimony. See, e.g., United States v. Jones, 107 F.3d 1147 (6th Cir. 1997) (no abuse of discretion in admitting the testimony of a handwriting examiner who had years of practical experience and extensive training, and who explained his methodology in detail); Tassin v. Sears Roebuck, 946 F.Supp. 1241, 1248 (M.D.La. 1996) (design engineer's testimony can be admissible when the expert's opinions "are based on facts, a reasonable investigation, and traditional technical/mechanical expertise, and he provides a reasonable link between the information and procedures he uses and the conclusions he reaches"). See also Kumho Tire Co. v. Carmichael, 119 S.Ct.1167, 1178 (1999) (stating that "no one denies that an expert might draw a conclusion from a set of observations based on extensive and specialized experience.").

If the witness is relying solely or primarily on experience, then the witness must explain how that experience leads to the conclusion reached, why that experience is a sufficient basis for the opinion, and how that experience is reliably applied to the facts.. The trial court's gatekeeping function requires more than simply "taking the expert's word for it." See Daubert v. Merrell Dow Pharmaceuticals, Inc., 43 F.3d 1311, 1319 (9th Cir. 1995) ("We've been presented with only the experts' qualifications, their conclusions and their assurances of reliability. Under Daubert, that's not enough."). The more subjective and controversial the expert's inquiry, the more likely the testimony should be excluded as unreliable. See O'Conner v. Commonwealth Edison Co., 13 F.3d 1090 (7th Cir. 1994) (expert testimony based on a completely subjective methodology held properly excluded). See also Kumho Tire Co. v. Carmichael, 119 S.Ct. 1167, 1176 (1999) ("[I]t will at times be useful to ask even of a witness whose expertise is based purely on experience, say, a perfume tester able to distinguish among 140 odors at a sniff, whether his preparation is of a kind that others in the field would recognize as acceptable.").

Subpart (1) of Rule 702 calls for a quantitative rather than qualitative analysis. The amendment requires that expert testimony be based on sufficient underlying "facts or data." The term "data" is intended to encompass the reliable opinions of other experts. See the original Advisory Committee Note to Rule 703. The language "facts or data" is broad enough to allow an expert to rely on hypothetical facts that are supported by the evidence. Id.

When facts are in dispute, experts sometimes reach different conclusions based on competing versions of the facts. The emphasis in the amendment on "sufficient facts or data" is not intended to authorize a trial court to exclude an expert's testimony on the ground that the court believes one version of the facts and not the other.

There has been some confusion over the relationship between Rules 702 and 703. The amendment makes clear that the sufficiency of the basis of an expert's testimony is to be decided under Rule 702. Rule 702 sets forth the overarching requirement of reliability, and an analysis of the sufficiency of the expert's basis cannot be divorced from the ultimate reliability of the expert's opinion. In contrast, the ``reasonable reliance'' requirement of Rule 703 is a relatively narrow inquiry. When an expert relies on inadmissible information, Rule 703 requires the trial court to determine whether that information is of a type reasonably relied on by other experts in the field. If so, the expert can rely on the information in reaching an opinion. However, the question whether the expert is relying on a sufficient basis of information—whether admissible information or not—is governed by the requirements of Rule 702.

The amendment makes no attempt to set forth procedural requirements for exercising the trial court's gatekeeping function over expert testimony. See Daniel J. Capra, The Daubert Puzzle, 38 Ga.L.Rev. 699, 766 (1998) ("Trial courts should be allowed substantial discretion in dealing with Daubert questions; any attempt to codify procedures will likely give rise to unnecessary changes in practice and create difficult questions for appellate review."). Courts have shown considerable ingenuity and flexibility in considering challenges to expert testimony under Daubert, and it is contemplated that this will continue under the amended Rule. See, e.g., Cortes-Irizarry v. Corporacion Insular, 111 F.3d 184 (1st Cir. 1997) (discussing the application of Daubert in ruling on a motion for summary judgment); In re Paoli R.R. Yard PCB Litig., 35 F.3d 717, 736, 739 (3d Cir. 1994) (discussing the use of in limine hearings); Claar v. Burlington N.R.R., 29 F.3d 499, 502-05 (9th Cir. 1994) (discussing the trial court's technique of ordering experts to submit serial affidavits explaining the reasoning and methods underlying their conclusions).

The amendment continues the practice of the original Rule in referring to a qualified witness as an "expert." This was done to provide continuity and to minimize change. The use of the term "expert" in the Rule does not, however, mean that a jury should actually be informed that a qualified witness is testifying as an "expert". Indeed, there is much to be said for a practice that prohibits the use of the term "expert" by both the parties and the court at trial. Such a practice "ensures that trial courts do not inadvertently put their stamp of authority" on a witness' opinion, and protects against the jury's being "overwhelmed by the so-called 'experts'." Hon. Charles Richey, Proposals to Eliminate the Prejudicial Effect of the Use of the Word "Expert" Under the Federal Rules of Evidence in Criminal and Civil Jury Trials, 154 F.R.D. 537, 559 (1994) (setting forth limiting instructions and a standing order employed to prohibit the use of the term "expert" in jury trials).

GAP Report—Proposed Amendment to Rule 702

The Committee made the following changes to the published draft of the proposed amendment to Evidence Rule 702:

1. The word "reliable" was deleted from Subpart (1) of the proposed amendment, in order to avoid an overlap with Evidence Rule 703, and to clarify that an expert opinion need not be excluded simply because it is based on hypothetical facts. The Committee Note was amended to accord with this textual change.

2. The Committee Note was amended throughout to include pertinent references to the Supreme Court's decision in Kumho Tire Co. v. Carmichael, which was rendered after the proposed amendment was released for public comment. Other citations were updated as well.

3. The Committee Note was revised to emphasize that the amendment is not intended to limit the right to jury trial, nor to permit a challenge to the testimony of every expert, nor to preclude the testimony of experience-based experts, nor to prohibit testimony based on competing methodologies within a field of expertise.

4. Language was added to the Committee Note to clarify that no single factor is necessarily dispositive of the reliability inquiry mandated by Evidence Rule 702.

PROPOSED RULE 703

Rule 703. Bases of Opinion Testimony by Experts

The facts or data in the particular case upon which an expert bases an opinion or inference may be those perceived by or made known to the expert at or before the hearing. If of a type reasonably relied upon by experts in the particular field in forming opinions or inferences upon the subject, the facts or data need not be admissible in evidence in order for the opinion or inference to be admitted. Facts or data that are otherwise inadmissible shall not be disclosed to the jury by the proponent of the opinion or inference unless the court determines that their probative value in assisting the jury to evaluate the expert's opinion substantially outweighs their prejudicial effect.

COMMITTEE NOTE

Rule 703 has been amended to emphasize that when an expert reasonably relies on inadmissible information to form an opinion or inference, the underlying information is not admissible simply because the opinion or inference is admitted. Courts have reached different results on how to treat inadmissible information when it is reasonably relied upon by an expert in forming an opinion or drawing an inference. Compare United States v. Rollins, 862 F.2d 1282 (7th Cir. 1988) (admitting, as part of the basis of an FBI agent's expert opinion on the meaning of code language, the hearsay statements of an informant), with United States v. 0.59 Acres of Land, 109 F.3d 1493 (9th Cir. 1997) (error to admit hearsay offered as the basis of an expert opinion, without a limiting instruction). Commentators have also taken differing views. See, e.g., Ronald Carlson, Policing the Bases of Modern Expert Testimony, 39 Vand.L.Rev. 577 (1986) (advocating limits on the jury's consideration of otherwise inadmissible evidence used as the basis for an expert opinion); Paul Rice, Inadmissible Evidence as a Basis for Expert Testimony: A Response to Professor Carlson, 40 Vand.L.Rev. 583 (1987) (advocating unrestricted use of information reasonably relied upon by an expert).

When information is reasonably relied upon by an expert and yet is admissible only for the purpose of assisting the jury in evaluating an expert's opinion, a trial court applying this Rule must consider the information's probative value in assisting the jury to weigh the expert's opinion on the one hand, and the risk of prejudice resulting from the jury's potential misuse of the information for substantive purposes on the other. The information may be disclosed to the jury only if the trial court finds that the probative value of the information in assisting the jury to evaluate the expert's opinion substantially outweighs its prejudicial effect. If the otherwise inadmissible information is admitted under this balancing test, the trial judge must give a limiting instruction upon request, informing the jury that the underlying information must not be used for substantive purposes. See Rule 105. In determining the appropriate course, the trial court should consider the probable effectiveness or lack of effectiveness of a limiting instruction under the particular circumstances.

The amendment governs only the disclosure to the jury of information that is reasonably relied on by an expert, when that information is not admissible for substantive purposes. It is not intended to affect the admissibility of an expert's testimony. Nor does the amendment prevent an expert from relying on information that is inadmissible for substantive purposes.

Nothing in this Rule restricts the presentation of underlying expert facts or data when offered by an adverse party. See Rule 705. Of course, an adversary's attack on an expert's basis will often open the door to a proponent's rebuttal with information that was reasonably relied upon by the expert, even if that information would not have been discloseable initially under the balancing test provided by this amendment. Moreover, in some circumstances the proponent might wish to disclose information that is relied upon by the expert in order to "remove the sting" from the opponent's anticipated attack, and thereby prevent the jury from drawing an unfair negative inference. The trial court should take this consideration into account in applying the balancing test provided by this amendment.

This amendment covers facts or data that cannot be admitted for any purpose other than to assist the jury to evaluate the expert's opinion. The balancing test provided in this amendment is not applicable to facts or data that are admissible for any other purpose but have not yet been offered for such a purpose at the time the expert testifies.

The amendment provides a presumption against disclosure to the jury of information used as the basis of an expert's opinion and not admissible for any substantive purpose, when that information is offered by the proponent of the expert. In a multi-party case, where one party proffers an expert whose testimony is also beneficial to other parties, each such party should be deemed a "proponent" within the meaning of the amendment.

GAP Report—Proposed Amendment to Rule 703

The Committee made the following changes to the published draft of the proposed amendment to Evidence Rule 703:

1. A minor stylistic change was made in the text, in accordance with the suggestion of the Style Subcommittee of the Standing Committee on Rules of Practice and Procedure.

2. The words "in assisting the jury to evaluate the expert's opinion" were added to the text, to specify the proper purpose for offering the otherwise inadmissible information relied on by an expert. The Committee Note was revised to accord with this change in the text.

3. Stylistic changes were made to the Committee Note.

4. The Committee Note was revised to emphasize that the balancing test set forth in the proposal should be used to determine whether an expert's basis may be disclosed to the jury either (1) in rebuttal or (2) on direct examination to "remove the sting" of an opponent's anticipated attack on an expert's basis.

Appendix E
Worker Trait Information

Specific Vocational Preparation

Specific Vocational Preparation (SVP) is defined as the amount of time required by a typical worker to learn the techniques, acquire information, and develop the facility needed for average performance in a specific job-worker situation.

This training may be acquired in a school, work, military, institutional, or vocational environment. It does not include the orientation time required of a fully qualified worker to become accustomed to the special conditions of any new job. Specific vocational training includes: vocational education, apprenticeship training, in-plant training, on-the-job training, and essential experience in other jobs.

Specific vocational training includes training in any of the following circumstances:

   a. vocational education (high school; commercial or shop training; technical school; art school; and that part of college training which is organized around a specific vocational objective);

   b. apprenticeship training (for apprenticeable jobs only);

   c. in-plant training (organized classroom study provided by a an employer);

   d. in-the-job training (serving as learner or trainee on the job under the instruction of a qualified worker);

   e. essential experience in other jobs (serving in less responsible jobs which lead to the higher grade job or serving in other jobs that qualify).

The following is an explanation of the various levels of specific vocational preparation:

Level   Time

1	Short demonstration only
2	Anything beyond short demonstration up to and including 1 month
3	Over 1 month up to and including 3 months
4	Over 3 months up to and including 6 months
5	Over 6 months up to and including 1 year
6	Over 1 year up to and including 2 years
7	Over 2 years up to and including 4 years
8	Over 4 years up to and including 10 years
9	Over 10 years

Note: The levels of this scale are mutually exclusive and do not overlap.

SKILL LEVEL

Unskilled	Jobs where SVP = 1 – 2
Semi-Skilled	Jobs where SVP = 3 – 6
Skilled	Jobs where SVP = 7 – 9

Note: Levels as established by the Social Security Administration.

SOURCE: The complete definitions of all the worker traits are contained in the *Revised Handbook for Analyzing Jobs* (1991).

General Educational Development (GED)

General Educational Development embraces those aspects of education (formal and informal) which are required of the worker for satisfactory performance. This is education of a general nature which does not have a recognized, fairly specific occupational objective. Ordinarily, such education is obtained in elementary school, high school or college. However, it may be obtained from experience and self-study.

The GED Scale is composed of three divisions: Reasoning Development, Mathematical Development and Language Development. The description of the various levels of language and mathematical development are based on the curricula taught in schools throughout the U.S. An analysis of mathematics courses in school curricula reveals distinct levels of progression in the primary and secondary grades and in college. These levels of progression facilitated the selection and assignment of six levels of GED for the mathematical development scale.

However, though language courses follow a similar pattern of progression in primary and secondary school, particularly in learning and applying the principle of grammar, this pattern changes at the college level. The diversity of language courses offered at the college level precludes the establishment of distinct levels of language progression for these four years. Consequently, language development is limited to five defined levels of GED inasmuch as levels 5 and 6 share a common definition, even though they are distinct levels.

REASONING

1: Apply commonsense understanding to carry out simple one- or two-step instructions. Deal with standardized situations with occasional or no variables in or from these situations encountered on the job.

2: Apply commonsense understanding to carry out detailed but uninvolved written or oral instructions. Deal with problems involving a few concrete variables in or from standardized situations.

3: Apply commonsense understanding to carry out instructions furnished in written, oral or diagrammatic form. Deal with problems involving several concrete variables in or from standardized situations.

4: Apply principles of rational systems to solve practical problems and deal with a variety of concrete variables in situations where limited standardization exists. Interpret a variety of instructions furnished in written, oral, diagrammatic or schedule form.

5: Apply principles of logical or scientific thinking to define problems, collect data, establish facts, and draw valid conclusions. Interpret an extensive variety of technical instructions in mathematical or diagrammatic form. Deal with several abstract and concrete variables.

6: Apply principles of logical or scientific thinking to a wide range of intellectual and practical problems. Deal with nonverbal symbolism in the most difficult phases. Deal with a variety of abstract and concrete variables. Comprehend the most abstruse classes of concepts.

MATHEMATICS

1: Add and subtract two digit numbers. Multiply and divide 10's and 100's by 2, 3, 4, 5. Perform the four basic arithmetic operations with coins as part of a dollar. Perform operations with units such as cup, pint, and quart; inch, foot, and yard; and ounce and pound.

2: Add subtract, multiply, and divide all units of measure. Perform the four operations with like common and decimal fractions. Compute ratio, rate, and percent. Draw and interpret bar graphs. Perform arithmetic operations involving all American monetary units.

3: Compute discount, interest, profit, and loss; commission, markup, and selling price; ratio and proportion, and percentage. Calculate surfaces, volumes, weights, and measures. ALGEBRA: Calculate variables and formulas; monomials and polynomials; ratio and proportion variables; square roots and radicals. GEOMETRY: Calculate plane and solid figures; circumference, area, and volume. Understand kinds of angles, and properties of pairs of angles.

4: ALGEBRA: Deal with system of real numbers; linear, quadratic, rational, exponential, logarithmic, angle and circular functions, and inverse functions; related algebraic solution of equations and inequalities; limits and continuity, and probability and statistical inference. GEOMETRY: Deductive axiomatic geometry, plane and solid; and rectangular coordinates. SHOP MATH: Practical application of fractions, percentages, ratio and proportion, mensuration, logarithms, slide rule, practical algebra, geometric construction, and essentials of trigonometry.

5: ALGEBRA: Work with exponents and logarithms, linear equations, quadratic equations, mathematical induction and binomial theorem, and permutations. CALCULUS: Apply concepts of analytic geometry, differentiations and integration of algebraic functions with applications. STATISTICS: Apply mathematical operations to frequency distributions, reliability of tests, normal curve, analysis of variance, correlation techniques, chi-square application and sampling theory, & factor analysis.

6: ADVANCED CALCULUS: Work with limits, continuity, real number systems, mean value theorems, and implicit function theorems. MODERN ALGEBRA: Apply fundamental concepts of theories of groups, rings, and fields. Work with differential equations, linear algebra, infinite series, advanced operations methods, and functions of real and complex variables. STATISTICS: Work with mathematical statistics, mathematical probability and applications, experimental design, statistical inference, and econometrics.

LANGUAGE

1: READING: Recognize meaning of 2,500 (two- or three- syllable) words. Read at rate of 95-120 words per minute. Compare similarities and differences between words and between series of numbers. WRITING: Print simple sentences containing subject, verb, and object, and series of numbers, names, and addresses. SPEAKING: Speak simple sentences using normal word order, and present and past tenses.

2: READING: Passive vocabulary of 5,000-6,000 words. Read at rate of 190-215 words per minute. Read adventure stories and comic books, looking up unfamiliar words in dictionary for meaning, spelling, and pronunciation. Read instructions for assembling model cars and airplanes. WRITING: Write compound and complex sentences, using cursive style, proper end punctuation, and employing adjectives and adverbs. SPEAKING: Speak clearly and distinctly with appropriate pauses and emphasis, correct pronunciation, variations in word order, using present, perfect, and future tenses.

3: READING: Read a variety of novels, magazines and encyclopedias. Read safety rules, instructions in the use and maintenance of shop tools and equipment, and methods and procedures in mechanical drawing and layout work. WRITING: Write reports and essays with proper format, punctuation, spelling, and grammar, using all parts of speech. SPEAKING: Speak before an audience with poise, voice control, and confidence, using correct English and well-modulated voice.

4: READING: Read novels, poems, newspapers, periodicals, journals, manuals, dictionaries, thesauruses, and encyclopedias. WRITING: Prepare business letters, expositions, summaries, and reports, using prescribed format and conforming to all rules of punctuation, grammar, diction, and style. SPEAKING: Participate in panel discussions, dramatizations, and debates. Speak extemporaneously on a variety of subjects.

5 & 6: READING: Read literature, book, and play reviews, scientific and technical journals, abstracts, financial reports, and legal documents. WRITING: Write novels, plays, editorials, journals, speeches, manuals, critiques, poetry, and songs. SPEAKING: Conversant in theory, principles, and methods of effective and persuasive speaking, voice and diction, phonetics, and discussion and debate.

Physical Demands

Physical Demands are a way of describing the physical activities that a job requires. Care must be exercised in evaluating the strength categories, particularly in evaluating the force and physical effort a person must exert. These can be expressed, with the exception of Strength, according to the following:

N Not Present Activity or condition does not exist
O Occasionally   Activity or condition exists up to 1/3 of the time;
F Frequently   Activity or condition exists from 1/3 to 2/3 of the time; and
C Constantly   Activity or condition exists 2/3 or more of the time.

1. Strength (St)

The Physical Demands Strength Rating reflects the estimated overall strength requirements of the job, expressed in terms of the letter corresponding to the particular strength rating. It represents the strength requirements which are considered to be important for average, successful work performance.

Estimating the Strength Factor rating for an occupation requires the exercise of care on the part of occupational analysts in evaluating the force and physical effort a worker must exert. For instance, if the worker is in a crouching position, it may be much more difficult to push an object than if pushed at waist height. Also, if the worker is required to lift and carry continuously or push and pull objects over long distances, the worker may exert as much physical effort as is required to similarly move objects twice as heavy, but less frequently and/or over shorter distances.

The strength rating is expressed by one of the five terms: Sedentary, Light, Medium, Heavy and Very Heavy. In order to determine the overall rating, an evaluation is made of the workers involvement in the following activities:

a. Standing, Walking, Sitting

   Standing: Remaining on one's feet in an upright position at a work station without moving about.
   Walking: Moving about on foot
   Sitting: Remaining in a seated position

b. Lifting, Carrying, Pushing, Pulling

   Lifting: Raising or lowering an object from one level to another (includes upward pulling)
   Carrying: Transporting an object, usually holding it in the hands or arms, or on the shoulder.
   Pushing: Exerting force upon an object so that the object moves away from the force (includes slapping, striking, kicking, and treadle actions).
   Pulling: Exerting force upon an object so that the object moves toward the force (includes jerking).
   Lifting, pushing and pulling are evaluated in terms of both intensity and duration. Consideration is given to the weight handled, position of the worker's body, and the aid given by helpers or mechanical equipment. Carrying most often is evaluated in terms of duration, weight carried, and distance carried.

c. Controls

   Controls entail the use of one or both arms or hands (hand/arm) and/or one of both feet or legs (foot/leg) to move objects on machinery or equipment. Controls include but are not limited to buttons, knobs, pedals, levers and cranks.

Following are descriptions of the five terms in which the Strength Factor is expressed and where

   occasionally indicates that an activity or condition exists up to 1/3 of the time;
   frequently indicates that an activity or condition exists from 1/3 to 2/3 of the time; and
   constantly indicates that an activity or condition exists 2/3 or more of the time.

(S) Sedentary Work

Exerting up to 10 pounds of force occasionally and/or a negligible amount of force frequently to lift, carry, push, pull, or otherwise move objects, including the human body. Sedentary work involves sitting most of the time, but may involve walking or standing for brief periods of time. Jobs are sedentary if walking and standing are required only occasionally and all other sedentary criteria are met.

(L) Light Work

Exerting up to 20 pounds of force occasionally, and/or up to 10 pounds of force frequently, and/or a negligible amount of force constantly to move objects. Physical demand requirements are in excess of those for Sedentary Work. Even though the weight lifted may be only a negligible amount, a job should be rated Light Work: (1) when it requires walking or standing to a significant degree; or (2) when it requires sitting most of the time but entails pushing and/or pulling of arm or leg controls; and/or (3) when the job requires working at a production rate pace entailing the constant pushing and/or pulling of materials even though the weight of those materials is negligible. NOTE: The constant stress and strain of maintaining a production rate pace, especially in an industrial setting, can be and is physically demanding of a worker even though the amount of force exerted is negligible.

(M) Medium Work

Exerting 20 to 50 pounds of force occasionally, and/or 10 to 25 pounds of force frequently, and/or greater than negligible up to 10 pounds of force constantly to move objects. Physical demand requirements are in excess of those for Light Work.

(H) Heavy Work

Exerting 50 to 100 pounds of force occasionally, and/or 25 to 50 pounds of force frequently, and/or 10 to 20 pounds of force constantly to move objects. Physical demand requirements are in excess of those for Medium Work.

(V) Very Heavy Work

Exerting in excess of 100 pounds of force occasionally, and/or in excess of 50 pounds of force frequently, and/or in excess of 20 pounds of force constantly to move objects. Physical demands are in excess of those for Heavy Work.

2. Climbing (Cl)

Ascending or descending ladders, stairs, scaffolding, ramps, poles and the like using the feet and legs and/or hands and arms. Body agility is emphasized. This factor is important if the amount and kind of climbing required exceeds that required for ordinary locomotion.

3. Balancing (Ba)

Maintaining body equilibrium to prevent falling when walking, standing, crouching or running on narrow, slippery or erratically moving surfaces; or maintaining equilibrium when performing gymnastic feats. This factor is important if the amount and kind of balancing exceeds that needed for ordinary locomotion and maintenance of body equilibrium.

4. Stooping (St)

Bending the body downward and forward by bending the spine at the waist. This factor is important if it occurs to a considerable degree and requires full use of the lower extremities and back muscles.

5. Kneeling (Kn)

Bending the legs at knee to come to rest on knee or knees.

6. Crouching (Co)

Bending body downward and forward by bending legs and spine.

7. Crawling (Cw)

Moving about on the hands and knees or hands and feet.

8. Reaching (Re)

Extending hands & arms in any direction.

9. Handling (Ha)

Seizing, holding, grasping, turning or working with hands. Fingers are involved only to the extent that they are an extension of the hand.

10. Fingering (Fi)

Picking, pinching, or otherwise working primarily with fingers rather than the whole hand or arm as in handling.

11. Feeling (Fe)

Perceiving attributes of items as size, shape, temperature or texture by means of receptors in the skin, particularly that of the fingertips.

12. Talking (Ta)

Expressing or exchanging ideas by means of the spoken word.

13. Hearing (He)

Perceiving the nature of sounds by the ear.

14. Tasting/Smelling (TS)

Distinguishing, with a degree of accuracy, differences or similarities in intensity or quality of flavors and/or odors, or recognizing particular flavors and/or odors, using tongue and/or nose.

15. Near Acuity (NA)

Clarity of vision at 20 inches or less. This factor is important when special and minute accuracy is demanded and when defective near acuity would adversely affect job performance and/or the safety of others.

16. Far Acuity (FA)

Clarity of vision at 20 feet or more. This factor is important when visual efficiency in terms of far acuity is required and defective far acuity would adversely affect job performance and/or the safety of others.

17. Depth Perception (DP)

Three-dimensional vision. Ability to judge distances and spatial relationships so as to see objects where and as they really are. This factor is important when depth perception is required for successful job performance and/or for reason of safety to oneself and others.

18. Accommodation (Ac)

Adjustment of lens of eyes to bring an object into sharp focus. This factor is important when doing near point work at varying distances from the eye.

19. Color Vision (CV)

Ability to identify and distinguish colors.

20. Field of Vision (FV)

Observing an area that can be seen up and down or to right and left when eyes are fixed on a given point. This factor is important when job performance requires seeing a large area while keeping the eye fixed.

Environmental Conditions

Environmental conditions are a means of describing the physical surroundings of a worker in a specific job and of indicating the hazards that pose a definite risk of bodily injury to the worker. The environmental condition identified for an occupation are those which are considered to be important or critical. Environmental Conditions can be expressed, with the exception of Noise Intensity Level, according to the following:

N Not Present Activity or condition does not exist
O Occasionally   Activity or condition exists up to 1/3 of the time;
F Frequently   Activity or condition exists from 1/3 to 2/3 of the time; and
C Constantly   Activity or condition exists 2/3 or more of the time.

1. Exposure to Weather (We)

Exposure to hot, cold, wet, humid, or windy conditions, caused by weather. This factor is rated important when exposure to weather results in marked bodily discomfort.

2. Extreme Cold (Co)

Exposure to nonweather-related cold temperatures. This factor is rated important when temperatures are sufficiently low to cause bodily discomfort.

3. Extreme Heat (Ho)

Exposure to nonweather-related hot temperatures. This factor is rated important when temperatures are sufficiently high to cause bodily discomfort.

4. Wet and/or Humid (Hu)

Contact with water or other liquids; or exposure to nonweather- related humid conditions. This factor is rated important when contact with water or other liquids or exposure to humidity causes bodily discomfort.

5. Noise Intensity (No)

Exposure to constant or intermittent sounds of a pitch or level sufficient to cause marked distraction of possible hearing loss. The levels for this factor are:

    1 Very Quiet   2 Quiet   3 Moderate   4 Loud   5 Very Loud

6. Vibration (Vi)

Exposure to a shaking object or surface. This factor is rated important when vibration causes a strain on the body or extremities.

7. Atmospheric Conditions (AC)

Exposure to conditions, such as fumes, noxious odors, dusts, mists, gases, and poor ventilation, that affect the respiratory system, eyes or skin. This factor is rated important if these conditions are present to a degree or length of time sufficient to cause marked bodily discomfort or possible injury.

Hazards

A hazard is a condition in the work environment that subjects or exposes the worker to the possibility of serious bodily injury or danger to the worker's life or health. A hazard is specific, related to the job, and has a greater likeness of occurring than it would away from the job. The following conditions are evaluated as possible hazards in specific jobs:

8.   Proximity to moving, mechanical parts (MP)   12. Working with Explosives (Ex)
9.   Exposure to electrical shock (ES)   13. Exposure to toxic or caustic chemicals (TC)
10. Working in high, exposed places (HE)   14. Other hazards (Ot)
11. Exposure to radiant energy (Ra)

337

If protective measures eliminate the hazard entirely and if the worker has no choice regarding their use, the hazard is considered to be reduced and the factor is not rated. However, if the protective device is subject to the worker's discretionary use, the hazard is not considered reduced, and if appropriate, is rated, irrespective of the presence of the device.

With regard to Factor 5: Noise, the current standards of the Occupational Safety and Health Administration (OSHA) for permissible noise exposure apply. Factor 5 is rated important when the noise level exceeds these standards. The following chart indicates those standards:

Permissible Noise Exposures

Duration Per Day, Hours	8	6	4	3	2	1.5	1	.5	.25
Sound Level DB	90	92	95	97	100	102	105	110	115

Aptitudes

Specific capacities and abilities of an individual in order to learn or perform adequately a task or job duty.

G INTELLIGENCE: General learning ability. The ability to catch on or understand instructions and underlying principles. Ability to reason and make judgments. Closely related to doing well in school.

V VERBAL: Ability to understand meanings of words and ideas associated with them, and to use them effectively. To comprehend language, to understand relationships between words, and to understand meanings of whole sentences and paragraphs. To present information or ideas clearly.

N NUMERICAL: Ability to perform arithmetic operations quickly & accurately.

S SPATIAL: Ability to comprehend forms in space and understand relationships of plane and solid objects. May be used in such tasks as blueprint reading and in solving geometry problems. Frequently described as the ability to visualize objects of two or three dimensions, or to think visually of geometric forms.

P FORM PERCEPTION: Ability to perceive pertinent detail in objects or in pictorial or graphic material. To make visual comparisons and discriminations and see slight differences in shapes and shadings of figures and widths and lengths of lines.

Q CLERICAL PERCEPTION: Ability to perceive pertinent detail in verbal or tabular material. To observe differences in copy, to proof-read words and numbers, and to avoid perceptual errors in arithmetic computation.

K MOTOR COORDINATION: Ability to coordinate eyes and hands or fingers rapidly and accurately in making precise movements with speed. Ability to make a movement response accurately and quickly.

F FINGER DEXTERITY: Ability to move the fingers and manipulate small objects with the fingers rapidly or accurately.

M MANUAL DEXTERITY: Ability to move the hands easily and skillfully. To work with the hands in **placing and turning motions.**

E EYE-HAND-FOOT COORDINATION: Ability to move the hand and foot coordinately with each **other in accordance with visual stimuli.**

C COLOR DISCRIMINATION: Ability to perceive or recognize similarities or differences in colors, or in shades or other values of the same color; to identify a particular color, or to recognize harmonious or contrasting color combinations, or to match colors accurately.

EXPLANATION OF LEVELS

The digits indicate how much of each aptitude the job requires for satisfactory (average) performance. The average requirements, rather than maximum or minimum, are cited. The amount required is expressed in terms of equivalent amounts possessed by segments of the general working population.

The following scale is used:

1 = The top 10 percent of the population. This segment of the population possesses an extremely high degree of the aptitude.

2 = The highest third exclusive of the top 10 percent of the population. This segment of the population possesses an above average or high degree of the aptitude.

3 = The middle third of the population. This segment of the population possesses a medium degree of the aptitude, ranging from slightly below to slightly above average.

4 = The lowest third exclusive of the bottom 10 percent of the population. This segment of the population possesses a below average or low degree of the aptitude.

5 = The lowest 10 percent of the population. This segment of the population possesses a negligible degree of the aptitude.

Temperaments

Temperaments for the purpose of collecting occupational data, are defined as personal traits required by a worker by specific job-worker situations. This component consists of the following 10 factors:

A   Working ALONE or apart in physical isolation from others.

D   DIRECTING, controlling, or planning activities of others.

E   EXPRESSING personal feelings.

I   INFLUENCING people in their opinions, attitudes, or judgments.

J   Making JUDGMENTS and decisions.

P   Dealing with PEOPLE.

R   Performing REPETITIVE or short-cycle work.

S   Performing effectively under STRESS.

T   Attaining precise set limits, TOLERANCES, and standards.

U   Working UNDER specific instructions

V   Performing a VARIETY of duties.

Guide To Occupational Exploration (GOE) Interest Areas

Interest Areas are categorized by the first two digits of the GOE code.

01 - ARTISTIC: Interest in creative expression of feelings.

02 - SCIENTIFIC: Interest in discovering, collecting, and analyzing information about the natural world and in applying scientific research findings to problems in medicine, life sciences, and natural sciences.

03 - PLANTS & ANIMALS: Interest in activities involving plants and animals, usually in an outdoor setting.

04 - PROTECTIVE: Interest in the use of authority to protect people and property.

05 - MECHANICAL: Interest in applying mechanical principles to practical situations, using machines, handtools, or techniques.

06 - INDUSTRIAL: Interest in repetitive, concrete, organized activities in a factory setting.

07 - BUSINESS DETAIL: Interest in organized, clearly defined activities requiring accuracy and attention to detail, primarily in an office setting.

08 - SELLING: Interest in bringing others to a point of view through personal persuasion, using sales and **promotional techniques.**

09 - ACCOMMODATING: Interest in catering to the wishes of others, usually on a one-to-one basis.

10 - HUMANITARIAN: Interest in helping others with their mental, spiritual, social, physical, or vocational needs.

11 - LEADING-INFLUENCING: Interest in leading and influencing others through activities involving high-level verbal or numerical abilities.

12 - PHYSICAL PERFORMING: Interest in physical activities performed before an audience.

Industries

01 - PROFESSIONAL, TECHNICAL, AND MANAGERIAL OCCUPATIONS

Occupations concerned with the theoretical and practical aspects of such fields of human endeavor as: architecture; engineering; mathematics; physical sciences; social sciences; medicine and health; education; museum, library and archival sciences; law; theology; the arts; recreations; administrative specialities; and management. Also included are occupations in support of scientists and engineers and other specialized activities such as piloting aircraft, operating radios, and directing the course of ships. Most of these occupations require substantial educational preparation, usually at the university, college, junior college, or technical institute level.

02 - CLERICAL AND SALES OCCUPATIONS

Clerical occupations include those activities concerned with transcribing, preparing, systematizing, and preserving written communications and records; distributing information and collecting accounts. Sales occupations include those activities concerned with influencing customers in favor of a commodity or service. Occupations closely identified with sales transactions are included even though they do not involve active participation in the transactions.

03 - SERVICE OCCUPATIONS

Occupations concerned with providing domestic services in private households; preparing and serving food and drink in commercial, institutional, or other establishments; providing lodging and related services; providing grooming, cosmetic, and other personal & health care services for children and adults; maintaining and cleaning clothing and other wearing apparel; providing protection for people and property attending to the comfort or requests of patrons of amusement and recreation facilities; and performing cleaning and maintenance services to interiors of buildings.

04 - AGRICULTURAL, FISHERY, FORESTRY AND RELATED OCCUPATIONS

Occupations concerned with propagating, growing, caring for, and gathering plant and animal life and products; logging timber tracts; catching, hunting, and trapping animal life; and caring for parks, gardens, and grounds. Also occupations concerned with providing related support services. Excluded are occupations requiring a primary knowledge or involvement with technologies, such as processing, packaging and stock checking, regardless of their industry designations.

05 - PROCESSING OCCUPATIONS

Occupations concerned with refining, mixing, compounding, chemically treating, heat treating, or similarly working materials in solid, fluid, semifluid or gaseous states to prepare them for use as basic materials,or stock for further manufacturing treatment, or for sale as finished products to commercial users. Knowledge of a process and adherence to formulas or other specifications are required to some degree. Vats, stills, ovens, furnaces, mixing machines, crushers, grinders, and related machines and equipment usually are involved.

06 - MACHINE TRADES OCCUPATIONS

Occupations concerned with the operation of machines that cut, bore, mill, abrade, print, and similarly work such as metal, paper, wood, plastics, and stone. A worker's relationship to the machine is of primary importance. The more complicated jobs require an understanding of machine functions, blueprint reading, making mathematical computations, and exercising judgment to attain conformance to specifications. In other jobs eye and hand coordination may be the most significant factor. Installation, repair, and maintenance of machines and mechanical equipment and weaving, knitting, spinning, and similarly working textiles are included.

07 - BENCHWORK OCCUPATIONS

Occupations concerned with using body members, handtools, and bench machines to fabricate, inspect, or repair relatively small products, such as jewelry, phonographs, light bulbs, musical instruments, tires, footwear, pottery and garments. The work is usually performed at a set position or station in a mill, plant or shop, at a bench, worktable, or conveyer. Workers in more complex jobs may be required to read blueprints, follow patterns, use a variety of handtools, and assume responsibility for meeting standards. Other jobs may only require workers to follow standardized procedures.

08 - STRUCTURAL WORK OCCUPATIONS

Occupations concerned with fabricating, erecting, installing, paving, painting, and repairing structures and structural parts, such as bridges, buildings, roads, motor vehicles, cables, internal combustion engines, girders, plates and frames. Generally, work is outside, except for factory production line occupations. The worker's relationship to handtools and power tools is more important than that to stationary machines, which are also used. Knowledge of the properties (stress, strain, durability, resistance) of the materials used (wood, concrete, metal, glass, clay) is often a requirement.

09 - MISCELLANEOUS OCCUPATIONS

Occupations concerned with the transportation of people and cargo from one geographical location to another by various methods; with the packaging of materials and the moving of material in and around establishments; with the extraction of minerals from the earth; with the production and distribution of utilities; with modeling for painters, sculptors and photographers; with providing various production services in motion pictures and radio and television broadcasting; with the production of graphic art work; and with other miscellaneous activities.

Work Fields

The Work Fields (001-299) can be arranged in the following general categories.

1 — Securing, producing, or cultivating raw materials, products or animals (livestock or game) on or below the surface of the earth; usually outdoor work.

001 Hunting-Fishing	004 Logging
002 Animal Propogating	005 Mining-Quarrying-Earth Boring
003 Plant Cultivating	

2 — Grading surfaces and building foundations.

007 Excavating-Clearing-Foundation Building

3 — Moving materials or people, by hand and/or machine power.

011 Material Moving	014 Pumping
013 Tranporting	

4 — Producing and/or distributing heat, power, or conditioned air.

021 Stationary Engineering

5 — Industrial, commercial and domestic cleaning.

031 Cleaning

6 — Shaping, pressing and stretching articles, usually with heat and steam, under tension and pressure.

032 Surface Finishing

7 — Coating objects with liquids and dry lubricants.

033 Lubricating

8 — Slaughtering livestock and preparing meats for marketing.

034 Butchering-Meat Cutting

9 — Packaging materials or products for distribution or storage.

041 Filling-Packing-Wrapping

10 — Working with machines and/or handtools to shape or cut materials and objects usually made of wood, metal, or plastics. Can also involve assembly of objects.

051 Abrading	055 Milling-Turning-Planing
052 Chipping	056 Sawing
053 Boring	057 Machining
054 Shearing-Shaving	

11 — Folding and assembling parts or materials, usually light, by means of fitting together or joining with sticky compounds and fastening devices, such as staples, grommets, and snaps.

061 Fitting-Folding	063 Gluing-Laminating
062 Fastening	

12 — Assembling parts or materials, usually of metal, wood, or plastics, by means of screws, nails, or rivets.

071 Bolting-Screwing	073 Riveting
072 Nailing	

13 — Joining or cutting materials by means of a gas flame, electric arc, combination welding process, laser beam and soldering.

081 Welding	083 Soldering
082 Flame Cutting-Arc Cutting-Beam Cutting	

14 — Building and repairing structures, and assembling structural parts, usually working with brick, cement, mortar, stone and other building material .

091 Masoning	094 Caulking
092 Laying-Covering	095 Paving

15 — All-round fabricating, installing, and/or repair of interior fittings; structures; and electrical, electronic, and mechanical units. Involves combinations of other Work Fields, usually 051 - 094.

101 Upholstering
102 Structural

111 Electrical-Electronic
121 Mechanical

16 — Compounding, melting, heat conditioning, and shaping objects, usually metal and plastics, by methods which involve heat or pressure or force.

131 Melting
132 Casting
133 Heat Conditioning

134 Pressing-Forging
135 Die Sizing
136 Molding

17 — Processing various materials, in solid, fluid, semi-fluid, or gaseous, states, during production process.

141 Baking-Drying
142 Crushing-Grinding
143 Mixing
144 Distilling

145 Separating
146 Cooking-Food Preparing
147 Processing-Compounding

18 — Coating and impregnating materials and products to impart decorative and protective finish and other specific quality.

151 Immersing-Coating
152 Saturating

153 Brushing-Spraying
154 Electroplating

19 — Converting fiber raw stock into yarn and thread, and interlacing and otherwise working yarns to form woven, nonwoven and tufted fabrics. Winding also includes coiling any material about an object.

161 Combing-Napping
162 Spinning
163 Winding

164 Weaving
165 Knitting
166 Tufting

20 — Joining, mending, or fastening materials, usually with needle and thread, and fitting and adjusting parts.

171 Sewing-Tailoring

21 — Cutting designs or letters into materials or products by sandblasting, applying acids, or action of sharp pointed tools.

182 Etching

183 Engraving

22 — Transferring letters or designs onto paper or other materials, by use of ink or pressure, includes setting type and preparing plates.

191 Printing

192 Imprinting

23 — Taking pictures and developing and processing film.

201 Photographing

202 Developing-Printing

24 — Evaluating or estimating the quality, quantity or value of things; ascertaining the physcial characteristics of materials and objects.

211 Appraising

212 Inspecting- Measuring-Testing

25 — Receiving, storing, issuing, shipping, requisitioning, and accounting for stores of materials.

221 Stock Checking

26 — Preparing and maintaining verbal or numerical records.

231 Verbal Recording-Record Keeping
232 Numerical Recording-Record Keeping

27 — Planning, developing, testing, evaluating, and executing a systematic sequence of activities or operations to process alphabetic, numeric, and symbolic data or to solve problems by means of computer systems.

233 Data Processing

28 — Plotting, tracing, or drawing diagrams and other directive graphic information for use in design or production; designing and constructing machinery, structures, or systems.

241 Laying Out
242 Drafting

243 Surveying
244 Engineering

29 — Controlled exploration of fundamental areas of knowledge, by means of critical and exhaustive investigation and experimentation.

251 Researching

30 — Creating, expressing or depicting one's own ideas in various media.

261 Writing
262 Artistic Painting-Drawing

263 Composing- Choreography
264 Styling

31 — Obtaining and evaluating data for purposes of completing business and legal procedures.

271 Investigating

272 Litigating

32 — Providing and effecting the transmission of information to other persons, indirectly (by electrical/electronic media) or directly (by voice or written statement).

281 Systems Communicating

282 Information-Giving

33 — Dealing with people to provide services of various types.

291 Accommodating
292 Merchandising-Sales
293 Protecting
294 Health Caring-Medical

295 Administering
296 Teaching
297 Entertaining
298 Advising-Counseling

Definitions of Codes

The various codes contained and/or referenced in this manual are drawn from several different government sources. Unless otherwise noted, the codes were developed by the US Department of Labor. The codes are:

Dictionary of Occupational Titles

The nine digit DOT code is assigned to each of the 12,741 titles contained within the Dictionary. A detailed explanation of this code is presented on pages xvii to xxxvii of Vol. 1 of the DOT (1991).

Guide to Occupational Exploration

The GOE (1978) arranges the 1977 edition DOT titles according to "interest" areas. The GOE code organizes the job titles by twelve interest areas (the first two digits), 66 work groups (the second two digits), and 348 sub-groups (the third two digits). The 1991 DOT references all titles within one of the twelve interest areas. A new GOE is scheduled for release by DOL sometime within 1992.

Data-People-Things

The DPT is not really a code, but rather, the middle three digits of the DOT code (see above). A full explanation of DPT is contained in the DOT (1991), pages 1005 to 1007 of Vol. 2.

Work Field Code

All Dot titles are clustered within one of the 96 work field codes. Work field codes arrange jobs according to their similarity to machines, tools, materials, aides, and behaviors. The work field code is most useful in identifying jobs within the transferability process. The Work Field arrangement is presented in the Revised Handbook for Analyzing Jobs (1991) on pages 4-1 to 4-29. However, a more detailed discussion of the Work Field is contained in the 1972 version of the Handbook for Analyzing Jobs.

Materials, Products, Subject Matter, Services

The MPSMS code, also useful for the transferability process, arranges all of the DOT titles within the majors areas of materials, products, subject matter, or services. Source: The Revised Handbook for Analyzing Jobs (1992), pp. 5-1 to 5-49.

Census

The Census code arranges all DOT titles within 501 codes (Revised with 1990 Census). The Census code is a survey code (provides estimates of the numbers of workers within a labor force) which may also be used as a useful arrangement in transferability. Source: U.S. Bureau of Census.

Standard Occupational Classification

The SOC code, also a survey code, is an occupational arrangement for the work setting (businesses and industries). All DOT titles are cross referenced to the SOC code. Source: U.S. Department of Commerce.

Standard Industrial Classification

The SIC code is perhaps the most widely used survey of all the occupational arrangements (both federal and state data). The SIC classifies establishments by the types of work activity in which they are engaged. The SIC Code is used to classify manufacturers and businesses within each state; a directory is usually published by each state's Chamber of Commerce. Source: U.S. Chamber of Commerce.

Industry

The Industry Code ranges from 1 - 9 and is determined by the first digit of the DOT code. Industry 1 includes DOT codes beginning with either zero or one.

Industry Designation

The Industry Designation is an arrangement of DOT titles by product or services.

Appendix F
Deposition Checklist
(Selected Items Relevant to the Vocational Expert)

1.3   Identification of Deponent — Defendant

1. Name
   (a) full name
   (b) maiden name
   (c) other names or changes

2. Address
   (a) home address
   (b) rent or own
   (c) home phone number
   (d) usiness address
   (e) business phone
   (f) previous addresses
   (g) any present or former landlord
   (h) present secondary addresses (cottage, etc.)

3. Age and citizenship
   (a) age in years
   (b) date of birth
   (c) place of birth
   (d) citizenship
   (e) where registered to vote

4. Identifying numbers
   (a) Social Security number
   (b) taxpayer's number (if no Social Security)
   (c) driver's license number
   (d) Selective service number
   (e) college student number (if student)

5. Marriage
   (a) name, age, birthplace of spouse
   (b) date of marriage
   (c) spouse's employer
   (d) type of work
   (e) hours
   (f) salary or wage
   (g) spouse's previous employers
   (h) time worked for each
   (i) if separated or divorced, when and why
   (j) address of spouse
   (k) custody of children
   (l) name and address of previous spouses
   (m) inclusive dates of previous marriages
   (n) how terminated
   (o) if divorced, give court, date of decree, grounds

6. Children
   (a) names and ages of all natural, step, foster, or adopted children
   (b) residence, occupation, marital status, and school of each
   (c) when, where, and result of any adoption applied for

7. Education
   (a) dates, degrees, and course of studies at all schools
   (b) ever expelled

8. Employment record
   (a) if self-employed, number of employees, annual earnings, partners
   (b) if employed, name and address of employer
   (c) nature of business
   (d) position held
   (e) duties, hours, salary or wage
   (f) name and address of supervisor
   (g) if unemployed, how long, benefits received, location of unemployment center
   (h) name, address, type of business of previous employers
   (i) job title and reason for leaving former jobs
   (j) if ever self-employed, dates, nature of business, annual earnings and reasons for discontinuing
   (k) previous periods of unemployment, dates, reason, benefits
   (l) if student, any part-time or summer work

9. Military service
   (a) branch
   (b) length of service
   (c) place(s) of service
   (d) ranks held
   (e) date, place, and type of discharge
   (f) if ever rejected for military service, why
   (g) present draft classification
   (h) ever disciplined while in service

10. Bias or interest
    (a) related to any other party
    (b) related to anyone involved
    (c) know any other party previous to occurrence
    (d) know anyone involved previous to occurrence
    (e) what clubs, organizations, and associations

1:6   Notice

1. Notice of occurrence
   (a) day, date, time notified of occurrence
   (b) by whom
   (c) how given
   (d) names and addresses of all employees giving notice
   (e) what was done by you after notice to help plaintiff
   (f) what was said to plaintiff by defendant or agent

2. Notice of claim
   (a) date notice first given
   (b) method
   (c) date and method of subsequent notice
   (d) content or substance of first notice

(e) content or substance of all subsequent notices

1:7   Written Statements and Reports

1. Written statement from plaintiff

    (a) date

    (b) substance

    (c) location of statement

2. Written reports or statements by agents or employees of defendant

    (a) name and address of person

    (b) position with defendant

    (c) duties with defendant

    (d) location at time of occurrence

    (e) date

    (f) location of all copies of report or statement

    (g) substance

3. Written statements received by defendant

    (a) name and address of person making statement

    (b) reason present

    (c) location at time of occurrence

    (d) date

    (e) location of all copies

    (f) substance

    (g) identify employee or agent to whom given

1:12   Prior Similar Occurrences

1. Description of prior similar occurrences

    (a) dates

    (b) time of day of each

    (c) identify persons involved

    (d) facts of each

    (e) location of each

2. Civil suits

    (a) name and address of court

    (b) name and address of plaintiffs

    (c) filing dates

    (d) status of lawsuits

    (e) disposition of each

    (f) money paid

3. Preventive measures

    (a) preventive measures after similar occurrences

    (b) preventive measures after this occurrence

1:13   Circumstances and Conditions

1. Time

2. Place

    (a) location

    (b) description

3. Persons present

    (a) identify all agents or employees in area

    (b) position of each with defendant

    (c) location at time

    (d) reason present

    (e) identify anyone else present in area

    (f) number of people in area

4. Detailed description

    (a) facts of occurrence

    (b) causes

(c) injuries sustained by plaintiff

(d) any other injuries

5. Plaintiff's conduct

    (a) before

    (b) after

    (c) during

    (d) anything done to cause occurrence

    (e) anything to prevent

    (f) could anything (else) be done

    (g) any warning given of danger by plaintiff

    (h) was plaintiff aware of danger

    (i) when (time, distance)

    (j) any contact with another person

2:10   Medical History (of claimant)

1. Congenital defects

    (a) describe

    (b) treatment

    (c) recovery

    (d) current effect on mobility, use of faculties or senses

2. Accidents

    (a) where and when (childhood, home, school, athletic accidents)

    (b) doctors

    (c) hospitalization

    (d) accident insurance carrier

    (e) claims

    (f) suits

    (g) family physician at time

    (h) temporary and permanent disabilities suffered

3. Illnesses and diseases

    (a) when and where

    (b) identify each

    (c) doctors

    (d) hospitalization

    (e) sickness insurance carrier

    (f) claims

    (g) suits

    (h) treatment

    (i) recovery

    (j) how long lasted

    (k) temporary and permanent disabilities suffered

4. Hospitalization

    (a) name and address of each hospital

    (b) reasons for hospitalization

    (c) length of stay

    (d) treatment and medication

    (e) operations

    (f) doctors

    (g) x-rays (what parts of body)

    (h) recovery

    (i) temporary and permanent disabilities suffered

5. Treatment by specialists (osteopaths, chiropractors, etc.)

    (a) reason

    (b) dates

    (c) recovery

6. Eyesight
    (a) date last checked
    (b) wear eyeglasses or contact lenses
    (c) prescription

7. Use other physical aids (cane, brace, hearing aid, etc.)
    (a) identify
    (b) reason
    (c) extent disabled

8. Ever had blackouts, amnesia, dizziness, fainting spells, epilepsy, loss of balance or equilibrium
    (a) when and how often
    (b) treatment
    (c) if epilepsy, first seizure date
    (d) how long afflicted
    (e) treatment

9. Mental health
    (a) ever seen psychiatrist - who and when
    (b) ever been admitted or committed to mental clinic or hospital - dates, place, doctors
    (c) physician ever prescribe tranquilizers, etc.   (d) ever take tranquilizers, bromides, etc., without prescription

10. Ever left employment for health reasons (or changed residence for same)
    (a) dates
    (b) employment or residence left
    (c) new employment or residence
    (d) reasons for change

11. Under any restraint orders ever
    (a) nature of restraint — type — poseybelt, bedsides, etc.
    (b) doctor who ordered
    (c) when order issued
    (d) orally or in writing
    (e) do you have copy
    (f) did doctor tell you of order
    (g) when told
    (h) where told
    (i) who else knew
    (j) restraint order in effect at time of occurrence

12. Alcohol
    (a) ever treated by physician or psychiatrist for alcoholism
    (b) ever discharged from work for insobriety
    (c) ever arrested for drunkenness or driving under the influence

13. Drugs and narcotics
    (a) when used and how long
    (b) effect
    (c) how obtained

14. Physical Examination - last 10 years
    (a) doctors - name and address
    (b) date
    (c) place
    (d) occasion or purpose
    (e) results - conclusions
    (f) diagnosis

(g) prognosis
(h) for employment
(i) for insurance

2:11 Physical Condition Before Occurrence

1. Physical condition
    (a) general health
    (b) any cold, illness, fever
    (c) weight normal
    (d) nervous, anxious, or depressed

2. Tiredness
    (a) tired, sleepy, groggy, ill
    (b) when last awoke
    (c) where last awoke
    (d) any impaired ability to think, ambulate, operate a motor vehicle

3. Activities
    (a) how long worked day of occurrence
    (b) what did on day of occurrence
    (c) any business or social activities
    (d) any business or social activities, day or night prior to occurrence

2:12 Physical Disabilities Before Occurrence

1. Eyesight
    (a) glasses or contact lenses
    (b) which eye or both
    (c) prescription
    (d) doctor prescribing and address
    (e) date of prescription
    (f) wearing at time
    (g) where now
    (h) any motor vehicle license restriction for eyesight
    (i) any difficulty judging distance
    (j) peripheral vision
    (k) color blindness
    (l) wearing dark glasses at time of occurrence
    (m) if so, describe
    (n) prescription or not
    (o) wear dark glasses now

2. Hearing
    (a) any hearing aids
    (b) one ear or both
    (c) ability impaired
    (d) who fitted aid
    (e) when
    (f) where
    (g) any doctor who examined and address
    (h) when doctor examined
    (i) regularly use aid
    (j) on at time of occurrence

3. Artificial limbs, eyes
    (a) any artificial limbs, eyes
    (b) difficulty
    (c) who fitted
    (d) when
    (e) where
    (f) how normal activity impaired
    (g) on at time of occurrence

4. Emotional problems
    (a) nature of problem
    (b) family problem
    (c) work problem
    (d) psychiatrist's treatment
    (e) name and address of psychiatrist
    (f) date first treatment
    (g) frequency or number of treatments
    (h) ulcers

5. Mental illness or nervous breakdown
    (a) confined or not
    (b) where
    (c) other medical attention
    (d) doctor's name and address
    (e) first treatment
    (f) how long suffered
    (g) recovery
    (h) relapse
    (i) present treatment

6. Venereal disease
    (a) nature
    (b) when contracted
    (c) date first treatment
    (d) confined or not
    (e) nature and extent of treatment
    (f) hospital and/or doctor's names and addresses
    (g) date of release or end of treatment

7. Tuberculosis
    (a) when contracted
    (b) confined or not
    (c) where
    (d) name and address of doctor
    (e) release
    (f) current condition

8. Diabetes
    (a) when contracted
    (b) treatment

9. Fainting spells
    (a) when started
    (b) how often, duration
    (c) any treatment
    (d) name and address of doctor
    (e) diagnosis

10. Epilepsy
    (a) when began
    (b) name and address of doctor
    (c) treatment

11. Other fits and convulsions
    (a) describe
    (b) how often occur
    (c) name and address of doctor
    (d) diagnosis
    (e) treatment

12. Defective balance
    (a) nature and extent
    (b) part of body affected
    (c) when first suffered
    (d) name and address of doctor
    (e) treatment
    (f) any aid or prosthetic device
    (g) using at time of occurrence

13. Other difficulty walking or functioning
    (a) describe
    (b) extent of difficulty
    (c) part of body affected
    (d) when first suffered
    (e) name and address of doctor
    (f) diagnosis
    (g) treatment
    (h) any aid or prosthetic device
    (i) using at time of occurrence

14. Ear infection (especially inner ear)
    (a) nature and extent
    (b) when
    (c) frequency
    (d) treatment
    (e) name and address of doctor

15. Insomnia
    (a) nature and extent
    (b) when
    (c) treatment
    (d) name and address of doctor
    (e) present sleeping habits

16. Other disabilities
    (a) describe
    (b) duration
    (c) name and address of doctor
    (d) treatment
    (e) confinement
    (f) where and when confined

17. Physical problems - past or present
    (a) eyes
    (b) ears
    (c) nose
    (d) blood pressure
    (e) circulation
    (f) wrists
    (g) feet
    (h) speech
    (i) memory
    (j) throat
    (k) chest
    (l) hips
    (m) heart
    (n) diabetes
    (o) alcoholism
    (p) headaches
    (q) venereal disease
    (r) elbows
    (s) abdomen
    (t) menstrual periods
    (u) lungs
    (v) hernia

(w) fractures

(x) back

(y) neck

(z) arms

(aa) legs

(bb) hands

(cc) shoulders

(dd) wounds

(ee) scars

(ff) miscarriages

(gg) knees

(hh) ankles

2:13 Habits Before Occurrence

1. Alcohol

    (a) had any in preceding 24 hours

    (b) 12 hours

    (c) 3 hours

    (d) when taken exactly

    (e) reason for consumption

    (f) where consumed

    (g) who present

    (h) who drinking with

    (i) type and brand of drinks consumed

    (j) quantity consumed

    (k) within what period consumed

    (l) how much regularly drink

    (m) ever treated for alcoholism

    (n) where

    (o) when

    (p) what treatment

    (q) sobriety test after occurrence

    (r) type given

    (s) how soon after occurrence

    (t) name and address of person administering

    (u) results

    (v) ever lose job for insobriety

2. Drugs

    (a) any taken within preceding 24 hours

    (b) 12 hours

    (c) 3 hours

    (d) describe

    (e) prescription

    (f) who prescribed, address

    (g) when prescribed

    (h) times renewed

    (i) prescription number

    (j) formula, if known

    (k) amount taken

    (l) how often taken

    (m) reason for taking

    (n) tranquilizer

    (o) narcotic

3. Tobacco

    (a) type of smoking

    (b) how long a smoker

    (c) average daily consumption

    (d) smoking at time of occurrence

4. Coffee or tea

    (a) average daily consumption

    (b) amount consumed within 12 hours preceding occurrence

2:14 Educational Background (of Claimant)

1. Years of formal education

2. High school

    (a) name and address

    (b) major course or study

    (c) dates of attendance

    (d) graduated

3. Vocational schools

    (a) name and address

    (b) major course of study

    (c) dates of attendance

    (d) graduated

4. Colleges

    (a) name and address

    (b) major course of study

    (c) dates of attendance

    (d) graduated

5. Post-graduate or professional school

    (a) name and address

    (b) major course of study

    (c) dates of attendance

    (d) graduated

6. Student at time of occurrence

    (a) school attending

    (b) part or full-time

    (c) grade in which studying

    (d) course studying

    (e) names and addresses of teachers

    (f) time missed due to occurrence

7. Ever expelled from any school

    (a) which and when

    (b) why

2:15 Employment Record

1. Occupation

2. If self-employed

    (a) name and address of place of business

    (b) nature of business

    (c) partners

    (d) corporation

    (e) length of time self-employed

    (f) annual earnings

    (g) number of employees

3. If employed

    (a) name and address of employer

    (b) principal business of employer

    (c) job title

    (d) department

    (e) duties and type of work

    (f) hours

    (g) how long there

    (h) salary or wage - weekly or monthly

(i) annual earnings
(j) name of immediate supervisor
(k) his job title
(l) promotions or demotions in present job

4. If unemployed
   (a) for how long
   (b) unemployment benefits receiving and received
   (c) location of unemployment center from which received

5. Prior employment
   (a) name each past employer
   (b) location of each
   (c) principal business of each
   (d) period of employment at each
   (e) job title at each
   (f) duties at each
   (g) immediate supervisor at each
   (h) salary or wage at each
   (i) reason for leaving each

6. Ever been self-employed before
   (a) name and address of place of business
   (b) nature of business
   (c) length of time self-employed
   (d) partners
   (e) corporation
   (f) annual earnings
   (g) number of employees
   (h) reason for discontinuing

7. Unemployment record
   (a) periods of unemployment
   (b) reasons for each
   (c) unemployment benefits claimed
   (d) location of unemployment center where claim made or benefits received

8. If student
   (a) part-time work
   (b) name and address of employer
   (c) type of work
   (d) number of hours per week
   (e) wage
   (f) summer employment
   (g) how many summers
   (h) names and addresses of employees
   (i) type of work
   (j) salary or wage
   (k) name immediate supervisor

2:16   Military Service
1. If formerly served in military
   (a) branch of service
   (b) length of service
   (c) place(s) served
   (d) all ranks held
   (e) date of discharge
   (f) place of discharge

2:18   Bias Toward Party or Interest in Outcome
1. Related to any party
   (a) how related

2. Acquainted with what parties
   (a) how acquainted
   (b) how long acquainted

3. What clubs and social organizations belong to

4. Church affiliation
   (a) name and address of church affiliated with
   (b) how long a member
   (c) how often attend
   (d) clergyman, Priest, Rabbi
   (e) church groups belong to
   (f) officer or positions held
   (g) services rendered church

5. Death action
   (a) relation to deceased
   (b) deceased die testate or intestate
   (c) who are beneficiaries if testate
   (d) if residuary clause, who named

2:19   Injuries
1. Description of each injury
   (a) part of body
   (b) which injuries painful
   (c) severity of pain
   (d) when pain noticed
   (e) how long pain lasted

2. What noticed externally
   (a) marks
   (b) cuts
   (c) bruises
   (d) blood

3. Loss of consciousness
   (a) when lost — date, hour, minute
   (b) what doing when lost
   (c) what happening when lost
   (d) how long unconscious
   (e) basis for that opinion
   (f) when recovered — date, hour, minute
   (g) location when recovered
   (h) what recollection before unconsciousness
   (i) first recollection when recovered

4. How felt
   (a) immediately after occurrence
   (b) first night thereafter
   (c) following morning
   (d) next night
   (e) next morning

5. Neck injuries
   (a) describe pain
   (b) direction it runs
   (c) frequency
   (d) pain in arms
   (e) numbness

6. Back injury
   (a) when first pain
   (b) now in pain
   (c) sleeping

(d) bending, stooping

(e) lifting

(f) coughing, sneezing

(g) extend down legs or not

7. Miscarriage

    (a) previous miscarriage

    (b) dates

    (c) doctor or hospital

    (d) times pregnant previously and how ended

    (e) when this miscarriage

    (f) last visit to doctor before occurrence

    (g) approximate date of pregnancy

    (h) pain prior to occurrence

    (i) doctor who attended

    (j) others present

    (k) place of miscarriage

    (l) other female problems

8. Head injury

    (a) describe below, severity

    (b) location on head

    (c) external signs

    (d) abrasion — scrape

    (e) contusion — blow

    (f) concussion — internal injury

    (g) spinal tap results

    (h) EEG results

9. Other injuries

    (a) part of body

    (b) describe pain

    (c) frequency of pain

    (d) now in pain

    (e) numbness

10. Immediately following injury, any:

    (a) bleeding

    (b) broken bones

    (c) cuts

    (d) bruises

    (e) dizziness

    (f) blackouts

    (g) shock

    (h) vomiting

    (i) paralysis

    (j) limitation of motion

    (k) numbness

    (l) unconsciousness

    (m) sprains

    (n) blindness

    (o) noise in ears

    (p) other

11. Dental injuries

    (a) nature and extent

    (b) name and address of dentist

    (c) treatment

    (d) dates of treatment

    (e) present condition of mouth and teeth

2:20 Medical, Hospital and Nursing Treatment (of Claimant)

1. First Aid

    (a) who administered

    (b) where administered

    (c) nature and extent

2. Doctors generally

    (a) how many seen

    (b) names and addresses of each

    (c) specialty of each

    (d) family doctor before occurrence

3. Each doctor — generally

    (a) name

    (b) address

    (c) specialty

    (d) family doctor

    (e) how chosen

    (f) referral by whom

    (g) date each visit

    (h) length of time treated

    (i) place of visits

    (j) charge each visit

    (k) total charge

    (l) treatment generally

    (m) diagnosis generally

    (n) prognosis generally

    (o) prior experience with doctor — dates, injuries, treatment, recover

4. Each visit to each doctor

    (a) name and address

    (b) place of examination or treatment

    (c) date and time of day

    (d) by appointment or emergency

    (e) medical history given

    (f) conversation with doctor

    (g) complaints of pain — location, extent, severity

    (h) physical examination — parts of body

    (i) diagnosis told you by doctor

    (j) advice or instructions

    (k) treatment — nature, extent, duration — what doctor did

    (l) medication or prescription

    (m) describe any drugs — instructions on use

    (n) prognosis told you by doctor

    (o) another appointment made — date

5. Diagnostic aids

    (a) parts of body x-rayed

    (b) x-ray reports — negative or positive

    (c) electroencephalogram

    (d) electrocardiogram

    (e) other aids

    (f) date of use of each

    (g) place — hospital, clinic

    (h) parts of body

    (i) person in charge

    (j) results

    (k) where copies of reports now

6. Ambulance

   (a) name and address of owner
   (b) name and address of driver and attendants

7. Hospitalization

   (a) name each hospital
   (b) address
   (c) inpatient or outpatient
   (d) admittance date
   (e) discharge date
   (f) reason for admittance
   (g) names of roommates
   (h) names of nurses
   (i) history given
   (j) examinations — description
   (k) examination — results, diagnosis
   (l) treatment
   (m) doctor's orders
   (n) laboratory reports
   (o) operations — description
   (p) operations — reason or purpose
   (q) operations — results

8. Therapeutic devices

   (a) wheel chair
   (b) braces
   (c) crutches
   (d) cane
   (e) special beds
   (f) special shoes
   (g) appliances
   (h) other
   (i) purpose for use of each
   (j) inclusive dates each used

9. Other medical or nursing care

   (a) nature and extent
   (b) names and addresses of those rendering
   (c) inclusive dates

10. Current treatment

   (a) nature and extent
   (b) name and address of doctor
   (c) parts of body still in pain
   (d) nature of pain
   (e) diagnosis, doctor's opinion of problems
   (f) prognosis, how long last
   (g) dates of future appointments

11. Future treatment or surgery

   (a) what required
   (b) what recommended
   (c) when recommended
   (d) by whom recommended
   (e) specialists recommended
   (f) estimated costs — doctor and hospital
   (g) time lost from employment or school

   12. Followed medical advise
   (a) date last doctor's appointment
   (b) kept it
   (c) discharge from hospital against medical advice
   (d) instructions given upon discharge

1. Confinement to bed

   (a) total or partial
   (b) reason
   (c) date first confinement
   (d) date last confinement

2. Confinement to home

   (a) total or partial
   (b) reason
   (c) date first confinement
   (d) date last confinement

3. Effect of occurrence — physical

   (a) sleep
   (b) weight
   (c) appetite
   (d) nerves
   (e) general health

4. Effect of occurrence — mental

   (a) impaired mental ability — describe
   (b) mental treatment — describe
   (c) by whom
   (d) psychiatric help
   (e) nervous breakdown — describe
   (f) give dates
   (g) treatment
   (h) doctors, hospitals, clinics involved
   (i) current condition

5. Recovery

   (a) dates of recovery as to each injury
   (b) if not recovered, doctor's program

6. Total disabilities

   (a) describe each
   (b) injury causing each
   (c) inclusive dates
   (d) date of resumption of normal activity
   (e) what unable to do yet

7. Partial disabilities

   (a) describe each
   (b) injury causing each
   (c) inclusive dates
   (d) date of resumption of normal activity
   (e) what unable to do yet

8. Disabilities — general

   (a) when first able to get out of bed to use toilet
   (b) sit up in bed
   (c) sit up in a chair for more than one hour
   (d) get out of bed so that no longer wholly confined
   (e) remain out of bed all day
   (f) climb stairs
   (g) join family regularly at meals
   (h) use washing machine or dryer
   (i) wash, dust, clean in home
   (j) prepare meal
   (k) make any bed
   (l) leave home
   (m) ride in car

(n) drive car

(o) attend social event outside home

(p) shop

(q) return to work part-time

(r) return to work full-time

(s) return to work on part-duty basis

(t) return to work on full-duty basis

9. Sports before and after (restrictions)

    (a) swimming

    (b) hunting

    (c) fishing

    (d) golf

    (e) tennis

    (f) bowling

    (g) water skiing

    (h) snow skiing

    (i) horseback riding

    (j) baseball

    (k) camping

    (l) hiking

    (m) bicycle riding

10. Activities at home before and after (restrictions)

    (a) cooking

    (b) laundry

    (c) cleaning

    (d) ironing

    (e) sewing

    (f) gardening

    (g) washing car

    (h) carrying children

    (i) sexual relations

    (j) entertaining guests

11. Social activities before and after (restrictions)

    (a) club affairs

    (b) school activities

    (c) dancing

    (d) luncheons and dinners

    (e) organization offices held

12. Permanent disabilities

    (a) describe

    (b) speaking impaired

    (c) hearing impaired

    (d) sight impaired

    (e) facial expression altered

    (f) cosmetic problems

    (g) scars or other permanent disfigurement

    (h) lost limb or member

    (i) limp

    (j) other

2:22　Death and Conscious Suffering

1. Death

    (a) exact time of occurrence

    (b) exact time of death (date, hour, minute)

    (c) exact time of determination of death

    (d) place of determination

    (e) who determined — official title

    (f) cause of death

    (g) autopsy

    (h) where record of determination

    (i) how long lived after occurrence

    (j) death instantaneous or not

2. Conscious suffering

    (a) evidence of conscious suffering

    (b) sounds or utterances

    (c) movements or actions

    (d) witnesses to suffering, names and addresses, other identification

    (e) date and page of hospital record relating to suffering

    (f) length of time of consciousness

    (g) date, time, place, and substance of any conversation

    (h) witnesses to any conversation, names and addresses

    (i) statements made by decedent to doctor or attendant

    (j) name and address of such doctor or attendant

2:23　Damages and Losses (of Claimant)

1. Doctors' bills (for each doctor and each bill)

    (a) date incurred

    (b) date bill received

    (c) amount of bill

    (d) amount paid

    (e) when payment made

    (f) amount still owing

2. Hospital bills (for each hospital)

    (a) date incurred

    (b) date bill received

    (c) amount of bill

    (d) amount paid

    (e) when payment made

    (f) amount still owing

3. Nursing bills

    (a) date incurred

    (b) date bill received

    (c) amount of bill

    (d) amount paid

    (e) when payment made

    (f) amount still owing

4. Housekeeper

    (a) name and address

    (b) related

    (c) services performed

    (d) hours per week

    (e) inclusive dates

    (f) pay rate

    (g) total bill

    (h) amount paid

    (i) when paid

    (j) amount still owing

5. Medicine and supplier

    (a) identify

    (b) when purchased or received

    (c) total amount of bills

    (d) amount paid

    (e) when paid

    (f) amount still owing

6. Other medical expenses
    (a) identify
    (b) date incurred
    (c) date of bill
    (d) total amount of bill
    (e) amount paid
    (f) when paid
    (g) amount still owing

7. Lost wages or earnings
    (a) inclusive dates out of work
    (b) name and address of employer
    (c) salary or wage
    (d) total amount lost

8. Loss of earning capacity
    (a) employed at time of occurrence
    (b) salary or wages
    (c) duties and responsibilities
    (d) inclusive dates of loss of earning capacity
    (e) if employment continued, any change in hours, duties, responsibility, conditions
    (f) in unemployed at time, last prior employer
    (g) salary or wage
    (h) duties and responsibilities
    (i) present salary or wage
    (j) present duties and responsibilities
    (k) raises since occurrence
    (l) when
    (m) amount of raises
    (n) any loss besides lost wages

9. Income tax (for 5 years prior to occurrence)
    (a) gross total
    (b) taxable income
    (c) amount of tax paid
    (d) where copies of returns

10. Property damage
    (a) what damaged
    (b) how damaged
    (c) repaired or not
    (d) name and address of person who repaired
    (e) cost of repairs
    (f) fair market value of property before
    (g) fair market value of property after repair
    (h) value now
    (i) amount paid for repairs
    (j) date of payment
    (k) amount still owing

11. Injury or damage to feelings (distress, anguish, humiliation, etc.)
    (a) nature, extent, duration
    (b) specific examples
    (c) how, wherein, and manner injury or damage was received
    (d) financial loss

12. Injury or damage to name or reputation
    (a) nature, extent, duration
    (b) specific examples
    (c) how, wherein, and manner injury or damage was received
    (d) financial losses

13. If claimant under 21
    (a) who paid expenses
    (b) bank accounts in own name

14. Other losses
    (a) identify
    (b) date incurred
    (c) date of bill
    (d) amount of bill
    (e) amount paid
    (f) date of payment
    (g) amount still owing

15. Since occurrence applied for insurance
    (a) what kind
    (b) name of companies
    (c) doctor's exam
    (d) name and address of doctor
    (e) date of exam
    (f) place of exam
    (g) results
    (h) if rejected, why

16. Remuneration
    (a) amount from employer
    (b) amount from insurance
    (c) amount from Workmen's Compensation
    (d) amount from unemployment insurance
    (e) amount from Medicare or similar agency
    (f) all other amounts

2:24   Prior Accidents or Civil Actions (of Claimant)

1. Any prior accidents or occurrences
    (a) date
    (b) time
    (c) location
    (d) names and addresses of people involved
    (e) how happened
    (f) legal proceedings
    (g) result of any settlement
    (h) attorneys involved

2. Civil suits for prior accidents or occurrences
    (a) name and address of court
    (b) plaintiff or defendant
    (c) filing date
    (d) status of suit
    (e) final results
    (f) money received or paid
    (g) attorneys involved

3. Accident claims (no suit filed)
    (a) when filed
    (b) name of person or firm against whom claim made
    (c) results of claim
    (d) names of any insurance companies involved
    (e) attorneys involved

4. Industrial accident claims
   (a) nature of accident
   (b) date of accident
   (c) where occurred
   (d) medical treatment
   (e) date claim filed
   (f) contents of papers executed for claim
   (g) amount received
   (h) compensation through any workmen's compensation act fund
   (i) dates through which received
   (j) amount received

5. Health policy claims
   (a) nature of illness
   (b) inclusive date of illness
   (c) date claim made
   (d) name of person or firm against whom claim made
   (e) results of claim
   (f) money received

6. Ever drawn social security benefits for disability
   (a) residence address at time
   (b) office through which claim filed
   (c) nature and extent of disability
   (d) inclusive dates of disability
   (e) nature and extent of disability, if any, on date or occurrence
   (f) inclusive dates of receipt of benefits
   (g) total amount received

7. Currently receiving payments through any claim made for prior illness, accident or disability
   (a) receiving from whom
   (b) inclusive dates of receipt
   (c) nature of illness, accident or disability
   (d) how arose
   (e) any present disability
   (f) nature and extent of present disability
   (g) total amount received plus aggregate amount expected in future

2:25 Subsequent Accidents or Civil Actions (of Claimant)

1. Any subsequent accidents, illnesses or occurrences
   (a) dates
   (b) time
   (c) location
   (d) names and addresses of people involved
   (e) how happened
   (f) legal proceedings
   (g) result of any settlement
   (h) attorneys involved
   (i) how was condition changed or effected

2. Civil suits for subsequent accidents or occurrences
   (a) name for subsequent accidents or occurrences
   (b) plaintiff or defendant
   (c) filing date
   (d) status of suit
   (e) any money paid or received
   (f) attorneys involved

3. Accident claims (no suit filed)
   (a) when filed
   (b) name of person or firm against whom made
   (c) results of claim
   (d) name of any insurance companies involved
   (e) attorneys involved

4. Industrial accident claims
   (a) nature of accident
   (b) date of accident
   (c) where occurred
   (d) medical treatment
   (e) date claim filed
   (f) contents of paper executed for claim
   (g) amount received
   (h) compensation through workmen's compensation act fund
   (i) dates through which received
   (j) amount received

5. Health policy claims
   (a) nature of illness
   (b) inclusive dates of illness
   (c) date claim made
   (d) name of person or firm against whom claim made
   (e) results of claim
   (f) money received

6. Social security benefits drawn for disability subsequent to occurrence
   (a) office through which claim filed
   (b) nature and extent of disability
   (c) inclusive dates of disability
   (d) inclusive dates of receipt of benefits
   (e) total amount received

7. Currently receiving payments through any claim made
   (a) receiving from whom
   (b) inclusive dates of receipt
   (c) nature of illness, accident or disability
   (d) how arose
   (e) any present disability
   (f) nature and extent of present disability
   (g) total amount received to date
   (h) aggregate amount expected to receivd in future

8. Any member of family made claim or filed suit for illness, accident or disability subse>quent to occurrence
   (a) which member
   (b) nature of illness, accident or disability
   (c) how arose
   (d) when arose
   (e) suit or claim
   (f) when filed
   (g) where or with whom filed
   (h) status of suit or claim

2:26 Other claims Resulting from Occurrence

1. Other claims related to this occurrence
   (a) names and addresses of parties
   (b) situation of parties
   (c) date suit filed

    (d) title and docket number

    (e) where filed

    (f) status of suit

    (g) terms of disposition

    (h) attorneys involved

2. Payment received from any source

    (a) from whom

    (b) amount

    (c) date received

    (d) releases, etc., signed

    (e) recommended by attorney

    (f) where copies of any settlement

3. Payment promised from any source

    (a) from whom

    (b) amount

    (c) date promised

    (d) date to be received

    (e) releases, etc., to be signed

    (f) recommended by attorney

4. Payments made or promised to anyone in connection with occurrence

    (a) to whom

    (b) amount

    (c) date promised and/or given

    (d) papers signed

    (e) recommended by attorney

    (f) copies of any settlement

5. Any agreement with anyone regarding suit or claim related to occurrence

    (a) with whom

    (b) terms

6. Any parties interested in outcome by way of subrogation assignment, etc.

    (a) identity

    (b) nature of interest

    (c) amount claimed

7. Any parties claim to be interested by way of subrogation, assignment, etc.

    (a) who

    (b) nature of interest

    (c) amount claimed

    8. Lien letters received

    (a) from whom

    (b) source of claim

    (c) amount of lien

Source: Lawyers Cooperative Publishing Company (1973).

Appendix G
What is O*NET?

O*NET, the Occupational Information Network, is a comprehensive database of worker attributes and job characteristics. As the replacement for the *Dictionary of Occupational Titles* (DOT), O*NET will be the nation's primary source of occupational information.

O*NET is being developed as a timely, easy-to-use resource that supports public and private sector efforts to identify and develop the skills of the American workforce. It provides a common language for defining and describing occupations. Its flexible design also captures rapidly changing job requirements. In addition, O*NET moves occupational information into the technological age.

As the basis for enhanced product development, the O*NET database can serve as the engine that drives value-added applications designed around core information. It provides the essential foundation for facilitating career counseling, education, employment, and training activities. The database contains information about knowledges, skills, abilities (KSAs), interests, general work activities (GWAs), and work context. O*NET data and structure will also link related occupational, educational, and labor market information databases to the system.

O*NET may be used to:

- Align educational and job training curricula with current workplace needs
- Create occupational clusters based on KSA information
- Develop job descriptions or specifications, job orders, and resumes
- Facilitate employee training and development initiatives
- Develop and supplement assessment tools to identify worker attributes
- Structure compensation and reward systems
- Evaluate and forecast human resource requirements
- Design and implement organizational development initiatives
- Identify criteria to establish performance appraisal and management systems
- Identify criteria to guide selection and placement decisions
- Create skills-match profiles
- Explore career options that capitalize on individual KSA profiles
- Target recruitment efforts to maximize person-job-organizational fit
- Improve vocational and career counseling efforts

What is the Foundation of O*Net?

Common Language

O*NET offers a common language for communication across the economy and among work force development efforts. It provides definitions and concepts for describing worker attributes and workplace requirements that can be broadly understood and easily accepted. Using comprehensive terms to describe the KSAs, interests, content, and context of work, O*NET provides a common frame of reference for understanding what is involved in effective job performance.

The goal of O*NET's common language is straightforward: "improve the quality of dialogue among people who communicate about jobs in the economy, generate employment statistics, and develop education and training programs". It provides the shared foundation of language upon which to build private and public sector workforce development efforts. Employer hiring requirements will have the same meaning for human resource practitioners, workers, education and training developers, program planners, and students.

The O*NET 3.0 database uses a coding structure consistent with the 1998 Standard Occupational Classification (SOC). O*NET 3.0 uses the 6-digit numerical code of the SOC and adds a 2-digit numerical suffix to define O*NET occupations.

Conceptual Framework

The conceptual foundation of O*NET is called the Content Model. The Content Model provides a framework for classifying, organizing, and structuring O*NET data.

The O*NET Content Model

The Content Model Forming the Foundation of O*NET

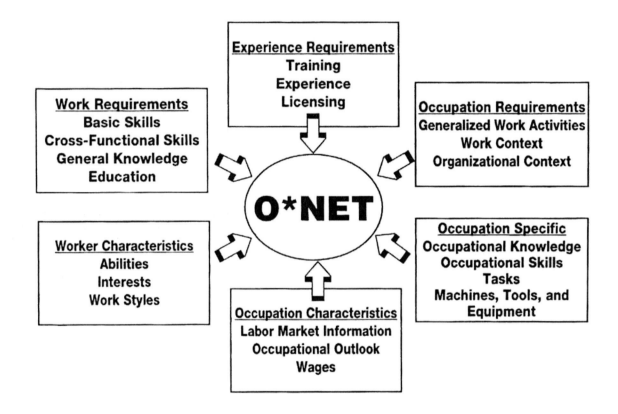

The Content Model is the conceptual foundation of O*NET. The Content Model provides a framework that identifies the most important types of information about work and integrates them into a theoretically and empirically sound system. The graphic below displays the parts of the Content Model and how they are related.

Classification of the Content Model

The Content Model was developed using research on job and organizational analysis. It embodies a view that reflects the character of occupations (via job-oriented descriptors) and people (via worker-oriented descriptors). The Content Model also allows occupational information to be applied across jobs, sectors, or industries (cross-occupational descriptors) and within occupations (occupational-specific descriptors). The table below shows how the parts of the O*NET Content Model are classified.

Cross Classification Table of O*NET Occupational Information

Type of Occupational Information

Specificity of Application	Job-Oriented Descriptors	Worker-Oriented Descriptors
Cross Occupation Descriptors	Generalized work activities Work Context Organizational context Labor Market Information Occupational Outlook Wages	Skills Knowledges Education Abilities Interests Work Styles Training Experience Licensing
Occupation Specific Descriptors	Tasks Machines, Tools, and Equipment Labor market Information Occupational Outlook Wages	Occupational Skills Occupational Knowledges Training Experience

Elements of Content Model

The Content Model is organized into six major domains. These are: Worker Characteristics, Worker Requirements, Experience Requirements, Occupation Requirements, Occupational Characteristics, and Occupation-Specific Information. The structure enables the user to focus on areas of information that specify the key attributes and characteristics of workers and occupations. The following sections briefly describe the information included within each domain.

A summary of the full O*NET information hierarchy by Content Model domain is presented below.

Worker Characteristics

- Abilities – enduring attributes of the individual that influence performance

  - Cognitive Abilities
  - Psychomotor Abilities
  - Physical Abilities
  - Sensory Abilities

- Interests – preferences for work environments and outcomes Holland Occupational Classification Occupational Values

- Work Styles – personal characteristics that describe important interpersonal and work style requirements

  - Achievement Orientation
  - Social Influence
  - Interpersonal Orientation
  - Adjustment
  - Conscientiousness
  - Independence
  - Practical Intelligence

Worker Requirements

- Basic Skills – developed capacities that facilitate learning and information acquisition
  - Content Skills – fundamental skills needed to work with or acquire more specific skills
    - Reading Comprehension
    - Active Listening
    - Writing
    - Speaking
    - Mathematics
    - Science
  - Process Skills – procedures that contribute to the more rapid acquisition of knowledge and skill
    - Critical Thinking
    - Active Learning
    - Leaning Strategies
    - Monitoring
- Cross-Functional Skills – developed capacities that facilitate performance of activities that occur across jobs
  - Social Skills – developed capacities used to work with people to achieve goals
    - Social Perceptiveness
    - Coordination
    - Persuasion
    - Negotiation
    - Instructing
    - Service Orientation
  - Complex Problem-Solving Skills – developed capacities used to solve novel, ill-defined problems in complex, real-world settings
    - Problem Identification
    - Information Gathering
    - Information Organization
    - Synthesis/Reorganization
    - Idea Generation
    - Idea Evaluation
    - Implementation Planning
    - Solution Appraisal
- Technical Skills – developed capacities used to design, set up, operate, and correct malfunctions involving application of machines or technological systems
  - Operations Analysis
  - Technology Design
  - Equipment Selection
  - Installation
  - Programming
  - Testing
  - Operation Monitoring
  - Operation and Control

- Product Inspection
- Equipment Maintenance
- Troubleshooting
- Repairing
- Systems Skills – developed capacities used to understand, monitor and improve socio-technical systems
  - Visioning
  - Systems Perception
  - Identifying Downstream Consequences
  - Identification of key Causes
  - Judgment and Decision-Making
  - Systems Evaluation
- Resource Management Skills – developed capacities used to allocate resources efficiently
  - Time Management
  - Management of Financial Resources
  - Management of Material Resources
  - Management of Personnel Resources
- Knowledges – organized sets of principles and facts applying in general domains
  - Business and Management
  - Manufacturing and Production
  - Engineering and Technology
  - Mathematics and Science
  - Health Services
  - Education and Training
  - Arts and Humanities
  - Law and Public Safety
  - Communications
  - Transportation
- Education – prior educational experience required to perform a job
- Level of Education
- Instructional Program Required
- Education Level in Specific Subjects

Experience Requirements

- Experience and Training – basic experience required for occupational readiness
- Licensing – licenses, certificates, or registration awarded to show that a job holder has gained certain skills; includes requirements for obtaining these credentials, and the organization or agency requiring their possession
  - License, Certificate or Registration required
  - Additional Education or Training
  - Organization and Agency Requirements

Occupational Characteristics

- The Bureau of Labor Statistics (BLS)

- The National Occupational Information Coordinating Committee (NOICC)
- The Department of Education (ED)
- The Office of Personnel Management (OPM)

Occupational Requirements

- Generalized Work Activities – general types of job behaviors occurring on multiple jobs
  - Information Input
  - Mental Processes
  - Work Output
  - Interacting with Others
- Organizational Context – characteristics of the organization that influence how people do work
  - Structural Characteristics
  - Social Processes
- Work Context – physical and social factors that influence the nature of work
  - Interpersonal Relationships
  - Physical Work Conditions
  - Structural Job Characteristics

Online Location: *www.doleta.gov/programs/onet*

Appendix H
Code of Professional Ethics for Rehabilitation Counselors

Adopted in June 2009 by the Commission on Rehabilitation Counselor Certification for its Certified Rehabilitation Counselors. This Code is effective as of January 1, 2010.

Developed and Administered by the Commission on Rehabilitation Counselor Certification (CRCC), 1699 East Woodfield Road, Suite 300 Schaumburg, Illinois 60173 (847) 944-1325 http://www.crccertification.com, Revised March 9, 2012

TABLE OF CONTENTS

PREAMBLE

Rehabilitation counselors provide services within the Scope of Practice for Rehabilitation Counseling. They demonstrate beliefs, attitudes, knowledge, and skills, to provide competent counseling services and to work collaboratively with diverse groups of individuals, including clients, as well as with programs, institutions, employers, and service delivery systems and provide both direct (e.g., counseling) and indirect (e.g., case review, feasibility evaluation) services. Regardless of the specific tasks, work settings, or technology used, rehabilitation counselors demonstrate adherence to ethical standards and ensure the standards are vigorously enforced. The Code of Professional Ethics for Rehabilitation Counselors, henceforth referred to as the Code, is designed to provide guidance for the ethical practice of rehabilitation counselors.

The primary obligation of rehabilitation counselors is to clients, defined as individuals with or directly affected by a disability, functional limitation(s), or medical condition and who receive services from rehabilitation counselors. In some settings, clients may be referred to by other terms such as, but not limited to, consumers and service recipients. Rehabilitation counseling services may be provided to individuals other than those with disabilities. Rehabilitation counselors do not have clients in a forensic setting. The subjects of the objective and unbiased evaluations are evaluees. In all instances, the primary obligation remains to clients or evaluees and adherence to the Code is required.

The basic objectives of the Code are to: (1) promote public welfare by specifying ethical behavior expected of rehabilitation counselors; (2) establish principles that define ethical behavior and best practices of rehabilitation counselors; (3) serve as an ethical guide designed to assist rehabilitation counselors in constructing a professional course of action that best serves those utilizing rehabilitation services; and, (4) serve as the basis for the processing of alleged Code violations by certified rehabilitation counselors.

Rehabilitation counselors are committed to facilitating the personal, social, and economic independence of individuals with disabilities. In fulfilling this commitment, rehabilitation counselors recognize diversity and embrace a cultural approach in support of the worth, dignity, potential, and uniqueness of individuals with disabilities within their social and cultural context. They look to professional values as an important way of living out an ethical commitment. The primary values that serve as a foundation for this Code include a commitment to:

- Respecting human rights and dignity;
- Ensuring the integrity of all professional relationships;
- Acting to alleviate personal distress and suffering;
- Enhancing the quality of professional knowledge and its application to increase professional and personal effectiveness;
- Appreciating the diversity of human experience and culture; and,

- Advocating for the fair and adequate provision of services.

These values inform principles. They represent one important way of expressing a general ethical commitment that becomes more precisely defined and action-oriented when expressed as a principle. The fundamental spirit of caring and respect with which the Code is written is based upon six principles of ethical behavior:

Autonomy: To respect the rights of clients to be self-governing within their social and cultural framework.

Beneficence: To do good to others; to promote the well-being of clients.

Fidelity: To be faithful; to keep promises and honor the trust placed in rehabilitation counselors.

Justice: To be fair in the treatment of all clients; to provide appropriate services to all.

Nonmaleficence: To do no harm to others.

Veracity: To be honest.

Although the Code provides guidance for ethical practice, it is impossible to address every possible ethical dilemma that rehabilitation counselors may face. When faced with ethical dilemmas that are difficult to resolve, rehabilitation counselors are expected to engage in a carefully considered ethical decision-making process. Reasonable differences of opinion can and do exist among rehabilitation counselors with respect to the ways in which values, ethical principles, and ethical standards would be applied when they conflict. While there is no specific ethical decision-making model that is most effective, rehabilitation counselors are expected to be familiar with and apply a credible model of decision-making that can bear public scrutiny. Rehabilitation counselors are aware that seeking consultation and/or supervision is an important part of ethical decision-making.

The Enforceable Standards within the Code are the exacting standards intended to provide guidance in specific circumstances and serve as the basis for processing complaints initiated against certified rehabilitation counselors.

Each Enforceable Standard is not meant to be interpreted in isolation. Instead, it is important for rehabilitation counselors to interpret standards in conjunction with other related standards in various sections of the Code. A brief glossary is located after Section L to provide readers with a concise description of some of the terms used in the Code.

Due to the length of this document, it is advised that the reader go to the CRCC website in order to download and print the full document.

CRCC Desk Reference on Professional Ethics:
A Guide for Rehabilitation Counselors

This 176 page booklet was developed by CRCC and is available from E&F, Inc.
For additional information, please visit www.elliottfitzpatrick.com

Appendix I
International Association of Rehabilitation Professionals:
Code of Ethics, Standards of Practice, and Competencies

Code of Ethics

Introduction

The International Association of Rehabilitation Professionals (IARP) is committed to promoting ethical and professional rehabilitation services at all times. IARP recognizes that medical and vocational rehabilitation services are provided under a variety of international, federal, local, and state laws or administrative codes, and in a wide variety of private and public venues. However, certain practices are applicable in any rehabilitation setting.

This document addresses nine areas of ethical practice followed by a Forensic Code of Ethics for IARP members who practice in a forensic setting. IARP expects its members to adhere to the standards and ethical guidelines applicable to their professional discipline, licensing, and/or credentialing organizations and to refer to those respective Codes of Ethics for specific guidelines as well as to the IARP guidelines. If there is a conflict in the respective Codes and IARP guidelines, the Code is binding. Note that life care planning standards and Codes are available through IARP's life care planning section.

A1) Conflict of Interest

- o IARP members are to respect the integrity and protect the welfare of the individuals or groups to whom their work pertains. IARP members' primary obligation is always to the client, defined as the person with or without a disability to whom their assignment pertains. There may be institutional recipients of services that are provided for the benefit of an organization, not that of a single individual.

A2) Detrimental/Exploitive Relationships

- o IARP members are to conduct themselves in the role for which their services are retained. Members may not use their professional position to promote other products or services. At the outset and throughout the professional relationship, members will disclose to their clients professional boundaries, particularly if those involve multiple services on the same case where there exists a high potential for ethical conflict.

A3) Objectivity.

- a) For purposes of this document, objectivity is defined as providing an evaluation and arriving at the same conclusions without bias given the same set of facts.

- b) It is the responsibility of IARP members to maintain objectivity in all cases and in appropriate situations. Members are also obligated to engage in the objective use of available resources and reference data in supporting an opinion or in the development of a rehabilitation or life care plan.

A4) Competency

- o IARP members, while practicing in a number of diverse fields and areas of expertise, are obligated to maintain professional and technical competency at such a level that the recipient receives the highest quality of service that the member's discipline(s) is capable of offering through their education, training, or supervised experience. Members will not misrepresent their current credentials or the extent of their expertise within related scopes of practice.

A5) Confidentiality

- a) The purpose of confidentiality is to safeguard information that is obtained in the course of practice. Disclosure of information is restricted to what is necessary, relevant, and verifiable with respect to the client's right to privacy. IARP members must be sure to obtain the necessary written authorizations from the client, and when a third party is involved, to make sure that the client is aware from the onset that the delivery of service is being monitored. Professional files, reports, records, and working environment shall be maintained under conditions of security and with provisions for proper destruction of records when appropriate.

b) IARP members should adhere to appropriate disclosure of confidential information to referral sources and other professionals providing services on the same case.

A6) Multicultural/Diversity Issues

a) IARP members should always be mindful of, and respect, the cultural/ ethnic differences of clients from other backgrounds. Members should avail themselves of workshops/trainings in diversity issues and, if possible, research those issues prior to the first meeting with the client, as well as be aware of their own biases and their potential impact on service delivery.

b) IARP members will not condone or engage in discrimination based on age, color, culture, disability, ethnic group, gender, race, religion, sexual orientation, marital status, military history, criminal record, or socioeconomic status.

c) Regarding language issues, IARP members will be proactive in securing interpreter or translator services when needed to facilitate communication with the client.

A7) Appropriate Role for Practitioner

a) IARP members are obligated to secure the most appropriate services for clients within the standards of local, state, or federal law and within the scope of practice. Those services may include:

   i. Providing the client with a professional disclosure statement, verbally and/or in writing and documenting such activity;

   ii. Setting clear, attainable rehabilitation goals;

   iii. Making appropriate referrals to allied professionals when needed and providing appropriate case coordination with other service providers;

   iv. Providing only those services that the member is qualified to provide;

   v. Referring an individual to another professional who may be more qualified to render needed services, when necessary;

   vi. Assisting in resolving conflicts that arise;

   vii. Conducting face-to-face contact with the client whenever possible or feasible

A8) Social Advocacy

o With regard to the individual with a disability, advocacy takes into account such issues as the legal rights of individuals with disabilities to achieve integration into the social, cultural, and economic life of the general community. The role of the IARP member as an advocate is to protect and promote the welfare of individuals with disabilities to maximize their potential for community integration to the best of their capabilities. IARP members are encouraged to stay informed about emerging legislation trends and issues within the rehabilitation field serving individuals with disabilities.

A9) Electronic Communication

a) IARP members will be held to the same level of expected ethical behavior regardless of the form of communication, e.g., cellular phones, electronic mail (e-mail), fax, video, or any and all other audio-visual media.

b) IARP members will exercise responsible, ethical behavior at all times; respect the need for confidentiality; and adhere to the standards set forth by their individual credentialing and/or licensing boards.

c) IARP members will not use electronic communications to send copies of copyrighted documents, if such a transmission would be in violation of copyright laws.

d) It may be difficult at times to verify the identity of a client, client's guardian, or the rehabilitation professional. IARP members will take the necessary steps to address these concerns by such means as professional disclosure to the client regarding the potential of imposters in electronic communication.

e) Attempting unauthorized access to data, attempting to breach any security measures on an electronic communication system, or attempting to intercept any electronic communication transmissions without proper authorization will represent a breach of acceptable behavior by an IARP member.

f) In situations where access to clients is allowed, IARP members are expected to inform clients and referral sources of the potential hazards of unsecured communications via e-mail and the Internet. Hazards may include authorized or unauthorized monitoring of transmissions and/or records of sessions and difficulty ensuring complete confidentiality of information transmitted through electronic communication over the Internet.

g) Case-related transmissions made by e-mail, facsimile, text message, or other communication media will be regarded as case documentation and will be stored in the case file and will be afforded the same degree of confidentiality as written progress notes and reports.

Forensic Code

For purposes of the Forensic Code section, the term Forensic Rehabilitation Experts/ Consultants is used to describe rehabilitation professionals who provide services in a forensic or litigation setting. Where applicable, statements differentiate between rules that apply for the Forensic Rehabilitation Expert versus rules for the Forensic Rehabilitation Consultant and the ethical responsibilities inherent in each role. Forensic Rehabilitation Experts/Consultants who are initially retained as primary service providers will adhere to the tenets of confidentiality and appropriate disclosure, as well as to other rules outlined in this Forensic Code.

General Definitions

• Client

  ○ Clients are defined as individuals with or without disabilities who are the subject of the litigation. The primary obligation and responsibility of Forensic Rehabilitation Experts/Consultants is to the client. Regardless of whether direct client contact occurs or whether indirect services are provided, the primary obligation remains to the client.

• Forensic Rehabilitation Expert

  ○ A rehabilitation professional who has been retained and disclosed as an expert for purposes of providing expert testimony

• Forensic Rehabilitation Consultant

  ○ A rehabilitation professional that has been retained to provide consulting services and has not been disclosed as an expert.

Specific Codes

B1) Confidentiality

  a) Clients have the right to expect confidentiality and will be provided with an explanation of its limitations, including disclosure to others, at the onset of service delivery. Forensic Rehabilitation Experts will discuss these limitations, as well as pertinent benefits available to clients they serve, in order to facilitate open, honest communication and avoid unrealistic expectations.

  b) When circumstances require the disclosure of confidential information, Forensic Rehabilitation Experts will endeavor to reveal only essential information that is relevant, necessary, and verifiable.

  c) Forensic Rehabilitation Experts will obtain written permission from the client/guardian prior to any video/audio taping and/or photographing of any interview session or interaction they may have with the client.

  d) When a referral source requests a records review, Forensic Rehabilitation Consultants may exchange confidential information that is relevant, necessary, and verifiable without the written consent of clients or their legal guardians.

B2) Objectivity

    a) So that justice is served by accurate determination of the facts involved, Forensic Rehabilitation Experts/Consultants use their abilities in an objective, unbiased, nonpartisan, impartial, and fair manner in arriving at findings, conclusions, and/or opinions.

    b) Forensic Rehabilitation Experts/Consultants are to use appropriate methods and techniques, carefully research and analyze the evidence in a case, and render opinions or conclusions that are demonstrably objective and reasonable.

    c) When testifying, Forensic Rehabilitation Experts have an obligation to present their findings, conclusions, evidence, or opinions in a fair and objective manner.

B3) Competence

    a) Forensic Rehabilitation Experts/Consultants have an obligation to provide services in a manner consistent with the highest quality standards of their profession. They are responsible for their own professional and ethical conduct and the conduct of those individuals under their direct supervision.

    b) Forensic Rehabilitation Experts/Consultants will not claim to possess any depth or scope of expertise greater than that demonstrated by professional achievement, knowledge, skill, experience, education, training, or credential.

    c) Forensic Rehabilitation Experts/Consultants recognize that their own personal values, moral beliefs, or personal and professional relationships with parties to a legal proceeding may interfere with their ability to practice competently. Under such circumstances, Forensic Rehabilitation Experts/Consultants are obligated to decline participation or to limit their assistance in a manner consistent with professional obligations.

    d) Forensic Rehabilitation Experts/Consultants will refer clients to other colleagues if the intended assignment is beyond their competence.

    e) Forensic Rehabilitation Experts/Consultants will not represent their membership status as bestowing any specialized expertise.

    f) Forensic Rehabilitation Experts/Consultants will practice in specialty areas new to them only after appropriate education, training, and/or supervised experience has been obtained. While developing skills in new specialty areas, Forensic Rehabilitation Experts/Consultants will take steps to ensure the competence of their work and to protect clients from possible harm.

    g) Because of their special status as persons qualified as experts to the Court, Forensic Rehabilitation Experts/Consultants have an obligation to maintain current knowledge of scientific, professional, and legal developments within their area of claimed competence. They are obligated to use that knowledge, consistent with accepted clinical and scientific standards, in selected data collection methods and procedures for an evaluation, treatment, consultation, conclusion, finding, opinion and/or scholarly/empirical investigation.

    h) Forensic Rehabilitation Experts/Consultants will take steps to maintain competence in the skills they use, will be open to exploring new and emerging techniques, seek consultation if deemed necessary, and develop and maintain competence for practice with the diverse and/or special populations with whom they work in order to provide the highest quality of services within their abilities.

    i) Forensic Rehabilitation Experts/Consultants avoid offering information from their evaluations that does not bear directly upon the legal purpose of their professional services. The submissions of written and/or oral reports will present data germane to the purposes of the referral.

    j) When Forensic Rehabilitation Experts/Consultants rely upon data or information gathered by others, the origins of those data are clarified in any professional product. Forensic Rehabilitation Experts/Consultants bear a special responsibility to ensure that such data, if relied upon, are gathered in a manner standard for the profession. Forensic Rehabilitation Experts/ Consultants will ensure that the resources used or accessed in supporting an opinion are credible and valid.

    k) Reports will be thorough and include competent research.

    l) Forensic Rehabilitation Experts/Consultants will not allow pursuit of financial gain or other personal benefit to interfere with the exercise of sound professional judgment and skills. They will not abuse their relationships with clients to promote personal or financial gain.

m) Forensic Rehabilitation Experts/Consultants understand and abide by the Code, demonstrate adherence to ethical standards, and ensure that standards are enforced.

n) Forensic Rehabilitation Experts/Consultants will not advocate, sanction, participate in, accomplish or otherwise carry out, or condone any act which is prohibited by the Code.

o) Forensic Rehabilitation Experts/Consultants may choose to consult with any other professionally competent persons about their cases. Care should be taken not to place the individual who is being consulted in a conflict of interest situation.

p) Forensic Rehabilitation Experts have an obligation to present to the Court the boundaries of their competence, the factual bases for their qualifications as an expert, and the relevance to the specific matters at issue.

q) Forensic Rehabilitation Experts are aware that hearsay exceptions and other rules governing expert testimony place a special ethical burden upon them.

When hearsay or otherwise inadmissible evidence forms the basis of their opinion, evidence, or professional product, they seek to minimize sole reliance upon such evidence. Where circumstances reasonably permit, Forensic Rehabilitation Experts seek to obtain independent and personal verification of data relied upon as part of their professional services to the Court or to a party in a legal proceeding.

B4) Disclosure

a) Forensic Rehabilitation Experts/Consultants will not intentionally withhold or omit any findings or opinions discovered during a forensic evaluation that would cause the facts of a case to be misinterpreted or distorted.

b) A clinical interview is an important part of the decision-making process and bears particular importance for the Forensic Rehabilitation Expert. When direct contact with the client is made, Forensic Rehabilitation Experts will generate written documentation, either in the form of case notes or a report, as to their involvement and/or conclusions or opinions. This is not required for Forensic Rehabilitation Consultants where there is no contact with the client and where the Consultant's role is not discoverable. In those cases where a Forensic Rehabilitation Consultant changes roles to a Forensic Rehabilitation Expert, the responsibility stipulated in this Code predominates. Forensic Rehabilitation Experts/Consultants will define the limits of their reports, testimony, or opinions, especially when an examination of the client has not been conducted.

c) During initial consultation with the referral source, Forensic Rehabilitation Experts/Consultants have an obligation to inform the party of factors that might reasonably affect the decision to contract with the rehabilitation expert/ consultant.

d) Forensic Rehabilitation Experts/Consultants shall be honest, thorough, and open in their analyses and shall not provide the retaining or opposing attorney, referral source, client, the Court, or any other entity involved in the case with any information, through commission or omission, that they know to be false or misleading. They shall exert due diligence and at all times strive to use competent judgment to avoid the use of invalid or unreliable information in the formulation of their opinions.

e) Forensic Rehabilitation Experts/Consultants will not misrepresent their role or competence to clients and referral sources and will provide information about their credentials, if requested.

f) Forensic Rehabilitation Experts/Consultants will actively disclose the sources of information relied upon in formulating their opinions.

g) Forensic Rehabilitation Experts/Consultants will disclose the existence of, and their adherence to, ethical standards and principles to those retaining them and to other participants involved in the case.

B5) Consistency

o Forensic Rehabilitation Experts/Consultants may be given a different assignment when retained in a forensic case by the plaintiff as opposed to the defense. For any given assignment, however, the basic assumptions, information sources, and methods should not change regardless of the party who retains the Forensic Rehabilitation Expert/Consultant to perform the assignment. There should be no change in methodology or process used to evaluate the case for purposes of favoring any party's claim. This tenet is not meant to preclude methodological changes as new knowledge becomes available.

B6) Informed Consent

   a) Forensic Rehabilitation Experts/Consultants shall inform clients and the retaining party with whom they have direct contact of the purposes, goals, techniques, procedures, limitations, potential risks, and/or benefits of services to be performed and other pertinent information, as well as the limits of the relationship between the evaluator and the client.

   b) Forensic Rehabilitation Experts/Consultants provide clear and unbiased reports.

   c) Unless Court ordered, Forensic Rehabilitation Experts will obtain the informed consent of the client or party, or their attorney or representative, before proceeding with their evaluation. If the client appears unwilling to proceed after receiving a thorough notification of the purposes, methods, and intended uses of the forensic evaluation, the evaluation should be postponed and the Forensic Rehabilitation Expert should take steps to place the client in contact with his/her attorney or representative for the purpose of legal advice on the issue of participation.

   d) In situations where the client or party may not have the capacity to provide informed consent for services or the evaluation is pursuant to a Court Order, the Forensic Rehabilitation Expert provides reasonable notice to the client's attorney or representative of the nature of the anticipated forensic service before proceeding. If the client's attorney or representative objects to the evaluation, the Forensic Rehabilitation Expert notifies the Court that issued the Order and responds as directed.

B7) Loyalty to Community and the Law

   a) Forensic Rehabilitation Experts/Consultants will be familiar with and observe the legal limitations of the services they offer.

   b) Forensic Rehabilitation Experts/Consultants will obey the laws and statutes of the legal jurisdiction in which they practice unless there is conflict with the Code, in which case they should seek immediate consultation and advice. When conflicts arise between professional standards and ethics and the requirements of legal standards, a particular court, or a directive by an officer of the court or legal authorities, the Forensic Rehabilitation Expert/Consultant has an obligation to make those legal authorities aware of the source of the conflict and to take reasonable steps to resolve it. Such steps may include, but are not limited to:

        i.   Obtaining the consultation of fellow rehabilitation experts;

        ii. Obtaining the advice of independent counsel; and

        iii. Conferring directly with the legal representative involved. In the absence of legal guidelines, the Code is binding.

B8) Loyalty to Colleagues (e.g., Professional Relationships)

   a) Forensic Rehabilitation Experts/Consultants will not discuss in a disparaging way the competency of other professionals or agencies. Differences in opinions, findings, methods, or plan development should be made based on work product, not on the individual or agency.

   b) When evaluating or commenting upon the professional work product or qualifications of another expert or party to a legal proceeding, Forensic Rehabilitation Experts/Consultants represent their professional disagreements with reference to a fair and accurate evaluation of the data, theories, standards, and opinions of the other expert or party.

   c) Forensic Rehabilitation Experts/Consultants shall at all times strive to practice within the boundaries of professional and disciplinary honesty and fairness. To this end, they must assume the responsibility of holding their colleagues in the profession accountable to the ethical principles promulgated herein.

   d) It is appropriate for Forensic Rehabilitation Experts/Consultants to offer criticism of breaches of these ethical principles, as long as such criticisms are not offered in a disparaging way.

   e) Forensic Rehabilitation Experts/Consultants shall act with integrity in relationships with colleagues, other organizations, agencies, institutions, referral sources, and other professions so as to facilitate the contribution of all specialists toward achieving optimum service delivery.

f) When referring clients to other professional colleagues or cooperating agencies, Forensic Rehabilitation Experts/Consultants shall supply all relevant information necessary to begin service delivery in a prompt manner.

B9) Business Practices

a) Forensic Rehabilitation Experts/Consultants will neither give nor receive commissions, rebates, contingency fees, or any other form of remuneration when accepting a case or referring clients for professional services. Payment for services will not be contingent upon a case outcome or award.

b) Forensic Rehabilitation Experts/Consultants will not enter into financial commitments that may compromise the quality of their services.

c) Forensic Rehabilitation Experts/Consultants will not enter into fee arrangements that could influence their opinions in a case and otherwise raise questions as to their credibility.

d) While all Forensic Rehabilitation Experts/Consultants have the discretionary right to accept retention in any case or proceed within their area(s) of expertise, they should decline involvement in any case when asked to take or support a predetermined position, or where there are ethical concerns about the nature of the requested assignment.

e) Forensic Rehabilitation Experts/Consultants should decline involvement in any case when they are asked to assume invalid representations of fact or alter their methodology or process without foundation or compelling reason.

f) Should a fee dispute arise during the course of evaluating a case and prior to trial, the Forensic Rehabilitation Expert/Consultant shall have the ability to discontinue his/her involvement in the case as long as no harm comes to the client.

g) If necessary to withdraw from a case after having been retained, the Forensic Rehabilitation Expert/Consultant will make a reasonable effort to assist the client and/or referral source in locating another Forensic Rehabilitation Expert/Consultant to take over the assignment.

B10) Detrimental/Exploitive Relationships

a) Forensic Rehabilitation Experts/Consultants will recognize potential conflicts of interest in dual/multiple relationships that are detrimental/exploitive, and seek to minimize their effects.

b) Forensic Rehabilitation Experts/Consultants will avoid providing professional services to parties in a legal proceeding with whom they have had personal or professional relationships that are inconsistent with the anticipated business and professional relationship.

c) When necessary to provide both evaluation and treatment services to a client involved in a legal proceeding, the Forensic Rehabilitation Expert will recognize the potential negative effects of these circumstances on the rights of the client, confidentiality, and the process of treatment and evaluation.

d) Forensic Rehabilitation Experts/Consultants will avoid establishing dual/multiple relationships with clients that could impair their professional judgment or increase the risk of exploitation.

e) Sexual conduct with clients is unethical and will not be tolerated during the course of an evaluation until the litigation has been concluded, unless otherwise restricted by other professional codes that may apply.

f) Forensic Rehabilitation Experts/Consultants will not be involved in surveillance set up, scheduling, and monitoring. Any knowledge of surveillance-related items must be divulged when rendering an expert opinion.

Standards of Practice and Competencies

IARP has chosen to focus on the predominant Standards of Practice and Competencies considered fundamental for medical case management, vocational counseling, and placement in the private sector. This format change recognizes that different methods may apply in various jurisdictions or systems as to medical case management, vocational assessment, rehabilitation plan development, job development and placement, on-the-job training, occupational retraining, and self-employment. IARP members should choose the methods applicable to their area of practice or refer to professional literature regarding accepted methods. Regardless of the method employed, IARP members ascribe to and support a basic level of Standards of Practice and Competencies as outlined below.

Medical case management and vocational rehabilitation services are provided directly to a client, the goal of which is to maximize medical recovery or return an individual to suitable gainful employment. IARP members recognize the uniqueness of providing medical case management or vocational rehabilitation services under various federal and state laws and insurance systems, and the importance of Standards of Practice and Competencies in the delivery of primary care services.

Standards of Practice and Competencies are defined as the knowledge, skills, abilities, personal qualities, experience, and related characteristics necessary to provide primary care services in vocational counseling/placement for individuals with or without disabilities. Beyond general Standards of Practice and Competencies, a member may have additional knowledge, skills, abilities, personal qualities, and professional experience resulting in specialized expertise that binds them to the Standards of Practice and Competencies of that specialty.

Medical Case Management Standards of Practice and Competencies

Medical case management is defined as the process of assessing, planning, coordinating, monitoring and evaluation of the services required to respond to an individual's health care needs to attain the goals of quality and cost effective care. This service may be performed in conjunction with managed care; however, it is differentiated from managed care, which is recognized as an organized process designed to ensure the medical necessity and cost effectiveness of a proposed service. Case management is designated to promote optimal recovery and rehabilitation by professional involvement in the rehabilitation process. Medical case management in the optimum sense is a balance in terms of both quality assurance and medical cost control. The case manager advocates on behalf of the individual to assure quality of care and attainment of appropriate goals, as well as promotes self-advocacy skills to achieve maximum independence.

C1) Professional Standards for Medical Case Management include:

a) Accepting referrals relevant to medical case manager's qualifications, expertise, education, licensure, or certification relevant to the diagnostic category, needed services, working guidelines, and on legislation;

b) Providing adequate information when referring a client to a provider (e.g., contact, identification, medical, purpose, special instructions, payor, etc.);

c) Understanding conditions of the assessment/evaluation

   i. Recognizing importance of timely client assessment (e.g., onset of injury/illness)

   ii. Release(s) of information

   iii. Medical/Mental health status review

   iv. Client's understanding/learning needs related to the diagnosis, treatment, resources, adjustment, and coping mechanisms

   v. Family knowledge base and need for education, health status, expectations, support or caregiver potential;

d) Developing/Implementing a plan that integrates the client and/or parties in the decision-making process to meet recommended and cost-effective short- and long-term goals and objectives, and recognition of potential complications. Plan may involve the identification, procurement, and coordination of services and resources to implement the plan, and may involve ongoing evaluation of client's progress and the effectiveness or appropriateness of the plan;

e) Acknowledging and compensating for strengths/weaknesses of on-site, electronic, and/or telephonic services;

f) Coordinating services among medical or allied health professionals and inpatient, outpatient, home services, or environmental modification providers;

g) Understanding rehabilitation principles for optimum delivery and outcome of services, including accelerated and/or alternative options;

h) Coordinating vendor and resource utilization involving medical equipment, supplies, medications, and services;

i) Identifying and addressing education needs of client, family, support system, or service provision team;

j) Awareness of laws, statutes, standards, and regulations covering written documentation and recordkeeping (e.g., cost/benefit analysis, individualized medical rehabilitation or independent living plans, initial or status reports, etc.);

k) Documenting termination of services to the client or representative; and

l) Coordinating communication formally or informally to resolve disputes between parties, documenting efforts appropriately, or referring parties to resources able to resolve such disputes.

Vocational/Placement Standards of Practice and Competencies

Vocational rehabilitation services are those vocational services provided directly to a client, the goal of which is to return a client to suitable gainful employment. IARP members recognize the uniqueness of providing vocational rehabilitation services under various federal and state laws and insurance overages. However, there remain broad services standards that should be applied regardless of this uniqueness. These standards of practice and competencies include vocational assessment, plan development, job development and placement, training, and self-employment.

D1) Understanding conditions of the assessment including the purpose of the evaluation; laws, rules, and/or regulations under which the member practices; responsibilities of the parties; timelines; and criteria for completion, termination, or suspension of services.

D2) Recognizing importance of client in assessment process as the main recipient of services.

D3) Selecting clinical interview methodology appropriate to the situation of the client.

D4) Analyzing records and their significance to assessment (e.g., pre-existing and current diagnoses and treatment, physical/cognitive/mental functional limitations, abilities, etc.).

D5) Considering variables relevant in the assessment process (e.g., vocational and/or avocational histories, formal, informal, or military education or training, pertinent individual assessment and appraisal, and/or labor market, etc.).

D6) Synthesizing information for vocational diagnosis, treatment/intervention planning, conclusions, and/or recommendations.

D7) Following professional standards

a) Developing rehabilitation/treatment/intervention plan (e.g., individual or group adjustment and/or career/vocational counseling, early return to work services, accommodations, rehabilitation technology, job development and/or placement, job seeking skills training, professional skills training, on the job training, academic retraining, apprenticeship, internship, self-employment, case management, referral, research, consultation, etc.)

b) Understanding specific barriers/opportunities (e.g., client, support system, labor market, environment, jurisdictional, legal, systemic, etc.) to successful implementation of the plan

c) Outlining specific objectives and/or goals associated with the plan d) Monitoring activities vis- -vis the plan and intervening whenever necessary through the provision of services or the referral to appropriate services

Reporting Suspected Violations

When there is a suspected violation of the Code by an IARP member, consultation should occur with the member or other colleagues to seek an informal resolution. When an informal resolution is not appropriate, violations can be reported to the Standard Compliance Review Board (SCRB). The SCRB is made up of an elected advisory panel of IARP professional members from the various disciplines to review the conduct of IARP professional members and determine if a particular action is in violation of the IARP Code of Ethics. The conduct in question is reviewed by the panel objectively and recommendations are made to the IARP Board that could include revocation of their IARP membership. A recommendation can be made to report the behavior in questions to that member's credentialing or licensing board.

Addendum
Clarification of the "Client" in Forensics
Approved 12/20/07

Purpose

Who is the "client" in a forensic rehabilitation evaluation has been the source of confusion and much debate among expert witnesses for many years. In an attempt to clarify the issue, several leaders within the rehabilitation forensic practice setting met in Las Vegas, Nevada on November 4, 2007 to review the various definitions of "client" among several of the codes of ethics to which forensic certificants or professional members adhere. The goal of the work group was to identify and define the intent of the relationship among the parties in a legal matter and to offer definitions to clarify those relationships utilizing terminology that might be universally accepted by certification and membership bodies to which many rehabilitation expert witnesses belong.

Roles of Parties in a Forensic Setting

The work group members agreed that:

○ in a forensic setting, the professional who is engaged as an expert witness has no client;

○ the responsibility of the expert witness is to communicate the truth of the matter based on the case-related facts and the education, training, and experience of the expert;

○ the opinion(s) communicated by the expert witness should be objective and unbiased and not advocate for any party in the legal matter, such as the interests of the referral source, person being evaluated, or any other party in the legal matter; and,

○ the expert witness must use sound methodology and empirical data, using their unique specialized knowledge and skills to analyze the empirical data, generate hypotheses, test their validity against the facts, and to use skilled clinical judgment to express opinions that reflect the issue(s) at hand.

Definitions of Parties in a Forensic Setting

Further, the work group agreed on the following definitions:

○ **Evaluee:** The person who is the subject of the objective and unbiased evaluation.

○ **Referral Source:** The individual who referred the case to the expert witness. This may be through self-referral of the evaluee, family member, attorney, insurance company, or other source.

○ **Payor:** The entity paying for the services provided by the forensic rehabilitation expert. This may be the evaluee, family member, attorney, insurance company, referral source, or other source.

Appendix J
International Academy of Life Care Planners (IALCP) Standards Of Practice

Life care planning has evolved from a practice primarily within the field of litigation support to application in elder care, chronic illness, and discharge planning. The need for standards of practice has become more critical with this growth.

As the professional transdisciplinary organization for life care planners, the International Academy of Life Care Planners has developed Standards of Practice. Committee Chairwoman Sharon Reavis, RN, MS, CRC, CCM, Karen Preston, PHN, MS, CRRN, and Roger Weed, PhD, CRC, CDMS, CCM, CLCP, worked more than two years to develop these standards, consistent with the diversity of practice settings and individual professional standards of practice.

These standards will evolve as they are influenced by changes in the various professions of life care planners and by external forces, such as accrediting bodies and courts of law.

The field reviewed standards, which apply to the current practice of life care planning in all settings, are presented here for the use of life care planners.

Questions regarding Standards of Practice as published by the IALCP, may be directed to the national office, via email (debbiew@tcag.com) or telephone: (847) 657-6964.

I. Introduction

A. Definition of Life Care Planning

The Life Care Plan is a dynamic document based upon published standards of practice, comprehensive assessment, data analysis and research, which provides an organized, concise plan for current and future needs with associated cost for individuals who have experienced catastrophic injury or have chronic health care needs.

B. Historical Perspective

The development of a comprehensive plan of care has always been considered an integral part of the medical and rehabilitation process. This type of plan has historically been used by multiple disciplines. Rehabilitation professionals create a rehabilitation plan. Nurses develop a nursing care plan. Physicians define a medical treatment plan, and other professions develop plans specific to their practice. Pursuant to rapid growth in medical technology and an increased emphasis on the cost of care, including concepts of managed care, information regarding the specific cost of care has become an increasingly important aspect of health care. This process of developing a comprehensive plan and delineating costs has evolved over an extensive period of time and is now utilized by case managers, counselors, and other professionals in many sectors. This concept represents an acceptable and pragmatic approach to the delivery of services within myriad sectors of the health care delivery system.

The concept of Rehabilitation/Life Care Plans has been utilized in a variety of health care and legal settings to provide information and documentation regarding the cost of services related to long-term care. These plans are also provided as valuable tools for rehabilitation planning, geriatric services implementation, management of health care resources, discharge planning, educational planning, and long-term managed care, among other areas.

C. Transdisciplinary Perspective

Life Care Planning is a transdisciplinary specialty practice. Each profession brings to the process of Life Care Planning practice standards which must be adhered to by the individual professional, and these standards remain applicable while the practitioner engages in Life Care Planning activities. Each professional works within specific standards of practice for their discipline to assure accountability, provide direction, and mandate responsibility for the standards for which they are accountable. These include, but are not limited to, activities related to quality of care, qualifications, collaboration, law, ethics, advocacy, resource utilization, and research. Moreover, each individual practitioner is responsible for following the Standards of Practice for Life Care Planning in addition to the standards for the qualifying profession.

In addition, the individual practitioner must examine their qualifications as applied to each individual case. Therefore, a thorough knowledge of the medical diagnosis, disability and long-term care considerations, by virtue of education and experience, is a necessary component of the practitioner's competency for each individual case.

D. Education/Preparation/Certification

The Life Care Planner must:

1. Possess the appropriate educational requirements as defined by their professional standards; e.g., nurses should possess the requirements to acquire licensure, rehabilitation counselors should possess the requisite Masters Degree, and other health professionals should possess the required degree for their field.

2. Maintain current professional licensure or National Board Certification within a professional health care discipline.

3. Demonstrate completion of an accredited program in nursing or a baccalaureate or higher level educational program in a professional health care field. Fields may include, but not be limited to, nursing, rehabilitation counseling, medicine, physical, occupational or speech therapy, or psychology.

4. Demonstrate professional discipline provides sufficient education and training to assure that the Life Care Planner has an understanding of human anatomy and physiology, pathophysiology, the health care delivery system, the role and function of various health care professionals, and clinical practice guidelines and standards of care.

5. Participate in specific continuing education, required to maintain the individual practitioner's licensure or certification within their profession.

6. Obtain continuing education and/or training to remain current in the knowledge and skills in the field.

II. Philosophical Overview/Goals of Life Care Planning

The Life Care Plan should be a working document that provides accurate and timely information which can be easily used by the client and interested parties. It should be a document that can be updated and serve as a lifelong guide to assist in the delivery of health care services in a managed format.

It is appropriate, if possible, for the care plan to be a collaborative effort among the various parties and should reflect goals that are preventive and rehabilitative in nature. As a dynamic document, the Life Care Plan will require periodic updating to accommodate changes and should have as its goal quality outcomes.

Goals / Life Care Plans:

In accordance with the professional Standards and Codes of Ethics for the various practitioners and clinicians who are able to perform life care planning, the client is considered the person with a disability or illness who receives services. In life care planning, the client is defined as the person who is the subject of the life care plan.

A. To assist the client in achieving optimal outcomes by developing an appropriate plan of prevention of complications and restoration. This may include recommendations for evaluations or treatment that may contribute to the client's level of wellness or provide information regarding treatment requirements.

B. To provide health education to the client and interested parties, when appropriate.

C. To develop accurate and timely cost information and specificity of service allocations that can be easily utilized by the client and interested parties.

D. To develop options for care that may be necessary for alternative situations.

E. To communicate the Life Care Plan and objectives to the client and interested parties, when appropriate.

F. To develop measurement tools, which can be used to analyze outcomes.

G. To routinely develop comprehensive assessments of the projected goals of the Life Care Plan, whenever possible.

III. Role and Functions of Life Care Planning

A. Scope of practice/applications

As a member of a health care profession, the Life Care Planner must remain within the scope of practice for that profession as determined by state or national bodies. The functions associated with performing Life Care Planning are within the scope of practice for health care professionals, or evidenced by assessment.

Research analysis of data and evaluation of care recommendations are key elements in the functions of life care planning. In performing these elements, the Life Care Planner will communicate with a variety of health care professionals regarding a case. The Life Care Planner does not assume decision-making responsibility beyond the scope of his/her own professional discipline.

B. Specialization features

The Life Care Planner must have skill and knowledge in understanding the health care needs addressed in a Life Care Plan. Consultation with others and obtaining education are expected when the Life Care Planner must address health care needs that are new or unfamiliar. The Life Care Planner must be able to locate appropriate resources when necessary. The Life Care Planner provides a consistent, objective, thorough methodology for constructing the Life Care Plan, while relying on appropriate medical and other health related information, resources, and personal expertise for developing the content of the Life Care Plan. The Life Care Planner relies on state-of-the-art knowledge and resources to develop a Life Care Plan.

Specialized skills are required to successfully develop a Life Care Plan. These include, but are not limited to, the ability to research, critically analyze data, manage and interpret large volumes of information, attend to details, demonstrate clear and thorough written and verbal communication skills, develop positive relationships, create and use networks for gathering information, work autonomously, and demonstrate a professional demeanor and appearance.

C. Functions

1. **Assessments** – Assessment is the process of data collection and analysis involving multiple elements and sources.

    a. Collects data that is systematic, comprehensive, and accurate.

    b. Collects data about medical, health, biopsychosocial, financial, educational, and vocational status and needs.

    c. Obtains information from medical records, client/family/significant others (when available or appropriate), and relevant treating or consulting health care professionals. If access to any source of information is not possible (e.g., denied permission to interview the client), this should be so noted in the report.

2. **Plan Development Research**

The determination of content and the cost research components of Life Care Planning require a consistent, valid and reliable approach to research, data collection, analysis, and planning. The Life Care Planner:

    a. Determines current standards of care and clinical practice guidelines from reliable sources, such as current literature or other published sources, collaboration with other professionals, education programs, and personal clinical practice.

    b. Researches options and costs for care, using sources that are reasonably available to the client.

    c. Considers appropriate criteria for care options such as admission criteria, treatment indications or contraindications, program goals and outcomes, whether recommended care is consistent with standards of care, duration of care, replacement frequency, ability of the client to appropriately use services/products, and care is reasonably available.

    d. A consistent method is used to determine available choices and costs.

    e.   When available and/or helpful in providing clarity, classification systems (e.g., ICD-9, CPT) are used to correlate care recommendations and costs.

    f.   Knowledge is maintained of care standards, services and products through continuing education, literature, exhibits, etc.

3. Data Analysis

    a.   Analyzes data to determine client needs and consistency of care recommendations with standards of care.

    b.   Assesses need for further evaluations or expert opinions.

4. Planning

    a.   Follows a consistent method for organizing data, creating a narrative Life Care Plan report and cost projections.

    b.   Develops and uses written documentation tools for reports and cost projections.

    c.   Develops recommendations for content of the Life Care Plan cost projections for each client and a method for validating inclusion or exclusion of content.

5. Collaboration

    a.   Develops positive relationships with all parties.

    b.   Seeks expert opinions, as needed.

    c.   Shares relevant information to aid in formulating recommendations and opinions.

6. Facilitation

    a.   Maintains objectivity and assists others in resolving disagreements about appropriate content for the Life Care Plan.

    b.   Provides information about the Life Care Planning process to involved parties to elicit cooperative participation.

7. Evaluation

    a.   Reviews and revises the Life Care Plan for internal consistency and completeness.

    b.   Reviews the Life Care Plan for consistency with standards of care and seeks resolution of inconsistencies.

    c.   Provides follow-up consultation to ensure that the Life Care Plan is understood and properly interpreted.

8. Testimony

If the Life Care Planner engages in practice that includes participation in legal matters, the Life Care Planner:

    a.   Acts as a consultant to legal proceedings related to determining care needs and costs.

    b.   May provide expert sworn testimony regarding development and content of the Life Care Plan.

    c.   Maintains records of research and supporting documentation for content of the Life Care Plan.

IV. Standards of Performance

A. Ethical

Ethics refers to a set of principles of "right" conduct, a theory or a system of moral values, or the rules or standards governing the conduct of a person or members of a profession. The primary goal of practice ethics is to protect clients, provide guidelines for practicing professionals, and to enhance the profession as a whole. Within the Life Care Planning industry all practitioners are members of one or more professional disciplines and/or are licensed or certified. It is expected that Life Care Planners follow appropriate relevant ethical guidelines within their areas of professional practice and expertise.

Life Care Planners are expected to maintain appropriate confidentiality, avoid dual relationships, adequately advise clients of the role of the Life Care Planner, and maintain competency in the profession.

1. Confidentiality: Appropriate confidentiality is a sensitive and important concept. Some professionals will have communications protected by "privilege" which is statutorily based in each state. For example, although no "Life Care Planners" are currently covered by privilege, many may be professional counselors, licensed psychologists or others who have the additional statutory protection. In addition, litigation has the additional component of attorney work product that may have an effect on what information may be disclosed. The Life Care Planner must be thoroughly informed on this topic.

2. Dual relationships: A personal relationship with a client is not appropriate during the course of service. Developing Life Care Plans for friends, co-workers, professional colleagues, or anyone where the objectivity and professionalism of the care plan is questions should be avoided.

3. Client advisement of role: Each client should be fully informed about the role of the Life Care Planner. For example, the client should be fully informed about who is requesting the Life Care Plan as well as the confidentiality of communications. Also, Life Care Planners who have dual role responsibilities should clarify that they are not acting as a case manager, psychologist, etc. and what the limits of their participation might be.

4. Competency: The Life Care Planner is expected to accurately represent any information received for a particular case. Medical recommendations are to have an appropriate medical foundation. Research information that the Life Care Planner has obtained for all aspects of care should be readily available for examination by appropriate reviewers.

B. Research

The Life Care Plan will have as its basis the Scientific Principles of medicine and health care. The involvement of the Life Care Planner in the area of research should include, but not limited to, the following objectives:

1. The Life Care Planner will strive to identify and participate in research independently or in collaboration with others, utilizing research tools and activities that will promote quality outcomes.

2. The Life Care Planner will critique literature for application to life care planning.

3. The Life Care Planner will use appropriate research findings in the development of Life Care Plans.

Interview Worksheet

Date: Time Start: Stop:

Location of interview:

Name:

   Date of Injury:

   Date of Birth:

   Social Security #:

Address:

Phone:

Attorney:

Referral Source:

Injury Incurred or Disability:

Social Information: (Include family history, where raised, what the parents did for work, health of family members, location of each and occupation, list of siblings or step-parents/brothers/sisters, family closeness, marital status, children and ages, relationship with spouse, religious orientation, history of illegal activity, etc.)

Family Information Supplement

Name	Age	Education	Work History	Health
Spouse/Partner				
Father				
Mother				
Siblings				
Grandparents				
Aunts/Uncles				

Comments:

Military: Branch:

Dates: Duties:

Location: Special Training:

Rank at discharges: Honorable?: Y/N

Hobbies/Leisure Time Activities: (Include before injury/illness and compare to post injury/illness, note avocation interests particularly if severe disability, TV program, reading interests and subscription, etc.)

Educational History: (Include high school and other schooling best and worst subjects, likes and dislikes, perceived success, outside activities, sports, vocational training, higher education, short course, etc.)

Employment History:

Dates|Age|Company |Job Title |Duties (include skills and tools) |Wage

(Also note reason for leaving, likes and dislikes, perceived employee ratings, etc.)

2222222222222

Employment Interests:

Skills/Strengths (include tools and expertise from paid and non-paid work):

Current Financial Status: (Include sources and amounts of income, rent costs, monthly expenses, loans, public assistance, social security, workers' compensation, SSDI, SSI, VA, Soc Sec retirement, food stamps, loans, etc.)

Medical History: (Include childhood diseases and residuals, accidents and residuals, hospitalizations, smoking, drinking and drug history, etc.)

Dominant Hand:

Height:

Weight: Before_____   After_____

Smoke: Drink: Substance abuse Hx?

Present Medical Treatment Information: (Information regarding the current treatment, such as the next appointment with the doctors and therapists)

DRUG	PRESCRIPTION) (size and amount	PURPOSE	SUPPLIER (pharmacy)	COST

SUPPLIES	MAKE/ ID NUMBER	PURPOSE	FREQUENCY OF USE	SUPPLIER	COST

MAKE/MODEL
EQUIPMENTNUMBERPURPOSESUPPLIERCOST

OTHER

Subjective Complaints: (Include the list from head to toe of the perceived current problems due to the accident/illness. Pain, paralysis, lack of feeling, headaches, ringing in the ears, etc.)

Functional Abilities: (To include the working conditions and physical demands consistent with the Department of Labor research on worker traits)

Lifting/strength limitations:

Walking:

Standing:

Sitting:

Climbing:

Balancing:

Stooping:

Kneeling:

Crouching:

Crawling:

Reaching:

Handling:

Fingering:

Feeling/sensation:

Talking:

Hearing:

Smell/taste:

Near acuity:

Far acuity:

Depth perception:

Accommodation:

Color vision:

Field of vision:

Exposure to weather:

Extreme cold:

Extreme heat:

Wet/humid areas:

Noise intensity:

Vibrations:

Atmospheric (fumes/odors/dust):

Proximity to moving mechanical parts:

Exposure to electrical shock:

Working in high, exposed places:

Exposure to radiation:

Working with explosives:

Exposure to toxic or caustic chemicals:

Other environmental conditions:

Sleeping:

Stamina:

Driving:

Other:

Daily Activity Schedule: (Include time up, eat, who fixes meals and does household duties, yard work, laundry and what does s/he do to keep busy, time to bed, etc. Note if daily routine is established or whether client is looking for things to fill in time)

Motivation/emotional tone/comments regarding the interview: (What was the attitude, how receptive to information, any psychological concerns noted that may require further study)

Approach to eval: + +/- -

Conclusions/Recommendations:

Things to do:

Medical evaluations: (Including basic medical, specialty, dental)

Physician Comments: (Including current treatment. Obtain release form)

Employer Comments: (Obtain release form)

Emotional Status:

Vocational Assessment plans:

Next appointment: (Include who is to do what)

Records to obtain:

People to contact:

Other:

FUNCTIONAL CONSIDERATIONS CHECKLIST

What handicaps does the client (or family member) believe they have?

One check (✓) if it is a problem, two checks (✓✓) if it is perceived to be a big problem

REDO THIS PAGE

Physical Demands

Standing

Walking

Sitting

Lifting

Carrying

Pushing

Pulling

Limited to sedentary work,

Climbing

light work, medium work,

Balancing

   heavy work, or very heavy work (circle)

Stooping,

Crouching

Kneeling,

Crawling

Reaching

Handling

Fingering

Feeling

Seeing (depth perception, accommodation,

Talking

   color vision, field, and

Hearing

   near/far acuity)

Smell/taste

Controls: right hand/arm

Controls: right foot/leg

Controls: left hand/arm

Controls: left foot/leg

Reduced physical stamina

Environmental Conditions

Inside, outside, or both

Extremes of cold plus

Extremes of heat plus

  temperature changes

temperature changes

Wet and/or humid

Hazards

Proximity to moving mechanical parts

Eye, hand, foot coordination

Fumes, odors, toxic conditions,

Noise

  dust, and

Vibration

  poor ventilation

Working in high exposed places

Working with explosives

Exposure to toxic/

Exposure to radiation

  caustic chemicals

Exposure to electrical shock

Atmospheric conditions

Cognitive

Problems with attention,

Problems with basic

concentration, memory

 academics

Difficulties handling money

Difficulties beginning or

Reduced frustration tolerance

 following through on tasks

Reduced ability to reason

Slowed thought process

  clearly and solve

Inability to say what is

  problems

  meant

Difficulty understanding

Trouble following directions

  others

Reduced ability to manage time

Poor insight into

Poor "executive function"

  problems

Reduced ability to be educated/

Perseveration

  trained

Lack of initiative

Distractibility

Confabulation

Reduced intelligence

Emotional

Irritability

Depression/Withdrawal

Impulsivity

Poor social interactions

Fear/Phobia

Difficulty controlling
behavior in social
situations

Reduced ability to subjectively
evaluate information

Anxiety

Changes in control of
temper

Anger, aggression, verbal
outbursts

Reduced ability to deal with people

Reduced ability to handle
stress

Reduced ability interpreting
feelings

FUNCTIONAL LIMITATIONS: GENERAL

1. Mobility Limitation

    The function of getting from one location to another is limited.

2. Motility Limitation

    The inability to move an object or to do another task normally performed by using the musculoskeletal system.

3. Restricted Environment

    Bound to a place or status, or limited in activity, atmosphere, or progress.

4. Sensory Limitation

    The result of defect(s) in the transmission of information from the environment to the brain.

5. Communication Limitation

    A breakdown in the process by which information is exchanged between individuals through common symbols, signs, or behavior.

6. Pain Limitation

    When pain is continuing, unremitting, uncontrollable, and severe, it may constitute a severe functional limitation to normal living.

7. Debilitation or Exertional Limitation

    A condition in which the individual is in a weakened state for an extended time period.

8. Atypical Appearance

    Characteristics of an individual's physique and carriage that are inconsistent with what is considered acceptable by a culture.

9. Invisible Limitation

    Concealed or unapparent conditions that limit functions.

10. Substance Dependency

    Physical and/or psychological dependency.

11. Mental Limitation

    Developmentally Delayed (MR) and Learning Disabilities.

12. Consciousness Limitation

    Unconsciousness and other defects in consciousness.

13. Uncertain Prognosis

    Involves the stress and ambiguity of those medical conditions that have an unpredictable course of termination.

14. Dysfunctional Behavior

    Emotional disorders with deviate behavior. Also behavior due to cultural disadvantages.

Source: Wright, G. (1981). Total Rehabilitation. Compiled by Maribeth Abrams and Roger Weed.

MEDICAL-LEGAL CONSULTATION CHECKLIST

✔ **Medical Records Analysis**

Organize and tab; define in layman's terms; describe number of operative procedures and invasive procedures; use of pain medication; special consultations; number of days in ICU or other special placements; complications experienced; physician names and specialties; discharge disposition

✔ **Medical Research**

Relevant articles and books; MEDLINE; software; networking; define content, highlight, organize, and educate attorney

✔ **Experts**

Location of appropriate experts; coordination of referral to expert; securing services of appropriate experts, including liability, causation, and damage experts

✔ **Deposition: Review and Summarization**

Development of deposition questions and attendance at deposition. Review and summarize deposition to highlight damage and treatment issues

✔ **Case Management**

Assessment of medical condition; coordination of medical care and physician referral; coordination of information with attorney, client/family, physician to physician

✔ **Attendance at Medical Exam**

Documentation of physician/client interview and assessment

✔ **Demonstrative Evidence**

Overheads; charts; graphs; photos; videotape; medical illustration and medical equipment; arrange for day-in-the-life and script; help develop settlement brochures

✔ **Life Care Plan/Life Care Plan Review**

Development of a life care plan that identifies appropriate and reasonable care for individuals who have sustained catastrophic injury or chronic illness; review of existing life care plan for overlap and duplication of services; check costs for regional accuracy; assess planner's potential for bias; check math calculations; review for effective rehabilitation and potential to avoid complications; assure all appropriate topics are included in plan

✔ **Vocational Issues**

Identify vocational experts and coordinate evaluation; discuss issues related to placeability, earnings capacity, rehabilitation plan, vocational handicaps, work life expectancy, and related issues

CHECKLIST FOR A COMPREHENSIVE MEDICAL RECORDS ANALYSIS

✔ **Primary/Secondary Diagnoses**: Have you thoroughly reviewed the records to identify primary and other diagnoses?

✔ **Hospitalization Days**: List all hospitals and treatment programs. Summarize the dates and days in each. Include the number of days in specialized care such as ICU or rehabilitation.

✔ **Operative Procedures**: What operations were performed, on what date, by whom, and what was the surgeon's specialty area (orthopedics, neurosurgery, plastic, ophthalmology, etc.)? What kind of anesthesia was used (local or general)? How long was the operation? Were their any complications?

✔ **Medications**: What medications were administered? Why were they administered (infections, pain, bowel or bladder program, blood loss, anxiety, etc.) ? Include the name, dosage, route of administration (oral, IV, IM, sublingual, catheter). Note any abnormal reactions and long term effects.

✔ **Treatment Team**: Identify all treating physicians by name, specialty, address, and telephone.

✔ **Consultations**: Have you identified all consultations during treatment (e.g., endocrinology, infectious disease, pulmonology, radiology, urology, cosmetic)?

✔ **Invasive Procedures**: Note Foley catheters, intravenous, g-tube feeds, etc. Include length of required treatment and how much.

✔ **Post Hospitalization Treatment**: What post-acute programs or treatment programs were included? Day treatment? Home care? Include dates, purpose, and outcomes.

✔ **Complications**: List complications and dates. For example, septic shock, chronic infections such as urinary and respiratory, contractures, skin breakdown, adverse reactions to medications, psychological, etc. Include future risk factors such as bone non-union, traumatic arthritis, etc.

✔ **Report Writing**: Have you explained the medical records so that your reader can understand them (e.g., decubitus = skin breakdown; debride = clean the wound)?

✔ **Recommendations**: Have you offered recommendations so your client and/or account will receive appropriate and cost effective services? Should additional evaluations or treatment be offered? What effect does the incident have on the client's ultimate functioning or work?

MEDICAL SUMMARY OUTLINE/WORKSHEET

Records Reviewed

Source/Name/Date	Source/Name/Date

Hospital or treatment program admission(s) and discharge date(s)

Hospital or Program	Admit	Discharge

Surgical Procedures (include projected treatment, if known)

Description	Date	Notes

Complications or Abnormal Findings

Description	Date	Notes

Treating Physicians

Name	Specialty	Phone or Location

Current Medications/Supplies/Equipment

Description	Size/amt/make	Purpose	Supplier/Notes

EXAMPLE QUESTIONS FOR PHYSICIANS

1. **Future Care** (Distinguish what is reasonable and appropriate vs. medically necessary vs. desirable)

   How long will the patient need follow-up?

   When will the patient reach maximum medical improvement?

   How long and how often will treatment be needed? (Include frequency and duration (e.g., every six months for 2 years then once per year thereafter)?

   What treatment is expected? (Follow-up visits, routine evaluations, etc.)

   How much will each visit cost?

   Are X-rays or lab work needed? If so how much will each cost?

   Do you anticipate any further surgeries or aggressive medical treatment? (e.g., several years from now due to complications. If so, what and how much will each cost?)

2. **Possible Complications**

   What complications are possible/expected? (Traumatic arthritis, contractures, adverse reactions to medications, etc.)

3. **Recommended Medical Follow-up by Other Specialties**

   Orthopedist

   Neurology?

   Physiatrist?

   Cosmetic Surgeon?

   Dermatology?

   Psychology/Neuropsychology?

   Occupational Therapist, Physical Therapist, Speech Therapy, Dietary, Recreation Therapy?

   Other?

   If you recommend any of the above, do you have an opinion regarding what treatment will be needed, how often it will be needed and expected costs?

4. Functional Limitations

4.1 In an 8 hour day, person can: (Circle full capacity for each activity.)

Key To Providing Following Guidelines
Occasionally   =   1% - 33%
Frequently   =   34% - 66%
Constantly   =   67% - 100%

4.2 Lifting

4.3 Carrying

4.4 Pushing/Pulling

4.5 Person can do repetitive movements as in operating controls: (Circle)

4.6 Person can:

4.7 Any difficulties with: (e.g., none, mild, moderate, severe and comments)

Talking _____

Hearing _____

Tasting _____

Smelling _____

Seeing near _____

Seeing far _____

Visual accommodation _____

Seeing color _____

Visual field _____

4.8 Any restrictions of activities involving: (e.g., none, mild, moderate, sever and comments)

Exposure to cold, heat, wet or humidity _____

Noise (include dB limit) _____

Vibration _____

Exposure to fumes, odors, chemicals, gases or dusts _____

Moving mechanical parts _____

Unprotected heights _____

Operating equipment _____

4.9 Is this individual taking medication that may affect his or her ability to work?

_____

4.10 Can this person work full time? Yes   No   Part-time? Yes No   Hrs/day? _____

4.11 If the client cannot work now, when?

4.12 Will these limitations require attendant care? _____
If so, how much? And what level? (e.g., companion, housekeeping, nurse's aide, LPN, RN, High Tech, etc.) _____

4.13 Add any comments that might impact the person's ability to work.

NEUROPSYCHOLOGIST QUESTIONS

Total Without Breaks (hours)										
Sit	0	1/2	1	2	3	4	5	6	7	8
Stand	0	1/2	1	2	3	4	5	6	7	8
Walk	0	1/2	1	2	3	4	5	6	7	8

Total During Entire 8-Hour Day (hours)										
Sit	0	1/2	1	2	3	4	5	6	7	8
Stand	0	1/2	1	2	3	4	5	6	7	8
Walk	0	1/2	1	2	3	4	5	6	7	8

In addition to the standard evaluation report, add the following as appropriate.

1. Please describe, in layman terms, the damage to the brain.

Lifting	Never	Occasionally	Frequently	Constantly
Up to 10 lbs.				
11-20 lbs.				
21-50 lbs.				
51-100 lbs.				

2. Please describe the effects of the accident on the client's ability to function.

Carrying	Never	Occasionally	Frequently	Constantly
Up to 10 lbs.				
11-20 lbs.				
21-50 lbs.				
51-100 lbs.				

3. Please provide an opinion to the following topics:

Pushing/Pulling	Never	Occasionally	Frequently	Constantly
Up to 10 lbs.				
11-20 lbs.				
21-50 lbs.				
51-100 lbs.				

   a. Intelligence level? (include pre- vs. post-incident if able)

Right Hand/Arm		Right Foot/Leg		Left Hand/Arm		Left Foot/Arm	
Yes	No	Yes	No	Yes	No	Yes	No

b. Personality style with regard to the workplace and home?

Functio	Never	Occasionally	Frequently	Constantly
Climb				
Balance				
Stoop				
Kneel				
Crouch				
Crawl				
Reach (all directions)				
Handle (gross manip-ulations)				
Finger (fine manipu-lation)				
Feel				

c. Stamina level?

d. Functional limitations and assets?

e. Ability for education/training?

f. Vocational implications – style of learning?

g. Level of insight into present functioning?

h. Ability to compensate for deficits?

i. Ability to initiate action?

j. Memory impairments (short-term, long-term, auditory, visual, etc.)?

k. Ability to identify and correct errors?

l. Recommendations for compensation strategies?

m. Need for companion or attendant care?

4. What is the proposed treatment plan?

a. Counseling? (individual and family)

b. Cognitive therapy?

c. Re-evaluations?

d. Referral to others? (e.g., physicians)

e. Other?

5. How much and how long? (Include the cost per session or hour and re-evaluations.)

CHILD CP & BRAIN INJURY INTERVIEW SUPPLEMENT

Name: _____ **Date:** _____

MUSCLE INVOLVEMENT
    Limbs involved
    Sensation intact
    Tremor
    Spastic
    Rigidity
    Startle reflex, effects of
    Motor control
    Effects on functional limitations/capabilities
    Other

ACTIVITIES OF DAILY LIVING (also see ADL checklist if old enough)
    Dressing (include use of adapted clothing)
    Hygiene
    Grooming
    Eating
    Transfer
    Other

AMBULATION CAPABILITIES
    (include bracing/cane/other aids)
    Power chair/manual chair/travel chair

CONTRACTURES
    Location
    Other

VISUAL
    Visual disturbance or impairments
    Visual field disturbance/limitations
    Effects on one eye or both
    Tests to support
    Other

AUDITORY
    Hearing loss
    Difficulty in interpreting/understanding language
    Other

SEIZURES
    Type
    Frequency
    Medications
    Effects of meds on behavior/cognition

FATIGUE
   Amount and kind of activity before fatiguing

SCOLIOSIS
   Effects on respiration
   Effects on spasticity

RESPIRATORY INFECTIONS
   How often
   How long
   How treated

SWALLOWING CAPABILITIES
   Aspiration of foods/liquids
   Cough reflex

NUTRITION

   Kinds and amounts of food or food supplement
   Able to chew or eat
   Enteral feeding (brand, schedule)

JOINT DISEASE
   specially hips

OSTEOPOROSIS
   Especially hips

BOWEL/BLADDER
   Incontinence
   Aware of need but unable to respond adequately
   Constipation
   If incontinent, potential for continence

DENTAL NEEDS
   Medications for seizures
   Ability to brush teeth

PSYCHOSOCIAL
   Dependency
   Relationships with others

ANTICIPATED MEDICAL TREATMENT
   Contracture release
   Nerve blocking/surgery
   Medication follow along
   Lab tests

Other

ACTIVITIES OF DAILY LIVING

NAME: _____ DISABILITY: _____ DATE: _____

CODES: 1 = Can do without difficulty. 2 = Can do with some difficulty. 3 = Can do with great difficulty and/or needs assistance from attendant. 4 = Dependent on someone else to do.

FEEDING

	Code	Comments or amount of time required
Fix meal		
Open cans/jars/tubes/boxes		
Open containers/packages/empty contents		
Use manual or electric can opener (note if there is a difference)		
Use microwave		
Use stove/oven (turn on/use)		
Refrig/cupboard accessible		
Open refrigerator		
Open drawers		
Transport items short distance		
Use forks/spoon/knife (note if adapted utensils are used)		
Cut with knife		
Butter bread		
Eat soup with spoon		
Make sandwich/light meal		
Reaching meal area		
Eat meal		
Get drink		
Drink from cup/glass with/without adaption		
Other		

HYGIENE

Reach sink area		
Reach/turn faucets		
Brush teeth		
Wash and dry self (note if there is a difference with hands/face/entire body)		
Use shower (note if roll-in is required)		
Use tub		
Bed bath		
Apply deodorant		
Comb/brush hair (continued next page)		

CODES: 1 = Can do without difficulty. 2 = Can do with some difficulty. 3 = Can do with great difficulty and/or needs assistance from attendant. 4 = Dependent on someone else to do.

FEEDING

	Code	Comments or amount of time required
Shaving		
Makeup		
Shampoo and dry hair		
Nail cutting/cleaning		
Other		

BOWEL/BLADDER

Sitting balance without assistance		
Use catheter		
Irrigate catheter/prepare equipment		
Change catheter/prepare equipment		
Handle urinal		
Empty leg bag		
Leg bag on/off		
Tubing connections on/off		
Bowel care (note if dil, suppository)		
Cleanse self after toileting		
Flush toilet/empty commode		
Manage clothing before/after toileting		
Transfer to/from toilet/commode		

BED ACTIVITIES

Transfer to/from bed		
Sit up		
Check skin		
Operate bed controls		
Sit at side of bed		
Roll side to side		
Turn over		

DRESSING

Select appropriate clothes and match colors		
Button garment with/without adaptive aid		
Fastenings (slippers, snap, belt		
Shirt on/off		
Slack/underpant/skirt on/off		
Corset or binder on/off		
Socks on/off (continued next page)		

CODES: 1 = Can do without difficulty. 2 = Can do with some difficulty. 3 = Can do with great difficulty and/or needs assistance from attendant. 4 = Dependent on someone else to do.

FEEDING

	Code	Comments or amount of time required
Shoes on/off		
Tie shoe laces		
Coat/sweater on/off		
Elastic or TED hose on/off		
Clothes in/out drawers/closet		

COMMUNICATION

Write		
Speak with normal voice		
Summon emergency assistance		
Use telephone - dial/push-button/cordless		
Use wordprocesser/typewriter		
Use augmentative communications		

ENVIRONMENT

Use ECU (note brand/options)		
Effectively control temperature		
Open/close door		
Use keys		
Light on/off		
Use TV/radio/stereo		
Set and/or read clock/watch		
Manipulate newspaper/book		
Use scissors		
Plug in cord		
Pick up things off floor		
Adaptive aids		
Open/read mail		

MOBILITY

Maneuver power/manual wheelchair (note if Quad pegs/one hand/joy stick/sip & puff, etc.)		
Transfer from chair to vehicle		
Wheelchair manipulation		
Utilize and adjust armrests		
Manage leg rests		
Brakes on/off		
Safety belt on/off (continued next page)		

CODES: 1 = Can do without difficulty. 2 = Can do with some difficulty. 3 = Can do with great difficulty and/or needs assistance from attendant. 4 = Dependent on someone else to do.

FEEDING

	Code	Comments or amount of time required
Remove items from wheelchair		
Use lap board/bag/caddy/ashtray		
Utilize cushion		
Do chair maintenance		
Body handling in chair		
Weight shift		
Floor to chair		
Hook arm/reach forward		
Reposition in chair with/without assistance		
Cross/uncross legs		
Negotiate ramps/curbs		
Negotiate rough/smooth terrain		
chair in/out of car/van		
Drive		
If drive, adaptions		
Use public transportation		

ORTHOTICS/PROSTHESIS

Upper extremities orthotics/braces off/on		
Upper extremities prosthetics off/on		
Lower extremity prosthetics on/off		
Lower extremity orthotics/braces on/off		
AFOs or KAFO on/off/adjust		
Splint/sling off/on		

PERSONNEL/ATTENDANTCARE NEEDS

	X if required	Comments
Independent-no need		
Needs companion for judgment (due to TBI)		
Needs guardian (incl. money management)		
Occasional e.g. morning/eve/weekends		
Live-in attendant (10 - 12 hours per day and night safety)		
24 hour attendant awake		
24 hour skilled/high tech awake		
House cleaning/meals/laundry		
House maintenance interior/exterior		
Errands/doctor appointment		
Other		

JOB ANALYSIS CHECKLIST

✔ Have You Included All **Physical Demands** of the Job? (Strength, sit, stand, walk, lift, carry, push, climb, balance, stoop, kneel, crouch, crawl, bend, reach, handle, finger, feel, talk, hear, smell/taste, right & left hand, Vision – near, far, depth, color, accommodation)

✔ Have you included the **Environmental Conditions**? (Inside, outside, cold, heat, wet, humid, noise, vibrations, hazards, fumes, odors and dust, exposure to electric shock, radiation, and toxic chemicals.)

✔ What Are the **General Educational Development** Levels? (Reasoning, Math and Language.)

✔ What Are the Entry Level **Training Requirements**? (High-School, Vocational School, On-The-Job, College, Etc.)

✔ What **Aptitudes** Are Required? (general learning ability, verbal, numerical, spatial, form perception, clerical perception, motor coordination, finger dexterity, manual dexterity, eye-hand-foot coordination, and color discrimination.)

✔ What **Interests** Are Appropriate? (Refer to the Guide for Occupational Exploration)

✔ What **Personality** Factors (Temperaments) Are Important? (Directing, Repetitive, Influencing Others, Variety, Expressing Feelings, Work Alone, Stress, Precise Tolerances, Under Instructions, Dealing With People, Judgments.)

✔ Have you obtained the employers **job description**?

✔ What are the "**essential functions**"?

✔ Have you compared the description with the DICTIONARY OF OCCUPATIONAL TITLES definition?

✔ What are the normal **work hours**? Is **overtime** likely?

✔ Did you **observe** the job long enough to fully understand all of the details and requirements?

✔ Would **pictures** or a **video** of the job be appropriate to describe the job?

✔ Will the employer **modify** the job? (flex time, restructure, job share, etc.)

✔ Special **Clothing /Tools** Required?

✔ Will **Job Accommodation** or **Technology** Make the Job More Accessible to the Client?

✔ What **Architectural Barrier**s Exist?

✔ Did the **Employer Approve** the Job As Analyzed?

✔ Did the **Client Approve** the Job As Analyzed? (if applicable)

© ?????. Roger O. Weed

411

Job Analysis Worksheet
ADA Essential Functions.

Job Title: _____

D.O.T. Code: _____ S.I.C. Code: _____

Consultant _____

Company _____

Address _____

City, State, Zip _____

Contact Person: _____

Education/Training/Experience/License Required

    Circle: 8th   HS: 1 2 3 4   Col: 1 2 3 4 5 6 7

    Special Training: _____

    Certification/License: _____

Suggested resources for completing the **Job Analysis Worksheet**

ADA Manual for Rehabilitation Consultants, Field, T. & Norton, L. (1992). Elliott & Fitzpatrick, Inc. Athens, GA

The **Revised Classification of Jobs**, Field, J. & Field, T. (1992). Elliott & Fitzpatrick, Inc., Athens, GA.

The **Revised Dictionary of Occupational Titles**. (1991). U.S. Government Printing Office.

The **Revised Handbook for Analyzing Jobs**. (1991). U.S. Government Printing Office.

Evaluate each of the following job elements that are critical to the performance of the job; leave blank if not applicable.

* Critical to the performance of the job.

* Enter percent of time performing task, e.g. "Standing" — 60% / Time

* Risk to self or others (enter "S" or "O").

* Relevant to Essential Function # _____ (see page 8).

1

Elliott & Fitzpatrick, Inc.

Specific Vocational Preparation

> ### Rate Level of Performance
>
> SVP: "1" = Low; "9" = High.
> GED: "6" = High level of performance; "1" = Low level.
> Aptitudes: "1" = High; "5" = Low

Factor	Time	Rating	Relevant to Function #
Duration *For the purpose of rating jobs, TRAINING TIME is defined as the amount of general educational development and specific vocational preparation required of a worker to acquire the knowledge and abilities necessary for average performance in a particular job-worker situation.*	____	____	____

> 1. Short time only
> 2. Anything beyond short demonstration up to and including 30 days.
> 3. Over 30 days up to and including 3 months.
> 4. Over 3 months up to and including 6 months.
> 5. Over 6 months up to and including 1 year.
> 6. Over 1 year up to an including 2 years.
> 7. Over 2 years up to an including 4 years.
> 8. Over 4 years up to and including 10 years.
> 9. Over 10 years.

General Educational Development

Factor	Time	Rating	Relevant to Function #
1. **Reasoning**	____	____	____
2. **Mathematics**	____	____	____
3. **Language**	____	____	____

GED embraces those aspects of education (formal and informal) which contributes to the worker's (a) reasoning development and ability to follow instructions, and (b) acquisition of "tool" knowledge P=3 such as language and mathematical skills. This is education of a general nature which does not have a recognized, fairly specific occupational objective. Ordinarily, such education is obtained in elementary school, high school, or college. However, it derives also from experience and self-study.

Aptitudes

> ## Rate Level of Performance
>
> 1. The top 10 percent of the population. This segment of the population possesses an extremely high degree of the aptitude.
> 2. The highest third exclusive of the top 10 percent of the population. This segment of the population possesses an above average degree of the aptitude.
> 3. The middle third of the population. This segment of the population possesses a medium degree of the aptitude, ranging from slightly below to slightly above average.
> 4. The lowest third exclusive of the bottom 10 percent of the population. This segment of the population possesses a below average or low degree of the aptitude.
> 5. The lowest 10 percent of the population. This segment of the population possesses a negligible degree of the aptitude.

Factor	Time	Rating	Relevant to Function #
1. **Intelligence** *General learning ability.*	___	___	___
2. **Verbal** *Ability to understand meanings of words and ideas associated with them, and to use them effectively.*	___	___	___
3. **Numerical** *Ability to perform arithmetic operations quickly and accurately.*	___	___	___
4. **Spatial Perception** *Ability to comprehend forms in space and understand relationships of plane and solid objects.*	___	___	___
5. **Form Perception** *Ability to perceive pertinent detail in objects of in pictorial or graphic material.*	___	___	___
6. **Clerical Perception** *Ability to perceive pertinent detail in verbal or tabular matter.*	___	___	___
7. **Motor Coordination** *Ability to coordinate eyes and hands or fingers rapidly and accurately in making precise movements.*	___	___	___
8. **Finger Dexterity** *Ability to move the fingers and manipulate small objects with the fingers rapidly and accurately.*	___	___	___
9. **Manual Dexterity** *Ability to move the hands easily and skillfully.*	___	___	___
10. **Eye/Hand/Foot Coordination** *Ability to move the hand and foot coordinately with each other in accordance with visual stimuli.*	___	___	___
11. **Color Discrimination** *Ability to perceive or recognize similarities or differences in colors, or in shades or other values of the same color or to identify a particular color.*	___	___	___

Elliott & Fitzpatrick, Inc.

Physical Demands

Factor	Time	Critical to Performance	Risk	Relevant to Function #
1. Strength				
– Standing *Remaining on one's feet in an upright position at a work station without moving about.*	___	___	___	___
– Walking *Moving about on foot.*	___	___	___	___
– Sitting *Remaining in the normal seated position.*	___	___	___	___
– Lifting *To exert physical strength necessary to move objects from one level to another.*	___	___	___	___

	Never	Rarely	Occas.	Freq.	Cont.
Under 10 lbs.	___	___	___	___	___
10 to 25 lbs.	___	___	___	___	___
26 to 60 lbs.	___	___	___	___	___
61 to 75 lbs.	___	___	___	___	___
76 to 100 lbs.	___	___	___	___	___
Over 100 lbs.	___	___	___	___	___

Factor	Time	Critical to Performance	Risk	Relevant to Function #
– Carrying *Transporting an object, usually holding it in the hands or arms shoulders.*	___	___	___	___

	Never	Rarely	Occas.	Freq.	Cont.
Under 10 lbs.	___	___	___	___	___
10 to 25 lbs.	___	___	___	___	___
26 to 60 lbs.	___	___	___	___	___
61 to 75 lbs.	___	___	___	___	___
76 to 100 lbs.	___	___	___	___	___
Over 100 lbs.	___	___	___	___	___

Factor	Time	Critical to Performance	Risk	Relevant to Function #
– Pushing *Exerting force upon an object so that the object moves away from the force (includes slapping, striking, kicking, and treadle actions).*	___	___	___	___
– Pulling *Exerting force upon an object so that the object moves toward from the force (includes jerking).*	___	___	___	___
2. Climbing *To ascend or descend ladders, scaffolding, stairs, poles, inclined surfaces.*	___	___	___	___

Physical Demands (cont.)

Factor	Time	Critical to Performance	Risk	Relevant to Function #
3. Balancing *To maintain a body equilibrium to prevent falling when walking, standing, crouching, or running on narrow, slippery or erratically moving surfaces.*	____	____	____	____
4. Stooping *Bending the body downward and forward by bending the spine at the waist. This factor is important if it occurs to a considerable degree and requires full use of lower extremities and back muscles.*	____	____	____	____
5. Kneeling *Bending the legs at the knees to come to rest on the knee or knees.*	____	____	____	____
6. Crouching *Bending body downward and forward by bending legs and spine.*	____	____	____	____
7. Crawling *Moving about on hands and knees or hands and feet.*	____	____	____	____
8. Reaching *Extending the hand(s) and arm(s) in any direction.*	____	____	____	____
9. Handling *Seizing, holding, grasping, turning or otherwise working with hand or hands (fingering not involved).*	____	____	____	____
10. Fingering *Picking, pinching, or otherwise working with fingers primarily (rather than with whole hand or arm as in handling).*	____	____	____	____
11. Feeling *Perceiving attributes of objects such as size, shape, temperature or texture by means of receptors in skin, particularly those of finger tips.*	____	____	____	____
12. Talking *Expressing or exchanging ideas by means of the spoken word.*	____	____	____	____
13. Hearing *Perceiving the nature of sounds by the air.*	____	____	____	____
14. Tasting/Smelling *Distinguishing, with a degree of accuracy, differences or similarities in intensity or quality of flavors and/or odors, using tongue and/or nose.*	____	____	____	____
15. Near Acuity *Clarity of vision at 20 inches or less. This factor is important when special and minute accuracy is demanded and when defective near acuity would adversely affect job performance and/or the safety of others.*	____	____	____	____
16. Far Acuity *Clarity of vision at 20 feet or more. This factor is important when visual efficiency in terms of far acuity is required and defective far acuity would adversely affect job performance and/or the safety of others.*	____	____	____	____
17. Depth Perception *Three-dimensional vision. Ability to judge distances and spatial relationships so as to see objects where and as they really are. This factor is important when depth perception is required for successful job performance and/or for reason of safety to oneself and others.*	____	____	____	____

Elliott & Fitzpatrick, Inc.

Physical Demands (cont.)

Factor	Time	Critical to Performance	Risk	Relevant to Function #
18. **Accommodation** *Adjustment of lens of eye to bring an object into sharp focus. This factor is important when doing near point work at varying distances from eye.*	____	____	____	____
19. **Color Vision** *Ability to identify and distinguish colors.*	____	____	____	____
20. **Field of Vision** *Observing an area that can be seen up and down or right to left when eyes are fixed on a given point. This factor is important when job performance requires seeing a large area while keeping eye fixed.*	____	____	____	____

Environmental Conditions

Factor	Critical to Performance	Risk	Relevant to Function #
1. **Exposure to Weather** *Exposure to hot, cold, wet, humid, or windy conditions, caused by the weather. This factor is rated important when exposure to weather results in marked bodily discomfort.*	____	____	____
2. **Extreme Cold** *Exposure to nonweather-related cold temperatures. This factor is rated important when temperatures are sufficiently low to cause marked bodily discomfort.*	____	____	____
3. **Extreme Heat** *Exposure to nonweather-related cold temperatures. This factor is rated important when temperatures are sufficiently high to cause marked bodily discomfort.*	____	____	____
4. **Wet and/or Humid** *Contact with weather or other liquids; or exposure to nonweather-related humid conditions. This factor is rated important when contact with water or other liquids or exposure to humidity causes marked bodily discomfort.*	____	____	____
5. **Noise** *Exposure to constant or intermittent sounds of a pitch or level sufficient to cause marked distraction or possible hearing loss.*	____	____	____

Code	Level	Illustrative Examples
____ 1	Very Quiet	isolation booth for hearing test; deep sea diving; forest trail
____ 2	Quiet	library; many private offices; funeral reception; golf course; art museum
____ 3	Moderate	business office where typewriters are used; deparmtnet store; grocery store; light traffic; fast food restaurant at off-hours
____ 4	Loud	can manufacturing department; large earth-moving equipment; heavy traffic
____ 5	Very Loud	rock concert - front row, jackhammer work; rocket engine testing area during test

Environmental Conditions (cont.)

Factor	Critical to Performance	Risk	Relevant to Function #
6. **Vibration** *Exposure to a shaking object or surface. This factor is rated important when vibration causes a strain on the body or extremities.*	_____	_____	_____
7. **Atmospheric Conditions** *Exposure to conditions, such as fumes, noxious odors, dusts, mists, gases, and poor ventilation, that affect the respiratory system, eyes, or the skin. This factor is rated important if these conditions are present to a degree or length of time sufficient to cause marked bodily discomfort or possible injury.*	_____	_____	_____

8. **Hazards**

A hazard is a condition in the work environment that subjects or exposes the worker to the possibility of serious bodily injury or danger to the worker's life or health. A hazard is specific, related to the job, and has a greater likelihood of occurring than it would away from the job. The following conditions are evaluated as possible hazards in specific jobs.

	Critical to Performance	Risk	Relevant to Function #
a. **Moving Parts**	_____	_____	_____
b. **Electrical Shock**	_____	_____	_____
c. **High, Exposed Places**	_____	_____	_____
d. **Radiant Energy**	_____	_____	_____
e. **Explosives**	_____	_____	_____
f. **Toxic Chemicals**	_____	_____	_____
g. **Other Hazards**	_____	_____	_____

Temperaments

Factor	Time	Critical to Performance	Relevant to Function #
1. **Working Alone** *Performing work activities by oneself and away from others.*	_____	_____	_____
2. **Directing Others** *Adaptability to accepting responsibility for the direction, control, or planning of an activity*	_____	_____	_____
3. **Expressing Personal Feelings** *Adaptability to situations involving the interpretation of feelings, ideas, or facts in terms of personal viewpoint.*	_____	_____	_____
4. **Influencing People** *Adaptability to influencing people about the opinions, attitudes, or judgments about ideas or things.*	_____	_____	_____

Elliott & Fitzpatrick, Inc.

Temperaments (cont.)

Factor	Time	Critical to Performance	Relevant to Function #
5. **Making Judgments** *Adaptability to making generalizations, evaluations or decisions based on sensory or judgmental criteria.*	_____	_____	_____
6. **Performing Repetitive Work** *Adaptability to performing repetitive work, or to continuously performing the same work, according to set procedures, sequence, or pace.*	_____	_____	_____
7. **Performing Under Stress** *Adaptability to performing under stress when confronted with emergency, critical, unusual, or dangerous situations; or in situations in which working speed and sustained attention are make or break aspects of the job.*	_____	_____	_____
8. **Attaining Tolerances** *Adaptability to situations requiring the precise attainment of set limits, tolerances, or standards.*	_____	_____	_____
9. **Working Under Instructions** *Adaptability to dealing with people beyond giving and receiving instructions.*	_____	_____	_____
10. **Performing a Variety of Duties** *Adaptability to performing a variety of duties, often changing from one task to another of a different nature without loss of efficiency or composure.*	_____	_____	_____

Essential Functions

Brief Narrative Description of Essential Job Functions (tasks and activities)

1. _____

2. _____

3. _____

4. _____

5. _____

JOB ACCOMODATION CHECKLIST

Client Name _____

Employer _____ Contact _____

Job Title _____

Describe the essential functions requiring accommodation:

_____

_____

_____

WORK ENVIRONMENT

____ remove physical barriers
     ____ rearrange furniture (plants, decorations, etc.)
     ____ rearrange equipment (move printer, relocate control panel, etc.)
     ____ rearrange supplies (lower item from top shelf to bottom)
____ adjust lighting, temperature, ventilation, noise level
____ relocate office, work area to an already accessible area
____ acquire special furnishings, equipment, tools (height adjustable chairs, desks, electric staplers)

         POWER NEEDS AND SOURCES
         ____ battery (rechargeable or replacement)
         ____ amps required
         ____ outlets, cord lengths
         ____ other

MODIFY THE JOB

____ modify work hours
     ____ flexible hours (shorter,longer workdays)
     ____ extended, off-time breaks or lunch hours
____ restructure the job(s)
     ____ job share
     ____ reassign tasks
     ____ "lump work" (certain tasks at certain times)

MODIFY OR MAKE THE BEST USE OF EXISTING EQUIPMENT

____ add lever handles, grips, wheels, new keyboard, etc.
____ exchange equipment (laser for dot matrix printer, keyboards, chairs, computers)
     ____ who approves permanent alterations or exchanges?

PROVIDE PERSONAL ASSISTANCE

_____ job coaching
_____ notetaker (coworker or outside hire)
_____ orientation assistance (coworker)
_____ interpreter (ASL or PSE)
_____ transportation
     _____ frequency of need
     _____ who will arrange or schedule
     _____ costs per hour or day
_____ other

ORIENT/EDUCATE COWORKERS

_____ awareness training or orientation of employee"s disability and accommodations
_____ position supervisor or supportive coworker in close proximity to employee"s work area

REASSIGN EMPLOYEE TO VACANT POSITION

_____ identify position requiring fewer accommodations
_____ provide training that will allow for transfer to another job

PROVIDE NEW DEVICE, PRODUCT OR EQUIPMENT(S)

_____ off the shelf
     _____ Aids for Vision
          _____ magnifiers
          _____ lighting
          _____ audible alert device
          _____ speech output device
          _____ assistance dog
          _____ large print screen or printed materials
          _____ other _____

               POWER NEEDS AND SOURCES
               _____ battery (rechargeable or replacement)
               _____ amps required
               _____ outlets, cord lengths
               _____ other

     _____ Aids for Hearing
          _____ TDD
          _____ visual alert device
          _____ vibrating beeper
          _____ sound enhancement system
          _____ other _____

               POWER NEEDS AND SOURCES
               _____ battery (rechargeable or replacement)
               _____ amps required
               _____ outlets, cord lengths
               _____ other

     _____ Computer Related Accessories
          _____ input alternatives (voice, braille)
          _____ output alternatives (voice, braille)
          _____ special software (voice recognition, text enlargement, color contrast, keystroke saver)

_____ modified or alternate keyboards (L or R hand, oversized, ergonomic design)
_____ non-traditional operating switches
_____ aids (forearm supports, disk guides, adjustable monitor stands, wrist rests)
_____ alternate access (headstick, infrared beams, touchscreens, trackballs, screen pens, chin or foot switches)
POWER NEEDS AND SOURCES
_____ battery (rechargeable or replacement)
_____ amps required
_____ outlets, cord lengths
_____ other _____

_____ Electronic and Powered Aids
_____ Environmental Control Units (ECU)
_____ powered equipment or tools (electric stapler, screwdriver, nail gun)
POWER NEEDS AND SOURCES
_____ battery (rechargeable or replacement)
_____ amps required
_____ outlets, cord lengths
_____ other

_____ Augmentative Communication
_____ electronic (speech synthesizer, artificial larynx, voice enhancement)
_____ non-electronic (picture boards or books, written phrases or words)
POWER NEEDS AND SOURCES
_____ battery (rechargeable or replacement)
_____ amps required
_____ outlets, cord lengths
_____ other

_____ Wheelchairs/Mobility Aids
_____ manual and electric wheelchair (portable, standing, positioning)
_____ walker
_____ standing frame
_____ crutches
_____ three-wheel scooter
_____ utility vehicle (golf cart, ATV)
_____ assistance animal
POWER NEEDS AND SOURCES
_____ battery (rechargeable or replacement)
_____ amps required
_____ outlets, cord lengths
_____ other _____

_____ Vehicle Needs or Modifications
_____ adaptive driving aids
_____ hand controls
_____ restraint system or tie downs
_____ wheelchair or scooter lift
_____ modified vans

_____ Seating and Positioning

_____ modify wheelchair or seating system
_____ add cushions (body, trunk, head, posture support)
_____ seats (reduce skin pressure, maximize respiration)
_____ recline or tilt feature

POWER NEEDS AND SOURCES
_____ battery (rechargeable or replacement)
_____ amps required
_____ outlets, cord lengths
_____ other

_____ Prototype**
_____ Rehabilitation Engineer, Industrial Designer, etc. been consulted?
_____ proposal has been obtained and includes:
_____ itemized costs (labor, materials, installation, etc.)
_____ date of delivery
_____ maintenance agreement
_____ installation agreement
_____ training or orientation to the device

POWER NEEDS AND SOURCES
_____ battery (rechargeable or replacement)
_____ amps required
_____ outlets, cord lengths
_____ other

**PROTOTYPE CONSIDERATIONS

Have you contacted the resources below to discuss the accommodation you have in mind?

_____ Center for Rehabilitation Technology (800) 726-9119
_____ Regional Disability & Business Technical Assistance Centers (800) 949-4232
_____ Job Accommodation Network (800) 526-7234
_____ Abledata (800) 346-2742
_____ Special Organizations (American Foundation of the Blind, Epilepsy Foundation, Spinal Cord Injury Association, National Head Injury Foundation, etc.)
_____ Catalogs (Activities of Daily Living, Office Supply, Furniture, Recreational, Farming, Safety)

Comments or ideas you have obtained from these sources: _____
_____
_____
_____

Disability related information

_____ presently stable (amputation, paralysis)

_____ progressive (neuromuscular diseases, eye diseases)

_____ consider items or devices that can be upgraded or are interchangeable

_____ consider renting

*PRODUCT OR EQUIPMENT SUGGESTED _____

Vendor or Source _____

 Function of the device/product:
  ____ client has experienced "hands on" use of the device/product?
  ____ device/product enables the employee to perform the essential function of the job adequately?
 Level of understanding of the device/product:
  ____ client has learned, or demonstrates the ability to learn, its use?
  ____ employer/supervisor can learn its use?
   ____ if no, what training will be needed?

 Purchase:
  ____ new item
  ____ used item
   ____ has contact been made with two or more vendors/sellors?
   ____ have comparisons (pros & cons list) been made?
   ____ opinions obtained from users of the device/product?
   ____ questions about the safety and reliability of the device/product been answered?
   ____ has a price or reduced package price (equipment, maintenance agreement, installation, etc.) been agreed upon by the vendor/sellor and the purchaser?
   ____ is this information in writing?

 Rental or lease considerations:
  ____ cost per hour, day, week, month?
  ____ maintenance agreement (who is responsible for the cost and is a replacement provided during repair)?

 Maintenance:
  ____ owners manual/instruction guide obtained?
  ____ warranty signed and sent to vendor or manufacturer?
  ____ nearest service center identified?
  ____ costs associated with repairs/replacement understood?

 Training in use of the device:
  ____ is it needed?
  ____ if so, who will provide it? _____
  ____ type of training (on site, one-on-one, telephone support)?
  ____ anticipated length of training or support (1 hour, 6 months)?
  ____ cost (per hour, per visit)?

Funding (evaluations, consultations,equipment, job coaching, transportation, training, maintenance, etc.):

_____	employer	_____%
_____	vocational rehabilitation	_____%
_____	private insurance	_____%
_____	medicare/medicaid/PASS	_____%
_____	workers compensation insurance	_____%
_____	Tech Act (P.L. 100-407)	_____%
_____	veterans administration	_____%
_____	charitable organizations	_____%
_____	religious organizations	_____%
_____	employee	_____%
_____	other	_____%
	Total	100%

Employer ideas:

Employee"s ideas:

Rehabilitation Professional"s ideas:

Describe action to be taken:

Steps involved and those responsible in achieving these:

Time frames:

Plans for follow-up:

individualization of accommodation(s)
_____ employee has been integral in accommodation process
_____ accommodation will fit in to work setting and be accepted by coworkers
_____ accommodation will be utilized
_____ employee will be satisfied

LABOR MARKET SURVEY CHECKLIST

Labor market research (LMR) specifically examines the availability of employment for adult clients. This study addresses the question of placeability rather than employability. A job analysis, following the LMR, will help determine if the probable occupation is within the client's capabilities (see also job analysis checklist). In order to standardize the information and assure obtaining respectable data, the following checklist is recommended.

INTRODUCTION (include the following identifying information for report.)
- _____ Name
- _____ Age
- _____ Date of injury
- _____ Type of injury
- _____ Functional limitations
- _____ Work experience
- _____ Education
- _____ Other historical information
- _____ Vocational test results
- _____ Other

METHODS USED (What method(s) was (were) used to obtain the information? Suggest starting with residual employability profile by VDARE for worker traits.)

Personal contacts (as appropriate) with
- _____ Personal network
- _____ Chamber of Commerce
- _____ Professional and trade associations
- _____ Employment services (private and public)
- _____ Vocational rehabilitation
- _____ Other

Publications/On-line Resources
- _____ O*Net
- _____ Occupational Outlook Handbook (on-line)
- _____ State career information systems (or similar)
- _____ City directory or Haynes directory
- _____ Occupational supply and demand (state Dept. of Industry and Trade or Labor)
- _____ Wage rates for selected occupations (state)
- _____ Manufacturing directories (SIC codes)
- _____ Bureau of Labor Statistics, e.g. Area Wage Survey (federal)
- _____ Census Bureau (federal) and Current Population Surveys (CPS)
- _____ Classified ads
- _____ Identified discreet jobs related to client's experience
- _____ Job flyers
- _____ Other

RESULTS
- _____ Employer's contacted – approximately 10
- _____ Jobs(s) available (last 3 months, now and future expectations - within next 3-6 months)
- _____ Wages
- _____ Training/education needed
- _____ Benefits (holidays, vacation, sick, medical, dental, personal leave, etc.)
- _____ Willingness to work with disabled
- _____ Accessibility/architectural barriers
- _____ Willingness to participate in job analysis if appropriate
- _____ Other

CONCLUSIONS (professional's opinion)

Placeability

Expected outcome

Other related comments

Copyrighted by Dr. Roger Weed, 2001 (rev. 2011). Published by E & F, Inc., Athens, GA

LIFE CARE PLAN CHECKLIST

Projected Evaluations: Have you planned for different types of non-physician **evaluations** (for example; physical therapy, speech therapy, recreational therapy, occupational therapy, music therapy, dietary assessment, audiology, vision screening, swallow studies, etc.)?

Projected Therapeutic Modalities: What therapies will be needed (based on the evaluations above)? Will a case manager help control costs and reduce complications? Is a behavior management, or rehab psychologist, pastoral counseling or family education appropriate?

Diagnostic Testing/Educational Assessment: What testing is necessary and at what ages? Vocational evaluation? Neuropsychological? Educational levels? Educational consultant to maximize IDEA?

Wheelchair Needs: What types and configuration of wheelchairs will the client/evaluee require: power? shower? manual? specialty? ventilator? reclining? quad pegs? recreational?

Wheelchair Accessories and Maintenance: Has each chair been listed separately for maintenance and accessories (bags, cushions, trays, etc.?) Have you considered the client's/evaluee's activity level?

Aids for Independent Functioning: What can this individual use to help him or herself? environmental controls? adaptive aids? omni-reachers?

Orthotics/Prosthetics: Will the client/evaluee need braces? Have you planned for replacement and maintenance?

Home Furnishings and Accessories: Will the client/evaluee need a specialty bed? portable ramps? Hoyer or other lift?

Drug/Supply Needs: Have prescription and non-prescription drugs been listed including size, quantity, and rate at which to be consumed? All supplies such as bladder and bowel program, skin care, etc.?

Home Care/Facility Care: Is it possible for the client/evaluee to live at home? How about specialty programs such as yearly camps? What level of care will he/she require?

Future Medical Care - Routine: Is there a need for an annual evaluation? Which medical specialties? orthopedics? urology? internist? vision? dental? lab?

Transportation: Are hand controls sufficient or is a specialty van needed? Can local transportation companies be used?

Health and Strength Maintenance: What specialty recreation is needed- blow darts? adapted games? Rowcycle? annual dues for specialty magazines? (Specialty wheelchairs should be placed on wheelchair page.)

Architectural Renovations: Have you considered ramps, hallways, kitchen, fire protection, alternative heating/cooling, floor coverings, bath, attendant room, equipment storage, etc.?

Future Medical Care/Surgical Intervention or Aggressive Treatment: Are there plans for aggressive treatment? Additional surgeries such as reconstruction?

Orthopedic Equipment Needs: Are walkers, standing tables, tilt tables, body support equipment needed?

Vocational/Educational Plan: What are the costs of vocational counseling, job coaching, tuition, fees, books, supplies, technology, etc.?

Potential Complications: Have you included a list of potential complications which can occur such as skin breakdown, infections, psychological trauma, contractures, etc.? (Usually "possible" rather than "probable.")

Labor Market Survey Summary
Employer Sampling Results

Client/Evaluee: _____

Employer/Contact Name	Job avail (A) Job exist (E) Both (B)	Job Title	Wages High	Wages Low	Wages Ave	Required Educ/Training	Benefits	History of work with person with dis? (Y, N, ?)	Accessible? (Y, N, ?)	Other (e.g., shift work, special tools, etc.)
1.										
2.										
3.										
4.										
5.										
6.										
7.										
8.										
9.										
10.										

Conclusions

Employment potential estimate	Expected income range
Percent access to labor market (document method)	Other

EARNINGS CAPACITY CHECKLIST

Typical Topics

See RAPEL Checklist for reporting format.

- **Earnings v. Earnings Capacity**: Did the individual have an extensive work history? Do the earnings represent the capacity? For example, is the client a housewife, prisoner, farmer, military person or someone who recently changed jobs?
- **Work History**: Have you obtained tax records? Do you have depositions or other records from the employer? Do you have an opinion as to the client's work capability?
- **Industry**: If the person has a work history, did the job have clear advancement potential for career progression? (For example, a union job that begins as a helper, apprentice, them becomes a master.)
- **Transferable Skills**: Does the individual possess work skills that can be transferred to other occupations? Does the individual have the worker traits necessary to be able to learn new skills?
- **Labor Market Survey**: Have you considered a specific labor market survey for the selected industry?
- **Loss of Opportunity**: Does the disability cause a vocational handicap to the labor market? Is there a loss of access to chosen jobs?
- **Vocational Handicaps**: List physical, mental and emotional handicaps that result from the incident.
- **Impact on employability**: Does the disability restrict access to existing jobs?
- **Impact on Placeability**: Will your client have difficulty in finding a job? Will the client need professional rehabilitation services? Will job skills training, employment coaching, etc. help overcome the handicap?
- **Work Life Expectancy**: (labor force participation rate): Will this person be able to work full-time or part-time? Will there be long periods of time that the person will be unable to work due to complications? Will it take longer for this individual to find employment? Will the person "retire" early?
- **Vocational Development Options**: What was the pre-incident level of capability for education or training? Post-incident? Is there a difference?
- **Vocational Alternative**: What were the pre-incident reasonable jobs for the client? Post-incident? Is there a difference?
- **Earnings Capacity**: What is the average wage for jobs available pre-incident compared to jobs available post-incident? Is there a diminution of capacity?

TRANSFERABILITY OF WORK SKILLS WORKSHEET

Date _____ Phone # _____

Name of Client/Student _____

Address _____

City/State/Zip _____

SS# _____ Age _____ Height _____ Weight _____

Level of Education Completed _____ Date _____

Special Training _____ Date _____

Counselor _____

_____

Previous Work History

1. _____ From _____ To_____
2. _____ From _____ To_____
3. _____ From _____ To_____
4. _____ From _____ To_____
5. _____ From _____ To_____
6. _____ From _____ To_____
7. _____ From _____ To_____

Notes:

Client's Name

D.O.T. Code #

D.O.T. TITLE

Section	Rows
WORK HISTORY	1, 2, 3, 4, 5, 6, 7
JOB POSSIBILITIES	1, 2, 3, 4, 5, 6, 7
VOCATIONAL OUTCOME	1, 2, 3, 4, 5, 6, 7

Code Code Code

Pre-Vocational Profile (Summary Of Job History)

Worker Traits To Be Evaluated (check)

Residual Functional Capacity (Transferability To Current Level Of Functioning)

Consultants Reports & Vocational/Assessment Procedures Utilized (footnote)

FOOTNOTES on Consultant's Reports & Vocational/Assessment Procedures

Duration D (1-9) S V P

GED (1 — 6) (low) (high)
- R Reasoning
- M Math
- L Language

APTITUDES (low) 5 4 3 2 1 (high)
- G Intelligence
- V Verbal
- N Numerical
- S Spatial Perception
- P Form Perception
- Q Clerical Perception
- K Motor Coordination
- F Finger Dexterity
- M Manual Dexterity
- E Eye/Hand/Foot Coord.
- C Color Discrimination

- 1 Strength (SLMHV)
- 2 Climbing
- 3 Balancing
- 4 Stooping
- 5 Kneeling
- 6 Crouching

GOE INTEREST AREAS (Y,N)

1. Artistic
2. Scientific
3. Plant & Animal
4. Protective
5. Mechanical
6. Industrial
7. Administrative
8. Selling
9. Accommodating
10. Humanitarian
11. Leading
12. Sports

TEMPERAMENTS (Y,N)

- A. Working Alone
- D. Directing Others
- E. Expressing Personal Feelings
- I. Influencing People
- J. Making Judgments
- P. Dealing With People
- R. Performing Repetitive Work
- S. Performing Under Stress
- T. Attaining Tolerances
- U. Working Under Instructions
- V. Performing a Variety of Duties

ENVIRONMENTAL CONDITIONS (N,O,F,C)*

1. Exposure to Weather
2. Extreme Cold
3. Extreme Heat
4. Wet and/or Humid
5. Noise (1-5)
6. Vibration
7. Atmospheric Conditions

HAZARDS

8. Moving Parts
9. Electrical Shock
10. High, Exposed Places
11. Radiant Energy
12. Explosives
13. Toxic Chemicals
14. Other Hazards

PHYSICAL DEMANDS (N,O,F,C)

7. Crawling
8. Reaching
9. Handling
10. Fingering
11. Feeling
12. Talking
13. Hearing
14. Tasting/Smelling

VISION

15. Near Acuity
16. Far Acuity
17. Depth Perception
18. Accommodation
19. Color Vision
20. Field of Vision

Note: This form to be used with the **Dictionary of Occupational Titles** (1991), and the **Classification of Jobs** (1992 revised edition).

STANDARD D.O.L. DEFINITIONS

Specific Vocational Preparation (SVP) is defined as the amount of time required by a typical worker to learn the techniques, acquire information, and develop the facility needed for average performance in a specific job-worker situation. *Levels are mutually exclusive and do not overlap.*

Level	Time
1	Short demonstration only
2	Anything beyond short demonstration up to and including 1 month
3	Over 1 month up to and including 3 months
4	Over 3 months up to and including 6 months
5	Over 6 months up to and including 1 year
6	Over 1 year up to and including 2 years
7	Over 2 years up to and including 4 years
8	Over 4 years up to and including 10 years
9	Over 10 years

General Educational Development (GED) embraces those aspects of education (formal and informal) which are required of the worker for satisfactory performance. The GED Scale is composed of three divisions: Reasoning Development, Mathematical Development and Language Development. GED levels are expressed as a range of 1 (low) to 6 (high).

Aptitudes are expressed in a range of 5 (low) to 1 (high). The digits indicate how much of each aptitude the job requires for satisfactory (average) performance. The average requirements, rather than maximum or minimum, are cited. The amount required is expressed in terms of equivalent amounts possessed by segments of the general working population. The following scale is used:

1. The top 10 percent of the population. This segment of the population possesses an extremely high degree of the aptitude.
2. The highest third exclusive of the top 10 percent of the population. This segment of the population possesses an above average or high degree of the aptitude.
3. The middle third of the population. This segment of the population possesses a medium degree of the aptitude, ranging from slightly below to slightly above average.
4. The lowest third exclusive of the bottom 10 percent of the population. This segment possesses a below average or low degree of the aptitude.
5. The lowest 10 percent of the population. This segment of the population possesses a negligible degree of the aptitude.

Physical Demands are a means of a describing the physical activities that a job requires. The physical demands can be expressed, with the exception of Strength, according to the following:

N	Not Present	Activity or condition does not exist
O	Occasionally	Activity or condition exists up to 1/3 of the time;
F	Frequently	Activity or condition exists from 1/3 to 2/3 of the time;
C	Constantly	Activity or condition exist 2/3 or more of the time.

Strength is coded as S (Sedentary), L (Light), M (Medium), H (Heavy) and V (Very Heavy).

Environmental Conditions are a means of describing the physical surroundings of a worker in a specific job and of indicating the hazards that pose a definite risk of bodily injury to the worker. The environmental condition identified for an occupation are those which are considered to be important or critical. Environmental Conditions can be expressed, with the exception of Noise Intensity Level, in the same manner as physical demands.

Noise Intensity is rated as   1 Very Quiet   2 Quiet   3 Moderate   4 Loud   5 Very Loud

Temperaments are defined as personal traits required by a worker by specific job-worker situations. The client should have "Y" where temperament is relevant, "N" otherwise.

GOE Interest Areas are based on the first two digits of the Guide to Occupational Exploration Code. Client should have "Y" where interest area is relevant, "N" otherwise.

Functional Capacity Checklist

Name: _____   Date: _____

For each of the questions choose one of the following responses for how you are able to perform after the injury as compared to before.

(0) I don't know.
(1) No change.
(2) A little more difficult to do.
(3) Can be done but only with some pain.
(4) Very difficult to do.
(5) Impossible to do or can do only with great pain.

Please your answers in the space provided to the left of each question.

Walking short distances (several yards)
____ 1. within your own residence.
____ 2. over smooth ground outdoors.
____ 3. over uneven ground.
____ 4. on gravel.
____ 5. on pavement.
____ 6. up a ramp.
____ 7. down a ramp.
____ 8. Sitting on a soft surface that moves, like a car or truck seat.
____ 9. Standing, moving your feet occasionally, as you would if you were waiting in line.

Lifting relatively heavy objects (like a small child, a chair, or a portable television set)
____ 10. from the floor.
____ 11. from waist level.
____ 12. up above your head (lifting up).
____ 13. from above your head (lifting down).

Bending from your waist from a standing position, to pick up something from the floor with your
____ 14. right arm.
____ 15. left arm.
____ 16. Carrying moderately heavy objects for short distances (like carrying a full laundry basket to a washing machine).
____ 17. Kneeling on a hard surface for several minutes.

Climbing steps (5 or fewer)
____ 18. going up.
____ 19. going down.

Reaching for an object above your head with your
____ 20. right arm.
____ 21. left arm.
____ 22. Balancing on a flat, small surface several inches from the ground, like a stool.

Focusing your eyes on reading material for an hour or more
____ 23. at eye level.
____ 24. below eye level.
____ 25. above eye level.

Picking up and holding
____ 26. a pen or pencil.
____ 27. a knife, fork or spoon.
____ 28. a hairbrush or comb.
____ 29. your house or car keys.
____ 30. stamps (loose).
____ 31. coins.
____ 32. Pulling a stopper out of a bottle.

Walking moderate distances (several hundred yards)
____ 33. over smooth ground outdoors.
____ 34. over uneven ground.
____ 35. on gravel.
____ 36. on pavement.
____ 37. Crawling under a table, as you would to pick up something.

For each of the questions choose one of the following responses for how you are able to perform after the injury as compared to before.

(0) I don't know.
(1) **No change.**
(2) **A little more difficult** to do.
(3) Can be done but **only with some pain.**
(4) **Very difficult** to do.
(5) **Impossible** to do or can do only **with great pain.**

Please your answers in the space provided to the left of each question.

Lifting objects of moderate weight (like a sack of groceries, a tool kit, a full laundry basket or a stack of books)

____ 38. from the floor.
____ 39. from waist level.
____ 40. up above your head (lifting up).
____ 41. from above your head (lifting down)

While you are standing up. putting on

____ 42. shirt/dress.
____ 43. pants.
____ 44. socks.
____ 45. slip on shoes.
____ 46. underwear.
____ 47. jewelry.
____ 48. makeup.

Sitting comfortably for more than a few minutes in a room that is

____ 49. cold.
____ 50. very warm.
____ 51. Standing while holding something, like a tool.
____ 52. Getting out of or into a car as a passenger.
____ 53. Depositing coins in a pay telephone.
____ 54. Sitting on a firm chair without moving much, as in a waiting room.

When climbing up or down, grasping handrail with your

____ 55. right hand.
____ 56. left hand.
____ 57. Carrying very heavy objects (over 50 lbs.) for short distances.
____ 58. Driving a car.
____ 59. Kneeling on the floor, moving your hands, arms and shoulders, as you would if you were working on something in front of you.

Pushing open a door

____ 60. with a knob (as in your own residence).
____ 61. with no knob (as in a public restroom).
____ 62. Opening your purse or wallet and taking out paper money.
____ 63. Getting into or out of bed without help.

Climbing stairs (6 to 20) within a building

____ 64. going up.
____ 65. going down.

Using

____ 66. safety pins.
____ 67. a screwdriver.
____ 68. pliers.
____ 69. a hammer.

Moving your arms, hands and upper body, as you would when you are working on something while you are sitting in a

____ 70. soft chair.
____ 71. firm chair.
____ 72. Signing your name.
____ 73. Standing in one spot, reaching with your arms and hands and bending slightly from your waist.
____ 74. Performing your daily activities without getting tired too fast.
____ 75. Balancing on a flat, large surface several feet from the ground, like a platform.

Reaching for an object at shoulder level with your

____ 76. right arm.
____ 77. left arm.
____ 78. Washing your hair.

Lifting objects of relatively light weight (like a telephone, a briefcase or a purse)
___ 79. from the floor.
___ 80. from waist level.
___ 81. up above your head (lifting up).
___ 82. from above your head (lifting down).

Bending over, using both hands to put on shoes with laces while you are
___ 83. standing up.
___ 84. sitting down.

Walking long distances (a mile or more)
___ 85. over pavement.
___ 86. over uneven ground.
___ 87. uphill or downhill.
___ 88. Sitting for more than several minutes on a firm surface that moves, like the seat of a crane or tractor.
___ 89. Stooping for more than several minutes while working with your arms or hands.
___ 90. Carrying relatively heavy objects for short distances (like carrying a chair or portable television from one room to another).
___ 91. Bending at the waist, as you would to look under something.
___ 92. Dialing a telephone.
___ 93. Spending more than a few minutes reading material which is resting on a table so that you must look down to read it.

Unlocking and opening
___ 94. a car door.
___ 95. a door to your residence.

Pulling open a door
___ 96. with a handle, like in a public place.
___ 97. with a knob, like in your house.
___ 98. Opening mail.

Lifting very heavy objects (over 50 lbs.)
___ 99. from the floor.
___ 100. from waist level.
___ 101. up above your head (lifting up).
___ 102. from above your head (lifting down),

___ 103. Balancing on an unsteady, large surface, like scaffolding.
___ 104. Sitting in a comfortable chair, without moving much, to watch a movie on television.

Dressing or undressing, using
___ 105. buttons.
___ 106. zippers.
___ 107. Carrying relatively light objects for short distances (like carrying garbage to garbage pail or dumpster).
___ 108. Standing, moving several feet, then standing again.

Sitting down in a
___ 109. firm chair.
___ 110. soft chair.

Reaching for an object at eye level with your
___ 111. right arm.
___ 112. left arm.
___ 113. Pushing a cork into a bottle.

Stooping, bending your knees, to pick up an object from the floor using your
___ 114. right hand.
___ 115. left hand.

Being in a room for more than a few minutes where
___ 116. many people are smoking.
___ 117. there is much dust in the air.
___ 118. there are drafts.

Climbing a ladder
___ 119. indoors (5 steps or less).
___ 120. outdoors (more than 5 steps).
___ 121. Selecting proper coin from within your pocket.
___ 122. Standing with your feet in one spot, moving your arms and hands.
___ 123. Getting on a bus.

Reaching for an object at waist level with your
___ 124. right arm.
___ 125. left arm.

or each of the questions choose one of the following responses for how you are able to perform after the injury as compared to before.

(0) I don't know.
(1) **No change.**
(2) **A little more difficult** to do.
(3) Can be done but **only with some pain.**
(4) **Very difficult** to do.
(5) **Impossible** to do or can do only **with great pain.**

Please your answers in the space provided to the left of each question.

Sitting, bending to pick something up from the floor while in a

126. firm chair.
127. soft chair.
128. Screwing a lid off a jar.
129. Feeling different surfaces with your fingers.
130. Standing, shifting your position, then continuing to stand for several minutes.
131. Sitting, bending your neck to look down, as you would to work on a flat surface.
132. Writing a letter by hand.
133. Standing while holding on to something to the front or side of you.
134. Changing a lightbulb in a ceiling fixture.

Getting up from a

135. firm chair.
136. soft chair.
137. Standing, reaching up, as to use a tool above your head.
138. Getting off a bus.
139. Standing while writing on a flat surface at chest level.
140. Showering/bathing.
141. Screwing on lids of jars.
142. Standing, looking up, as at the ceiling.
143. Balancing on unsteady, small surface, like the top of a ladder.
144. Sitting, looking up, with head tilted slightly back.
145. Detecting differences in surfaces with your feet.
146. Standing without shifting position for several minutes.
147. Sitting, looking straight ahead or from side to side.
148. Standing while writing on a clipboard.
149. Opening a mailbox.

150. Fastening a button or hook behind your back.
151. Pulling an object of moderately heavy weight, like a door that is stuck.
152. Hearing a person who is speaking to you in a normal tone of voice.
153. Seeing objects that are several yards away, such as street signs from within a moving car.
154. Pushing an object of moderately heavy weight, like a loaded shopping cart.
155. Talking to a person who is in the same room with you for more than a few minutes.
156. Hearing small changes in noises, as when a machine motor (like in a mixer or a car) changes speeds.
157. Seeing objects that are close to you, like a newspaper you are reading.
158. Pulling a heavy object, like a sofa, bed or other large piece of furniture.
159. Being able to see approaching cars well enough to safely cross a street on foot.
160. Seeing objects to one side of you while you are looking straight ahead.
161. Being able to accurately tell what color an object is.
162. Being able to tell how far away your hand or foot is from something you are reaching for like a cup or a stair.
163. Being able to look up from close work, like reading or sewing, and to clearly see across the room at once.
164. Seeing well enough to safely drive a car.
165. Pushing a heavy object, like a sofa, bed or other large piece of furniture.

Index

3.92